The Handbook of Infrared and Raman Spectra of Inorganic Compounds and Organic Salts (a 4-volume set)

VOLUME 3

INFRARED AND RAMAN SPECTRAL ATLAS OF INORGANIC COMPOUNDS AND ORGANIC SALTS: INFRARED SPECTRA

The Handbook of Infrared and Raman Spectra
of Inorganic Compounds and Organic Salts
(a 4-volume set)

Volume 3

Infrared and Raman Spectral Atlas of Inorganic Compounds and Organic Salts:

INFRARED SPECTRA

Richard A. Nyquist, Curtis L. Putzig, and M. Anne Leugers
The Dow Chemical Company
Midland, Michigan

ACADEMIC PRESS
San Diego London Boston
New York Sydney Tokyo Toronto

This book is printed on acid-free paper. ∞

ACADEMIC PRESS
525 B Street, Suite 1900, San Diego, CA 92101-4495, USA
1300 Boylston Street, Chestnut Hill, Massachusetts 02167
http://www.apnet.com

ACADEMIC PRESS LIMITED
24–28 Oval Road, London NW1 7DX, UK
http://www.hbuk.co.uk/ap/

LIBRARY OF CONGRESS CATALOGING-IN-PUBLICATION DATA

Nyquist, Richard A.
Infrared and Raman spectral atlas of inorganic compounds and organic salts / Richard A. Nyquist, Curtis L. Putzig, M. Anne Leugers.
p. cm.
Includes bibliographical references and indexes.
Contents: v. 1. Text and explanations — v. 2. Raman spectra — v. 3. Infrared spectra
ISBN 0-12-523445-7 (v. 1). — ISBN 0-12-523446-5 (v. 2). — ISBN 0-12-523447-3 (v. 3)
1. Infrared spectra—Tables. 2. Raman effect—Tables. 3. Inorganic compounds—Spectra—Tables. 4. Organic compounds—Spectra—Tables. I. Putzig, Curtis L. II. Leugers, M. Anne. III. Title.
QC457.N927 1996
543′.08583—dc20 96-22175
CIP

PRINTED IN THE UNITED STATES OF AMERICA
96 97 98 99 EB 9 8 7 6 5 4 3 2 1

CONTENTS

Infrared Spectra

A. NUMERICAL INDEX OF RAMAN (R) AND INFRARED (IR) SPECTRA OF IONIC INORGANIC COMPOUNDS

Spectrum Number	Compound	Formula	Spectra IR	Spectra R		Vol. 4 IR
1	Boric acid	H_3BO_3	X	X		16
2	Lithium tetraborate	$Li_2B_4O_7$	X			18
3	Sodium tetraborate	$Na_2B_4O_7 \cdot 5H_2O$	X	X		20
4	Potassium tetraborate	$K_2B_4O_7 \cdot 8H_2O$	X	X		22
5	Sodium cyanide	NaCN		X		—
6	Potassium cyanide	KCN		X		—
7	Nickel (II) cyanide	$Ni(CN)_2 \cdot 4H_2O$	X	X		27
8	Copper (I) cyanide	CuCN	X	X		28
9	Zinc cyanide	$Zn(CN)_2$	X	X		29
10	Silver cyanide	AgCN	X			30
11	Platinous cyanide	$Pt(CN)_2 \cdot xH_2O$	X	X		31
12	Mercury (II) cyanide	$Hg(CN)_2$		X		32
13	Potassium cyanoargenate	$KAg(CN)_2$	X	X		33
14	Potassium cyanocuprate	$KCu(CN)_2 \cdot xH_2O$	X	X		34
14a	Potassium ferricyanide	$K_3Fe(CN)_6$		X		35
15	Sodium nitroferricyanide	$Na_2Fe(CN)_5NO_2 \cdot 2H_2O$		X		36
16	Sodium ferrocyanide	$Na_4Fe(CN)_6$		X		37
17	Potassium ferrocyanide	$K_4Fe(CN)_6$	X	X	(X)	38
18	Potassium calcium ferrocyanide	$K_2CaFe(CN)_6$	X	X		39
19	Calcium ferrocyanide	$Ca_2Fe(CN)_6$		X		—
20	Potassium copper (II) ferrocyanide	$K_2Cu(CN)_6$		X		40
21	Lead ferrocyanide	$Pb_2Fe(CN)_6 \cdot xH_2O$	X	X		41
22	Iron (III) ferrocyanide	$Fe_4[Fe(CN)_6]_3$	X			42
23	Sodium cyanate	NaOCN	X	X		44
24	Silver cyanate	AgOCN	X			45
24a	Potassium thiocyanate	KSCN			(X)	46
25	Lead thiocyanate	$Pb(SCN)_2$	X	X		47
26	Iron (II) thiocyanate	$Fe(SCN)_2 \cdot 3H_2O$	X			48
27	Copper (I) thiocyanate	CuSCN	X	X		49
28	Silver thiocyanate	AgSCN	X	X		50

(X) in water solution

Multiple Xs denotes more than one spectra

NUMERICAL INDEX

Spectrum Number	Compound	Formula	Spectra IR	R		Vol. 4 IR
29	Sodium bicarbonate	$NaHCO_3$	X	X	(X)	54
30	Potassium bicarbonate	$KHCO_3$	X	X		55
31	Lithium carbonate	Li_2CO_3	X	X		56
32	Sodium carbonate	Na_2CO_3	X	X	(X)	57
32a	Potassium carbonate	K_2CO_3	X		(X)	
33	Calcium carbonate (calcite)	$CaCO_3$		X		61
34	Barium carbonate	$BaCO_3$		X		63
35	Lead carbonate	$PbCO_3$	X	X		64
36	Cadmium carbonate	$CdCO_3$	X	X		68
37	Guanidinium carbonate	$[(H_2N_2)C{=}NH_2]_2CO_3$	X	X		—
38	Barium thiocarbonate	$BaCS_3$	X	X		75
39	Magnesium silicide	Mg_2Si	X			76
40	Calcium silicide	Ca_2Si	X			77
41	Boron silicide	B_6Si	X			78
42	Titanium silicide	$TiSi_2$	X			79
43	Vanadium silicide	VSi_2	X			80
44	Manganese silicide	$MnSi_2$	X			81
45	Molybdenum silicide	$MoSi_2$	X			85
46	Cobalt orthosilicate	$CoSiO_4 \cdot xH_2O$	X			—
47	Barium zirconium silicate	$BaZrSiO_5$	X			97
48	Strontium titanate (IV)	$SrTiO_3$		X		102
49	Barium titanate (IV)	$BaTiO_3$	X	X		103
50	Strontium zirconate (IV)	$SrZrO_3$	X			115
51	Lead zirconate (IV)	$PbZrO_3$	X	X		117
52	Zinc zirconate (IV)	$ZnZrO_3$	X			119
53	Cerium zirconate (IV)	$Ce(ZrO_3)_2$	X	X		121
54	Aluminum nitride	AlN	X			133
55	Titanium nitride	Ti_3N_4	X			135
56	Vanadium nitride	VN	X			136
57	Molybdenum nitride	Mo_2N	X			140
58	Sodium azide	NaN_3	X	X	(X)	143
59	Potassium nitrite	$KNO_2 \cdot xH_2O$	X	X		—
60	Lead nitrite	$Pb(NO_2)_2 \cdot xH_2O$		X		151
61	Sodium hexanitrocobaltate (III)	$Na_3Co(NO_2)_6$		X		153
62	Ammonium nitrate	NH_4NO_3	X	X		154
63	Sodium nitrate	$NaNO_3$		X	(X)	155
64	Potassium nitrate	KNO_3	X	X	(X)	156
65	Cesium nitrate	$CsNO_3$	X	X		158
66	Calcium nitrate	$Ca(NO_3) \cdot 4H_2O$		X		159
67	Strontium nitrate	$Sr(NO_3)_2$	X	X		160
68	Aluminum nitrate	$Al(NO_3)_3 \cdot 9H_2O$	X	X		162
69	Thallium nitrate	$Tl(NO_3)_3$	X	X		165
70	Lead nitrate	$Pb(NO_3)_2$	X	X		166
71	Bismuth nitrate	$Bi(NO_3)_3 \cdot 5H_2O$	X	X		168
72	Chromium nitrate	$Cr(NO_3) \cdot 9H_2O$	X			170
73	Iron (III) nitrate	$Fe(NO_3)_3 \cdot xH_2O$	X			171
74	Zinc nitrate	$Zn(NO_3)_2 \cdot xH_2O$	X	X		174
75	Zirconium nitrate	$Zr(NO_3)_4 \cdot 5H_2O$	X			176
76	Silver nitrate	$AgNO_3$	X	X		177

Spectrum Number	Compound	Formula	Spectra IR	Spectra R		Vol. 4 IR
77	Lanthanum nitrate	$La(NO_3)_3 \cdot 6H_2O$	X	X		
78	Cerium nitrate	$Ce(NO_3)_3 \cdot 6H_2O$	X	X		181
79	Bismuth subnitrate	$BiONO_3 \cdot H_2O$	X	X		192
80	Tellurium nitrate (basic)	$4TeO_2 \cdot N_2O_5 \cdot 1\ 1/2H_2O$	X	X		193
81	Uranyl nitrate	$UO_2(NO_3)_2 \cdot 6H_2O$	X	X		195
82	Sodium cobaltic nitrate	$NaCo(NO_3)_4$	X			—
83	Neodymium ammonium nitrate	$NdNH_4(NO_3)_4$	X	X		—
84	Sodium hypophosphite	$NaH_2PO_2 \cdot H_2O$	X	X		206
85	Potassium hypophosphite	$KH_2PO_2 \cdot xH_2O$	X	X	(X)	207
86	Calcium hypophosphite	$Ca(H_2PO_2)_2$	X	X		208
87	Magnesium hypophosphite	$Mg(H_2PO_2)_2 \cdot xH_2O$	X	X		—
88	Barium hypophosphite	$Ba(H_2PO_2)_2$	X	X		—
89	Iron (III) hypophosphite	$Fe(H_2PO_2)_3$		X		210
89a	Sodium orthophosphite	$Na_2HPO_3 \cdot 5H_2O$			(X)	211
89b	Barium orthophosphite	$BaHPO_3$			(X)	212
90	Sodium metaphosphate	$(NaPO_3)_x \cdot xH_2O$	X	X		214
91	Potassium metaphosphate	$(KPO_3)_x \cdot xH_2O$		X		215
92	Beryllium metaphosphate	$[Be(PO_3)_2]_x \cdot xH_2O$	X	X		216
93	Calcium metaphosphate	$[Ca(PO_3)_2]_x \cdot xH_2O$	X	X		218
94	Strontium metaphosphate	$[Sr(PO_3)_2]_x \cdot xH_2O$	X	X		219
95	Lead metaphosphate	$[Pb(PO_3)_2]_x \cdot xH_2O$	X	X		222
96	Sodium orthophosphate (monobasic)	$NaH_2PO_4 \cdot xH_2O$	X	X		—
96a	Potassium orthophosphate (monobasic)	KH_2PO_4			(X)	225
97	Lead orthophosphate (monobasic)	$Pb(H_2PO_4)_2$		X		—
98	Sodium ammonium orthophosphate (dibasic)	$NaNH_4HPO_4$	X	X		—
99	Barium orthophosphate (dibasic)	$BaHPO_4 \cdot xH_2O$	X			231
100	Lithium orthophosphate	$Li_3PO_4 \cdot 1/2H_2O$		X		234
101	Sodium orthophosphate	$Na_3PO_4 \cdot H_2O$	X			235
102	Magnesium orthophosphate	$Mg_3(PO_4)_2 \cdot 8H_2O$	X			236
103	Barium orthophosphate	$Ba_3(PO_4)_2$		X		—
104	Boron orthophosphate (tetragonal)	BPO_4	X			239
105	Tin (II) orthophosphate	$Sn_3(PO_4)_2$ wet	X			241
106	Lead orthophosphate	$Pb_3(PO_4)_2$ wet	X	X		242b
107	Bismuth orthophosphate	$BiPO_4$	X	X		244
108	Chromium (III) orthophosphate	$CrPO_4 \cdot 6H_2O$	X			245
109	Iron (II) orthophosphate	$Fe_3(PO_4)_2 \cdot 8H_2O$	X			246
110	Iron (III) orthophosphate	$FePO_4 \cdot 2H_2O$	X			247
111	Nickel orthophosphate	$Ni_3(PO_4)_2 \cdot 8H_2O$	X			248
112	Copper (II) orthophosphate	$Cu_3(PO_4) \cdot 3H_2O$	X			249
113	Zinc orthophosphate	$Zn_3(PO_4) \cdot 4H_2O$		X		250
114	Cadmium orthophosphate	$Cd_3(PO_4) \cdot xH_2O$		X		252
115	Magnesium ammonium orthophosphate	$NH_4MgPO_4 \cdot H_2O$		X		254
116	Ammonium cobalt orthophosphate	$NH_4CoPO_4 \cdot xH_2O$	X			256
117	Dilithium sodium orthophosphate	$Li_2NaPO_4 \cdot xH_2O$	X			257

Spectrum Number	Compound	Formula	Spectra IR	Spectra R		Vol. 4 IR
118	Lead copper (I) orthophosphate	$PbCuPO_4$	X			259
119	Sodium pyrophosphate	$Na_4P_2O_7$		X		260
120	Calcium pyrophosphate (δ-form) (some POH present)	$Ca_2P_2O_7$	X		(X)	268
121	Barium pyrophosphate (α form)	$Ba_2P_2O_7$		X		270
122	Titanium pyrophosphate	TiP_2O_4		X		—
123	Tin pyrophosphate	$Sn_2P_2O_7$		X		272
124	Sodium tripolyphosphate	$Na_5P_3O_{10} \cdot xH_2O$	X	X		278
125	Diamylammonium phosphate	$(C_5H_{11}O)_2PO_2NH_4$		X		—
125a	Sodium metaarsenite	Na_2AsO_2			(X)	286
126	Zinc metaarsenite	$Zn(AsO_2)_2$	X			288
127	Antimony orthoarsenite	$SbAsO_3$	X			289
128	Iron (III) orthoarsenite(basic)	$2FeAsO_3 \cdot Fe_2O_3 \cdot xH_2O$	X			290
129	Lead pyroarsenate (monobasic)	$Pb_2As_2O_7$		X		294
129a	Potassium orthoarsenate (monobasic)	KH_2AsO_4			(X)	295
130	Ammonium orthoarsenate (dibasic)	$(NH_4)_2HAsO_4$	X	X		296
131	Antimony orthoarsenate	$SbAsO_4 \cdot xH_2O$	X	X		298
132	Iron (II) orthoarsenate	$Fe_3(AsO_4)_2 \cdot 6H_2O$	X			299
133	Cobalt orthoarsenate	$Co(AsO_4) \cdot 8H_2O$	X			300
134	Copper (II) orthoarsenate	$Cu_3(AsO_4)_2 \cdot 4H_2O$	X			301
135	Zinc orthoarsenate	$Zn_3(AsO_4)_2 \cdot 8H_2O$	X	X		302
136	Mercury (II) orthoarsenate	$Hg_3(AsO_4)_2$		X		303
137	Ammonium metavanadate	NH_4VO_3	X	X		305
138	Sodium metavanadate	$NaVO_3 \cdot xH_2O$	X	X		—
138a	Sodium pyrovanadate	$Na_4V_2O_7 \cdot xH_2O$		X	(X)	306
139	Lead pyrovanadate	$Pb_2V_2O_7 \cdot xH_2O$	X			—
140	Magnesium vanadate	$Mg(VO_3)_2$		X		—
140a	α-aluminum oxide	Al_2O_3		X		—
141	Indium sesquioxide	In_2O_3	X			320
142	Silicon dioxide (cristobalite)	SiO_2	X			322
143	Germanium dioxide	GeO_2	X			325
144	Tellurium dioxide	TeO_2	X	X		330
145	Titanium dioxide (anatase)	TiO_2	X	X		332
146	Titanium dioxide (rutile)	TiO_2	X	X		332
147	Vanadium tetroxide	$V_2O_4 \cdot H_2O$	X			333
148	Vanadium oxide	V_6O_{13} wet	X			334
149	Tantalum pentoxide	Ta_2O_5 wet	X	X		356
150	Uranium oxide (orthorhomic)	U_3O_8	X			367
151	Strontium peroxide	SrO_2		X		369
152	Zinc peroxide	ZnO_2		X		370
153	Lithium hydroxide	$LiOH \cdot H_2O$	X			372
154	Barium hydroxide	$Ba(OH)_2 \cdot 8H_2O$	X			375
155	α-aluminium hydroxide (gibbsite)	$Al(OH)_3$	X			376
156	Nickel hydroxide	$Ni(OH)_2$	X			377
157	Copper (II) hexahydroxostannate (IV)	$CuSn(OH)_6$	X			380
158	Zinc hexahydrostanate (IV)	$ZnSn(OH)_6$	X			381

Spectrum Number	Compound	Formula	Spectra IR	Spectra R		Vol. 4 IR
159	Cadmium hexahydrostannate (IV)	$CdSn(OH)_6$	X			382
160	Arsenic disulfide	As_2S_2	X			395
161	Antimony trisulfide	Sb_2S_3	X			397
162	Bismuth trisulfide	Bi_2S_3	X			398
163	Tellrurium sulfide	TeS_2	X			399
164	Titanium sesquisulfide	Ti_2S_3	X			400
165	Nickel monosulfide	NiS	X			401
166	Silver sulfide	Ag_2S	X			406
167	Tantalum disulfide	TaS_2	X			409
168	Ammonium imidodisulfate	$(NH_4)_2S_2NHO_6$	X	X		413
169	Sodium hydrogen sulfate	$NaHSO_4 \cdot H_2O$		X	(X)	415
170	Potassium hydrogen sulfate	$KHSO_4$		X		416
171	Potassium thiosulfate	$K_2S_2O_3 \cdot 1/3H_2O$	X	X	(X)	418
172	Barium thiosulfate	$BaS_2O_3 \cdot H_2O$	X	X		420
173	Lead thiosulfate	$PbS_2O_3 \cdot xH_2O$ or wet	X			421
174	Sodium pyrosulfite	$Na_2S_2O_5$	X	X		422
175	Potassium pyrosulfite	$K_2S_2O_5$		X		423
176	Ammonium sulfite	$(NH_4)_2SO_3$		X		—
177	Sodium sulfite	Na_2SO_3		X		424
178	Potassium sulfite	K_2SO_3		X		—
179	Magnesium sulfite	$MgSO_3 \cdot xH_2O$	X	X		425
180	Strontium sulfite	$SrSO_3$		X		426
181	Barium sulfite	$BaSO_3 \cdot xH_2O$ or wet	X	X		427
182	Sodium dithionate	$Na_2S_2O_6$		X		—
183	Potassium dithionate	$K_2S_2O_6$		X		429
184	Silver pyrosulfite	$Ag_2S_2O_7 \cdot xH_2O$	X			430
185	Lithium sulfate	$Li_2SO_4 \cdot H_2O$	X	X		432
186	Sodium sulfate	Na_2SO_4	X	X	(X)	433
187	Potassium sulfate	K_2SO_4	X	X		434
188	Beryllium sulfate	$BeSO_4 \cdot 4H_2O$	X	X		437
189	Magnesium sulfate	$MgSO_4 \cdot 7H_2O$	X	X		439
190	Calcium sulfate	$CaSO_4 \cdot 2H_2O$	X	X		441
191	Strontium sulfate	$SrSO_4$	X	X		442
192	Barium sulfate	$BaSO_4$	X	X		443
193	Aluminum sulfate	$Al_2(SO_4)_3 \cdot 18H_2O$	X	X		444
194	Thallium sulfate	$Tl(SO_4)_3$	X	X		447
195	Lead sulfate tribasic	$3PbO \cdot PbSO_4 \cdot xH_2O$		X		448
196	Antimony sulfate	$Sb_2(SO_4)_3 \cdot xH_2O$	X	X		449
197	Bismuth sulfate	$Bi_2(SO_4)_3 \cdot xH_2O$	X	X		450
198	Vanadyl sulfate	$VSO_4 \cdot xH_2O$	X	X		
199	Iron (III) sulfate	$Fe_2(SO_4)_3 \cdot 9H_2O$		X		454
200	Cobalt (II) sulfate	$CoSO_4 \cdot 7H_2O$	X	X		455
201	Copper (II) sulfate	$CuSO_4 \cdot 5H_2O$	X			457
202	Zinc sulfate	$ZnSO_4 \cdot 6H_2O$	X	X		458
203	Zirconium sulfate	$Zr(SO_4)_2 \cdot 4H_2O$	X	X		461
204	Silver sulfate	Ag_2SO_4	X	X		462
205	Cadmium sulfate	$CdSO_4 \cdot 7H_2O$	X	X		463
206	Cerium (III) sulfate	$Ce_2(SO_4)_3 \cdot 4H_2O$	X	X		467
207	Cerium (IV) sulfate	$Ce(SO_4)_2 \cdot 4H_2O$	X	X		468

Spectrum Number	Compound	Formula	Spectra IR	Spectra R		Vol. 4 IR
208	Thorium sulfate	$Th(SO_4)_2 \cdot xH_2O$	X	X		478
209	Ammonium manganese sulfate	$(NH_4)_2MnSO_4 \cdot xH_2O$	X	X		484
210	Ammonium iron (III) sulfate	$(NH_4)Fe(SO_4)_2 \cdot 3H_2O$	X	X		486
211	Ammonium iron (III) sulfate	$NH_4Fe(SO_4)_2 \cdot xH_2O$		X		487
212	Ammonium cobalt sulfate	$(NH_4)_2Co(SO_4)_2 \cdot 6H_2O$	X			488
213	Potassium chromium sulfate	$KCr(SO_4)_2 \cdot 12H_2O$		X		493
214	Aluminum sodium sulfate	$NaAl(SO_4)_2 \cdot xH_2O$	X	X		—
215	Cesium aluminum sulfate	$CsAl(SO_4)_2 \cdot 12H_2O$	X	X		499
216	Ammonium cadmium sulfate	$(NH_4)Cd(SO_4)_2 \cdot 6H_2O$		X		—
216a	Sodium peroxydisulfate	$Na_2S_2O_8$	X	X	(X)	502
217	Potassium peroxydisulfate	$K_2S_2O_8$	X	X		503
218	Gallium monselenide	GaSe	X			506
219	Tin (II) selenide	SnSe	X			507
220	Lead selenide	PbSe	X			508
221	Titatium diselenide	$TiSe_2$	X			509
221a	Sodium selenite	Na_2SeO_3			(X)	517
222	Zinc selenite	$ZnSeO_3$	X			520
223	Copper selenite	$Cu(OH)SeO_3H \cdot H_2O$	X			521
224	Ammonium selenate	$(NH_4)_2SeO_4$		X		522
224a	Sodium selenate	Na_2SeO_4			(X)	523
225	Calcium selenate	$CaSeO_4 \cdot 2H_2O$	X	X		526
226	Copper (II) selenate	$CuSeO_4 \cdot 5H_2O$	X			529
227	Zinc selenate	$ZnSeO_4$		X		—
228	Silver selenate	$Ag_2SeO_4 \cdot xH_2O$ or wet	X	X		530
229	Potassium alumino selenate	$KAl(SeO_4)_2 \cdot 8H_2O$	X	X		—
230	Tin (II) telluride	SnTe	X			531
230a	Zinc telluride	ZnTe	X			536
231	Ammonium dichromate	$(NH_4)_2Cr_2O_7$	X	X		542
232	Lithium dichromate	$Li_2Cr_2O_7 \cdot 2H_2O$	X		(X)	543
233	Sodium dichromate	$Na_2Cr_2O_7 \cdot 2H_2O$	X	X		544
234	Potassium dichromate	$K_2Cr_2O_7$		X		545
235	Calcium dichromate	$CaCr_2O_7 \cdot xH_2O$	X	X		547
236	Silver dichromate	$Ag_2Cr_2O_7 \cdot xH_2O$ or wet	X			549
237	Ammonium chromate	$(NH_4)_2CrO_4 \cdot xH_2O$	X	X		550
238	Lithium chromate	$Li_2CrO_4 \cdot xH_2O$	X	X		551
239	Sodium chromate	$Na_2CrO_4 \cdot xH_2O$		X		552
240	Potassium chromate	K_2CrO_4		X	(X)	553
241	Cesium chromate	Cs_2CrO_4	X	X		554
242	Magnesium chromate	$MgCrO_4$		X		555
243	Calcium chromate	$CaCrO_4$		X		556
244	Aluminum chromate	$Al_2(CrO_4)_3 \cdot xH_2O$	X	X		557
245	Lead chromate	$PbCrO_4$		X		558
246	Cadmium chromate (carbonate imp)	$CdCrO_4$	X			559
247	Potassium zinc chromate	$K_2CrO_4 \cdot 3ZnCrO_4 \cdot Zn(OH)_2$	X	X		561
248	Ammonium molybdate (VI)	$(NH_4)_2MoO_4$	X	X		—
249	Sodium molybdate (VI)	$Na_2MoO_4 \cdot 2H_2O$	X	X	(X)	563
250	Lead molybdate (VI)	$PbMoO_4 \cdot xH_2O$ or wet	X	X		568
251	Nickel molybdate (VI)	$NiMoO_4 \cdot H_2O$ or wet	X			570

Spectrum Number	Compound	Formula	Spectra IR	Spectra R		Vol. 4 IR
252	Copper (II) molybdate (VI)	$CuMoO_4 \cdot xH_2O$	X			571
253	Ammonium phosphomolybdate	$(NH_4)_3PMo_{12}O_{40}$	X	X		577
254	Sodium phosphomolybdate	$Na_3PMo_{12}O_{40}$		X		—
255	Ammonium tungstate	$(NH_4)_2WO_4$	X	X		—
256	Sodium tungstate	$Na_2WO_4 \cdot 2H_2O$	X	X	(X)	579
257	Calcium tungstate	$CaWO_4$	X	X		582
258	Zinc tungstate	$ZnWO_4 \cdot xH_2O$	X	X		587
259	Zirconium tungstate	$Zr(WO_4)_2 \cdot xH_2O$ or wet	X			588
260	Silver tungstate	Ag_2WO_4	X			589
261	Sodium paratungstate	$Na_6W_7O_{24} \cdot 16H_2O$	X	X	(X)	591
262	Potassium tungstate	$K_6W_7O_{24} \cdot xH_2O$	X			—
263	Barium borotungstate	$Ba_3(BW_{12}O_{40})_2 \cdot xH_2O$	X	X		595
264	Ammonium phosphotungstate	$(NH_4)_3PW_{12}O_{40} \cdot 4H_2O$	X	X		596
265	Sodium phosphotungstate	$Na_3PW_{12}O_{40} \cdot xH_2O$		X		597
266	Lead difluoride	PbF_2	X			608
267	Titanium tetrafluoride	$TiF_4 \cdot xH_2O$	X			614
268	Vanadium trifluoride	$VF_3 \cdot 3H_2O$	X			615
269	Cobalt (II) fluoride	$CoF_2 \cdot xH_2O$	X			622
270	Nickel fluoride	$NiF_2 \cdot xH_2O$	X			624
271	Copper (II) fluoride	$CuF_2 \cdot 2H_2O$	X			625
272	Zirconium fluoride	$ZrF_4 \cdot xH_2O$	X			628
273	Lanthanum fluoride	LaF_3	X			631
274	Samarium fluoride	SmF_3	X			634
275	Gadolimium fluoride	GdF_3	X			635
276	Dysprosium fluoride	DyF_3	X			636
277	Holmium fluoride	HoF_3		X		637
278	Erbrium fluoride	ErF_3	X			638
279	Thorium fluoride	$ThF_4 \cdot 4H_2O$	X			640
280	Ammonium tetrafluoroborate	NH_4BF_4	X	X		642
281	Sodium tetrafluoroborate	$NaBF_4 \cdot xH_2O$	X		(X)	644
282	Ammonium tetrafluoroaluminate	NH_4AlF_4	X			649
283	Ammonium hexafluorogallate	$(NH_4)_3GaF_6$	X			652
284	Ammonium hexafluorosilicate	$(NH_4)_2SiF_6$		X		653
285	Sodium hexafluorosilicate	Na_2SiF_6		X		655
286	Ammonium hexafluorogermanate	$(NH_4)_2GeF_6$	X			665
287	Barium hexafluorogermanate	$BaGeF_6$	X			667
288	Ammonium hexafluorophosphate	NH_4PF_6		X		681
289	Potassium hexafluorophosphate	$KPF_6 \cdot xH_2O$ or wet	X	X	(X)	682
290	Potassium hexafluoroarsenate	$KAsF_6$	X	X	(X)	685
291	Potassium hexafluorotitanate (IV)	K_2TiF_6	X			692
292	Potassium tetrafluorozincate	$K_2ZnF_4 \cdot xH_2O$	X			703
293	Sodium pentafluorozirconate	$NaZrF_5 \cdot xH_2O$	X	X		704
294	Potassium pentafluorozirconate	$KZrF_5 \cdot xH_2O$	X			705
295	Ammonium hexafluorozirconate	$(NH_4)_2ZrF_6$	X	X		706
296	Sodium hexafluorozirconate	Na_2ZrF_6	X	X		707
297	Potassium hexafluorozirconate	$K_2ZrF_6 \cdot xH_2O$	X			708
298	Indium hexafluorozirconate	$In(ZrF_6)_3 \cdot xH_2O$	X			709
299	Potassium heptafluoroniobate (V)	K_2NbF_7		X		711
300	Potassium heptafluorotantalate	K_3TaF_7	X	X		713

Spectrum Number	Compound	Formula	Spectra IR	Spectra R		Vol. 4 IR
301	Sodium pentafluorouranate	$NaUF_5 \cdot H_2O$	X			714
302	Potassium oxopentafluoroniobate	$K_2NbOF_5 \cdot xH_2O$	X	X		—
303	Potassium oxohexafluorozirconate	K_3ZrOF_6		X		—
304	Ammonium chloride	NH_4Cl	X	X		715
304a	Sodium chlorite	$NaClO_2$			(X)	779
305	Sodium chlorate	$NaClO_3$		X	(X)	780
306	Strontium chlorate	$Sr(ClO_3)_2 \cdot xH_2O$	X	X		782
307	Barium chlorate	$Ba(ClO_3)_2 \cdot H_2O$	X	X		783
308	Ammonium perchlorate	NH_4ClO_4		X		784
309	Sodium perchlorate	$NaClO_4 \cdot H_2O$	X	X	(X)	786
310	Rubidium perchlorate	$RbClO_4$	X			787
311	Cesium perchlorate	$CsClO_4$	X	X		788
312	Magnesium perchlorate	$Mg(ClO_4)_2 \cdot 6H_2O$		X		789
313	Zinc perchlorate	$Zn(ClO_4)_2 \cdot 6H_2O$		X		793
314	Ammonium bromide	NH_4Br	X	X		795
315	Barium bromide	$BaBr_2 \cdot 2H_2O$	X	X		801
316	Antimony bromide	$SbBr_3$	X			806
317	Bismuth bromide	$BiBr_3 \cdot xH_2O$	X			807
318	Tellurium bromide	$TeBr_4 \cdot xH_2O$	X			808
319	Iron (II) bromide	$FeBr_2 \cdot xH_2O$	X			809
320	Cadmium bromide	$CdBr_2$	X			812
321	Mercury (I) bromide	Hg_2Br_2		X		814
322	Sodium bromate	$NaBrO_3$		X	(X)	819
323	Potassium bromate	$KBrO_3$	X	X		820
324	Rubidium bromate	$RbBrO_3$	X	X		821
325	Cesium bromate	$CsBrO_3$		X		822
326	Magnesium bromate	$Mg(BrO_3)_2 \cdot 6H_2O$	X	X		823
327	Barium bromate	$Ba(BrO_3)_2 \cdot H_2O$		X		824
328	Aluminum bromate	$Al(BrO_3)_3 \cdot 9H_2O$	X	X		825
329	Lead bromate	$Pb(BrO_3)_2 \cdot H_2O$		X		826
330	Cadmium bromate	$Cd(BrO_3)_2 \cdot xH_2O$		X		828
331	Potassium iodide	KI	X			831
332	Rubidium iodide	RbI	X			832
333	Barium iodide	$BaI_2 \cdot 2H_2O$	X			834
334	Thallium iodide	TlI	X			835
335	Arsenic iodide	AsI_3	X			839
336	Antimony iodide	SbI_3	X			840
337	Bismuth iodide	$BiI_3 \cdot xH_2O$ or wet	X			841
338	Zirconium iodide	$ZrI_4 \cdot xH_2O$	X			844
339	Palladium iodide	PdI_2	X			846
340	Silver iodide	AgI_2	X			847
341	Mercury (II) iodide	HgI	X			849
342	Ytterbium iodide	$YbI_3 \cdot xH_2O$	X			850
343	Potassium bismuth iodide	$K_4BiI_7 \cdot xH_2O$	X			851
344	Potassium tetraiodomercurate (II)	$K_2HgI_4 \cdot xH_2O$	X			—
345	Potassium iodocadmate	$K_2CdI_4 \cdot xH_2O$	X			853
346	Ammonium iodate	NH_4IO_3	X	X		854
347	Sodium iodate	$NaIO_3$	X	X		856
348	Rubidium iodate	$RbIO_3$	X	X		858

Spectrum Number	Compound	Formula	Spectra IR	R		Vol. 4 IR
349	Cesium iodate	$CsIO_3 \cdot xH_2O$	X	X		859
350	Calcium iodate	$Ca(IO_3)_2 \cdot 6H_2O$	X	X		860
351	Strontium iodate	$Sr(IO_3)_2 \cdot xH_2O$	X	X		861
352	Barium iodate	$Ba(IO_3)_2 \cdot H_2O$		X		862
353	Lead iodate	$Pb(IO_3)_2$	X	X		863
354	Chromium (III) iodate	$Cr(IO_3)_3 \cdot xH_2O$	X	X		864
355	Nickel iodate	$Ni(IO_3)_2 \cdot xH_2O$	X			865
356	Silver iodate	$AgIO_3$	X	X		866
357	Cerium iodate	$Ce(IO_3)_4 \cdot xH_2O$	X			867
358	Cobalt iodate	$Co(IO_3)_2 \cdot H_2O$	X			—
359	Zinc iodate	$Zn(IO_3)_x \cdot xH_2O$	X	X		—
360	Sodium periodate	$NaIO_4$		X		868
361	Potassium periodate	KIO_4		X	(X)	869
362	Potassium permanganate	$KMnO_4$	X		(X)	874

(X) water solution.
Vols. 2–3 = Nyquist, Putzig, and Leugers.
Vol. 4 = Nyquist and Kagel, "Infrared Spectra of Inorganic Compounds: 3800-45cm^{-1}".

B. NUMERICAL INDEX OF RAMAN (R) AND INFRARED (IR) SPECTRA OF NONIONIC INORGANIC COMPOUNDS AND HYDRAZINE SALTS

Spectrum Number	Compound	Formula	Spectra IR	R	Vol. 4 IR
	Boron				
363	Diborane	B_2H_6	XX		
364	Decaborane	$B_{10}H_{14}$	XX		
365	Hydrazine diborane	$B_2H_{10}N_2$	X		
366	Decaborane monohydrazine	$B_{10}H_{16}N_2$	X		
367	Boron trifluoride	BF_3	X		
368	Boron tribromide	BBr_3	X		
	Carbon				
369	Carbon monoxide	CO	X		
370	Carbon dioxide	CO_2	X		
371	Carbonyl sulfide	COS	X		
372	Carbon disulfide	CS_2	X	X	
373	Hydrogen cyanide	CHN	X		
374	Cyanogen	C_2N_2	X		
375	Cyanogen chloride	$CClN$	X		
376	Cyanogen bromide	$CBrN$	XX		
377	Cyanamide	CH_2N_2	X		
378	Cyanoquanidine	$C_2H_4N_4$	X		
379	Carbonyl fluoride	CF_2O	X		
380	Carbonyl chloride	CCl_2O	X		
	Nitrogen				

Spectrum Number	Compound	Formula	Spectra IR	R	Vol. 4 IR
381	Ammonia	NH_3	X		
382	Ammonia-d_3	ND_3	X		
383	Nitrous oxide	N_2O	X		
384	Nitric oxide	NO plus NO_2	X		
385	Nitrogen trifluoride	NF_3	X		
386	Nitrogen trichloride	NCl_3	X		
387	Hydrazine tetrafluoride	N_2F_4	X		
388	Thiazyl trifluoride	NF_3S	X		
389	Hydrazine dichloride	$N_2H_6Cl_2$	X		
	Phosphorus				
390	Phosphine	PH_3	XX		
391	Phosphorus trifluoride	PF_3	XX		
392	Phosphorus trichloride	PCl_3	XXXX		
393	Phosphorus tribromide	PBr_3	XX		
394	Phosphorus triiodide	PI_3	XX		
395	Phosphorus oxyfluoride	PF_3O	XX		
396	Phosphorus oxychloride	PCl_3O	XX		
397	Phosphorus oxybromide	PBr_3O	XX		
398	Thiophosphoryl dichloride fluoride	PCl_2FS	X	(R)	
399	Thiophosphoryl chloride	PCl_3S	XXX		
400	Thiophosphoryl bromide	PBr_3S	XX		
401	Phosphorus pentachloride	PCl_5	X	(R)	
402	Phosphorus pentabromide	PBr_5	XX		
403	Trichlorophosphazosulfuryl chloride	PCl_4NO_2S			
404	Phosphoric acid	PH_3O_4	X		
405	Phosphorus thioamide	PH_6N_3S	X		
406	Phosphorus pentasulfide	P_2S_5	X		
407	Chloromethylphosphonic dichloride	PCH_2Cl_3O	XX		
	Arsenic				
408	Arsine	AsH_3	X		
	Oxygen				
409	Ozone	O_3	X		
410	Water	OH_2	XX		
411	Deuteruim oxide	OD_2	X		
	Sulfur				
412	Sulfur	S_8	XX	X	811a
413	Hydrogen sulfide	SH_2	X		
414	Sulfur dioxide	SO_2	X		
415	Sulfur monochloride	S_2Cl_2	X		
416	Sulfur dichloride	SCl_2	X		
417	Sulfur monobromide	S_2Br_2	XX		
418	Thionyl fluoride	SF_2O	XX		
419	Thionyl chloride	SCl_2O	XXX	X	
420	Sulfuryl chloride	SCl_2O_2	XXX		
421	Pyrosulfuryl chloride	$S_2Cl_2O_5$	X		

Spectrum Number	Compound	Formula	Spectra IR	Spectra R	Vol. 4 IR
422	β-Sulfanuryl chloride	$S_3Cl_3N_3O_3$	X		
423	Sulfonamide	$SH_4N_2O_2$	X		
424	Sulfuric acid	SH_2O_4	X		
425	Sulfur hexafluoride	SF_6	X		
426	Decafluorodisulfide	S_2F_{10}	X		
427	Methyl chlorosulfinate	CH_3ClO_2S	X		
428	Potassium methyl sulfate	CH_3OSO_3K		X	
	Halogen				
429	Chlorine	Cl_2		(R)	
430	Bromine	Br_2		(R)	
431	Iodine	I_2		(R)	
432	Hydrogen chloride	ClH	X		
433	Deuterium chloride	ClD	X		
434	Hydrogen bromide	BrH	X		
435	Deuterium bromide	BrD	X		

(R) Recorded using a Spex Ramalog instrument equipped with a Spectra-Physics Model 125 He-Ne laser (70 mW at 6328A).
Vols. 2–3 = Nyquist, Putzig, and Leugers.
Vol. 4 = Nyquist and Kagel, "Infrared Spectra of Inorganic Compounds: 3800-45cm^{-1}".

C. NUMERICAL INDEX OF MISCELLANEOUS MINERALS

Spectrum Number	Compound	Formula	Spectra IR	Spectra R	Vol. 4 IR
436	Aragonite	$CaCO_3$	X	X	—
437	Asbestos (amphibole)		X		—
438	Asbestos (crocidolite)		X		—
439	Asbestos (serpentine chrysolite)		X		—
440	Gearksutite	CaAlF(OH)	X	X	—
441	Hydromagnesite	$3Mg \cdot Mg(OH)_2 \cdot 3H_2O$	X	X	—
442	Itacolumite		X	X	—
443	Kalinite	$AlK(SO_4)_2 \cdot 12H_2O$	X	X	—
444	Meyerhofferite	$2Ca \cdot 3B_2O_3 \cdot 7H_2O$	X	X	—
445	Quartz	SiO_2	X	X	892
446	Realgar	AsS	X	X	—
447	Stilbite	$H_4(Na_2,Ca)Al_2Si_6O_{18} \cdot 4H_2O$	X	X	—
448	Thaumasite	$CaSiO_3 \cdot CaCO_3 \cdot CaSO_4 \cdot 15H_2OX$	X	X	—
449	Vermiculite		X		—

D. NUMERICAL INDEX OF ORGANIC SALTS (OS) CARBOXYLIC ACID SALTS, PHENATES, AND BENZENESULFONATES

Spectrum Number OS	Compound	Formula	Spectra R	Spectra IR
1	Sodium formate	CHO_2Na	X	X
2	Magnesium formate	$(CHO_2)_2Mg \cdot xH_2O$	X	X
3	Calcium formate	$(CHO_2)_2Ca$	X	X
4	Strontium formate	$(CHO_2)_2Sr$	X	X
5	Barium formate	$(CHO_2)_2Ba$	X	X
6	Lead formate	$(CHO_2)_2Pb$	X	X
7	Zinc formate	$(CHO_2)_2Zn \cdot xH_2O$	X	X
8	Sodium acetate	$(CH_3CO_2)_2Na \cdot xH_2O$	X	X
9	Calcium acetate	$(CH_3CO_2)_2Ca \cdot xH_2O$	X	X
10	Strontium acetate	$(CH_3CO_2)_2Sr \cdot xH_2O$	X	X
11	Barium acetate	$(CH_3CO_2)_2Ba \cdot xH_2O$	X	X
12	Thallous acetate	$(CH_3CO_2)Tl \cdot xH_2O$	X	X
13	Guanidinium acetate	$(CH_3CO_2)(H_2N)_2C{=}NH_2$	X	X
14	Sodium butyrate	$(n\text{-}C_3H_7CO_2)Na$	X	X
15	Calcium butyrate	$(n\text{-}C_3H_7CO_2)_2Ca$	X	X
16	Sodium valerate	$(n\text{-}C_4H_9CO_2)Na \cdot xH_2O$	X	X
17	Potassium valerate	$(n\text{-}C_4H_9CO_2)K$	X	X
18	Sodium stearate	$(n\text{-}C_{17}H_{35}CO_2)Na$	X	X
19	Zinc stearate	$(n\text{-}C_{17}H_{35}CO_2)_2Zn$	X	X
20	Sodium cyanoacetate	$(NCCH_2CO_2)Na$	X	X
21	Lithium oxalate	$(C_2O_4)Li_2$	X	X
22	Sodium oxalate	$(C_2O_4)Na_2$	X	X
23	Potassium oxalate hydrate	$(C_2O_4)K_2 \cdot xH_2O$	X	
24	Calcium oxalate	$(C_2O_4)Ca$	X	X
25	Strontium oxalate	$(C_2O_4)Sr \cdot xH_2O$	X	X
26	Barium oxalate	$(C_2O_4)Ba \cdot xH_2O$	X	X
27	Lead oxalate	$(C_2O_4)Pb$	X	X
28	Manganese oxalate	$(C_2O_4)Mn \cdot xH_2O$	X	X
29	Stannous oxalate	$(C_2O_4)Sn$	X	
30	Bismuth oxalate	$(C_2O_4)Bi \cdot xH_2O$	X	X
31	Cadmium oxalate	$(C_2O_4)Cd$	X	X
32	Thallous malonate	$(CH_2(CO_2)_2)Tl_2 \cdot xH_2O$	X	X
33	Sodium succinate	$(CH_2CO_2)_2Na_2 \cdot xH_2O$	X	X
34	Potassium tartrate	$(CHOHCO_2)_2K_2$	X	
35	Strontium tartrate	$(CHOHCO_2)_2Sr$	X	X
36	Barium tartrate	$(CHOHCO_2)_2Ba$	X	X
37	Lead tartrate	$(CHOHCO_2)_2\ Pb \cdot xH_2O$	X	X
38	Lithium citrate	$((O_2CCH_2)C(OH)(CO_2))Li3$	X	X
39	Sodium citrate	$((O_2CCH_2)_2C(OH)(CO_2))Na_3$	X	X
40	Calcium citrate	$((O_2CCH_2)_2C(OH)(CO_2))_2Ca_3$	X	
41	Bismuth citrate	$((O_2CCH_2)_2C(OH)(CO_2))_2Bi_3$	X	X
42	Manganese citrate	$((O_2CCH_2)_2C(OH)(CO_2))_2Mn$	X	X
43	Bismuth ammonium citrate	$((O_2CCH_2)C(OH)(CO_2))BeNH_4$	X	X
44	Manganese sodium citrate	$((O_2CCH_2)C(OH)(CO_2))MnNa$	X	X
45	Stannous EDTA	$[CH_2\text{-}N(\text{-}CH_2\text{-}CO_2)]_2Sn_2$	X	
46	Lithium hippurate	$(C_6H_5C({=}O)NHCH_2CO_2)Li$	X	X

Spectrum Number OS	Compound	Formula	Spectra R	IR
47	Sodium hippurate	$(C_6H_5C(=O)NHCH_2CO_2)Na$	X	X
48	Calcium hippurate	$[((C_6H_5C(=O)NHCH_2CO_2)]Ca$	X	X
49	Lithium benzoate	$(C_6H_5CO_2)Li$	X	X
50	Sodium benzoate	$(C_6H_5CO_2)Na$	X	X
51	Calcium benzoate	$(C_6H_5CO_2)_2Ca$	X	X
52	Bismuth benzoate	$(C_6H_5CO_2)_2Bi$	X	X
53	Manganese benzoate	$(C_6H_5CO_2)_2Mn$	X	X
54	Zinc benzoate	$(C_6H_5CO_2)_2Zn$	X	X
55	Lead benzoate	$(C_6H_5CO_2)_2Pb$	X	X
56	Ammonium salicylate	$(o\text{-}(OH)C_6H_4CO_2)NH_4$	X	X
57	Lithium salicylate	$(o\text{-}(OH)C_6H_4CO_2)Li$	X	X
58	Sodium salicylate	$(o\text{-}(OH)C_6H_4CO_2)Na$	X	X
59	Calcium salicylate	$(o\text{-}(OH)C_6H_4CO_2)_2Ca$	X	X
60	Bismuth salicylate	$(o\text{-}(OH)C_6H_4CO_2)_2Bi$	X	X
61	Ferric salicylate	$(o\text{-}(OH)C_6H_4CO_2)_3Fe$	X	
62	Zinc salicylate	$(o\text{-}(OH)C_6H_4CO_2)_2Zn$	X	X
63	Cadmium salicylate	$(o\text{-}(OH)C_6H_4CO_2)_2Cd$	X	X
64	Potassium phthalate	$[o\text{-}C_6H_4(CO_2)_2]K_2$	X	X
65	Sodium cinnamate	$(C_6H_5CH=CHCO_2)Na$	X	X
66	Sodium 4-nitrophenate	$(4\text{-}NO_2C_6H_4O)Na$	X	
67	Sodium 2,4-dinitrophenate	$(2,4\text{-}(NO_2)C_6H_3O)Na$	X	
68	Sodium benzenesulfonate	$(C_6H_5SO_3)Na$	X	X
69	Sodium 4-hydroxybenzenesulfonate	$(4\text{-}(OH)C_6H_4SO_3)Na$	X	

E. NUMERICAL INDEX OF INORGANIC MATERIALS USED FOR INFRARED WINDOWS

Spectrum Number	Window Material	Spectra IR
W1	Pyrex	X
W2	Quartz	X
W3	Silicon wafer	X
W4	Silicon carbide	X
W5	Lithium fluoride	X
W6	Sodium chloride	X
W7	Potassium bromide	X
W8	Silver chloride	X
W9	Zinc selinide	X
W10	Cadmium telluride	X
W11	Barium fluoride sealed cell (0.026 mm pathlength)	X
W12	Sodium chloride sealed cell (0.108 mm pathlength)	X
W13	Calcium fluoride sealed cell (0.099 mm pathlength)	X
W14	Potassium chloride sealed cell (0.200 mm pathlength)	X

A. ALPHABETICAL INDEX OF SPECTRA FOR IONIC INORGANIC COMPOUNDS AND MINERALS

Compound	Vols. 2–3 Spectrum Number IR	R	R in water solution	Vol. 4 Spectrum Number
silicon				4
tantalum				3
tungsten				14, 15
vanadium				5
zirconium				9
Borotungstate, *see* Tungsten				
Bromate				
aluminum	328	328		825
barium		327		824
cadmium		330		828
cesium		325		822
lead		329		826
lithium				818
magnesium	326	326		823
potassium	323	323		820
rubidium	324	324		821
sodium		322	(322)	819
zinc				827
Bromide				
ammonium		314		795
ammonium cadmium				817
antimony (III)	316			806
arsenic				805
barium	315	315		801
bismuth	317			807
cadmium	320			812
cesium				799
holmium				816
indium				802
iron (II)	319			809
lanthanum				813
lead				804
mercury (I),(II)		321		814, 814a
neodymium				815
potassium				797
rubidium				798
silver				811
sodium				796
strontium				800
tellurium	318			808
tin				803
zinc				810
Cadmate				
iodo-, potassium	345			853
Carbonate				
barium		34		63

Compound	Vols. 2–3 Spectrum Number IR	R	R in water solution	Vol. 4 Spectrum Number
bismuth (basic)				70
cadmium	36	36		68
calcium		33		61, 61a
cesium				60
cobalt (basic)				66
copper (II) (basic)				72, 73
guanidinium	37	37		
lead	64	35	35	
lead (basic)				69
lithium	31	31		56
manganese				65
nickel				71
potassium			(32a)	59
silver				67
sodium	32	32	(32)	57, 58
strontium				62
zinc (basic)				74
bi-				
ammonium				53
potassium	30	30		55
sodium	29	29	(29)	54
thio-, barium	38	38		75
Carbide, boron				26
Cerate (III)				
pentanitrato-, ammonium				196
Cerate (IV)				
hexanitrato-				
ammonium				197
magnesium				199
potassium				198
Chlorate				
barium		307		783
potassium				781
sodium		305		780
strontium	306	306		782
per-				
ammonium		308		784
barium				790, 791
cerium	311	311		794
cesium				788
gallium				792
lithium				785
magnesium	312	312		789
rubidium	310			787
sodium	309	309	(309)	786
zinc		313		793

Compound	Vols. 2–3 Spectrum Number IR	R	R in water solution	Vol. 4 Spectrum Number
Chloride				
aluminum				726
ammonium		304		715
ammonium gallium				762
ammonium magnesium				758
barium				725
barium cadmium				776
cadmium				742
cerium				749
calcium				722, 723
cesium				720
chromium (III)				732, 733
cobalt				735
gadolinium				752
hafnium				744
hexammine cobalt				757
holmium				753
indium				727, 728
iron (II)				734
lanthanum				743
lead				730
lead fluoride				610
lithium				716
magnesium				721
mercury (I)				747
mercury (II)				748
mercury amide				755
nickel				736
niobium				739
palladium				740
palladium, diammine (trans)				756
potassium				718
potassium magnesium				759
praseodymium				750
rubidium				719
samarium				751
silver				741
sodium				717
sodium aluminum				761
strontium				724
tantalum				745
thallium				729
thorium				754
tungsten				746
uranyl				394
vanadium				731
yttrium				738

Compound	Vols. 2–3 Spectrum Number IR	R	R in water solution	Vol. 4 Spectrum Number
zinc				737
zirconyl				391
oxy-				
antimony				387
bismuth				388
molybdenum				392
Chlorite, sodium			(304a)	779
Chromate				
aluminum	244	244		557
ammonium	237	237		550
cadmium	246			559
calcium		243		556
cesium	221	221		554
lead		245		558
lithium	238	238	(238)	551
lithium sodium				560
magnesium		242		555
potassium		240	(240)	553
potassium zinc	247	247		561
sodium	239	239		552
di-				
ammonium	231	231		542
calcium	547	235	235	
lithium	232			543
potassium		234		545
rubidium				546
silver	236			549
sodium	233	233		544
zinc				548
hexafluoro-, potassium				696
Chromite				
copper (I)				540
copper (II)				541
Clay, kaolin				95
Cobaltite, lithium				881
Cobaltite (III)				
hexanitro-, sodium		61		153
Cuprate				
cyano-, potassium		14	14	34
tetrachloro-				
ammonium				769
potassium				770
Cyanamide, lead				52
Cyanate				
silver	24	24		45
sodium	23	23		44
thio-				

Compound	Vols. 2–3 Spectrum Number IR	R	R in water solution	Vol. 4 Spectrum Number
sodium				281
phosphorodi-, potassium				284
Fluoride				
aluminium				605
antimony				611
barium				604
bismuth				612
cadmium				630
calcium				602
cerium (III)				633
chromium (III)				617, 618
cobalt (II)	269			622
cobalt (III)				623
copper (II)	271			625
dysprosium	276			636
erbium	278			638
gadolinium	275			635
gallium				606
hafnium				632
holmium		277		637
iron (II)				620
iron (III)				621
lanthanum	273			631
lead (II)	266			608
lead (IV)				609
lithium				598
magnesium				601
manganese				619
nickel	270			624
potassium				600
samarium	274			634
silver				629
sodium				599
strontium				603
thallium				607
thorium	279			640
titanium (III)				613
titanium (IV)	267			614
uranyl				393
vanadium (III)	268			615
vanadium (IV)				616
ytterbium				639
yttrium				627
zinc				626
zirconium	272			628
hydrogen, sodium				641
Fluorosulfonate, *see* Sulfonate				

Compound	Vols. 2–3 Spectrum Number IR	R	R in water solution	Vol. 4 Spectrum Number
Imido disulfate, *see* Sulfate				
Iodate				
ammonium	346	346		854
barium		352		862
calcium	350	350		860
cesium	349	349		859
cerium	357			867
chromium (III)	354	354		864
cobalt	358			—
lead	353	353		863
lithium				855
nickel	355			865
rubidium	348	348		858
silver	356	356		866
sodium	347	347		856, 857
strontium	351	351		861
zinc	359	359		—
per-				
potassium		361	(361)	869
sodium		360		868
Iodide				
ammonium				829
antimony	336			840
arsenic	335			839
barium	333			834
bismuth	337			841
cesium				833
copper				843
germanium				836
lead				838
mercury (I)				848
mercury (II)	371			849
nickel				842
niobium				845
palladium	339			846
potassium	331			831
potassium bismuth	343			851
rubidium	332			832
silver	340			847
thallium	334			835
tin (IV)				837
ytterbium	342			850
zirconium	338			844
oxy-, bismuth				390
Iodocadmate, *see* Cadmate				
Kaolin clay, *see* Clay				
Manganate				

Compound	Vols. 2–3 Spectrum Number IR	R	R in water solution	Vol. 4 Spectrum Number
barium				871
hexafluoro-, potassium				697, 698, 699
per-				
barium				876
lithium				872
magnesium				875
potassium	362			874
sodium				873
zinc				877
Manganite, lithium				870
Mercurate				
tetraiodo-, copper	344			852
Metaarsenite, *see* Arsenite				
Metaphosphate, *see* Phosphate				
Metaphosphoric acid, *see* Phosphoric acid				
Metaniobate, *see* Niobate				
Metasilicate, *see* Silicate				
Metavanadate, *see* Vanadate				
Minerals				
albite				885
apatite				886
dolomite				887
hectorite				888
microcline				889
pyrite				890
serpentine				891
wavellite				892
Molybdate (VI)				
ammonium		248		—
barium				567
cadmium				575
calcium				565
cobalt				569
copper	252			571
lead	250	250		568
lithium				562
nickel	251			570
potassium				564
silver				574
sodium	249	249	(249)	563
stontium				566
zinc				572
zirconium				573
hexachloro-, potassium				771
para-, ammonium				576
phospho-, ammonium	253	253		577
phospho-, sodium		254		—

Compound	Vols. 2–3 Spectrum Number IR	R	R in water solution	Vol. 4 Spectrum Number
Niobate				
heptafluoro-, potassium		299		711
meta-, potassium				314
ortho-, potassium				315
oxy-, pentafluoro	302	302		—
Nitrate				
aluminum	68	68		162
ammonium	62	62		154
ammonium neodymium	83	83		—
barium				161
bismuth	71	71		168
cadmium				178
calcium		66		159
cerium	78	78		181
cesium	65	65		158
chromium	72			170
cobalt				172
dysprosium				186
erbium				188
gadolinium				184
gallium				163
holmium				187
indium				164
iron (III)	73			171
lanthanum	77	77		179
lead	70	70		166, 167
mercurous				180
neodymium				182
nickelous				173
potassium		63	(63)	156
rubidium				157
samarium				183
scandium				169
silver	76	76		177
sodium		82		155
sodium cobaltic		63	(63)	—
strontium	67	67		160
tellurium (basic)	80	80		193
terbium				185
thallium	69	69		165
thorium				191
thulium				189
uranyl	81	81		195
ytterbium				190
yttrium				175
zinc	74	74		174
zirconium	75			176

Compound	Vols. 2–3 Spectrum Number IR	R	R in water solution	Vol. 4 Spectrum Number
zirconyl				194
sub-, bismuth	79	79		192
Nitride				
aluminum	54			133
barium				131
boron				132
calcium				130
chromium				137
molybdenum	57			140
niobium				139
silicon				134
tantalum				141
titanium	55			135
vanadium	56			136
zirconium				138
Nitrite				
barium				150
lead		60		151
potassium	59	59		—
silver				152
sodium				149
hypo-, sodium				148
strontium	67	67		160
tellurium (basic)	80	80		193
terbium				185
thallium	69	69		165
thorium				191
thulium				189
uranyl	81	81		195
ytterbium				190
yttrium				175
zinc	74	74		174
zirconium	75			176
zirconyl				194
sub-, bismuth	79	79		192
Nitride				
aluminum	54			133
barium				131
boron				132
calcium				130
chromium				137
molybdenum	57			140
niobium				139
silicon				134
tantalum				141

Compound	Vols. 2–3 Spectrum Number IR	Vols. 2–3 Spectrum Number R	R in water solution	Vol. 4 Spectrum Number
titanium	55			135
vanadium	56			136
zirconium				138
Nitrite				
barium				150
lead		60		151
potassium	59	59		—
silver				152
sodium				149
hypo-, sodium				148
Nitroferricyanide, *see* Cyanide				
Orthoarsenate, *see* Arsenate				
Orthoarsenite, *see* Arsenite				
Orthoniobate, *see* Niobate				
Orthophosphate, *see* Phosphate				
Orthophosphite, *see* Phosphite				
Orthosilicate, *see* Silicate				
Orthovanadate, *see* Vanadate				
Oxide				
aluminum				319
αaluminum			140a	—
antimony				328, 329
cadmium				354
calcium				318
cerium (IV)				359
chromium (III)				336
cobalt				341, 342
copper(I)				344
copper (II)				345
dysprosium				361
erbium				363
germanium	143			325
hafnium				355
holmium				362
iodine				331
indium	141			320
iron (III) (hematite)				339
iron (magnetite)				340
lead				327
lithium				316
magnesium				317
manganese (II)				337
manganese (IV)				338
mercury (II)				358
molybdenum (IV)				351
molybdenum (VI)				352
nickel				343

Compound	Vols. 2–3 Spectrum Number IR	R	R in water solution	Vol. 4 Spectrum Number
Peroxydisulfate, *see* Sulfate				
Phosphate				
hexafluoro-				
ammonium		288		681
cesium				684
potassium	289	289	(289)	682
potassium and KHF_2				683
meta-				
aluminum				221
barium				220
beryllium	92	92		216
calcium	93	93		218
lead	95	95		222
magnesium				217
potassium	91	91		215
sodium	90	90		214
strontium	94	94		219
zinc				223
ortho-				
aluminum				240
ammonium (monobasic)				224
ammonium (dibasic)				226
ammonium cobalt	116			256
ammonium magnesium		115		254
ammonium manganese				255
ammonium sodium (dibasic)	98	98		—
antimony				243
barium (dibasic)		99		231
barium		103		—
bismuth	107	107		244
boron	104			239
cadmium		114		252
calcium				238
calcium (dibasic)				228
calcium nickel				258
chromium	108			245
cobalt				232
copper (II)	112			249
iron (II)	109			246
iron (III)	110			247
lead	106	106		242b
lead (monobasic)		97		—
lead (apatite)				242c
lead copper (I)	118			259
lithium		100		234
lithium (di)sodium	117			257
magnesium	102			236

Compound	Vols. 2–3 Spectrum Number IR	Vols. 2–3 Spectrum Number R	R in water solution	Vol. 4 Spectrum Number
magnesium (basic)				237
mercury				253
nickel	111			248
potassium (monobasic)			(96a)	225
potassium (dibasic)				227
silver				251
sodium		101		235
sodium (monobasic)		96		—
strontium (dibasic, α-form)				229
strontium (dibasic, β-form)				230
tin (II)	105			241
zinc		113		250
pyro-				
aluminum				269
barium				271
barium (α-form)		121		270
calcium (β-form)				264
calcium (δ-form)	120			—
calcium (γ-form)				268
cobalt				274
copper (II)				276
diamyl ammonium		125		—
lead				273
magnesium				263
nickel				275
potassium				262
potassium sodium				267
sodium	119			260, 261
sodium (dibasic)				233
strontium (α-form)				265
strontium (β-form)				266
tin		123		272
Pyrophosphate				
titanium		122		—
zinc				277
tripoly-				
potassium				279
sodium	124	124		278
Phosphide				
antimony				200
bismuth				201
zinc				203
Phosphite				
hypo-				
ammonium				204
barium	88	88		—
calcium	86	86		208

Compound	Vols. 2–3 Spectrum Number IR	R	R in water solution	Vol. 4 Spectrum Number
iron (II)				204
iron (III)				210
lithium				205
magnesium	87	87		—
manganese				209
potassium		85	(85)	207
sodium	84	84		206
ortho-				
barium				212
sodium				211
Phosphoric acid, meta-				
Phosphorodifluorodate, *see* Flurodate				
Phosphorofluoroidate, *see* Fluoride				
Phosphoromolybdate, *see* Molybdate				
Phosphorothioate, *see* Thioate				
Phosphorotungstate, *see* Tungstate				
Platinate				
cyani, barium				43
tetrachloro-				
ammonium				777
potassium				778
Pyroarsenate, *see* Arsenate				
Pyrophosphate, *see* Phosphate				
Pyrosulfate, *see* Sulfate				
Pyrosulfite, *see* Sulfite				
Pyrovanadate, *see* Vanadate				
Selenate				
ammonium		224		522
calcium	225	225		256
copper (II)		226		529
iron (II)				527
magnesium				525
nickel				528
potassium				524
potassium alumino	229	229		—
silver	228	228		520
sodium			(224a)	523
zinc		227		—
Selenide				
chormium				510
gallium				506
lead	220			508
molybdenum				514
niobium				513
tantalum				515
tin (II)	219			507
titanium	221			509

Compound	Vols. 2–3 Spectrum Number IR	R	R in water solution	Vol. 4 Spectrum Number
zirconium				82
Stannate (IV)				
barium				125
bismuth				127
calcium				123
cerium				129
iron				128
lead				126
magnesium				122
strontium				124
hexachloro-				
ammonium				765
cobalt				766
hexafluoro-				
calcium				677
cobalt				678
copper (II)				680
lithium				673
magnesium				676
nickel				679
potassium				675
sodium				674
hexahydroxo-				
cadmium	159			382
copper (II)	157			380
potassium				379
zinc	158			381
trichloro-				
ammonium				763
potassium				764
trifluoro-				
ammonium				668
iron (II)				671
potasisum				670
sodium				669
zinc				672
Subnitrate, *see* Nitrate				
Sulfamate, lead				412
Sulfate				
aluminum	193	193		444
aluminum sodium	214	214		—
ammonium				431
ammonium antimony trifluoride complex				482
ammonium cadmium	216	216		—
ammonium chromium				483
ammonium cobalt	212			488

Compound	Vols. 2–3 Spectrum Number IR	R	R in water solution	Vol. 4 Spectrum Number
Sulfite				
ammonium		176		—
barium	181	181		427
lead				428
magnesium	179	179		425
potassium		178		—
sodium		177		424
strontium		180		426
pyro-				
potassium		175		423
sodium	174	174		422
Sulfonate				
fluoro-				
ammonium				514
potassium				505
Sulfur				411a
Tantalate				
heptafluoro-, potassium	300	300		713
hexafluoro-, potassium				712
Telluric acid				539
Telluride				
bismuth				532
chromium				535
molybdenum				537
tin (II)	230			531
titanium				533
tungsten				538
vanadium				534
zinc	230a			536
Tetraborate, *see* Borate				
Tetrachlorcuprate, *see* Cuprate				
Tetrachloropalladate, *see* Palladate				
Tetrachloroplatinate, *see* Platinate				
Tetrafluoroaluminate, *see* Aluminate				
Tetrafluoroantimonate, *see* Antimonate				
Tetrafluoroborate, *see* Borate				
Tetraflorozirconate, *see* Zirconate				
Tetrahydroaluminate, *see* Aluminate				
Tetraiodomercurate, *see* Mercurate				
Tetrathiotungtate, *see* Tungstate				
Thiocarbonate, *see* Carbonate				
Thiocyanate, *see* Cyanate				
Thioate				
phosphoro-, sodium				280
Thionate				
di, potassium				429
di, sodium		182		—

Compound	Vols. 2–3 Spectrum Number IR	R	R in water solution	Vol. 4 Spectrum Number
Thiosulfate, *see* Sulfate				
Titanate(IV)				
barium	49	49		103
bismuth				105
calcium				101
cerium				110
cobalt				106
copper				108
europium				111
lead				104
lithium				100
nickel				107
strontium		48		102
zinc				109
hexafluoro-				
ammonium				689
barium				694
calcium				693
lithium				690
nickel				695
potassium	291			692
sodium				691
Trichlorostannate, *see* Stannate				
Trifluorostannate, *see* Stannate				
Tripolyphosphate, *see* Phosphate				
Tungstate				
aluminum				585
ammonium				592
ammonium	255	255		—
barium				584
cadmium				590
calcium	257	257		582
chromium				593
copper				586
lithium				578
magnesium				581
potassium				580
potassium	262			—
para, sodium	261	261,261		591
silver	260			589
sodium	256	256	(256)	579
strontium				583
zinc	258	258		587
zirconium	259			588
boro-, barium	263	263		595
pospho-				
ammonium				596

B. ALPHABETICAL INDEX OF SPECTRA FOR NONIONIC COMPOUNDS AND HYDRAZINE SALTS

Vol. 4

Compound	Spectrum Number IR	Spectrum Number R
ammonia	381	
ammonia-d_3	382	
arsine	408	
boron tribromide	368	
boron trifluoride	367	
bromine		430
carbon dioxide	379	
carbon disulfide	372	372
carbon monoxide	369	
carbonyl chloride	380	
carbonyl fluoride	370	
carbonyl sulfide	371	
chlorine		429
chloromethylphosphonic dichloride	407	
cyanamide	377	
cyanogen	374	
cyanogen bromide	376	
cyanogen chloride	375	
cyanoquanidine	378	
decafluorodisulfide	426	
decaborane	364	
decaborane monohydrazine	366	
decafluorodisulfide	426	
deuterium bromide	435	
deuterium chloride	433	
deuterium oxide	411	
diborane	363	
hydrazine diborane	365	
hydrazine dichloride	389	
hydrazine tetrafluoride	387	
hydrogen bromide	434	
hydrogen chloride	432	
hydrogen cyanide	373	
hydrogen sulfide	413	
iodine		431
methyl chlorosulfinate	427	427
nitric oxide	384	
nitrogen trichloride	386	
nitrogen trifluoride	385	
nitrous oxide	383	
ozone	409	
phosphine	390	
phophoric acid	404	
phophorous tribromide	393	
phosphorus trichloride	392	
phosphorus trifluoride	391	
phosphorus triiodide	394	

Compound	Spectrum Number IR	R	Vol. 4
phosphorus oxybromide	397		
phosphorus oxychloride	396		
phosphorus oxyfluoride	395		
phosphorus pentabromide	402		
phosphorus pentachloride	401		
phosphorus pentasulfide	406		
phosphorus thioamide	405		
potassium methylsulfate	428	428	
pyrosulfuryl chloride	421		
sulfonamide	423		
β-sulfonyl chloride	422		
sulfur	412	412	811a
sulfur dichloride	416		
sulfur dioxide	414		
sulfur hexafluoride	425		
sulfuric acid	424		
sulfur monobromide	417		
sulfur monochloride	415		
sulfuryl chloride	420		
thionyl chloride	419	419	
thionyl fluoride	418		
thiophosphoryl bromide	400		
thiophosphoryl chloride	399		
thiophosphoryl dichloride fluoride	398	398	
trichlorophosphazosulfuryl chloride	403		
water	410		
water-D_2O	411		

C. ALPHABETICAL INDEX OF MISCELLANEOUS MINERALS

Spectrum Number	Compound	Formula	Spectra IR	R	Vol. 4 No. IR
436	Aragonite	$CaCO_3$	X	X	
437	Asbestos (amphibole)		X		
438	Asbestos (crocidolite)		X		
439	Asbestos (serpentine chrysolite)		X		
440	Gearksutite	CaAlF(OH)	X	X	
441	Hydromagnesite	$3Mg \cdot Mg(OH)_2 \cdot 3H_2O$	X	X	
442	Itacolumite		X	X	
443	Kalinite	$AlK(SO_4)_2 \cdot 12H_2O$	X	X	
444	Meyerhofferite	$2Ca \cdot 3B_2O_3 \cdot 7H_2O$	X	X	
445	Quartz	SiO_2	X	X	892
446	Realgar	AsS	X	X	
447	Stilbite	$H_4(Na_2,Ca)Al_2Si_6O_{18} \cdot 4H_2O$	X	X	
448	Thaumasite	$CaSiO_3 \cdot CaCO_3 \cdot CaSO_4 \cdot 15H_2OX$	X	X	
449	Vermiculite		X		

D. ALPHABETICAL INDEX OF SPECTRA FOR ORGANIC SALTS

E. ALPHABETICAL INDEX FOR INFRARED WINDOWS

W

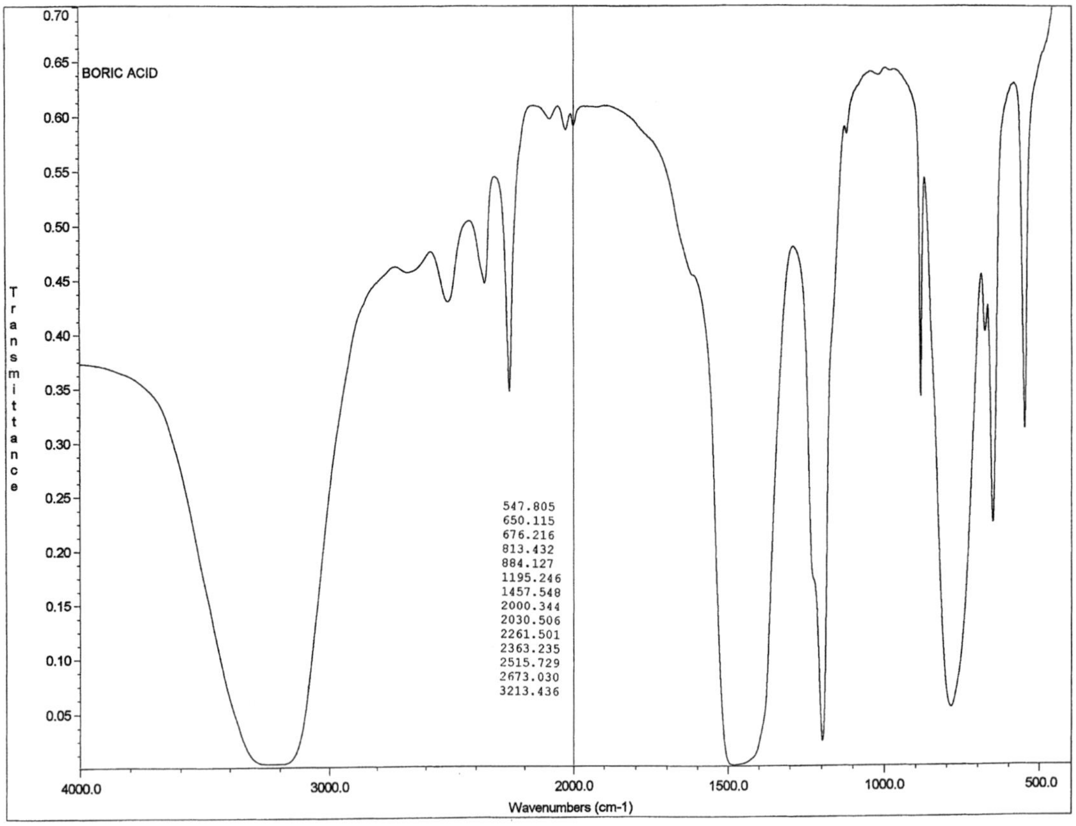

1 Boric acid H_3BO_3

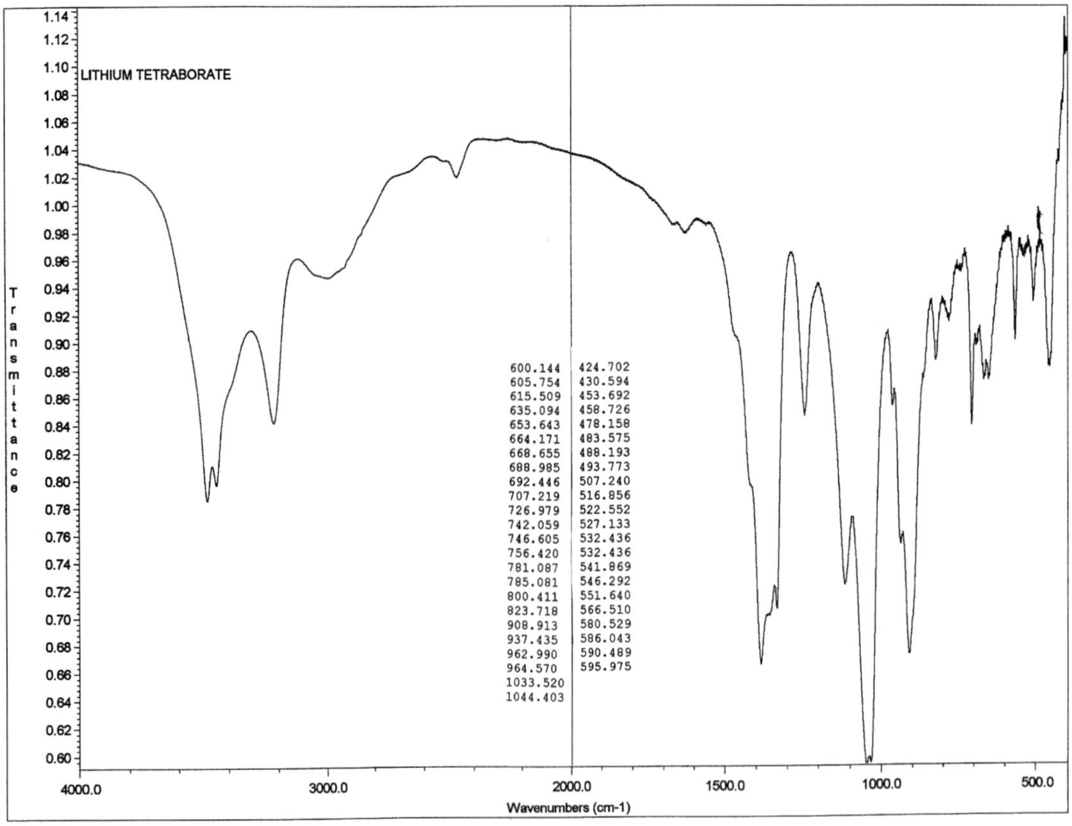

2 Lithium tetraborate $Li_2B_4O_7$

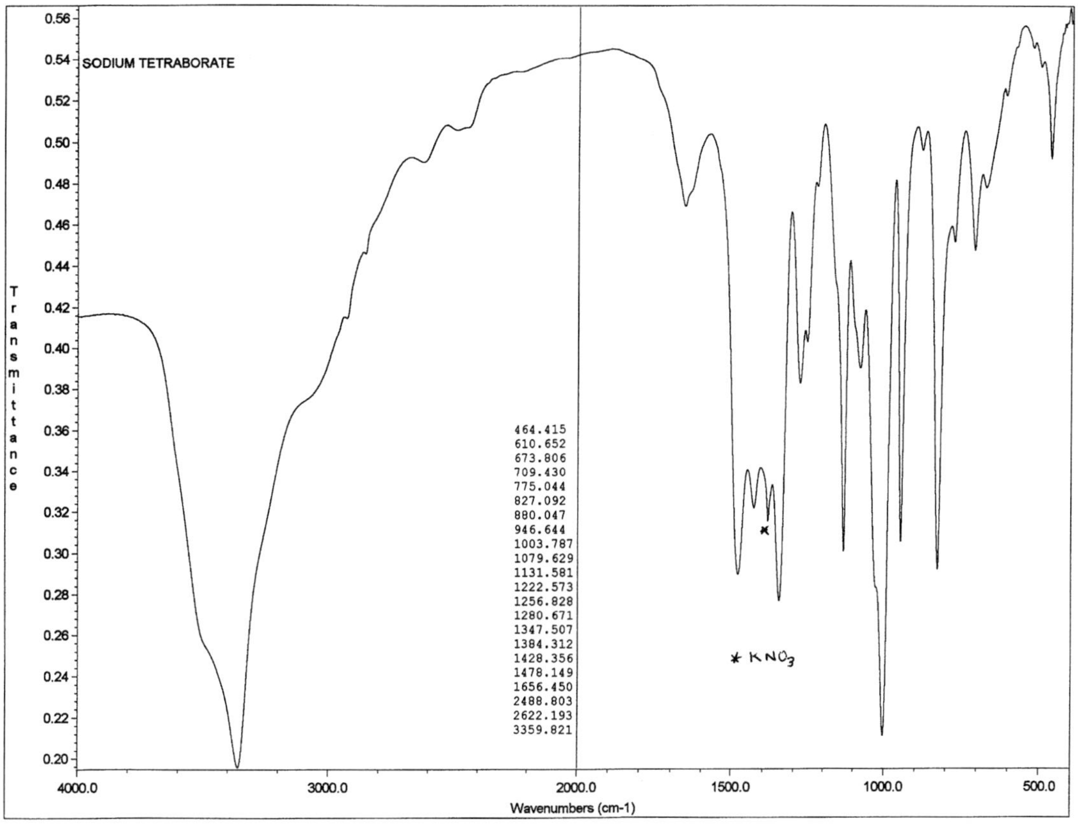

3 Sodium tetraborate $Na_2B_4O_7 \cdot 5H_2O$

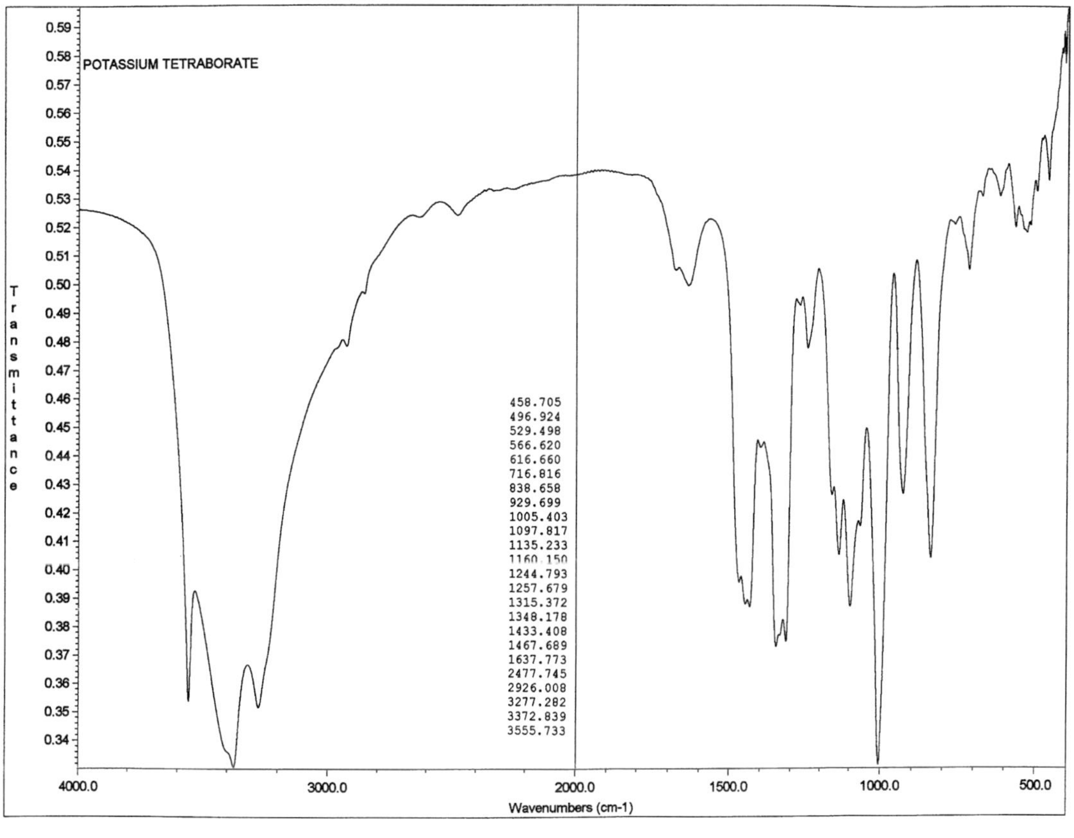

4 Potassium tetraborate $K_2B_4O_7 \cdot 8H_2O$

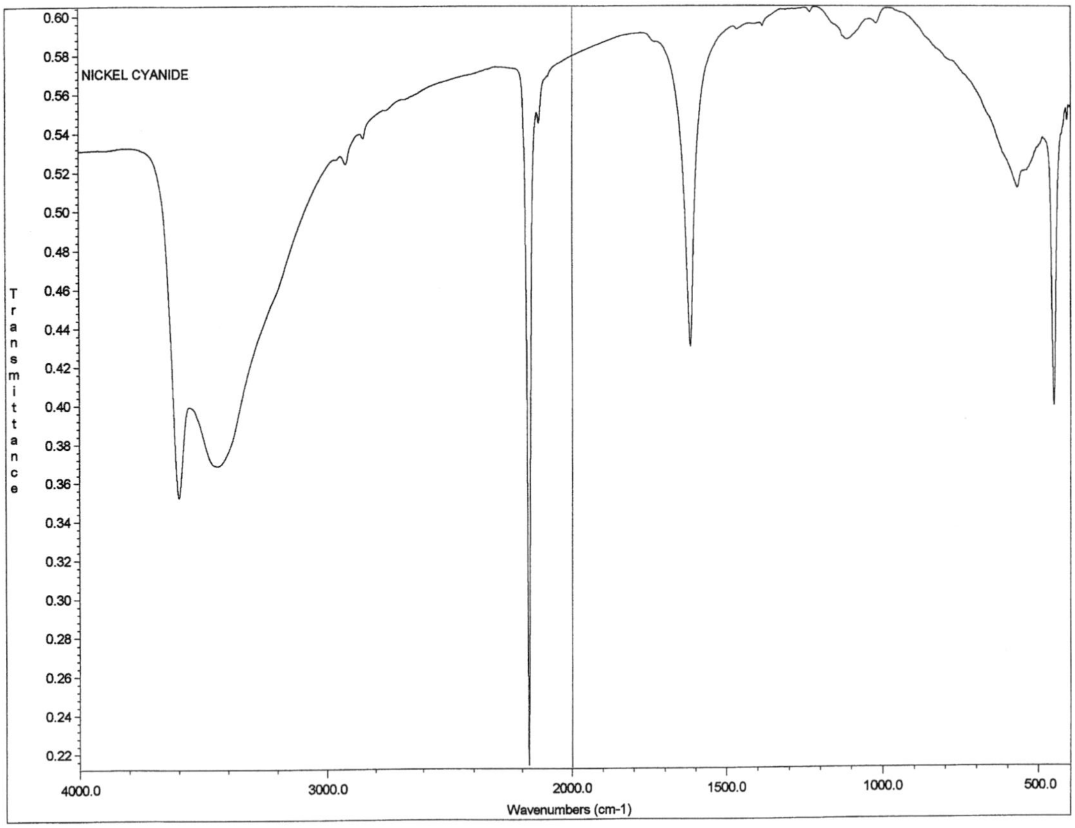

7 Nickel (II) cyanide $Ni(CN)_2 \cdot 4H_2O$

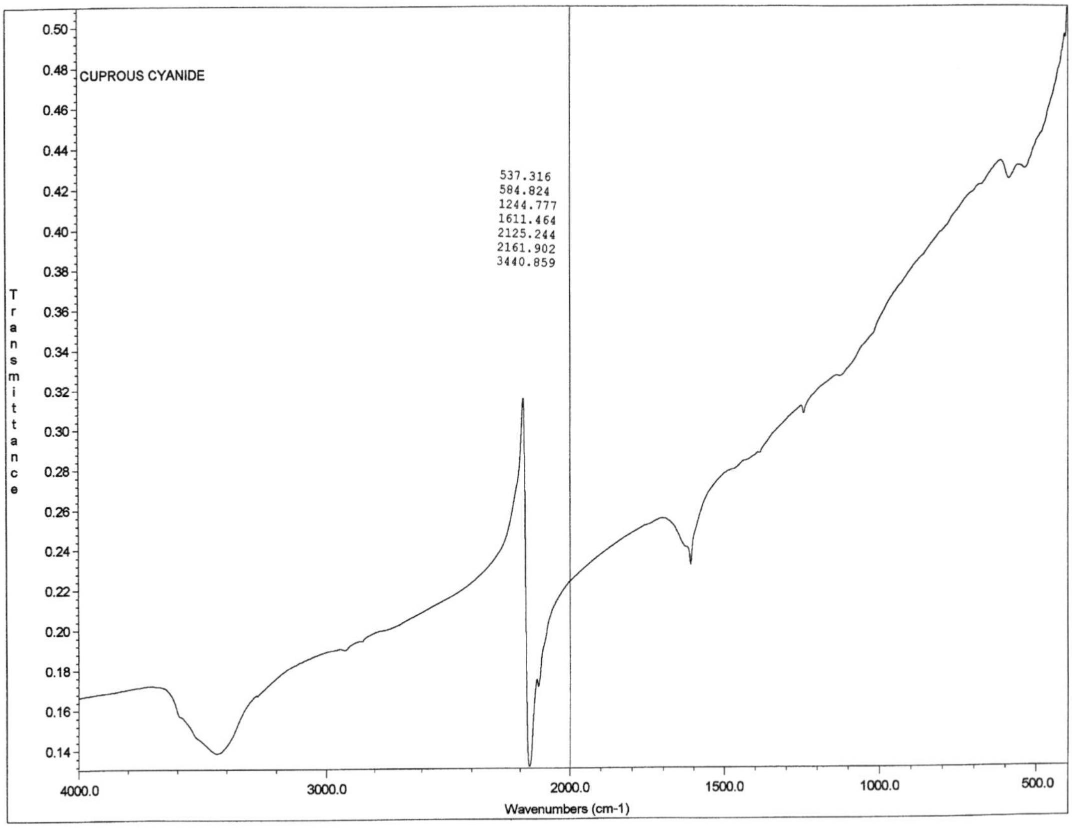

8 Copper (I) cyanide CuCN

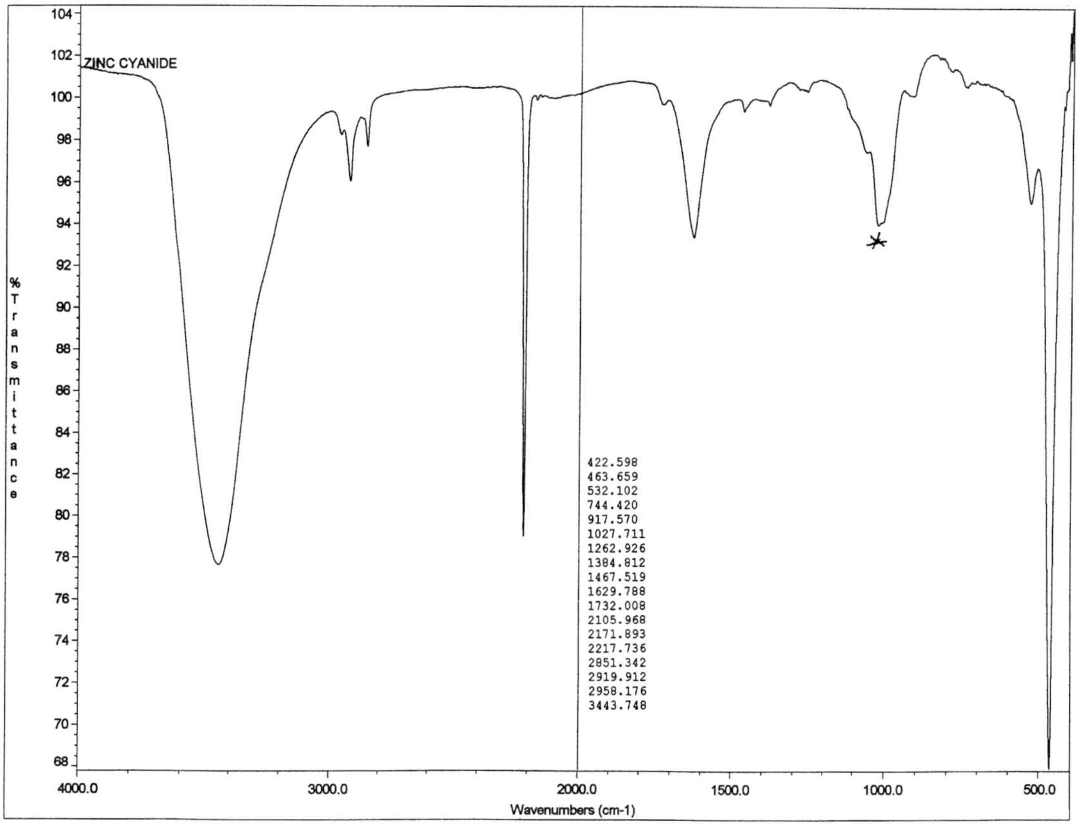

9 Zinc cyanide $Zn(CN)_2$

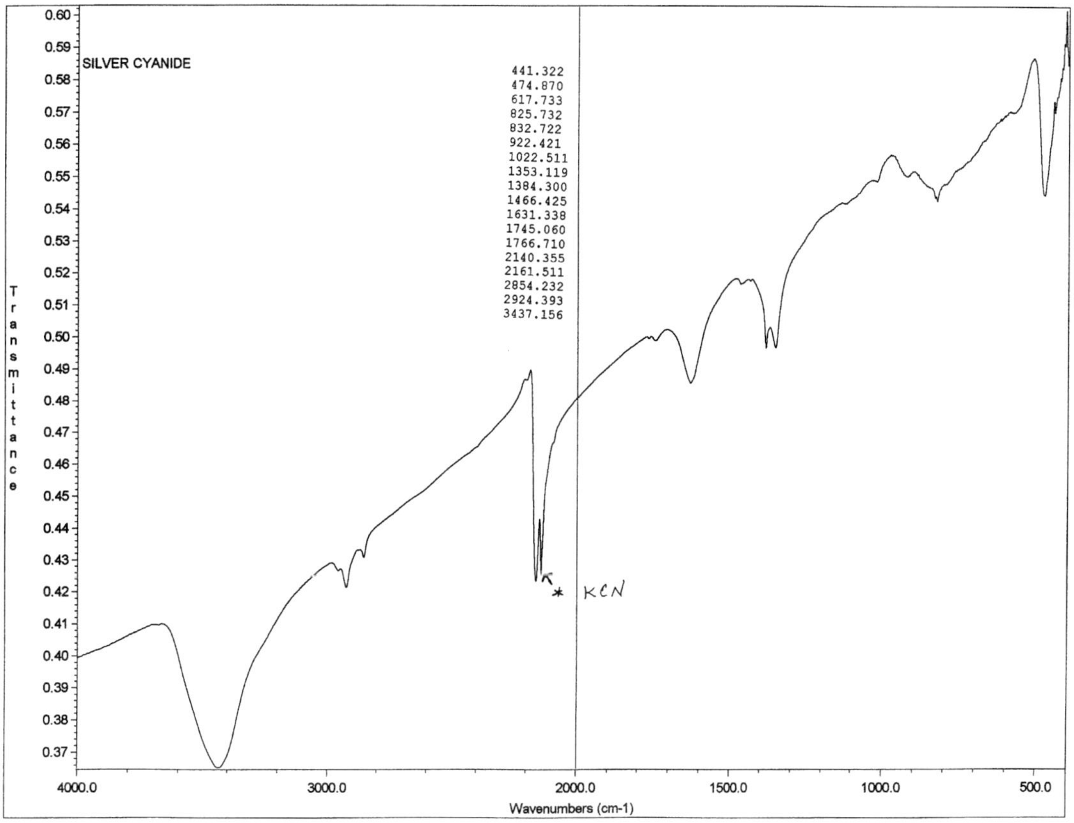

10 Silver cyanide AgCN

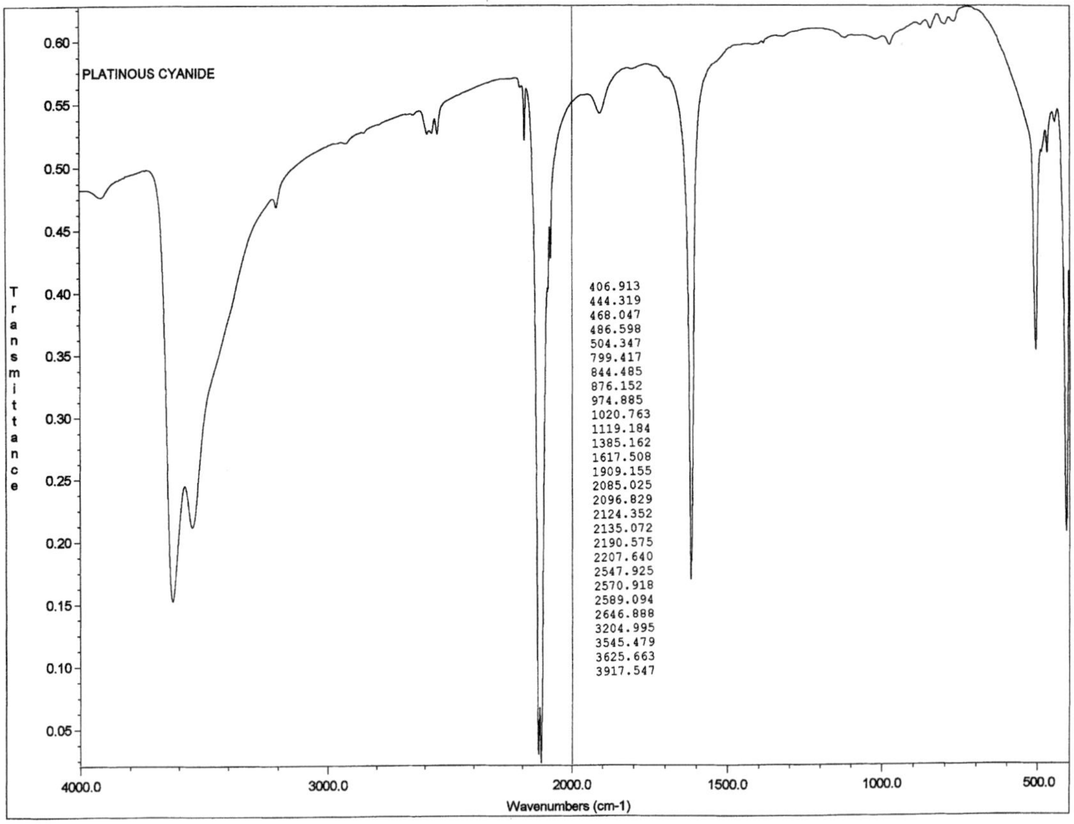

11 Platinous cyanide $Pt(CN)_2 \cdot xH_2O$

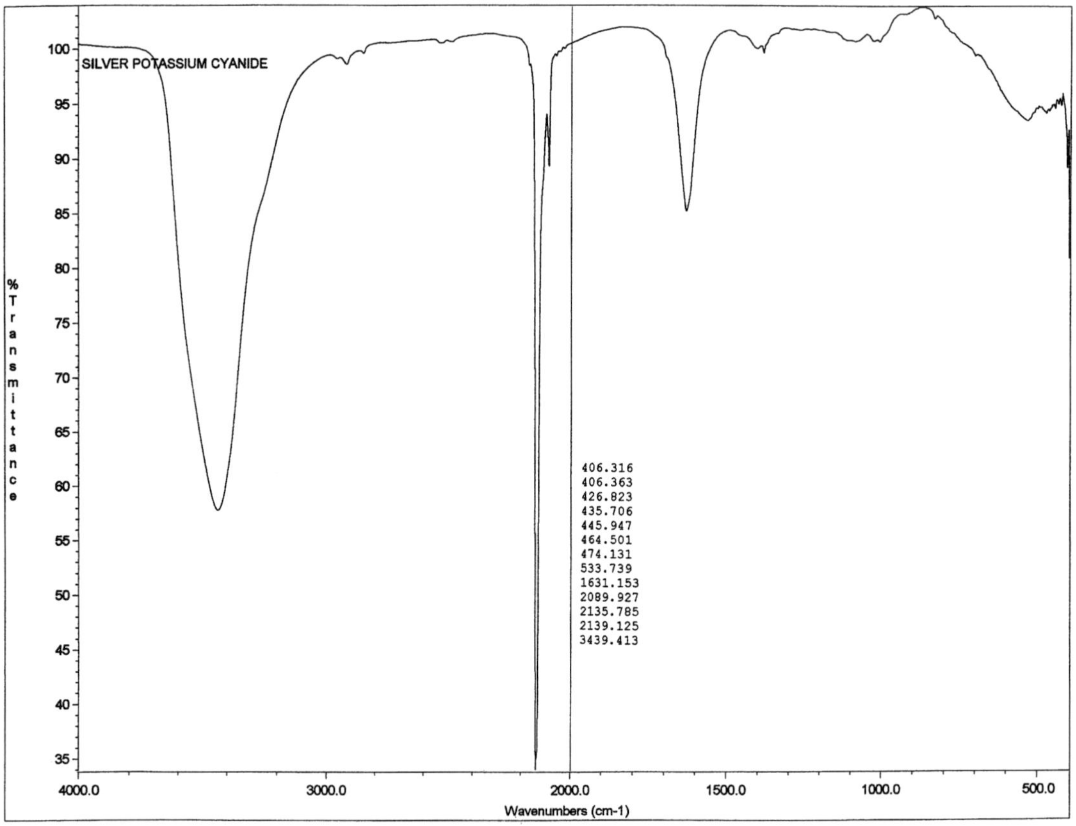

13 Potassium cyanoargenate $KAg(CN)_2$

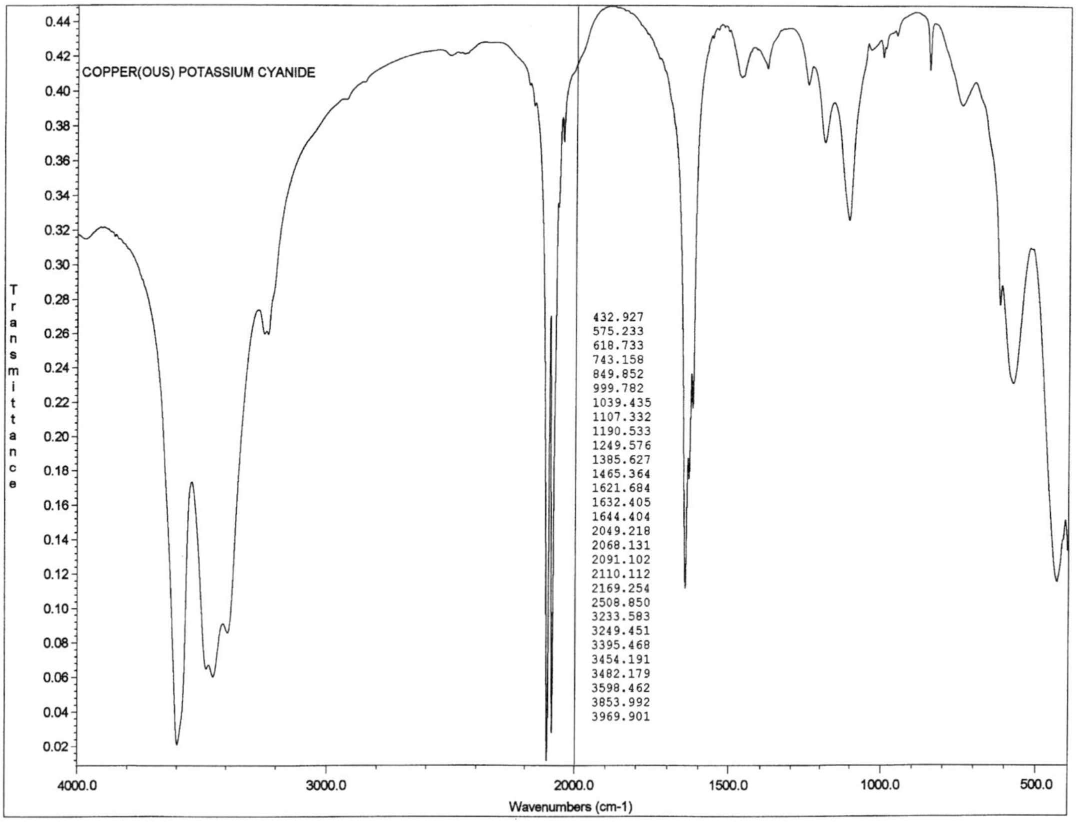

14 Potassium cyanocuprate $KCu(CN_2) \cdot xH_2O$

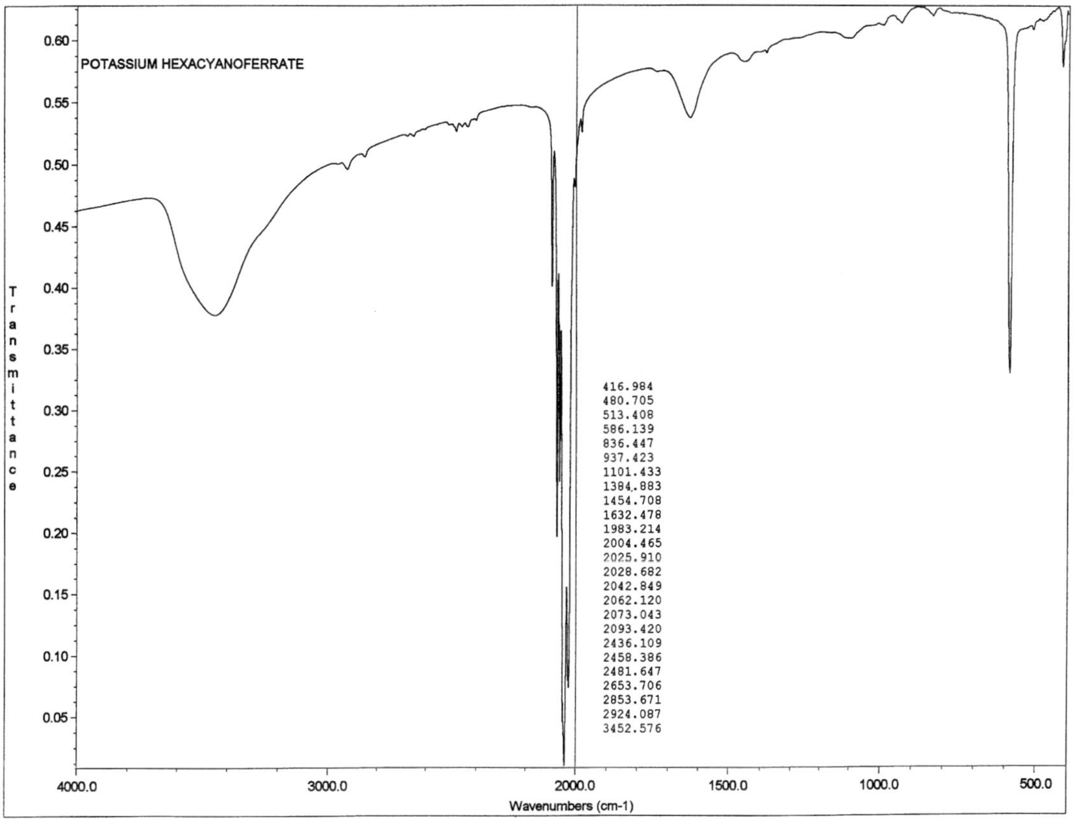

17 Potassium ferrocyanide $K_4Fe(CN)_6$

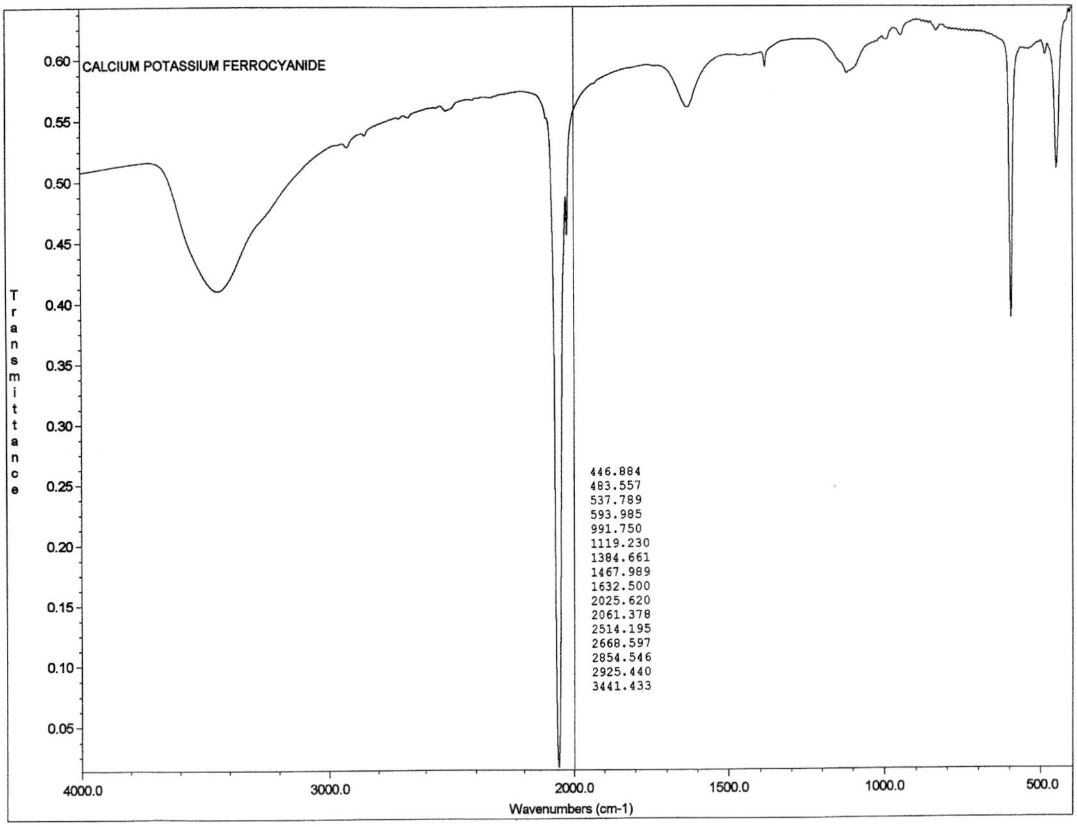

18 Potassium calcium ferrocyanide $K_2CaFe(CN)_6$

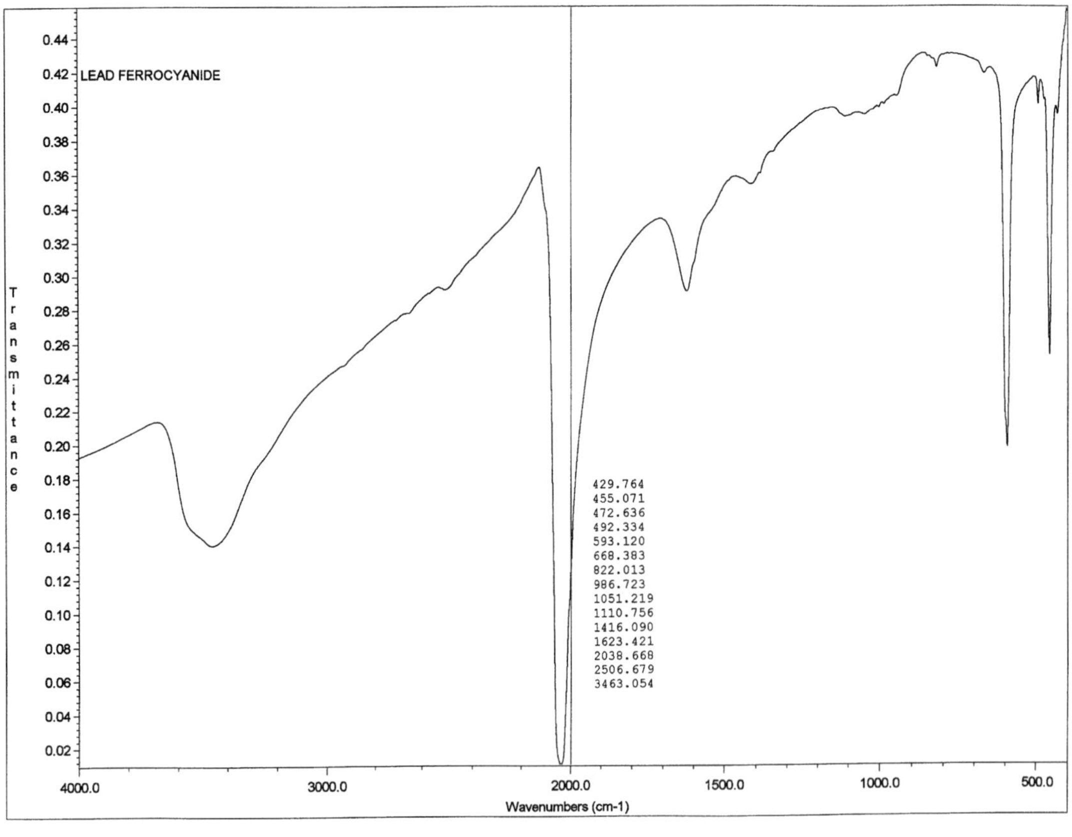

21 Lead ferrocyanide $Pb_2Fe(CN)_6 \cdot xH_2O$

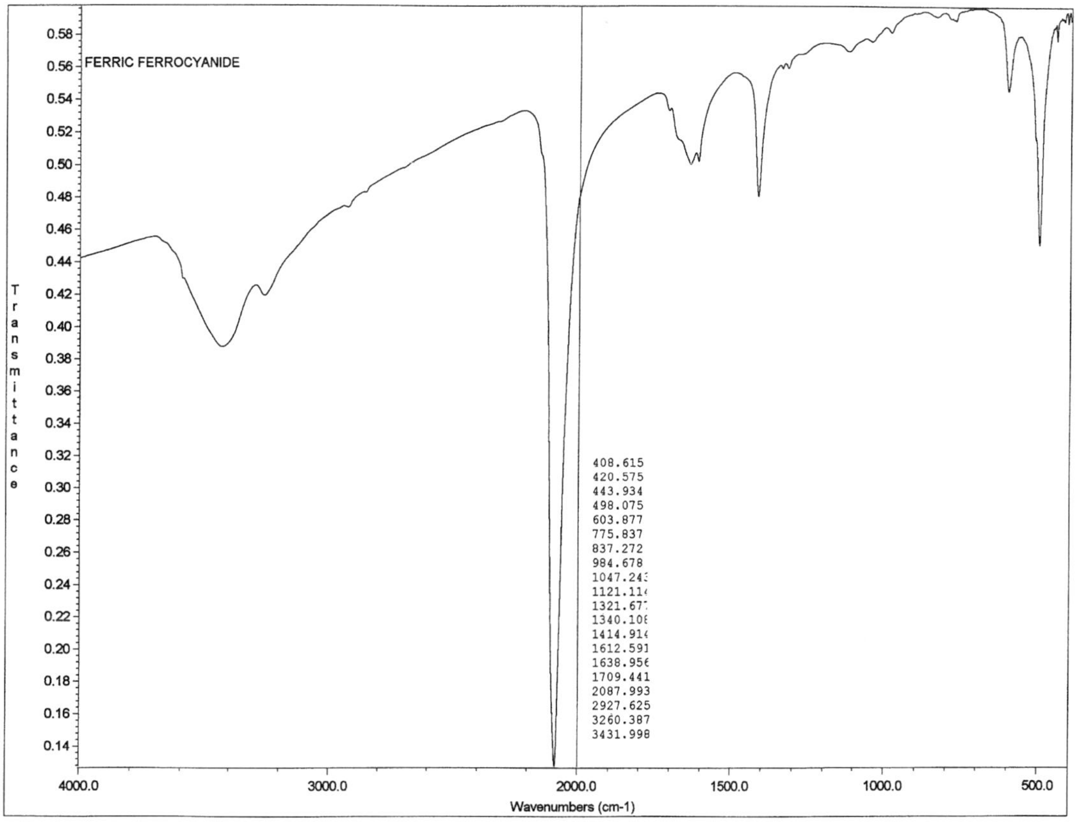

22 Iron (III) ferrocyanide $Fe_4[Fe(CN)_6]_3$

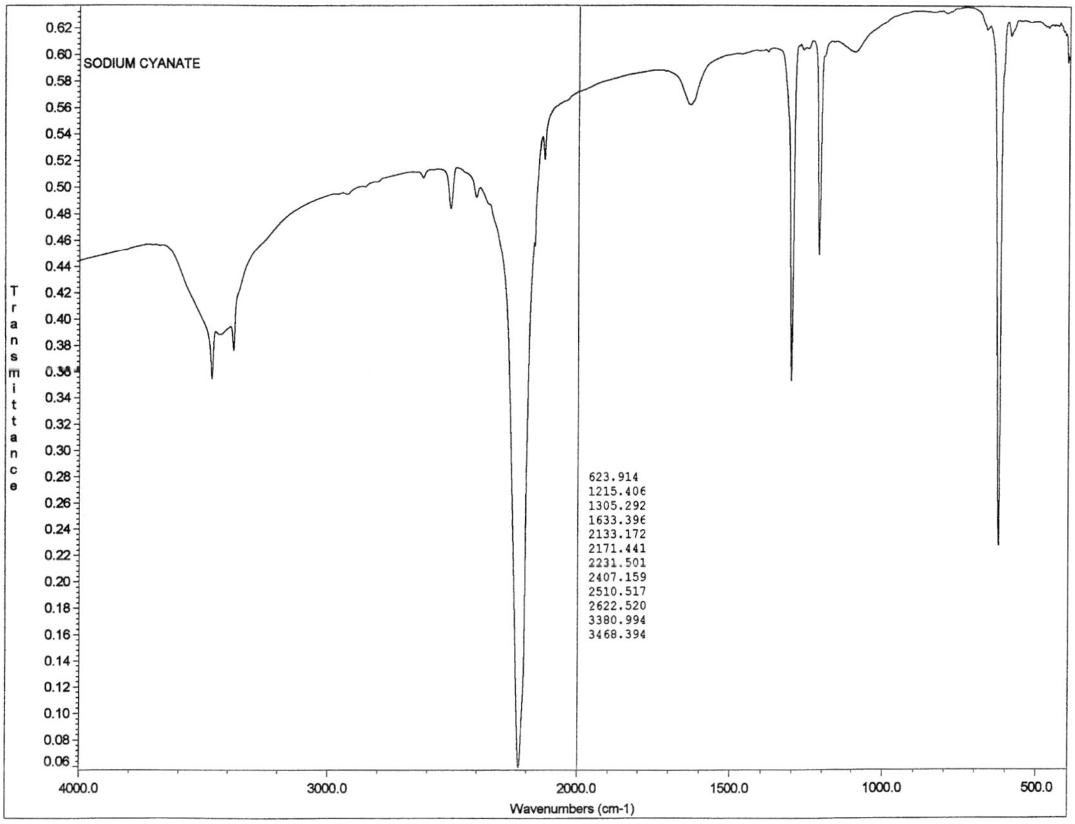

23 Sodium cyanate NaOCN

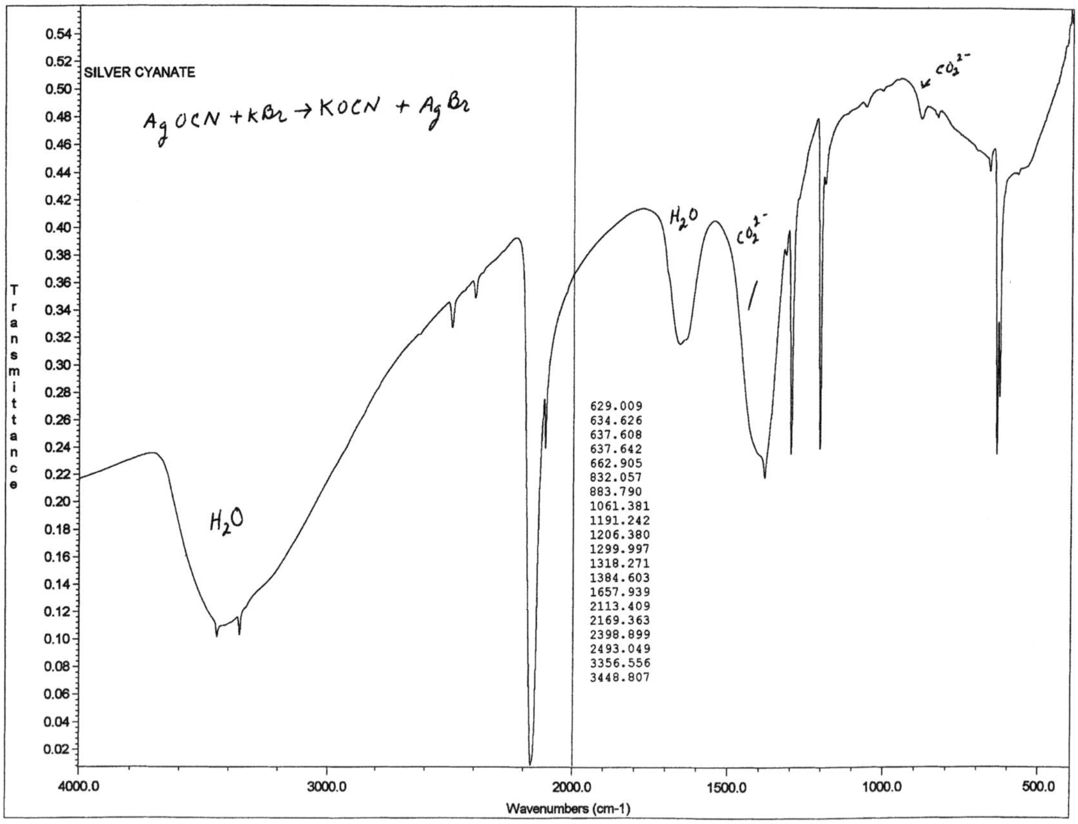

24 Silver cyanate AgOCN

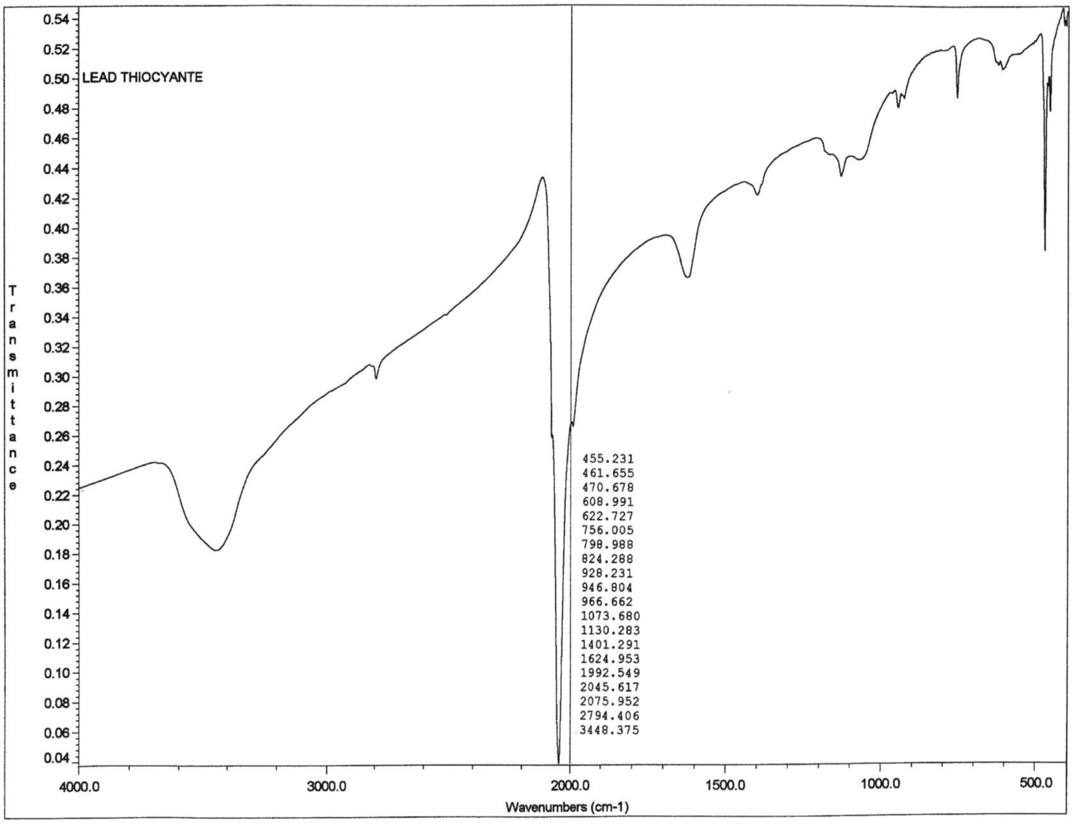

25 Lead thiocyanate $Pb(SCN)_2$

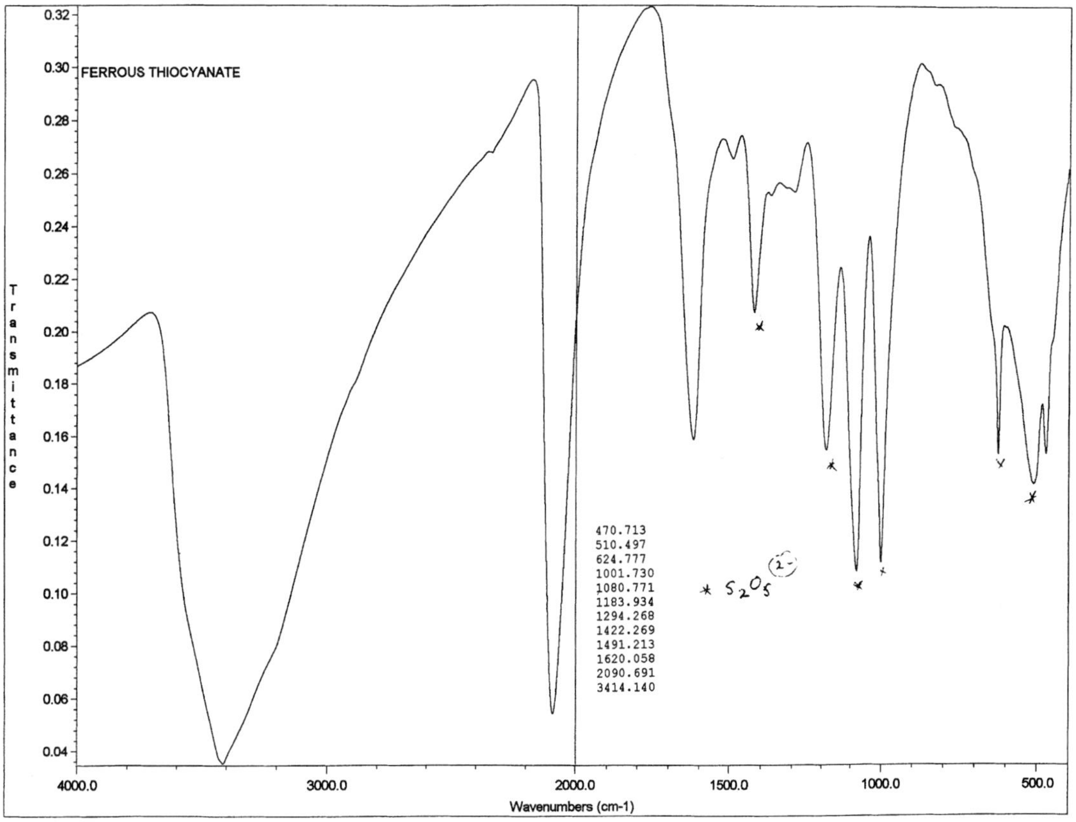

26 Iron (II) thiocyanate $Fe(SCN)_2 \cdot 3H_2O$

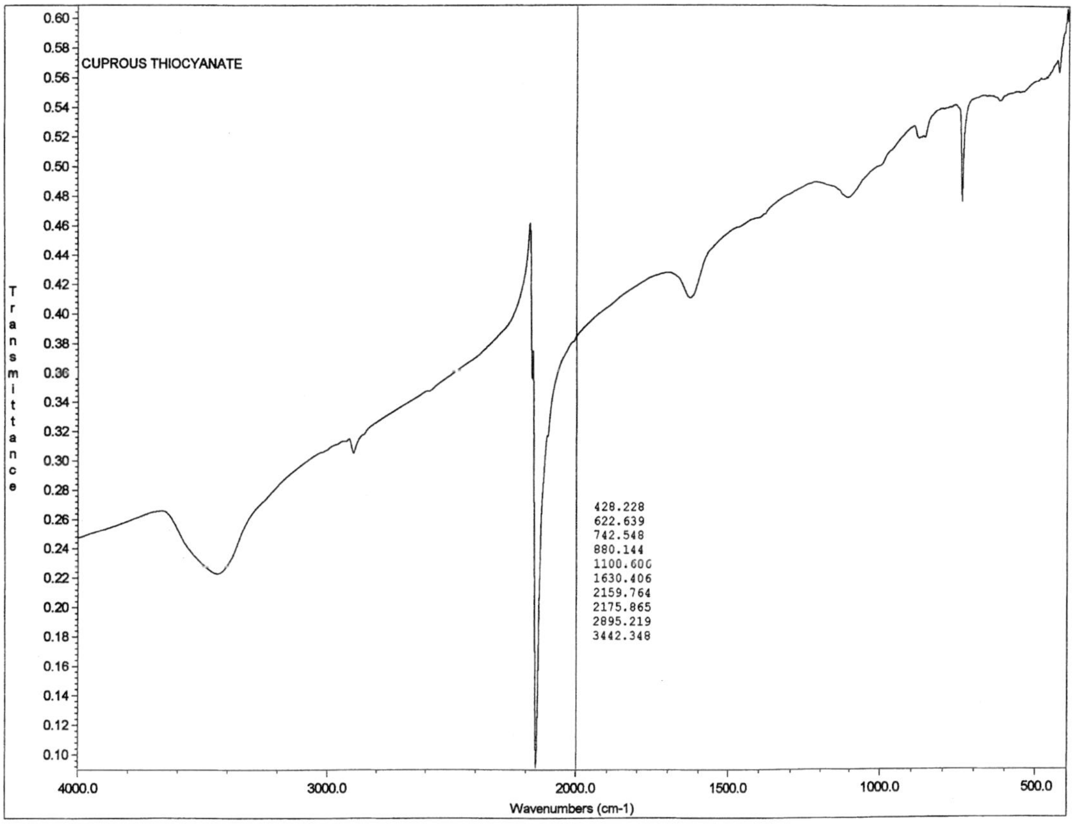

27 Copper (I) thiocyanate CuSCN

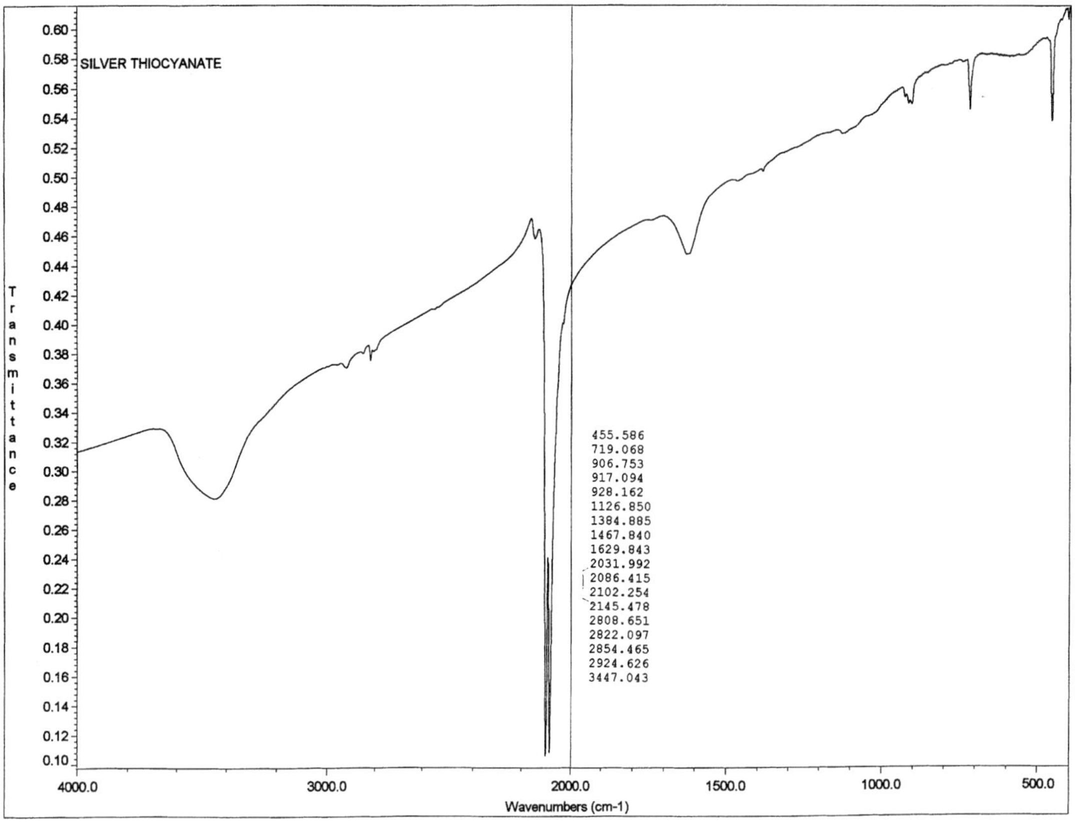

28 Silver thiocyante AgSCN

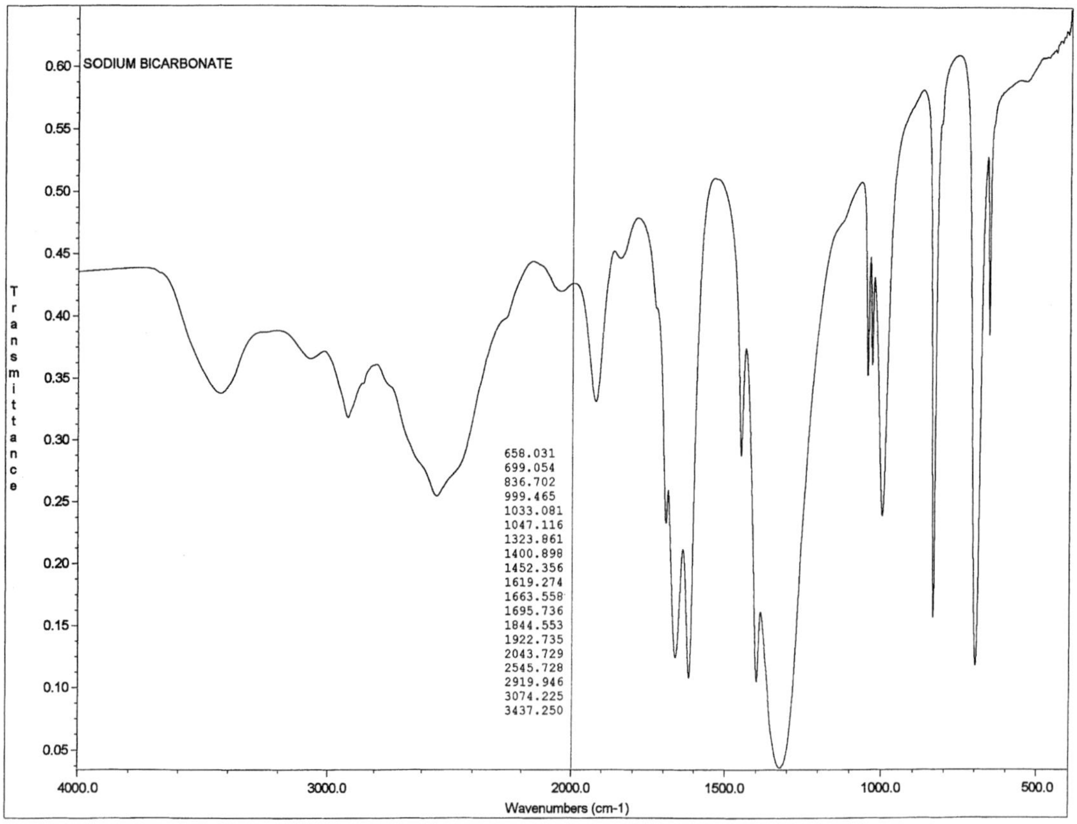

29 Sodium bicarbonate $NaHCO_3$

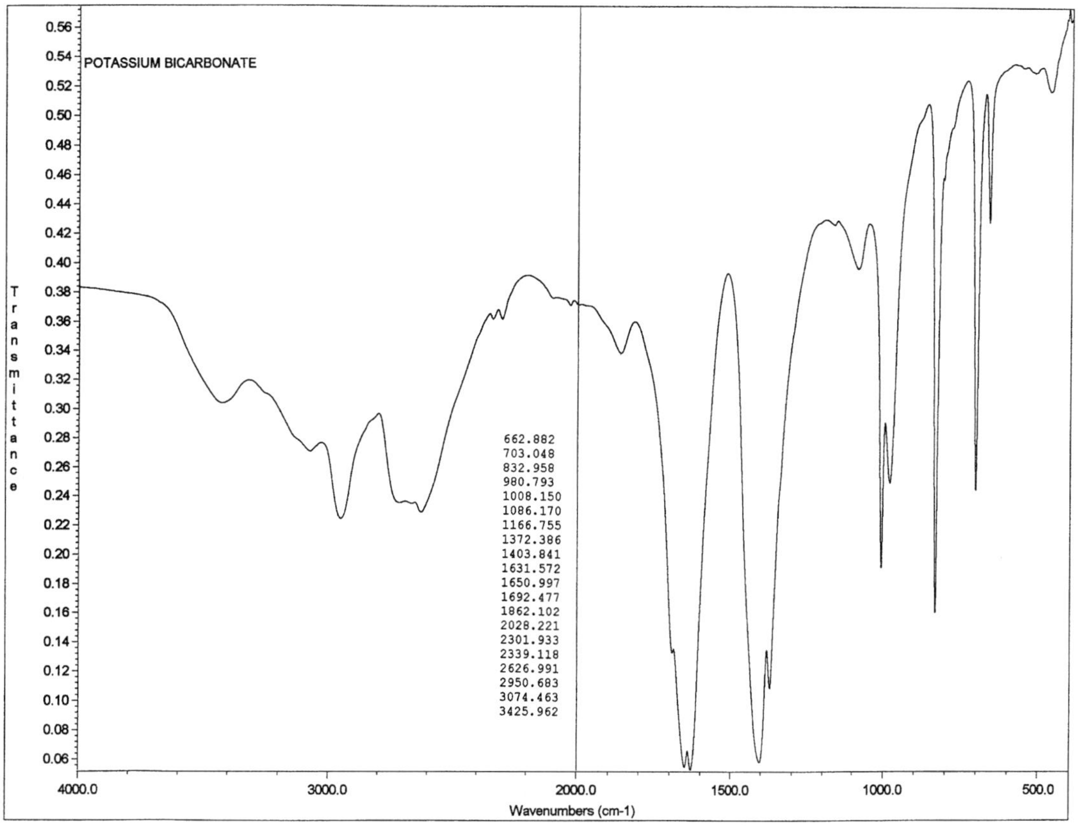

30 Potassium bicarbonate $KHCO_3$

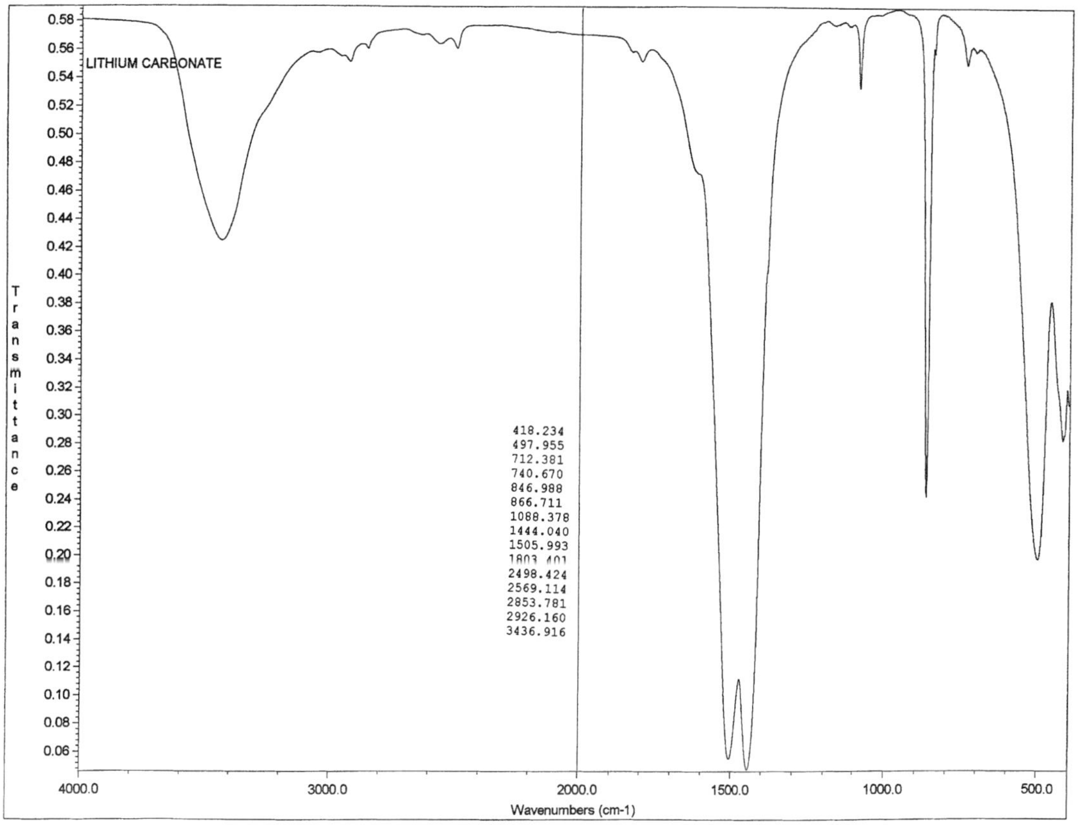

31 Lithium carbonate Li_2CO_3

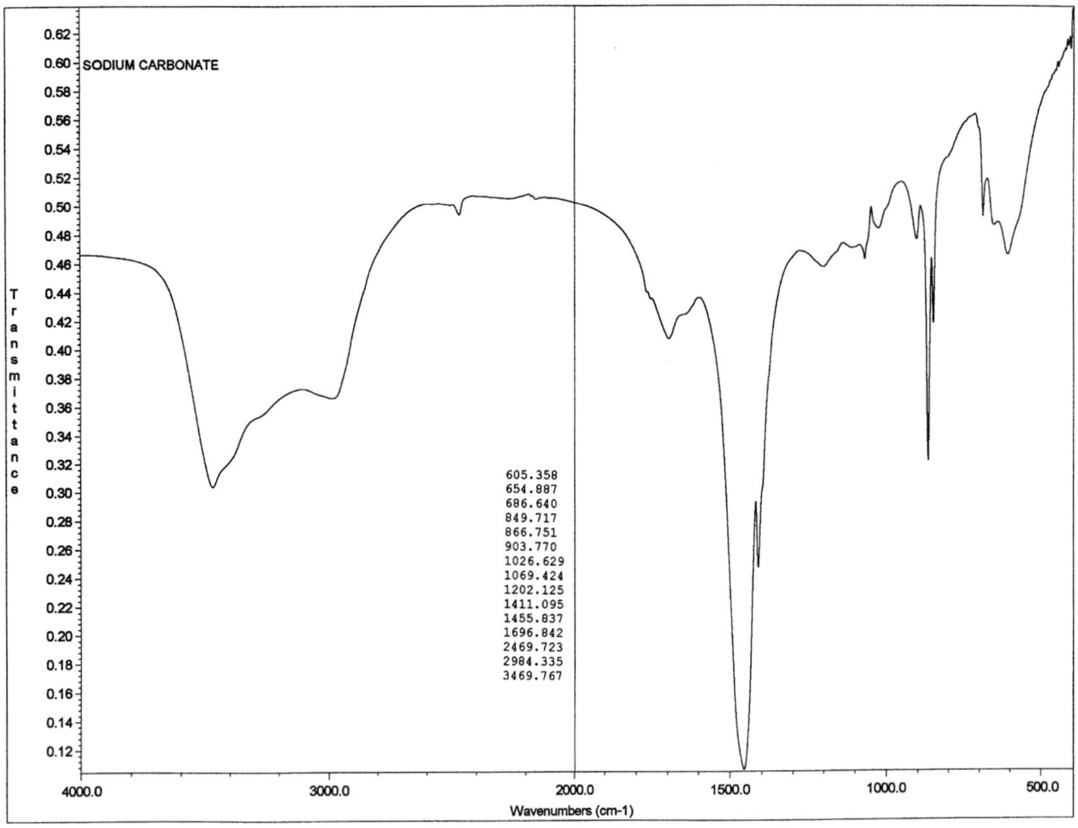

32 Sodium carbonate Na_2CO_3

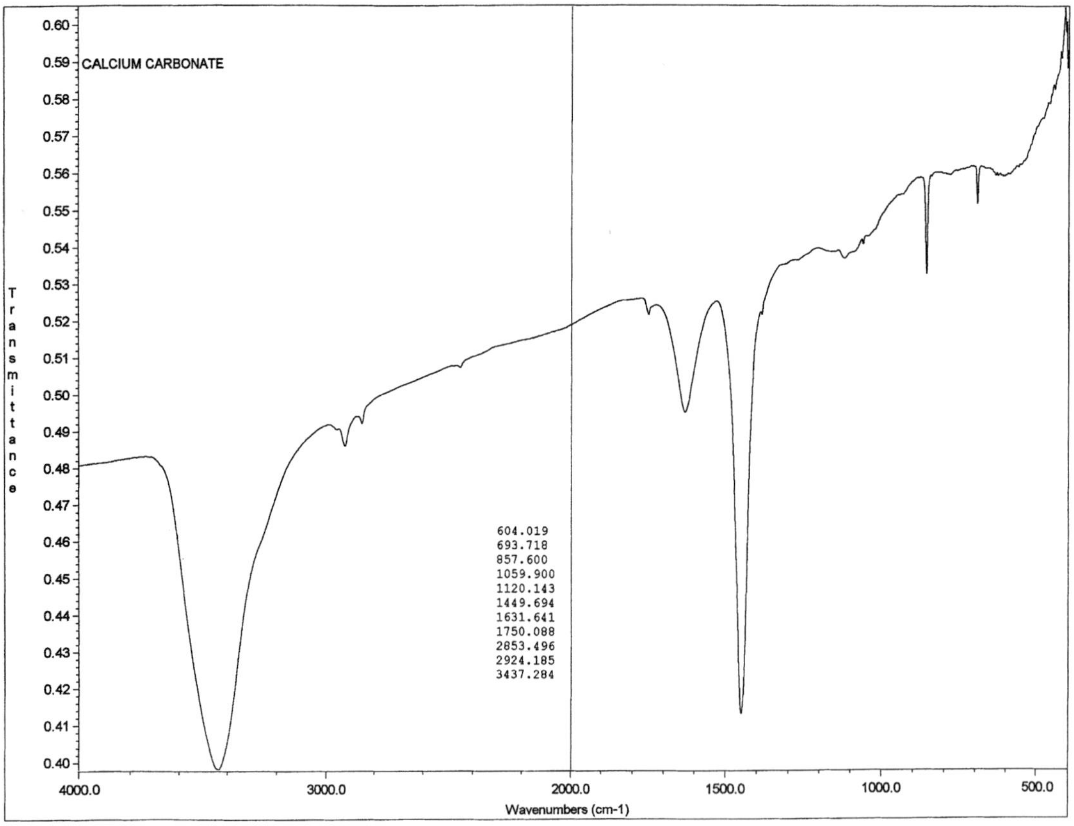

33 Calcium carbonate (calcite) $CaCO_3$

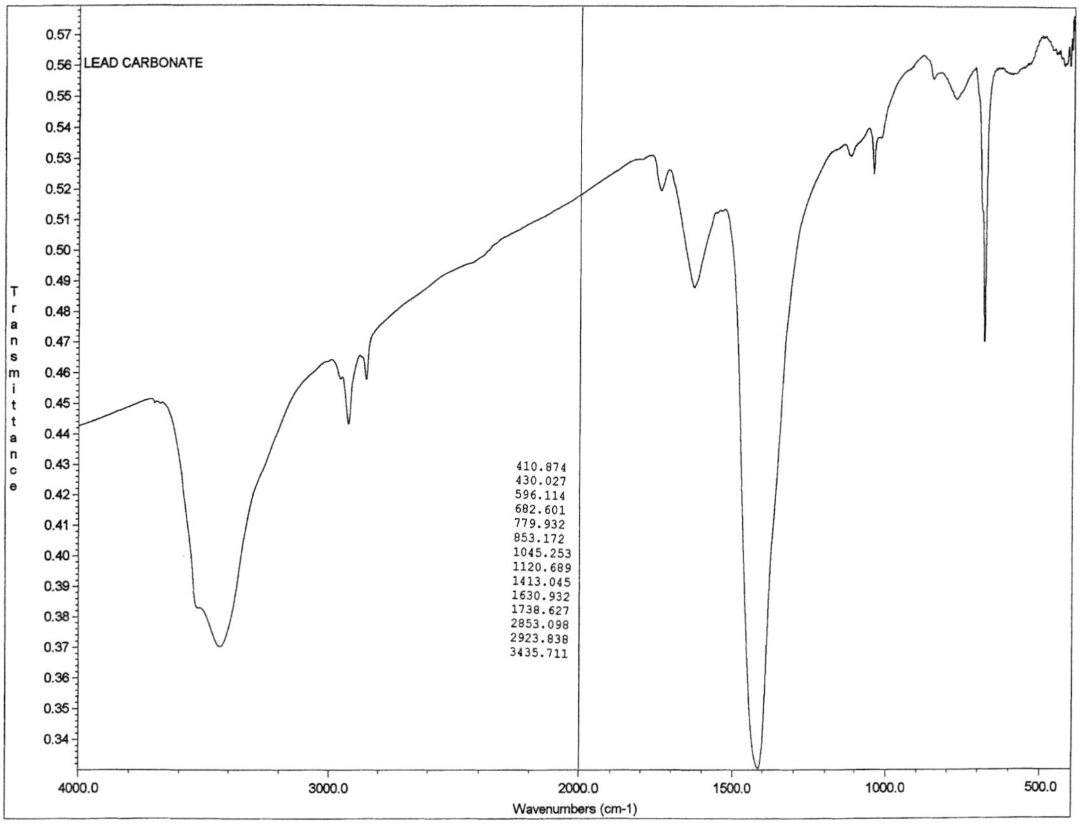

35 Lead carbonate $PbCO_3$

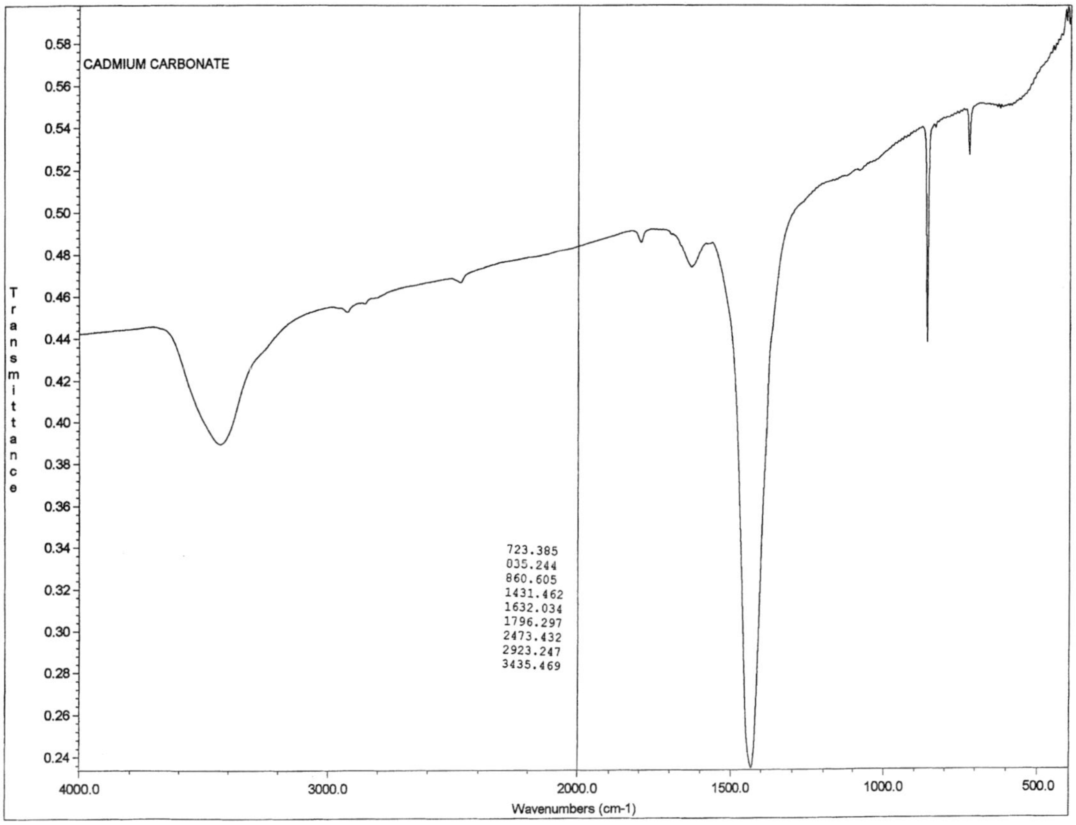

36 Cadmium carbonate $CdCO_3$

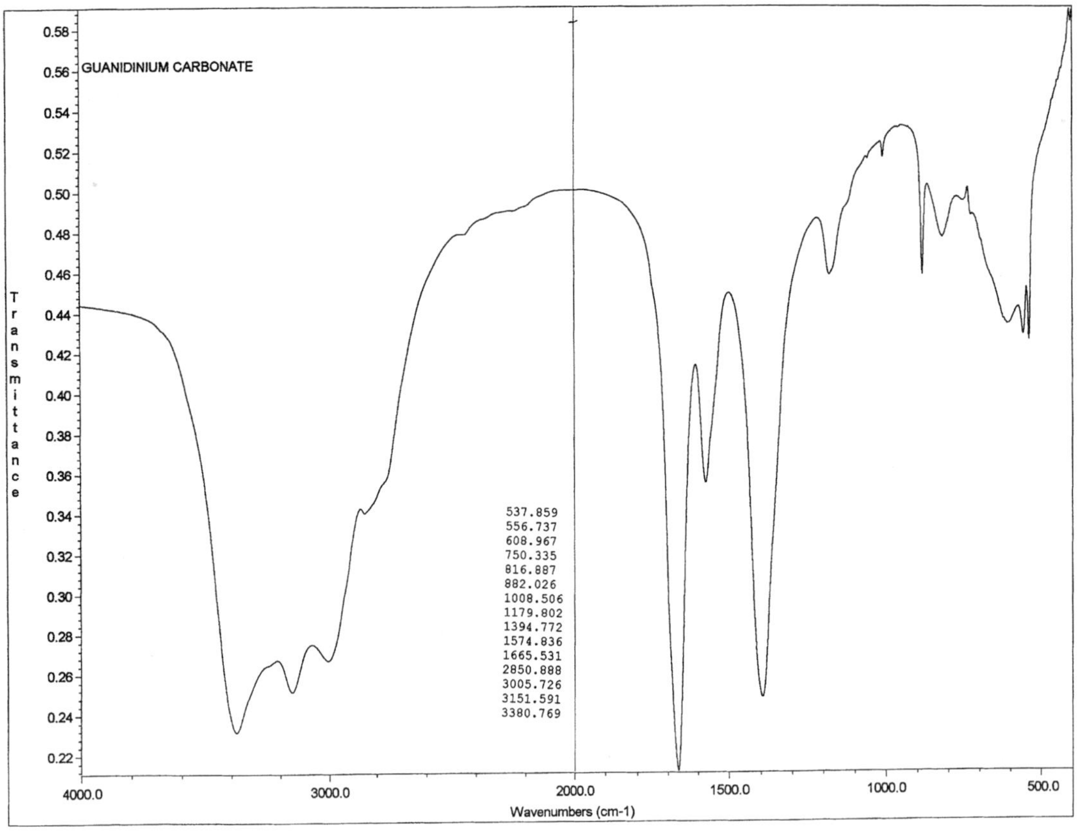

37 Guanidinium carbonate $[(H_2N_2)C{=}NH_2]_2CO_3$

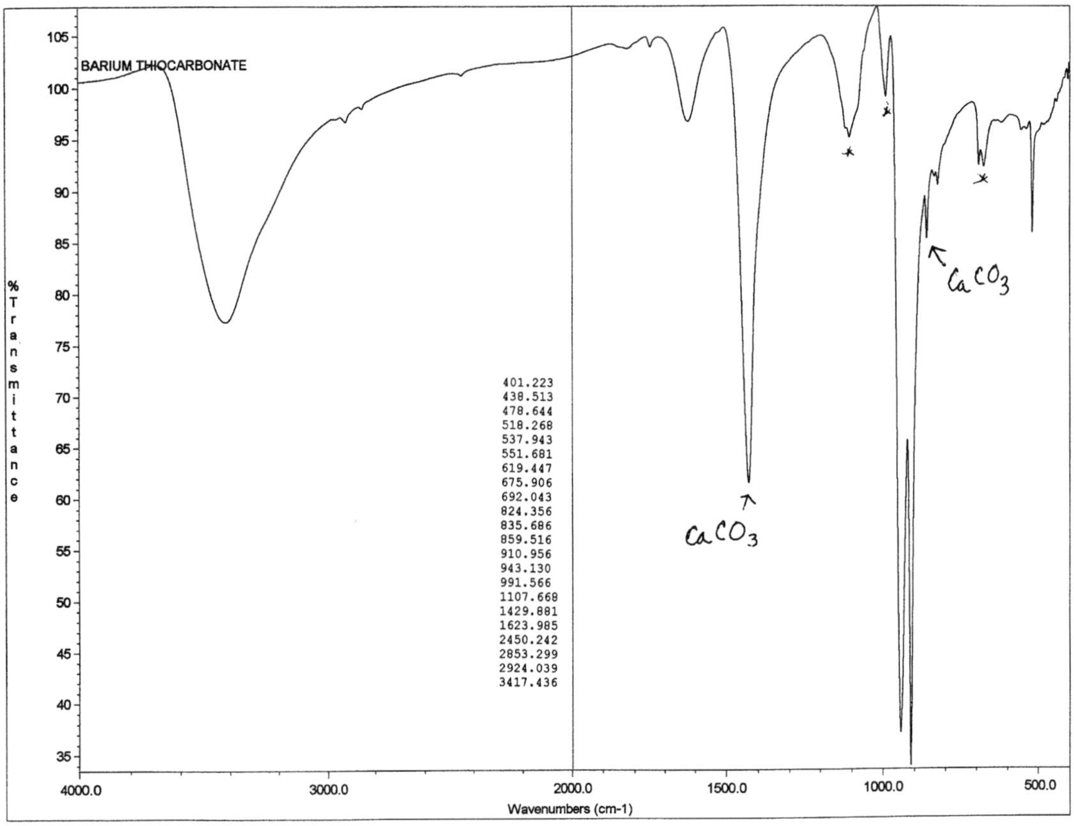

38 Barium thiocarbonate $BaCS_3$

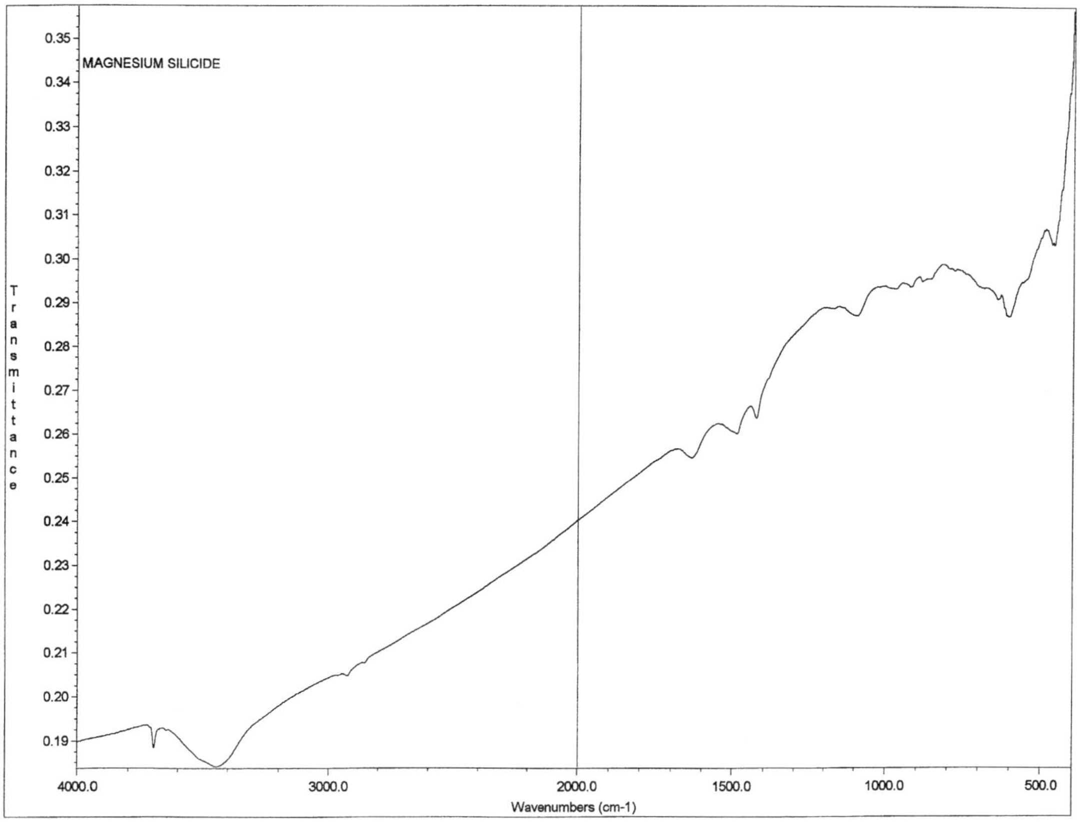

39 Magnesium silicide Mg_2Si

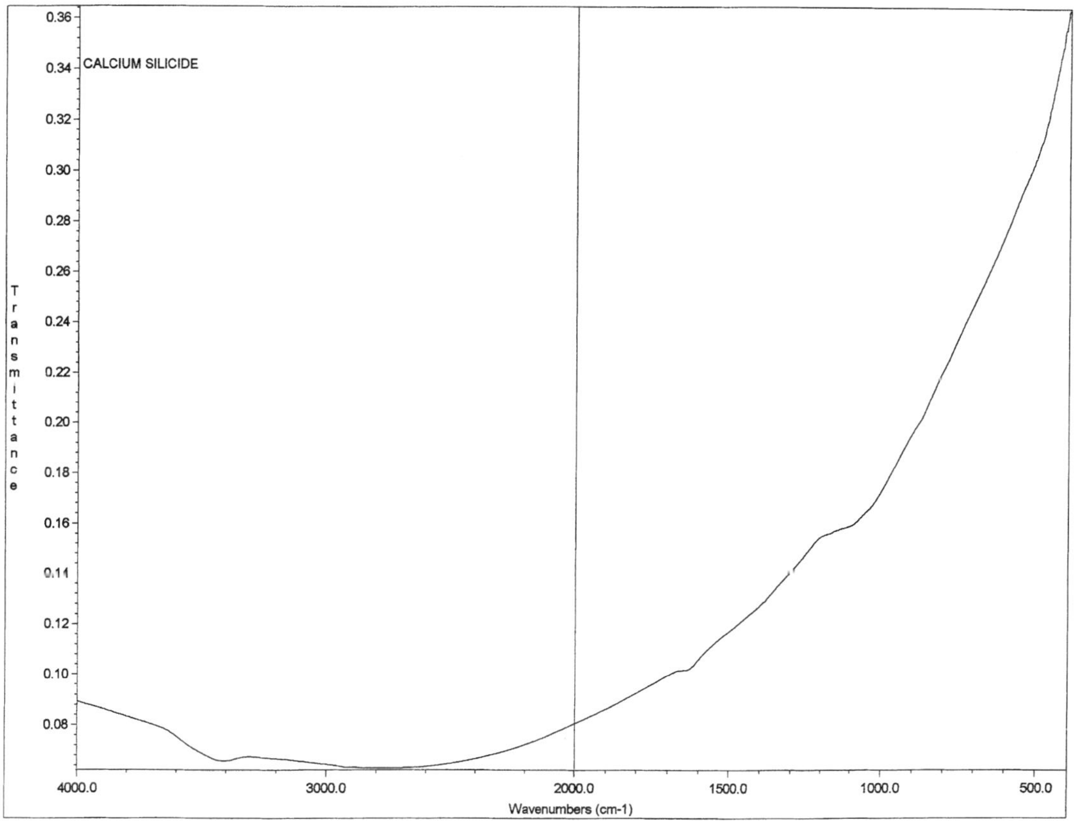

40 Calcium silicide Ca_2Si

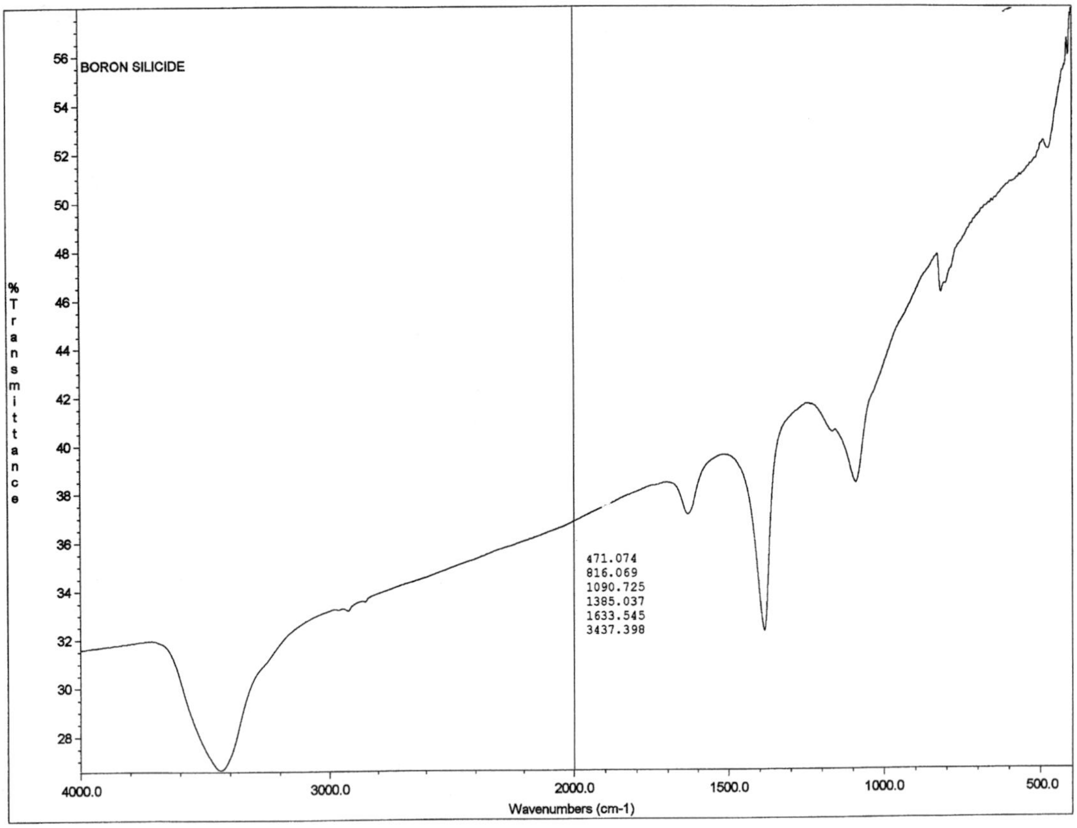

41 Boron silicide B_6Si

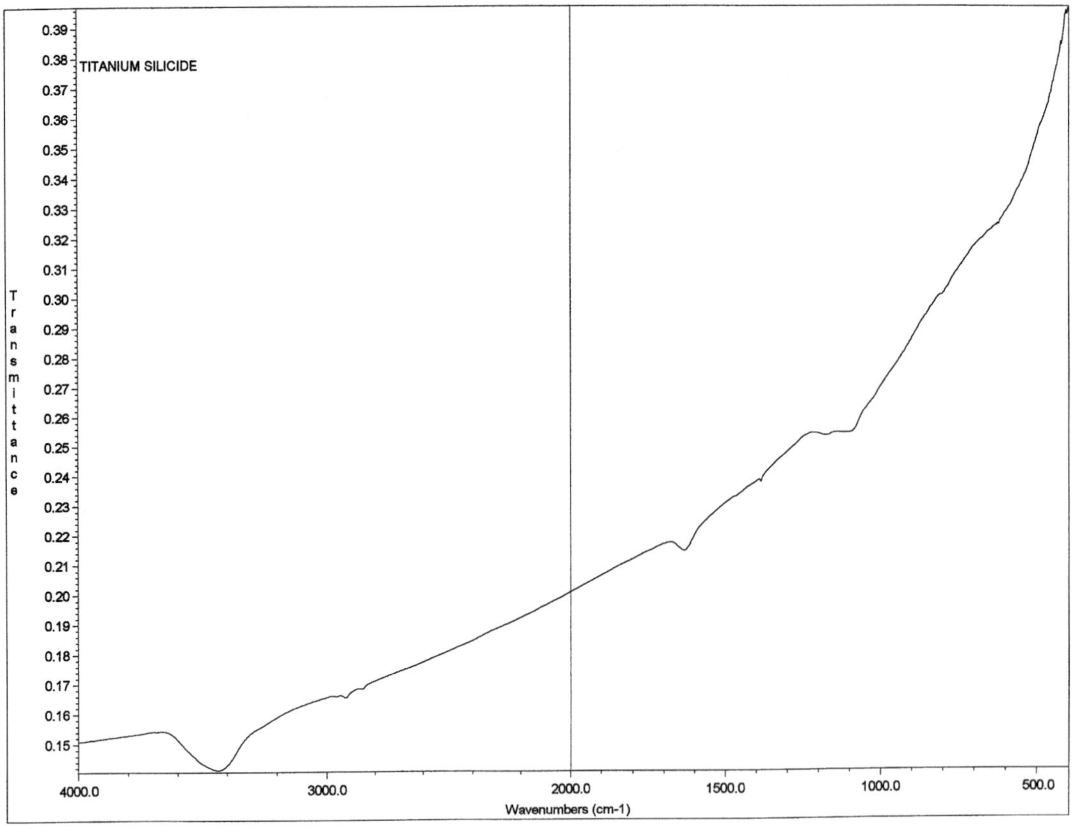

42 Titanium silicide $TiSi_2$

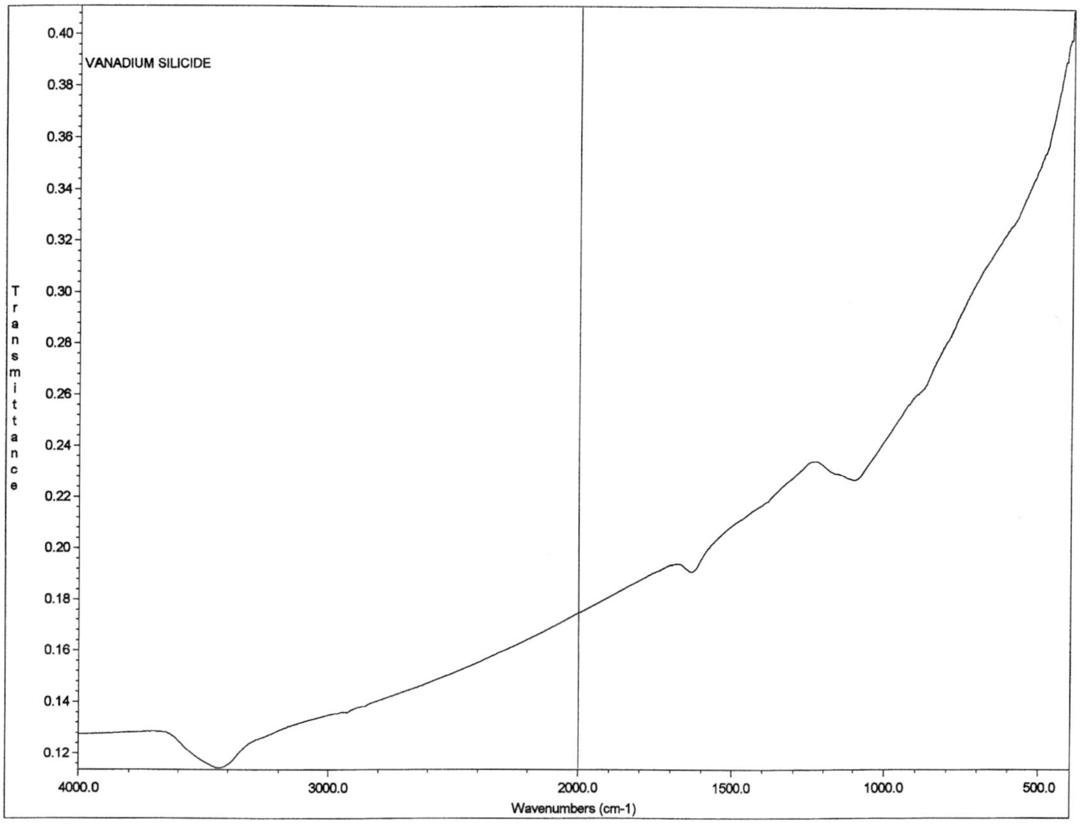

43 Vanadium silicide VSi_2

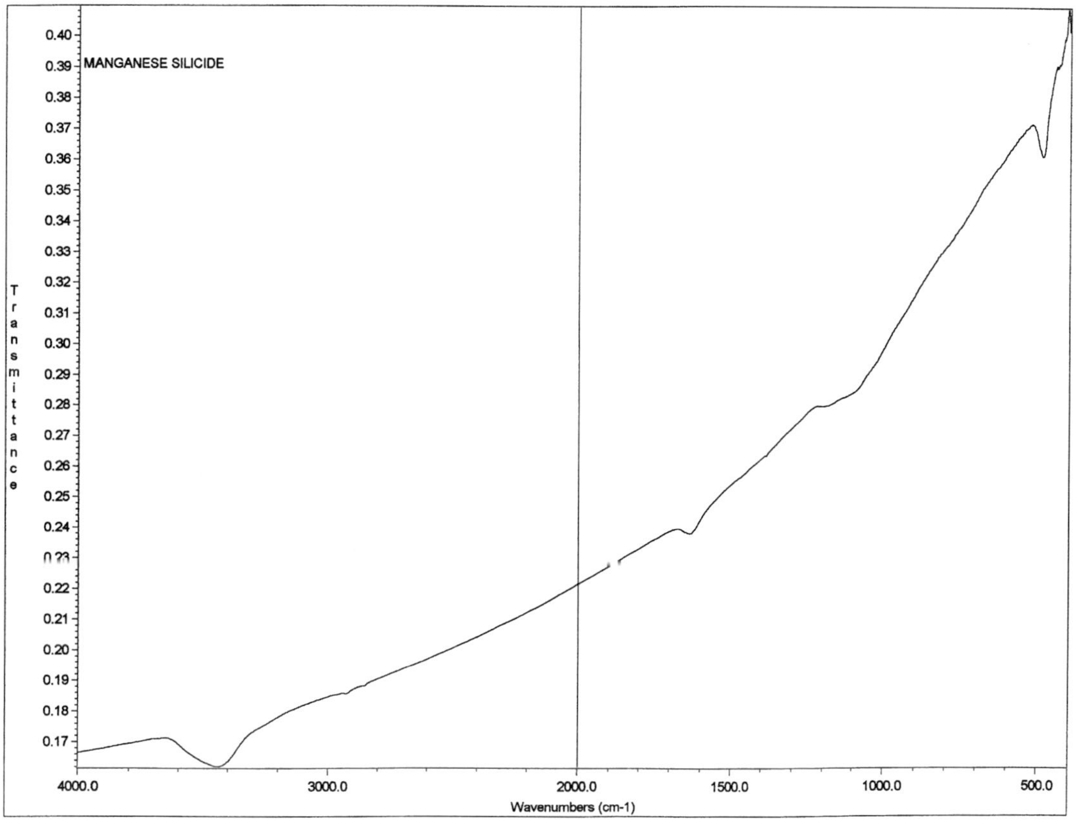

44 Manganese silicide $MnSi_2$

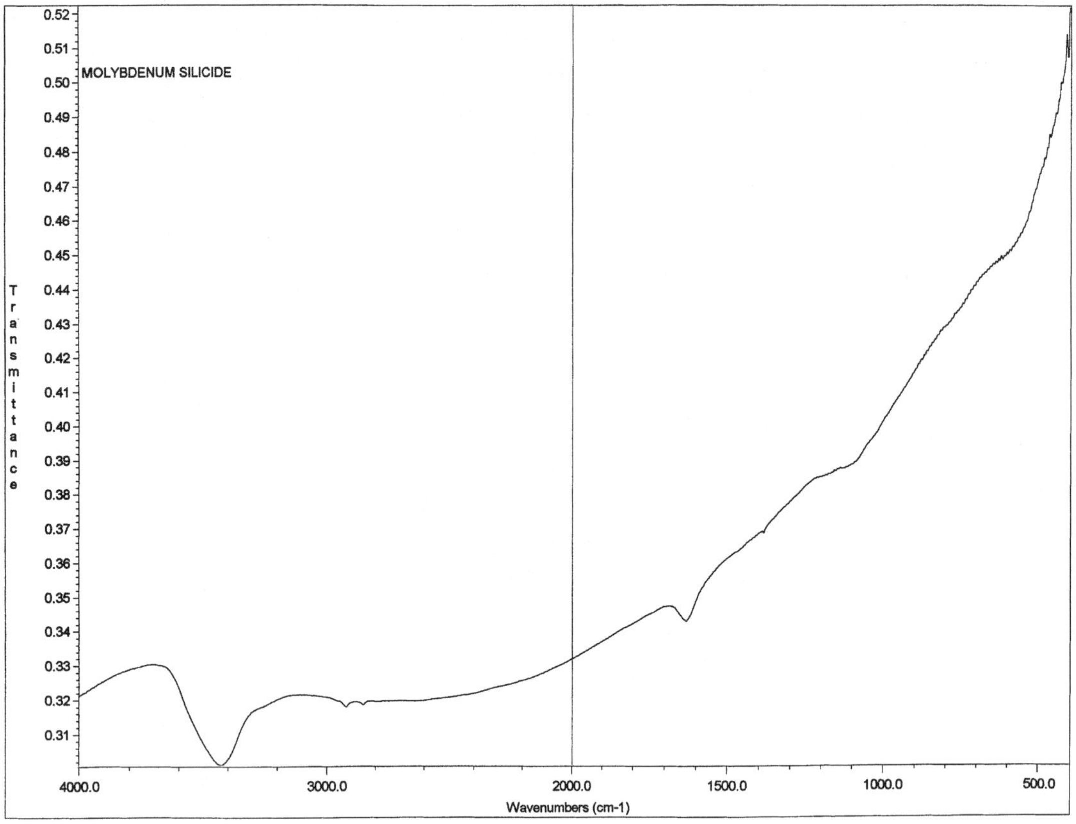

45 Molybdenum silicide $MoSi_2$

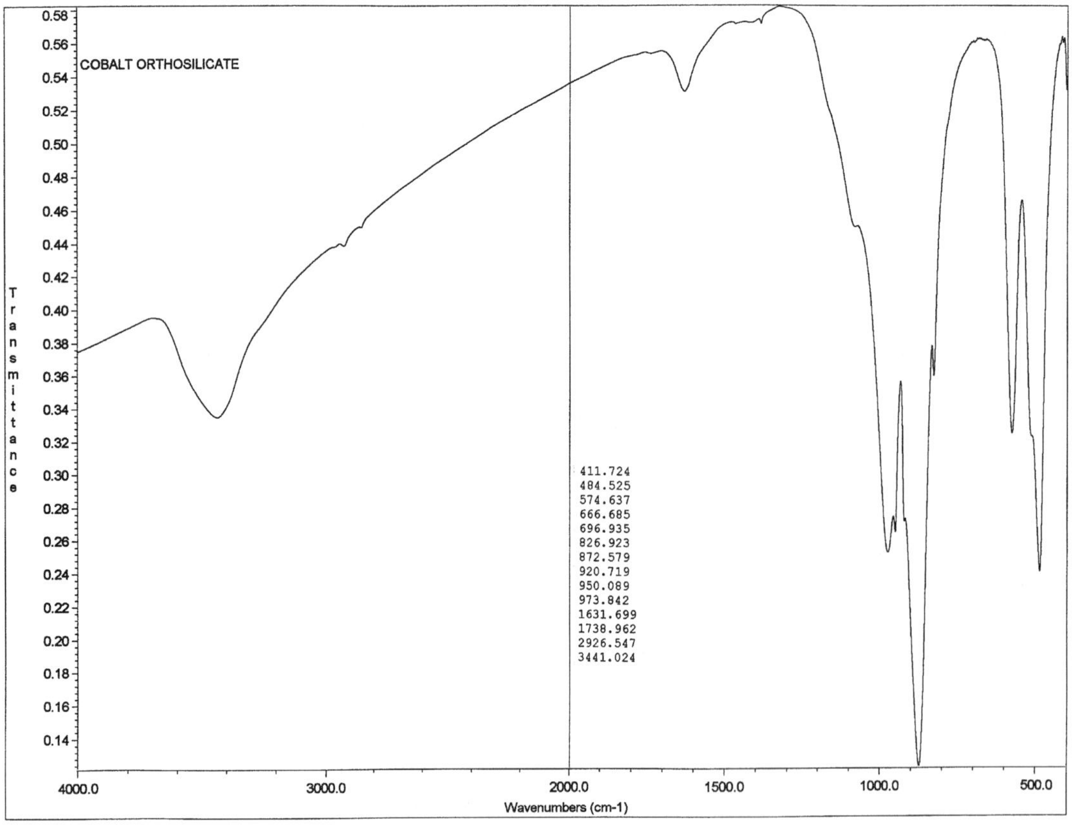

46 Cobalt orthosilicate $CoSiO_4 \cdot xH_2O$

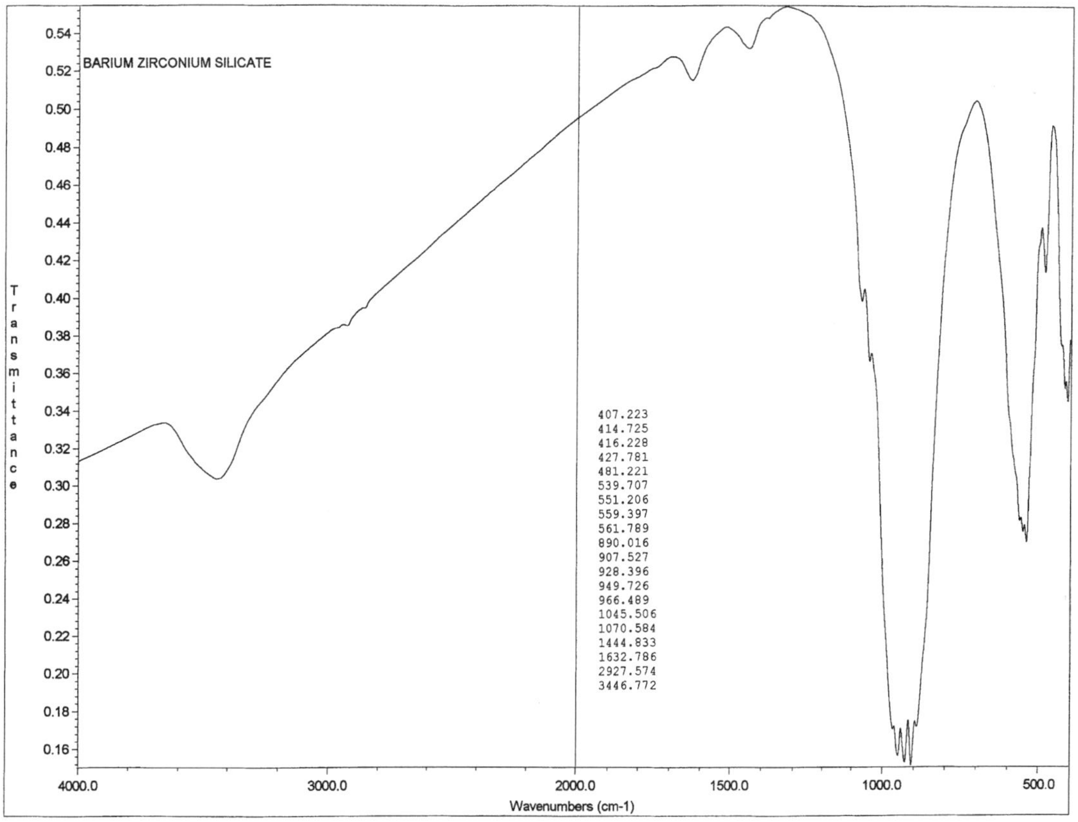

47 Barium zirconium silicate $BaZrSiO_5$

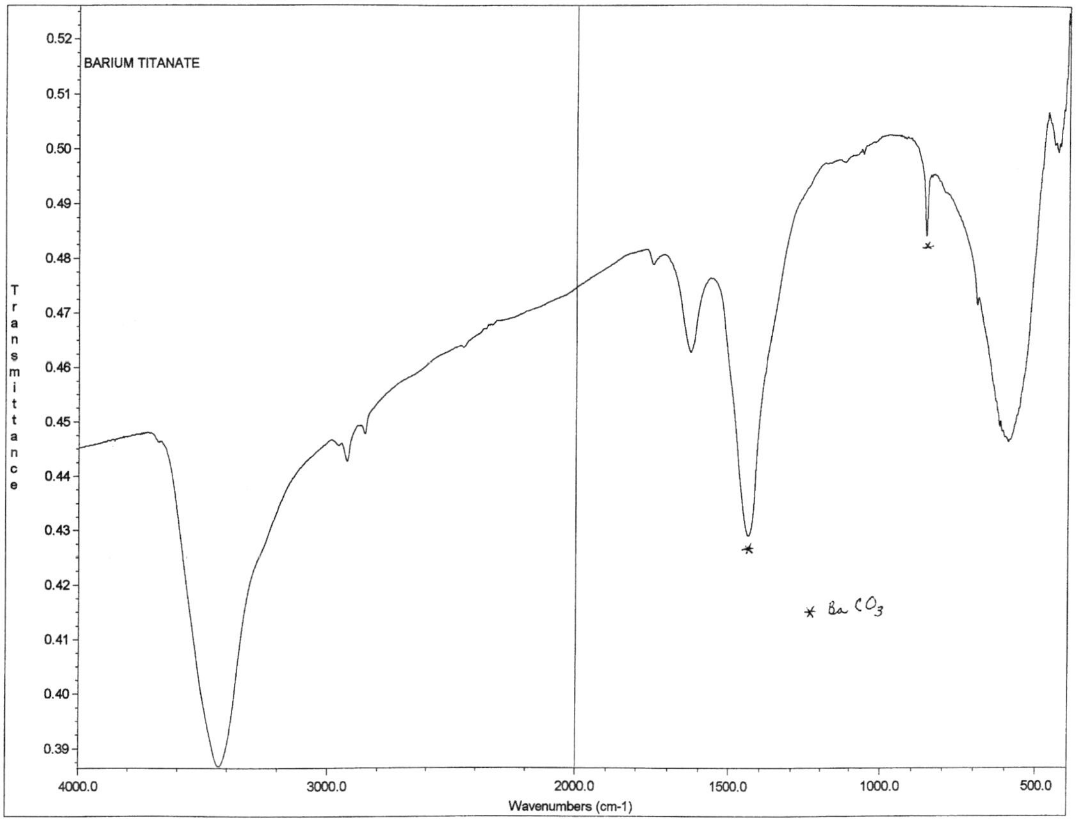

49 Barium titanate (IV) $BaTiO_3$

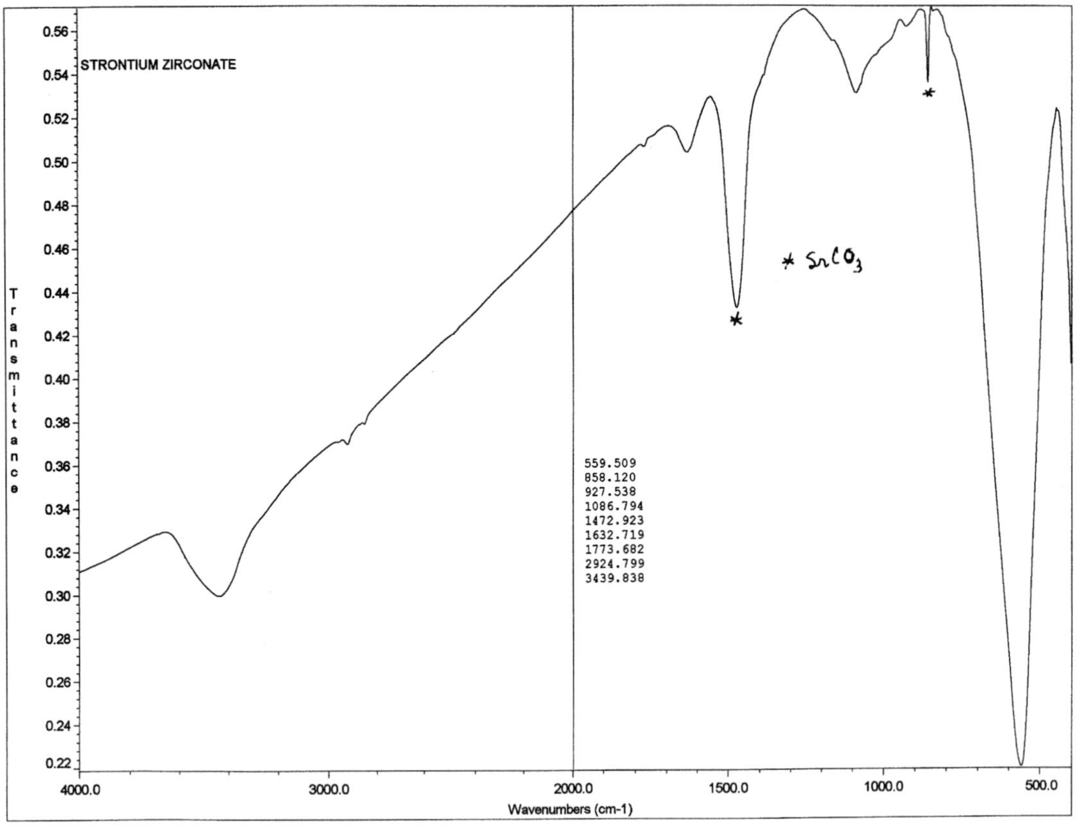

50 Strontium zirconate (IV) $SrZrO_3$

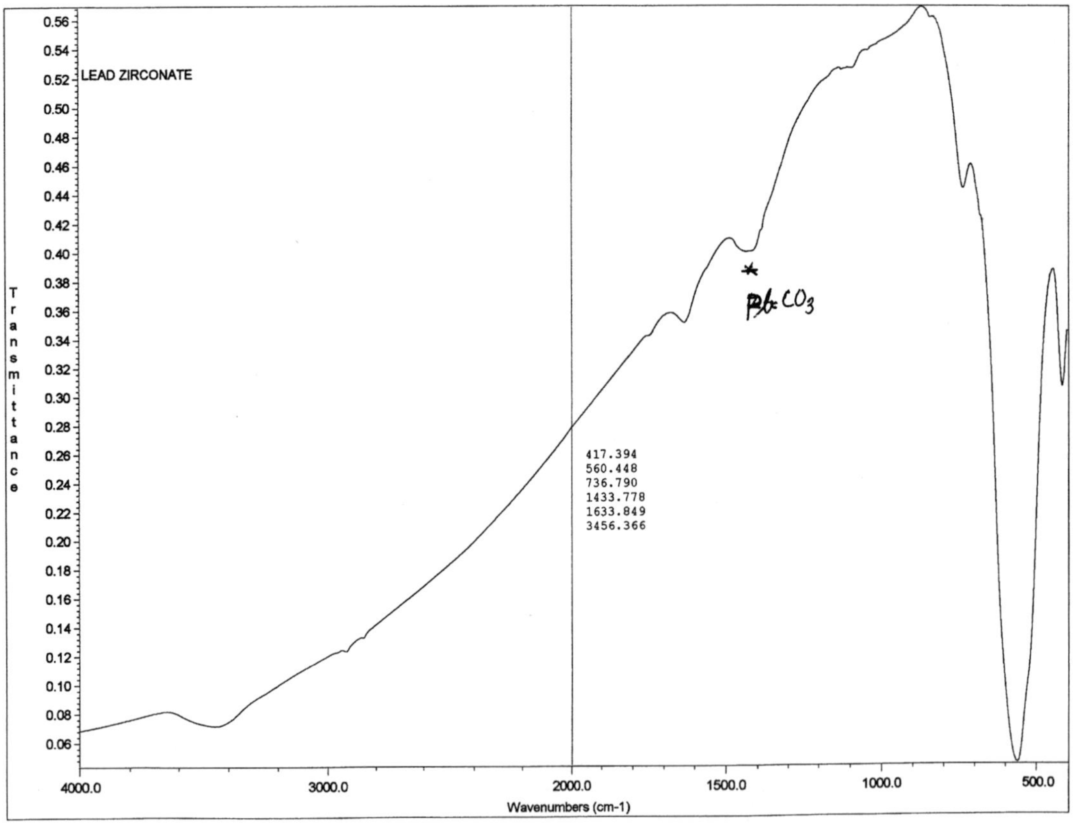

51 Lead zirconate (IV) $PbZrO_3$

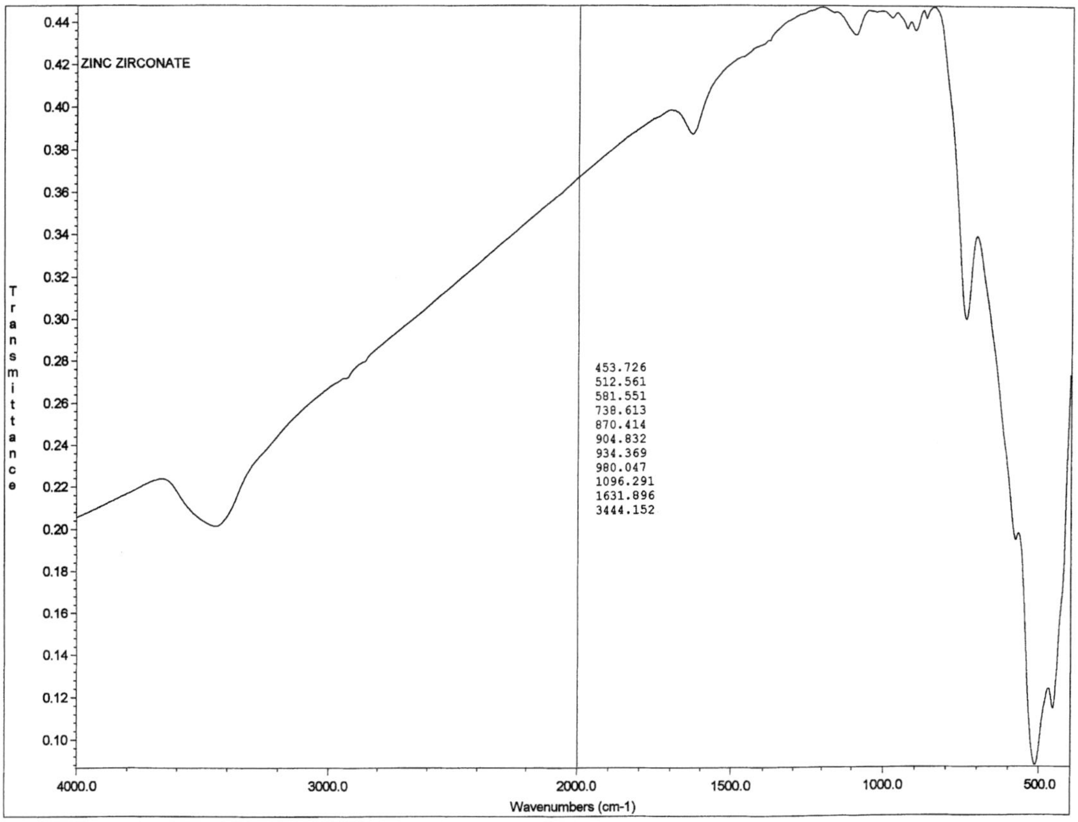

52 Zinc zirconate (IV) $ZnZrO_3$

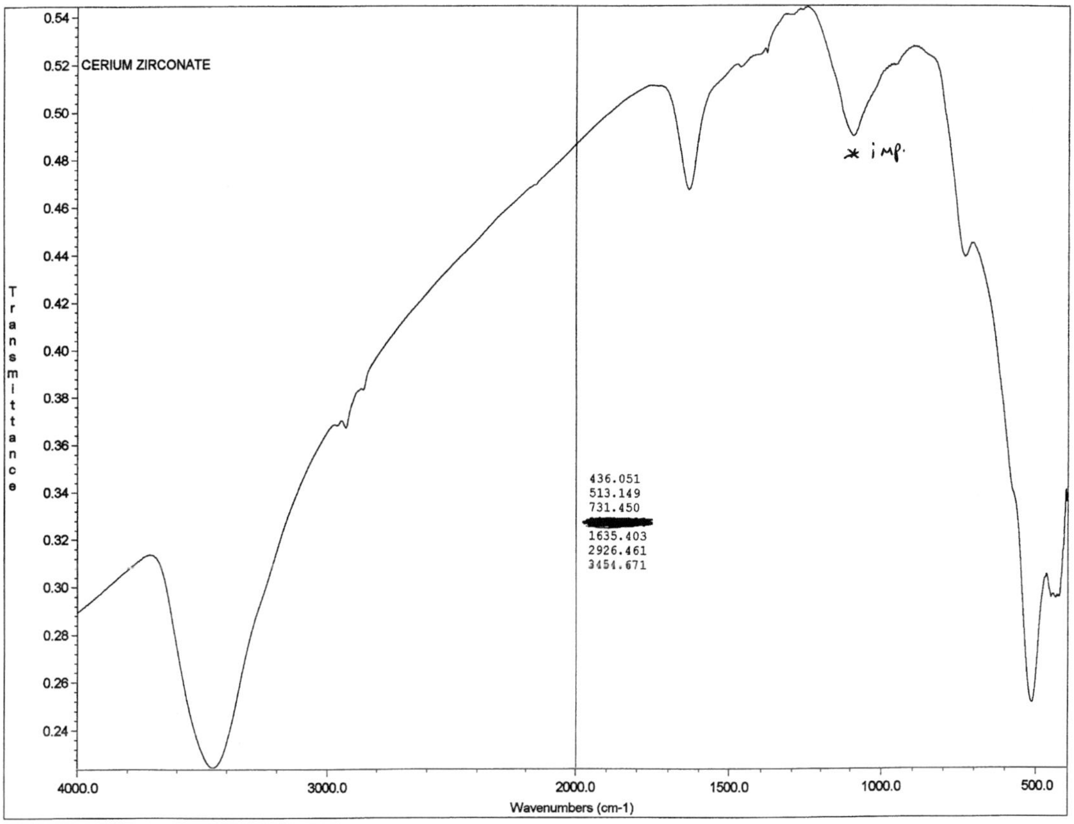

53 Cerium zirconate (IV) $Ce(ZrO_3)_2$

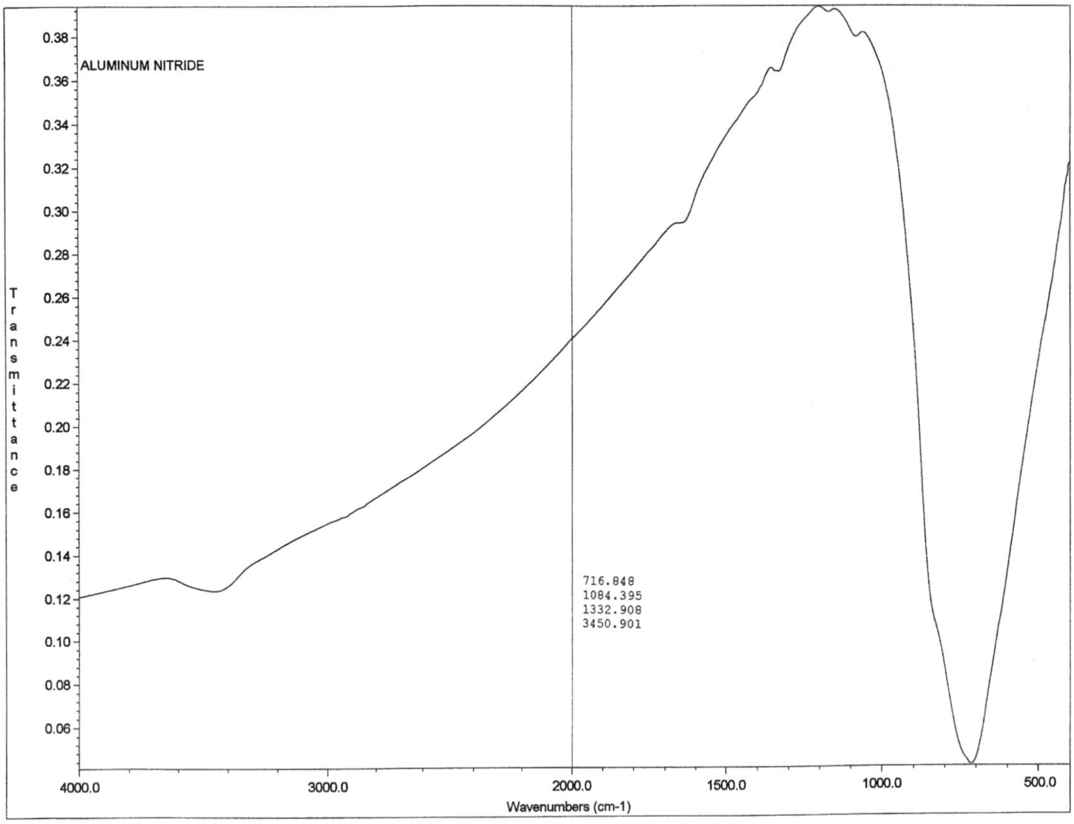

54 Aluminum nitride AlN

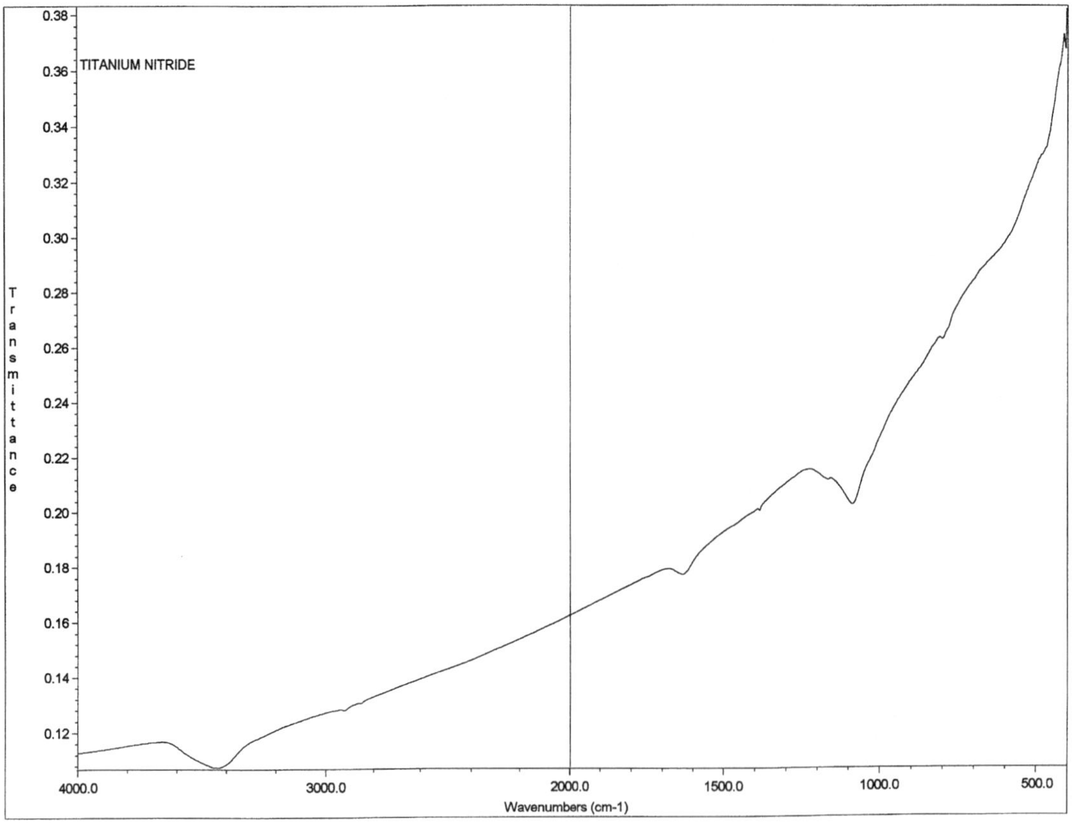

55 Titanium nitride Ti_3N_4

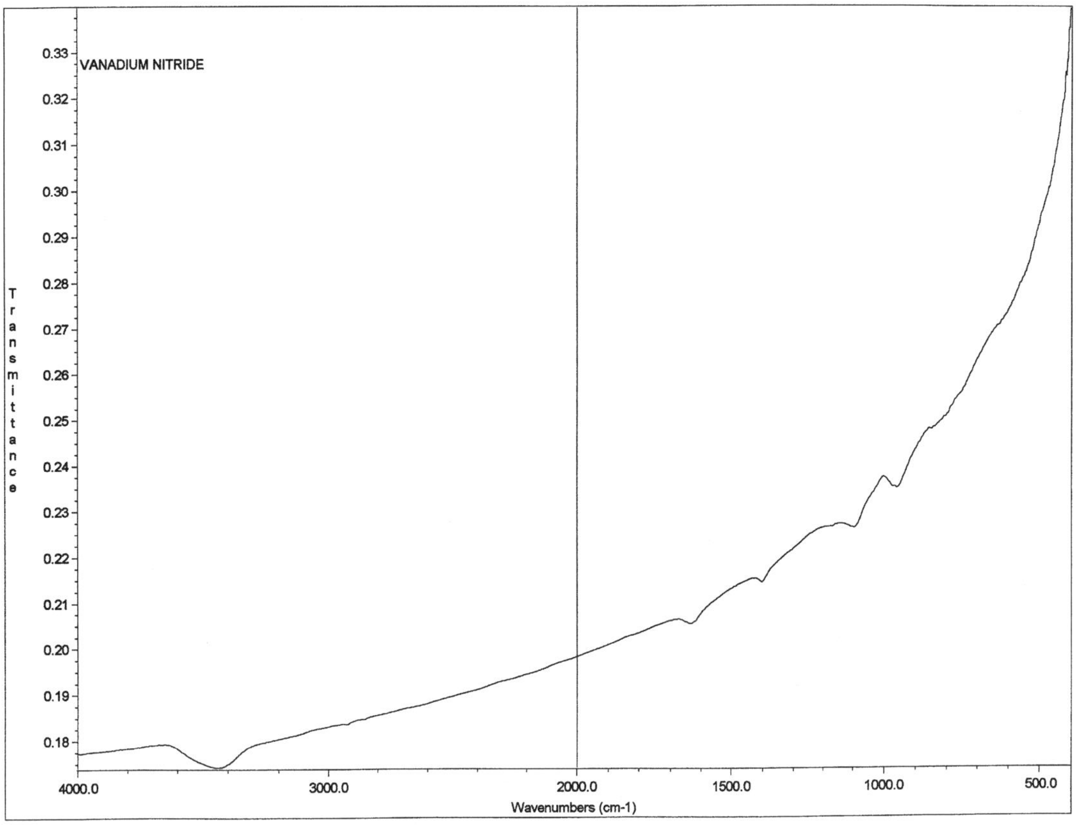

56 Vanadium nitride VN

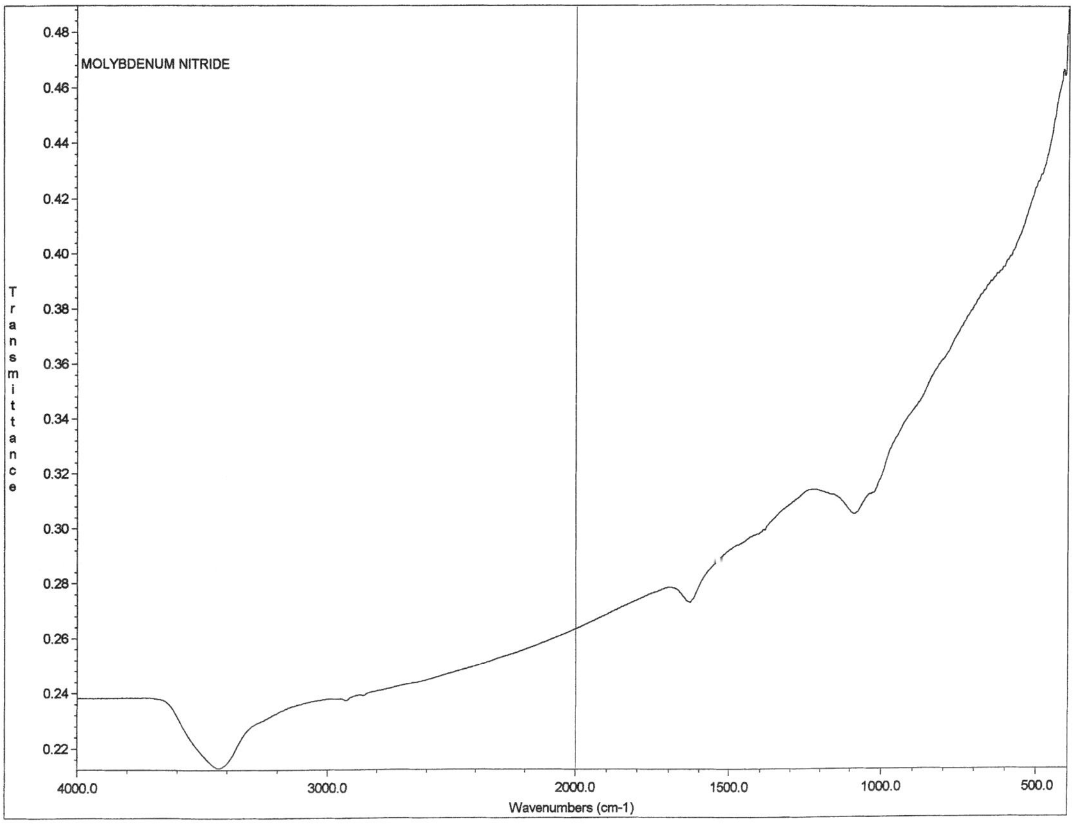

57 Molybdenum nitride Mo_2N

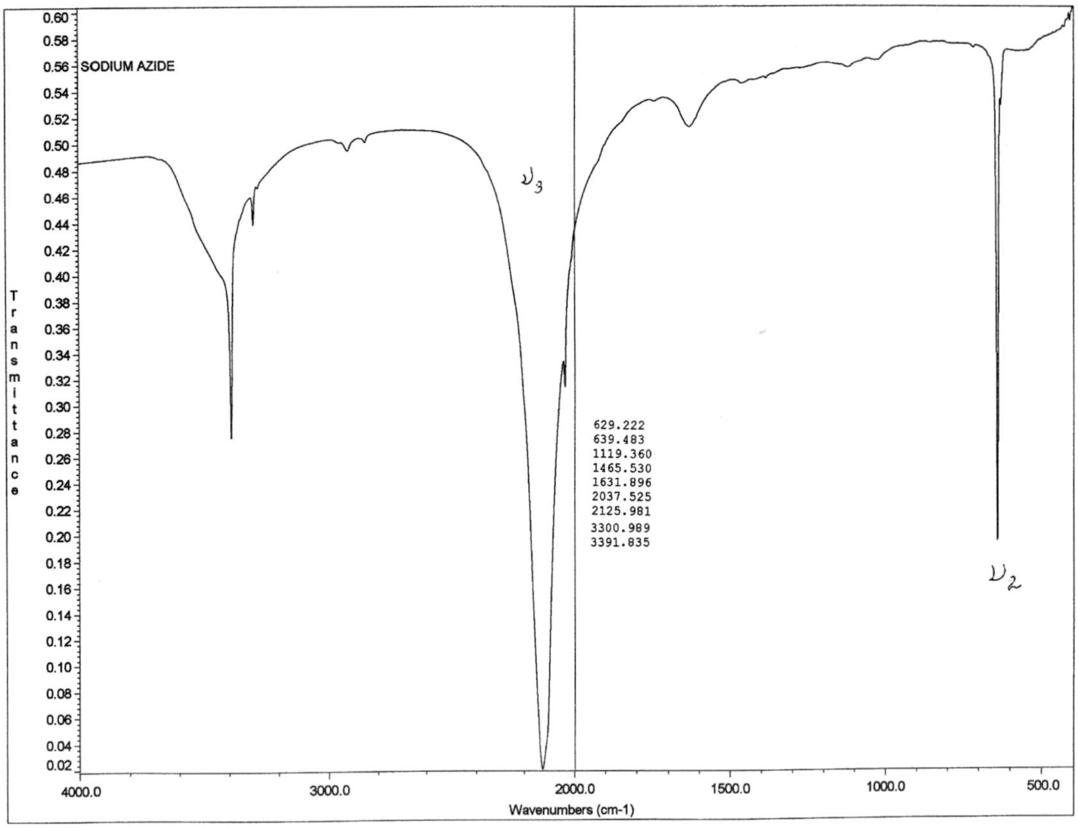

58 Sodium azide NaN_3

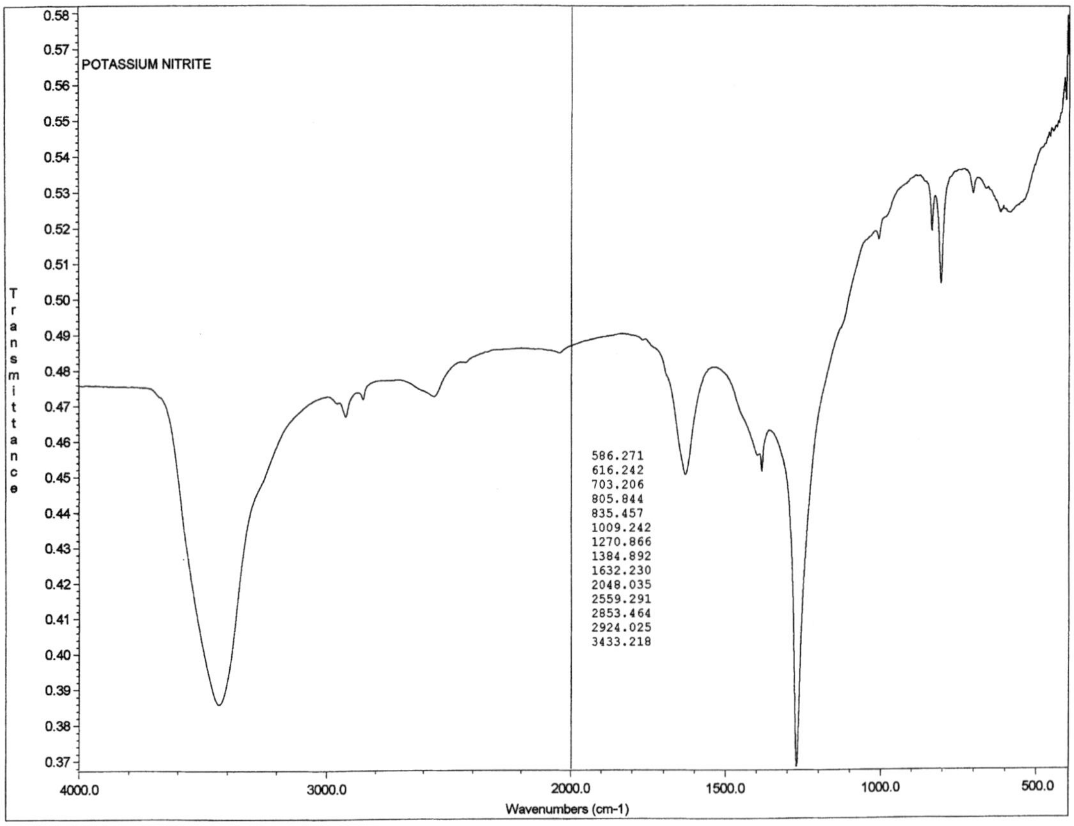

59 Potassium nitrite $KNO_2 \cdot xH_2O$

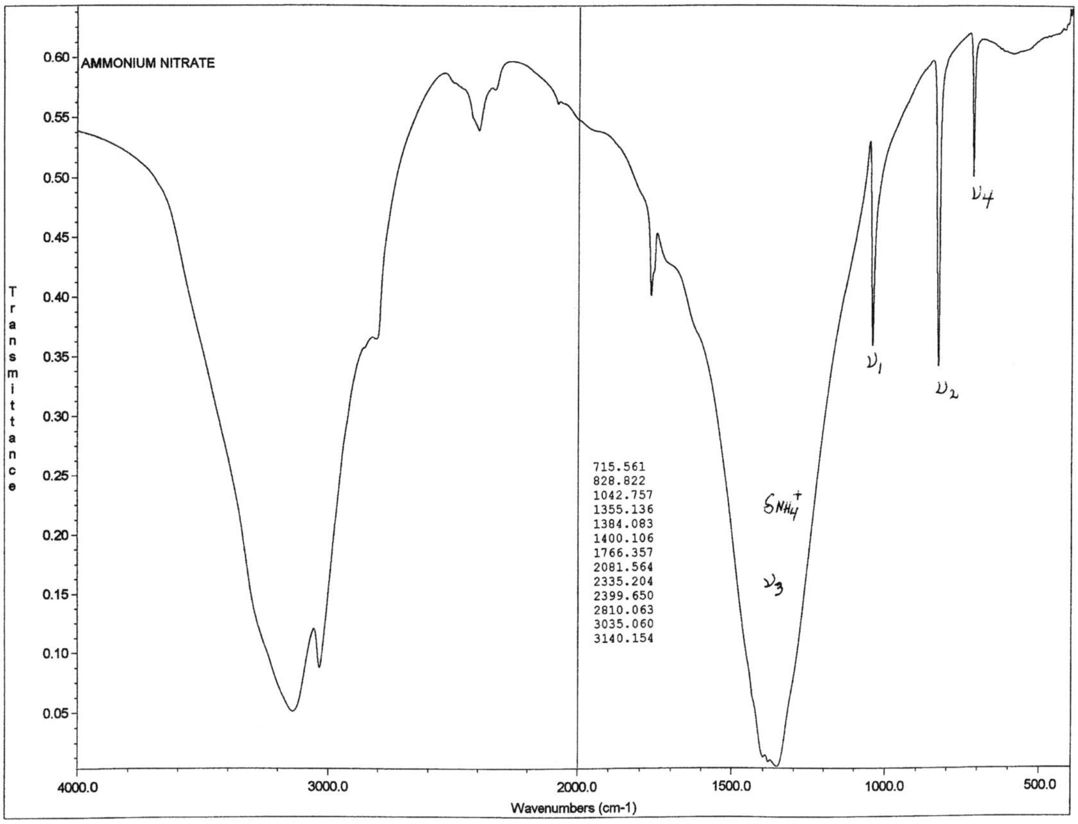

62 Ammonium nitrate NH_4NO_3

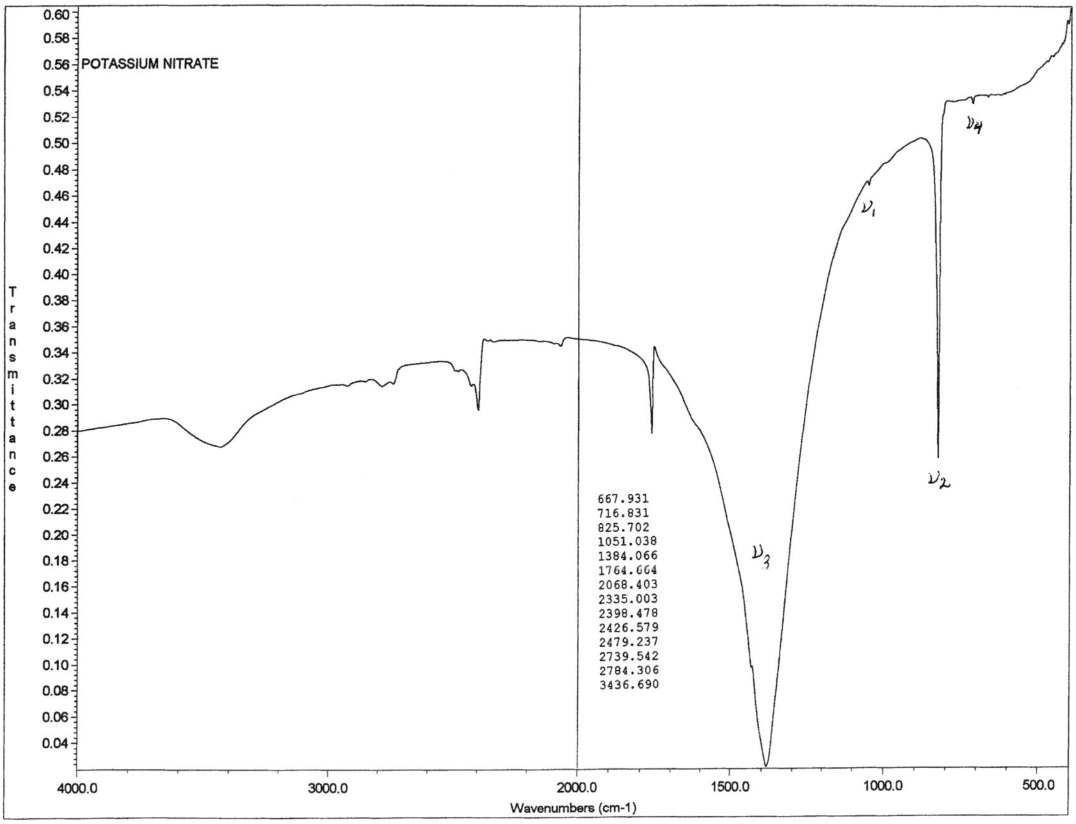

64 Potassium nitrate KNO_3

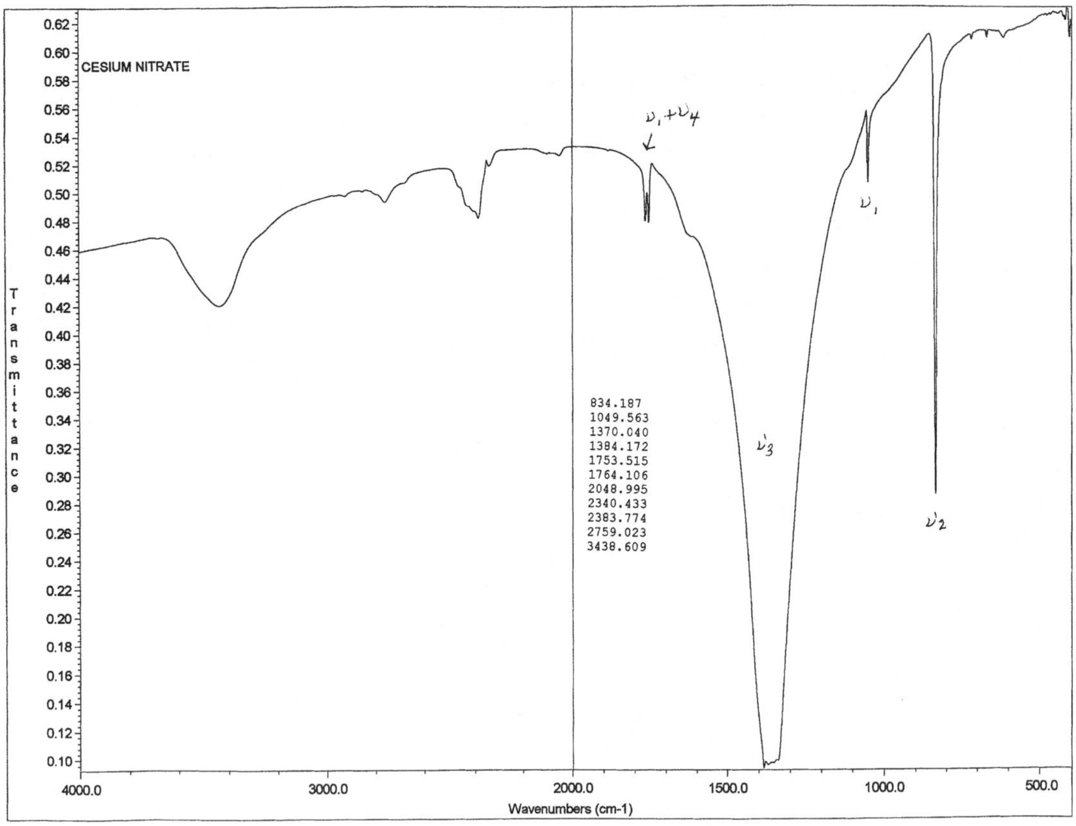

65 Cesium nitrate $CsNO_3$

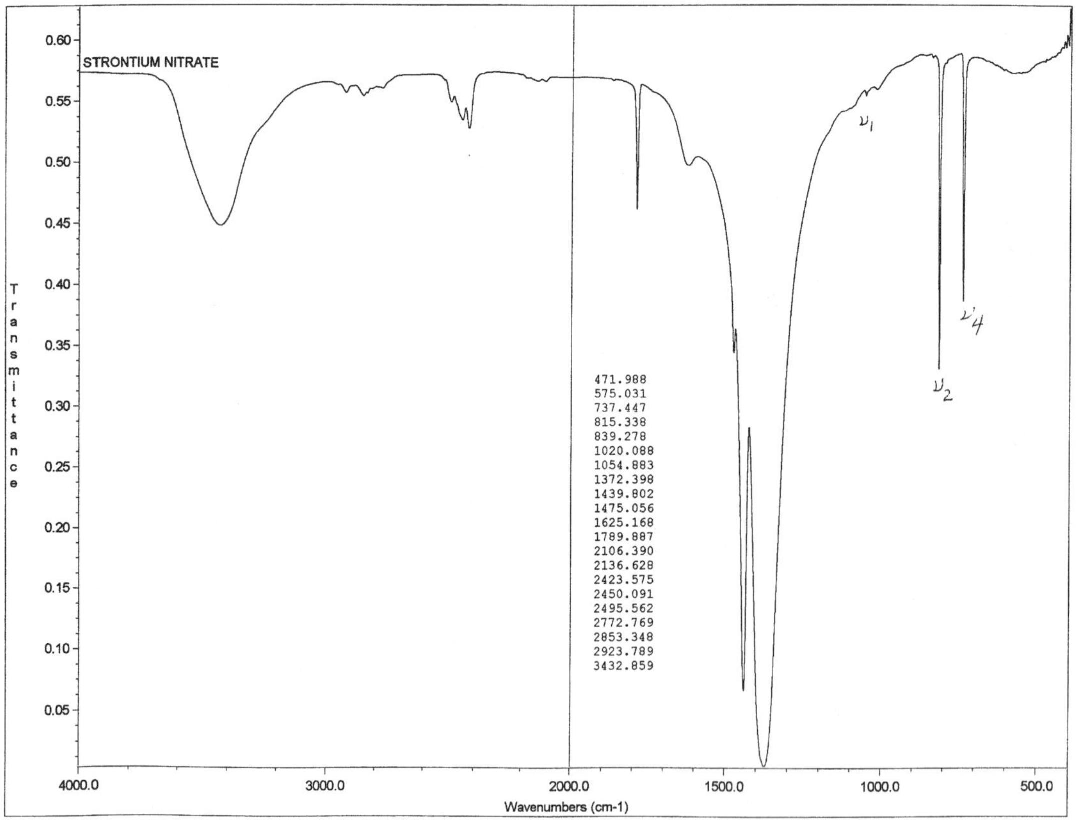

67 Strontium nitrate $Sr(NO_3)_2$

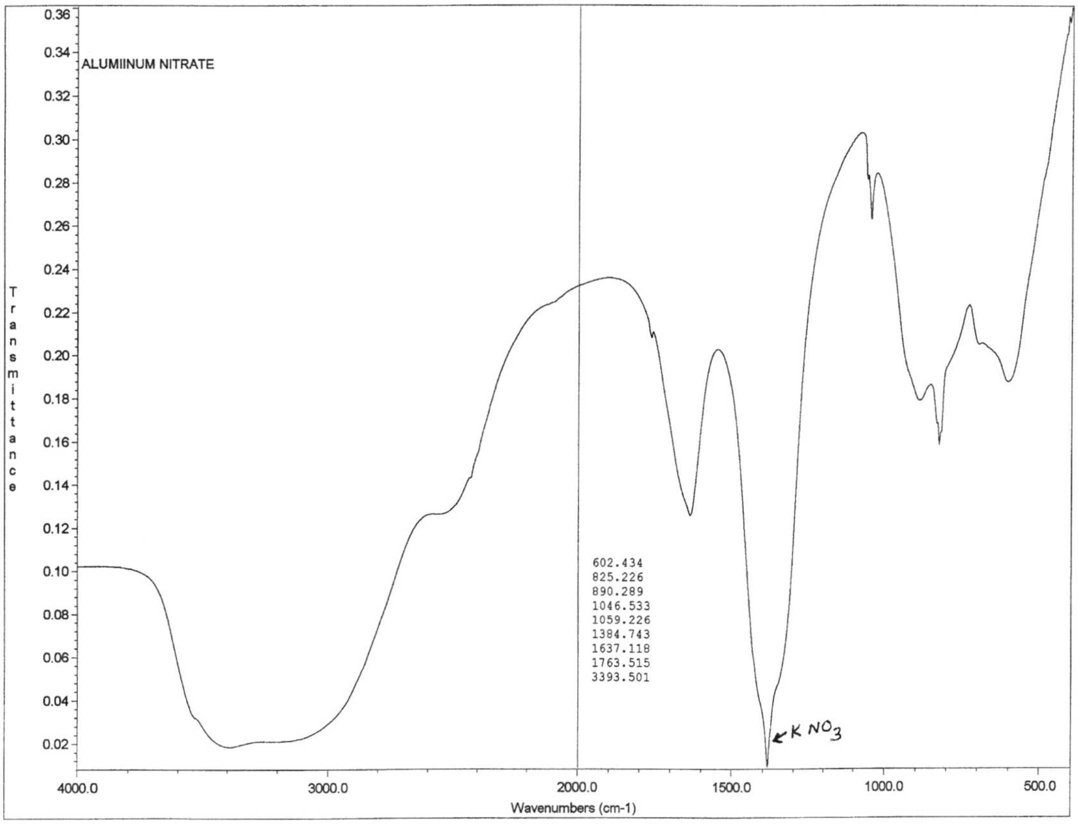

68 Aluminum nitrate $Al(NO_3)_3 \cdot 9H_2O$

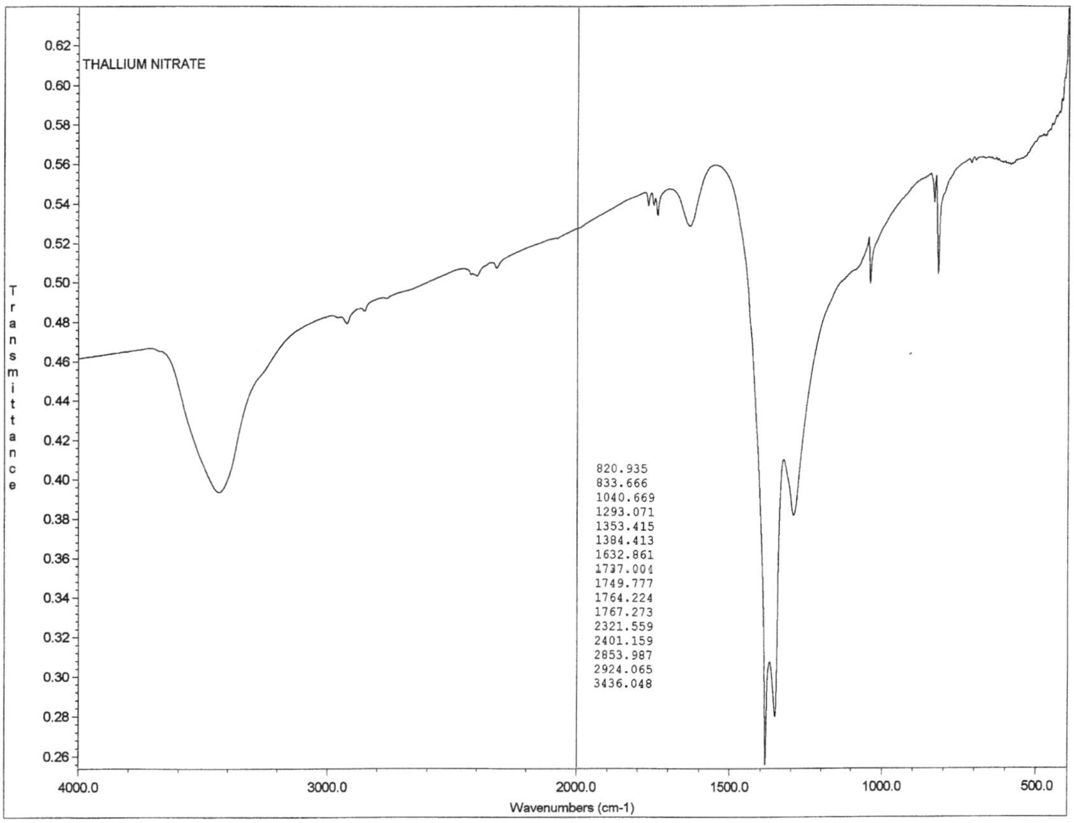

69 Thallium nitrate $Tl(NO_3)_3$

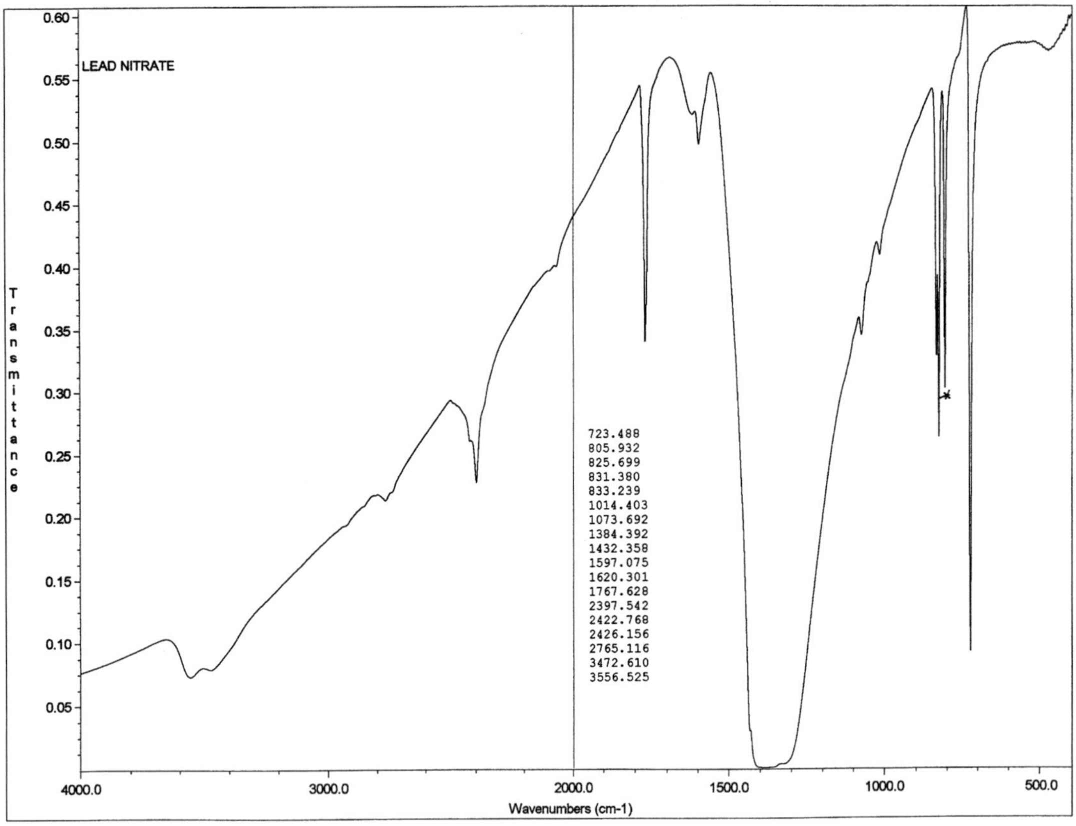

70 Lead nitrate $Pb(NO_3)_2$

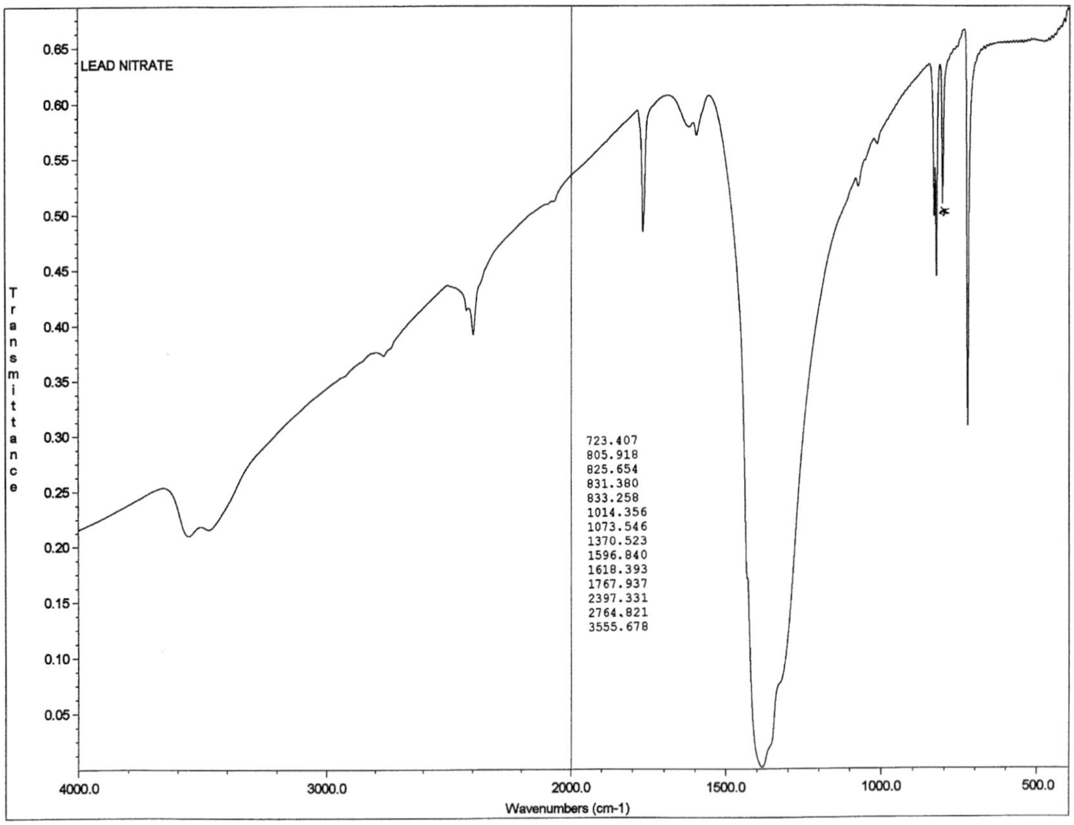

70a Lead nitrate $Pb(NO_3)_2$

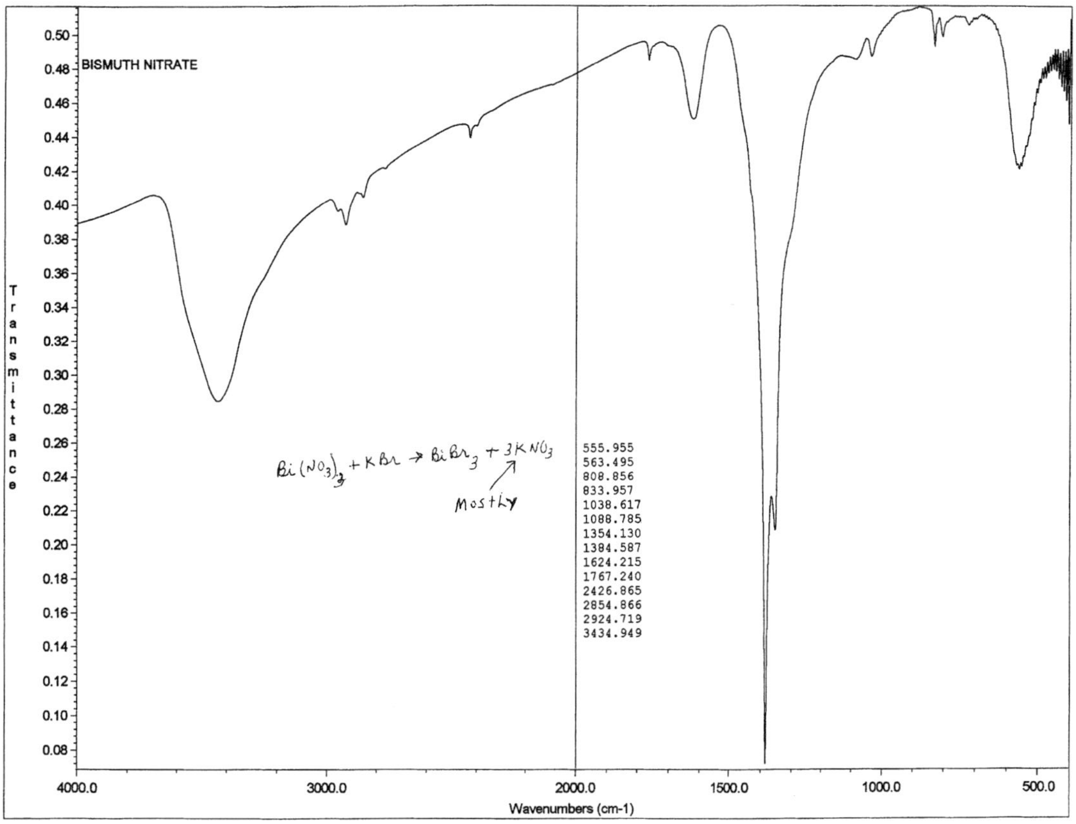

71 Bismuth nitrate $Bi(NO_3)_3 \cdot 5H_2O$

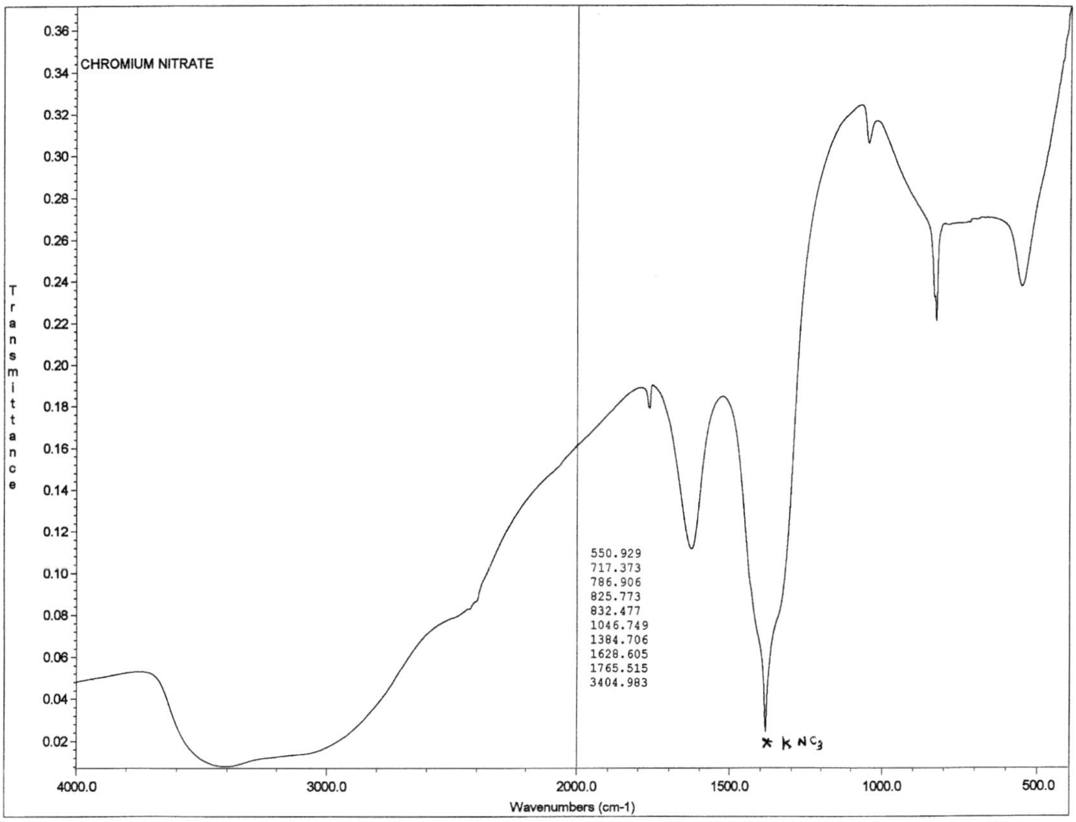

72 Chromium nitrate $Cr(NO_3)_3 \cdot 9H_2O$

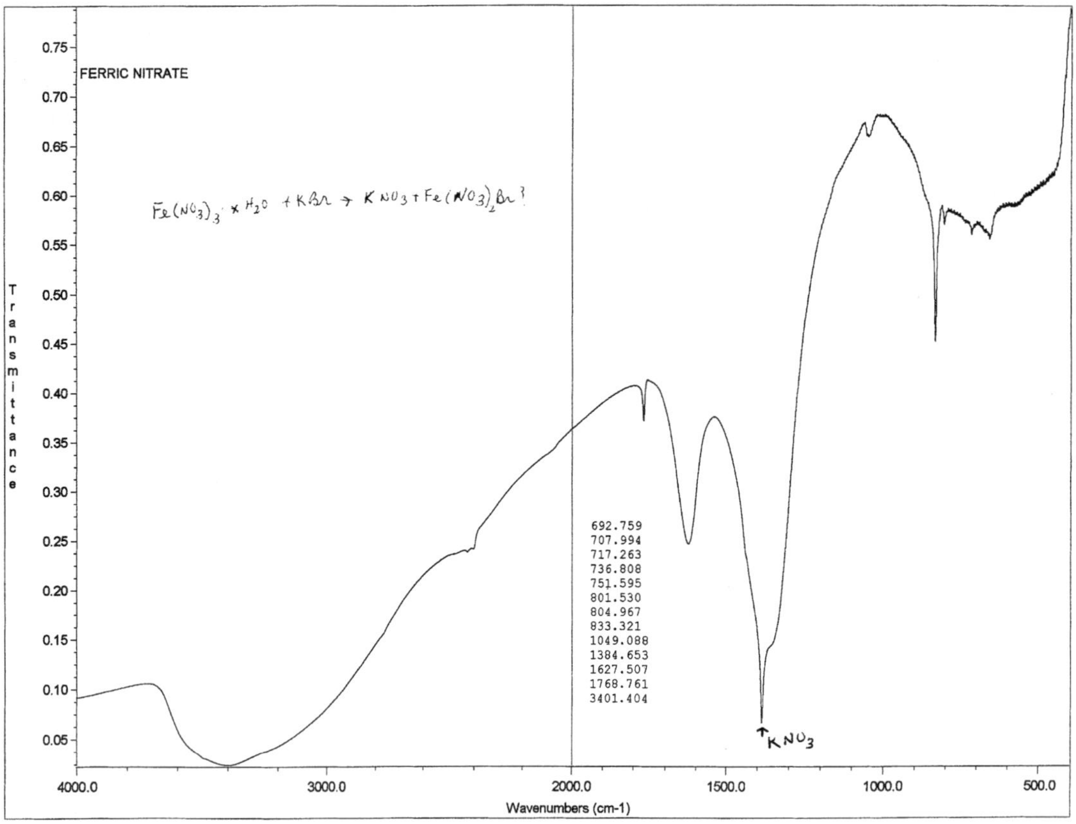

73 Iron (III) nitrate $Fe(NO_3)_3 \cdot xH_2O$

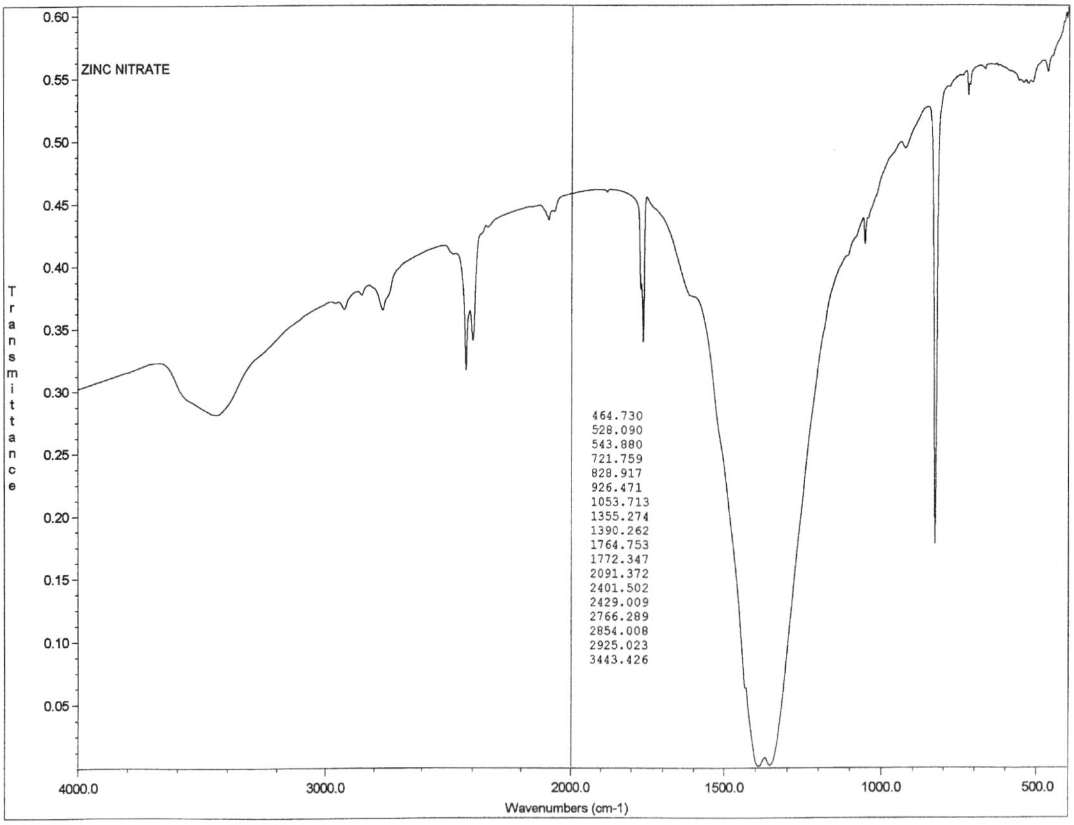

74 Zinc nitrate $Zn(NO_3)_2 \cdot xH_2O$

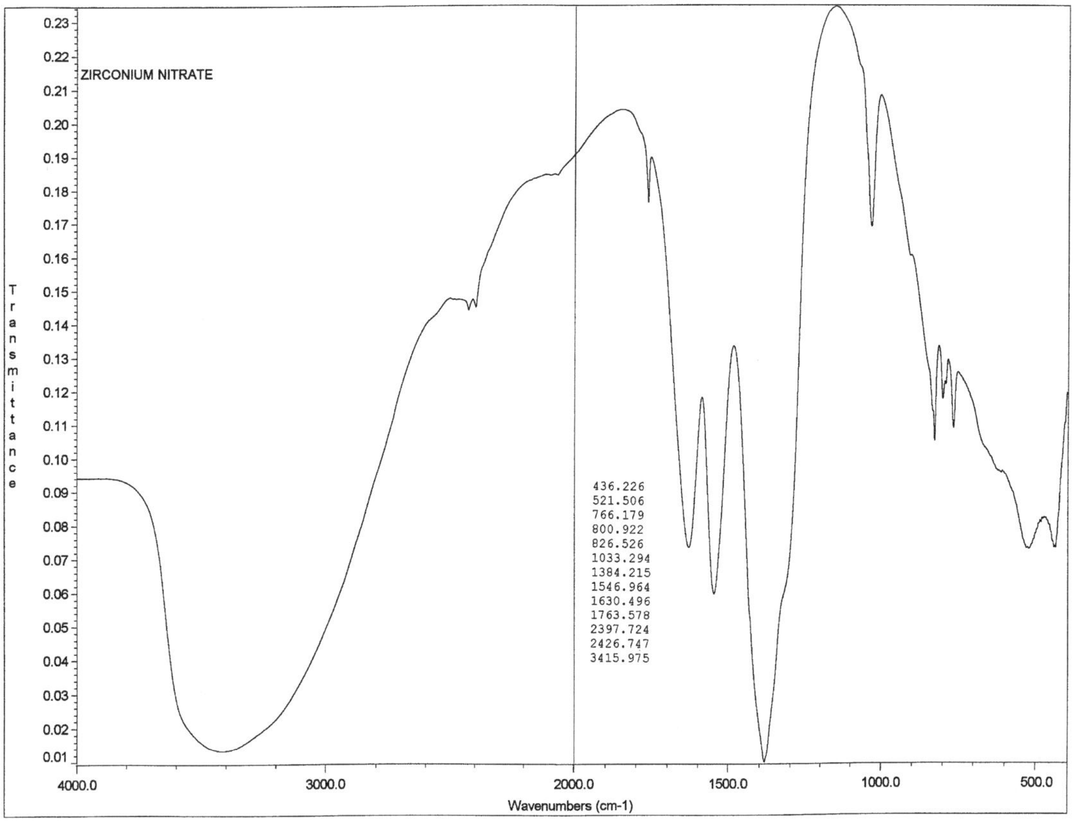

75 Zirconium nitrate $Zr(NO_3)_4 \cdot 5H_2O$

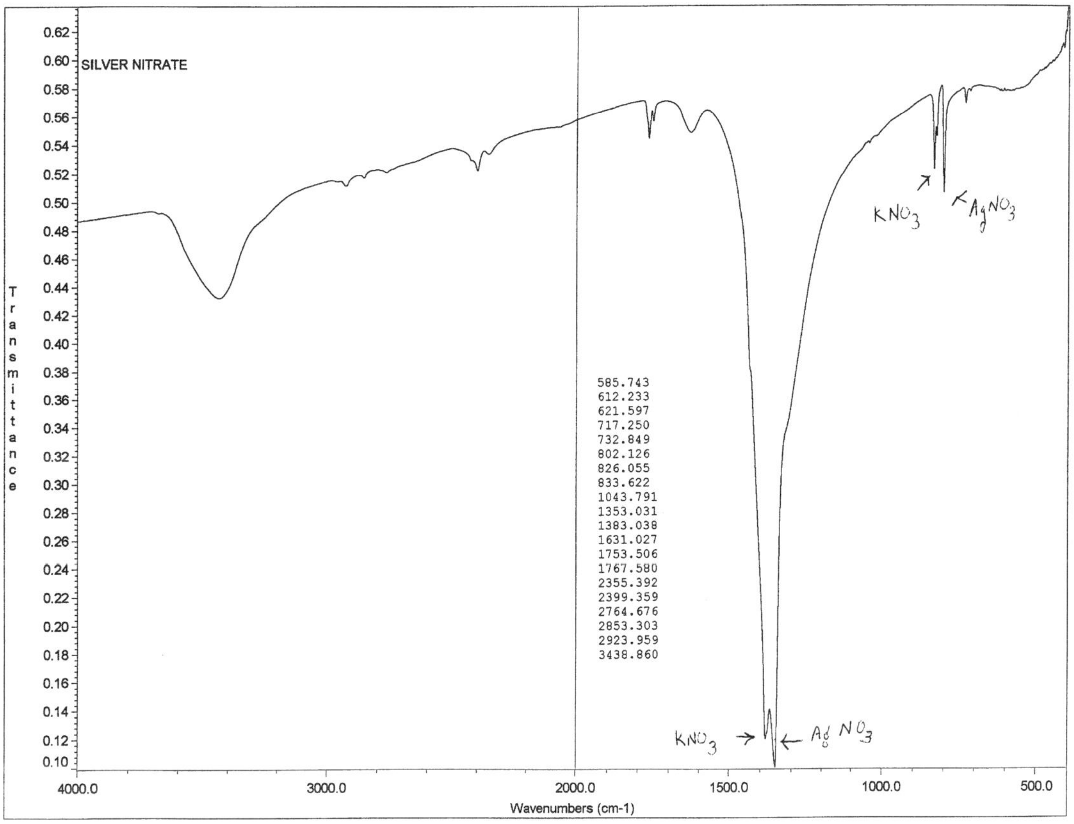

76 Silver nitrate $AgNO_3$

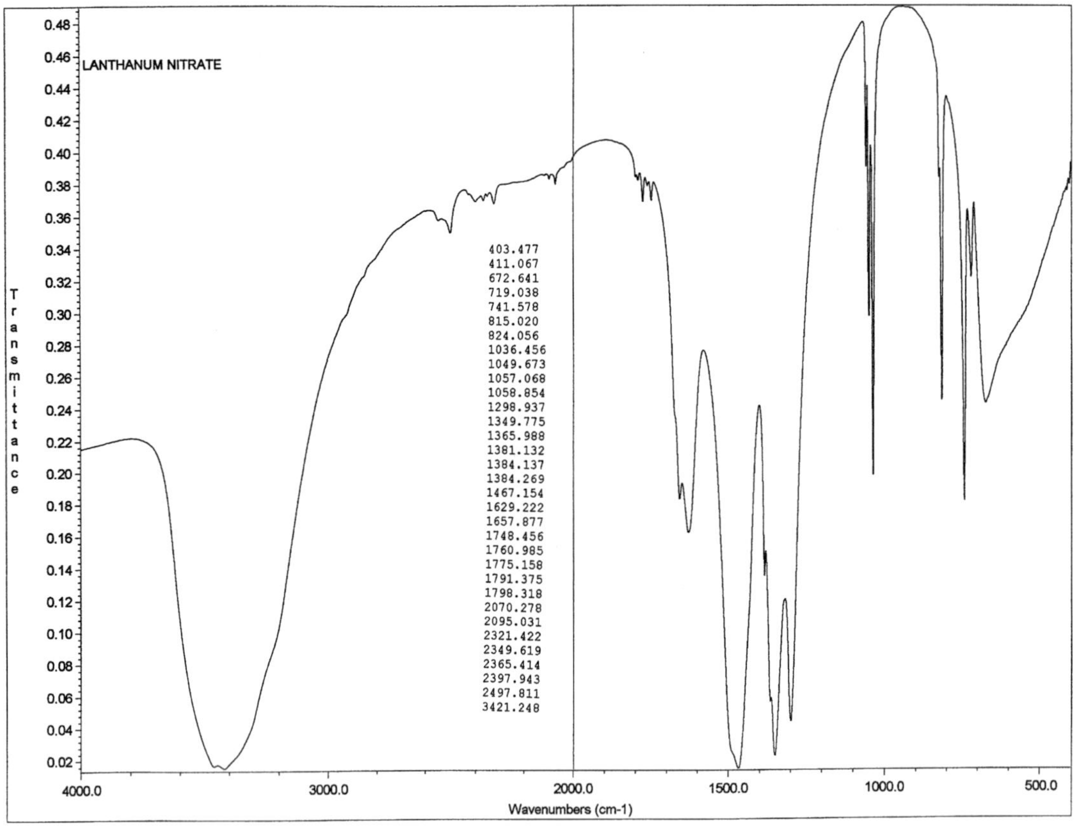

77 Lanthanum nitrate $La(NO_3)_3 \cdot 6H_2O$

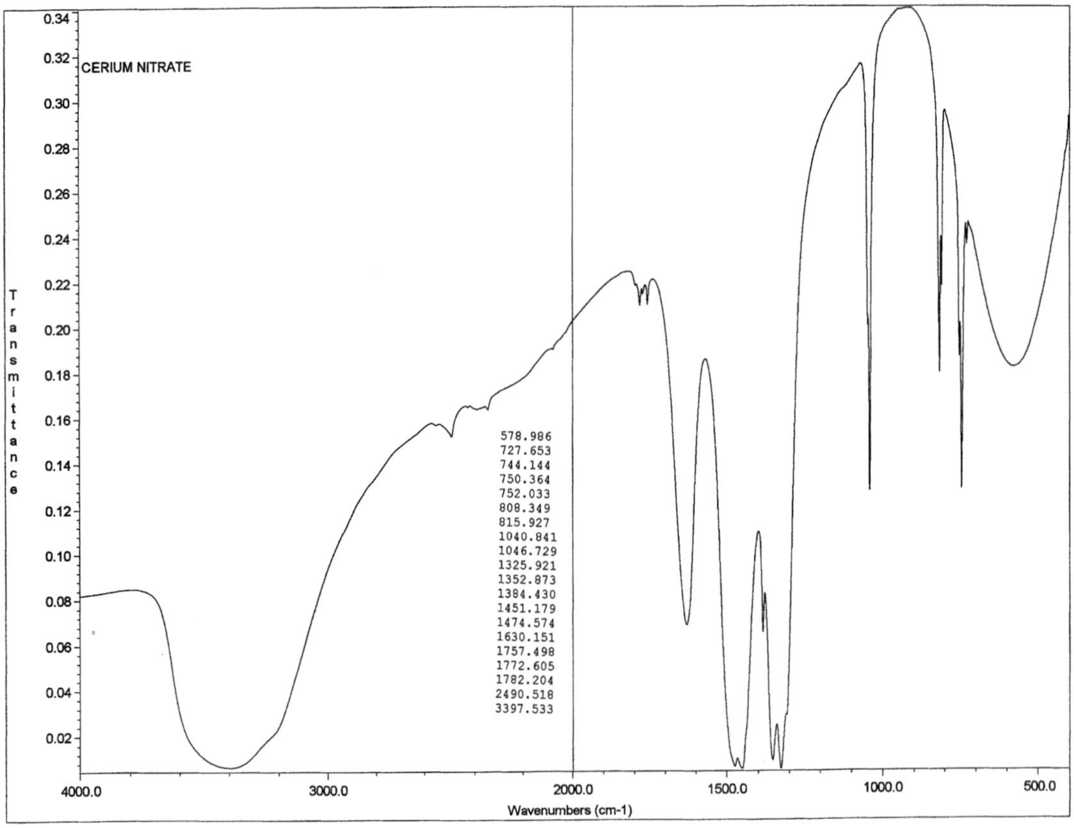

78 Cerium nitrate $Ce(NO_3)_3 \cdot 6H_2O$

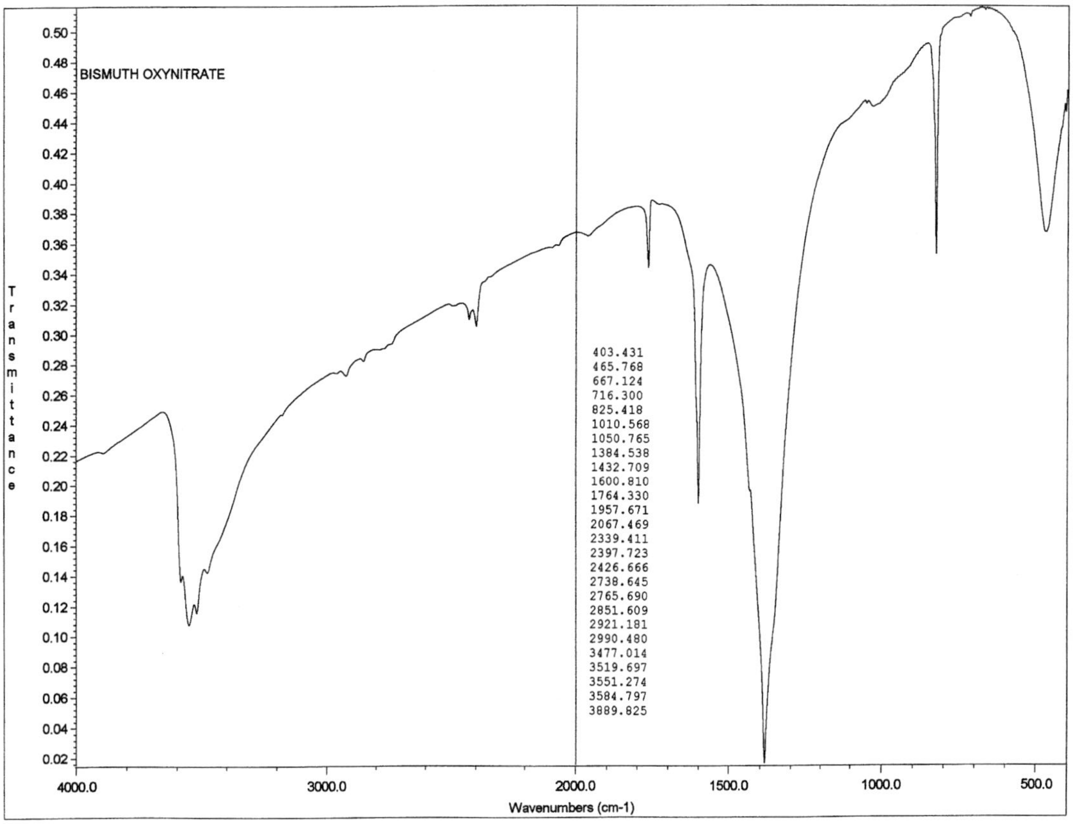

79 Bismuth subnitrate $BiONO_3 \cdot H_2O$

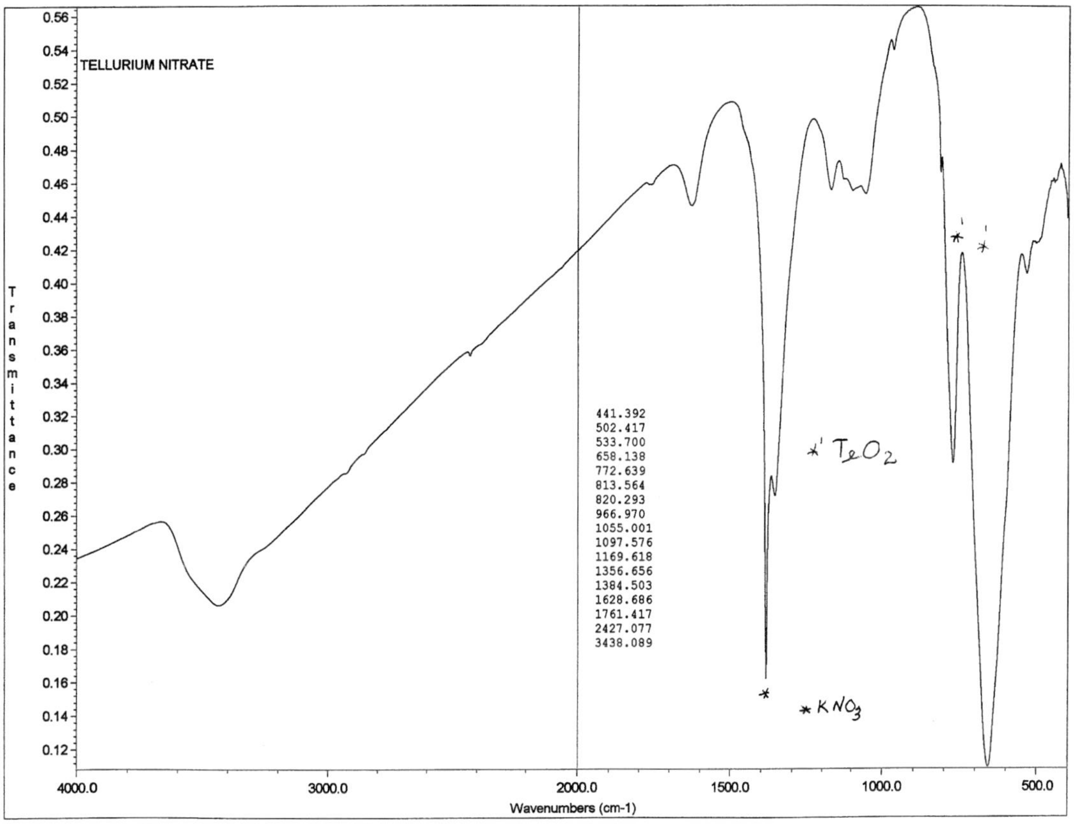

80 Tellurium nitrate (basic) $4TeO_2 \cdot N_2O_5 \cdot 1^1/_2H_2O$

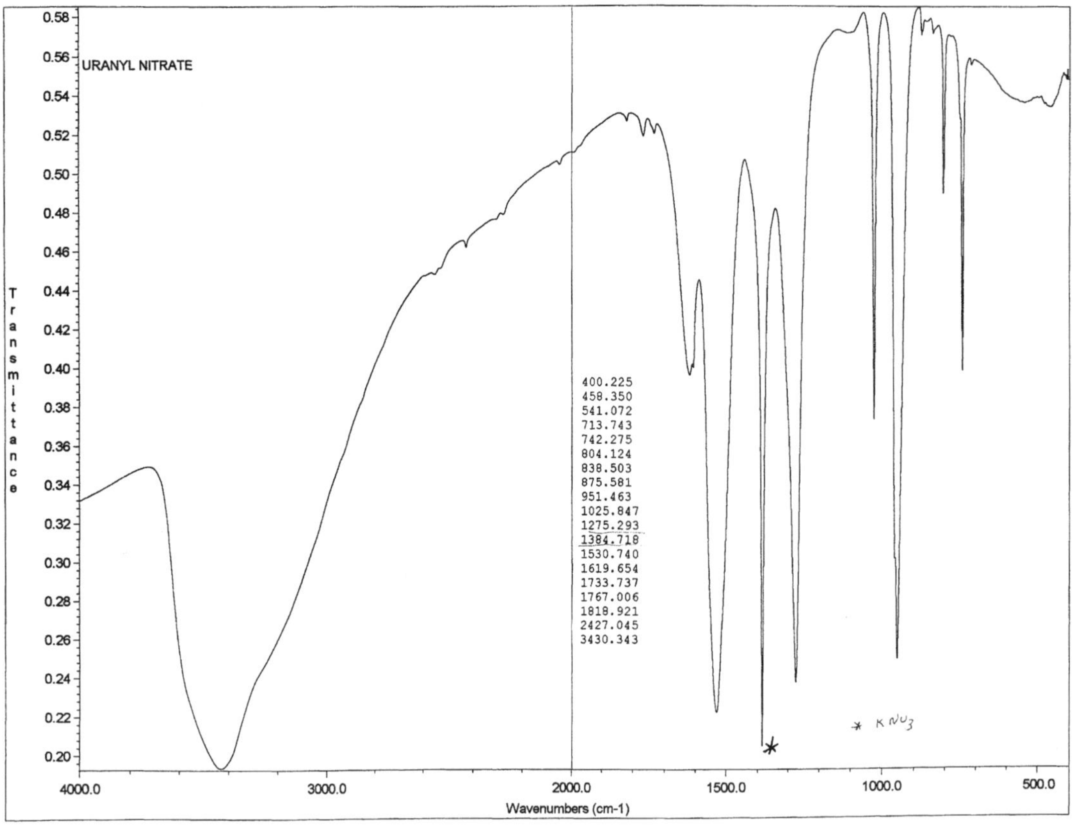

81 Uranyl nitrate $UO_2(NO_3)_2 \cdot 6H_2O$

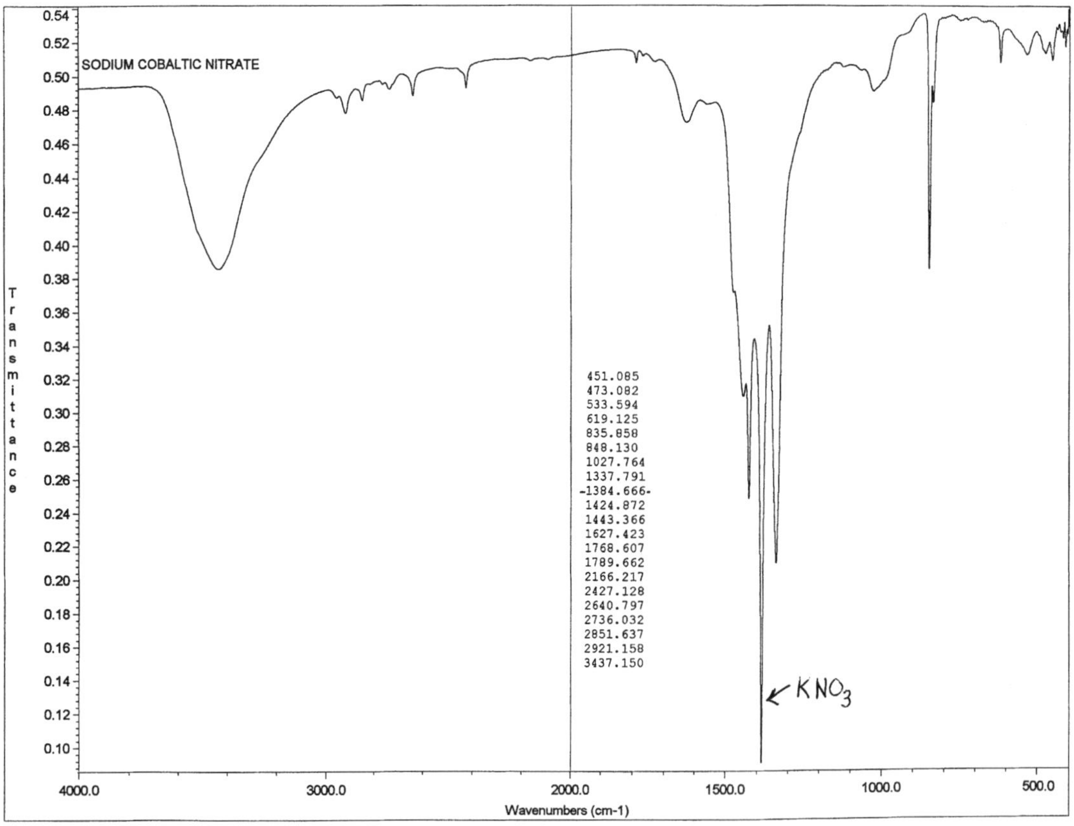

82 Sodium cobaltic nitrate $NaCo(NO_3)_4$

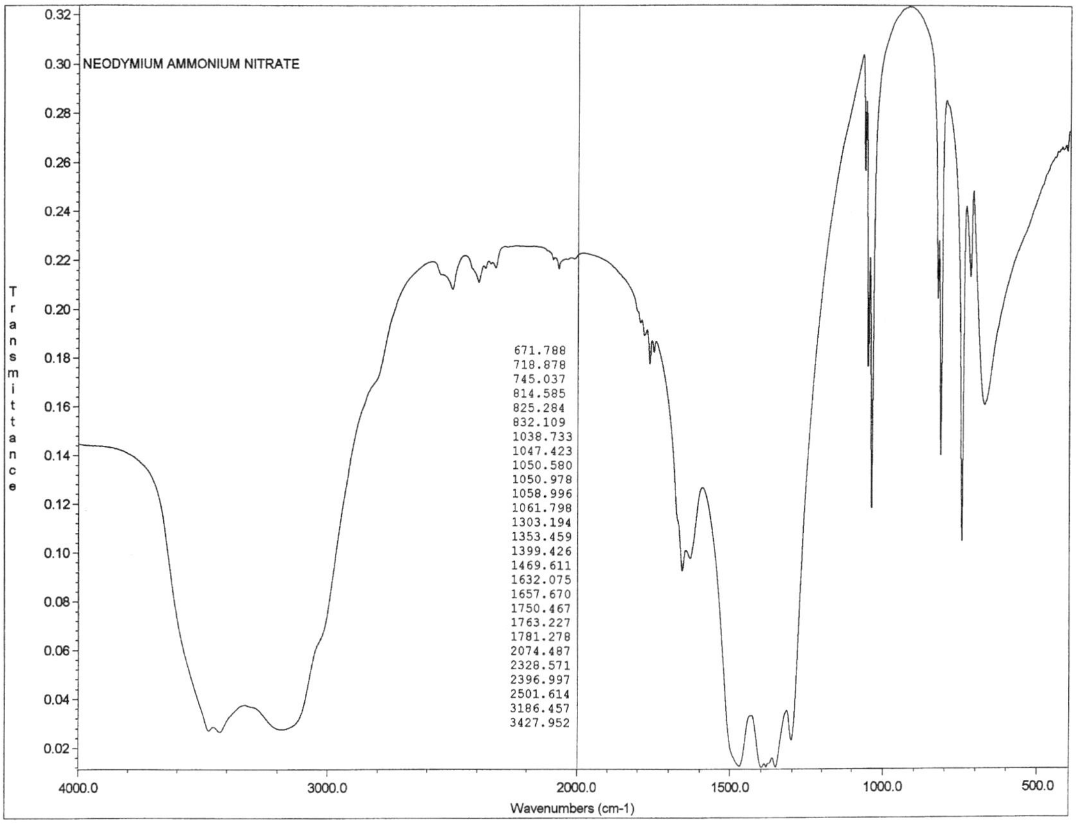

83 Neodymium ammonium nitrate $NdNH_4(NO_3)_4$

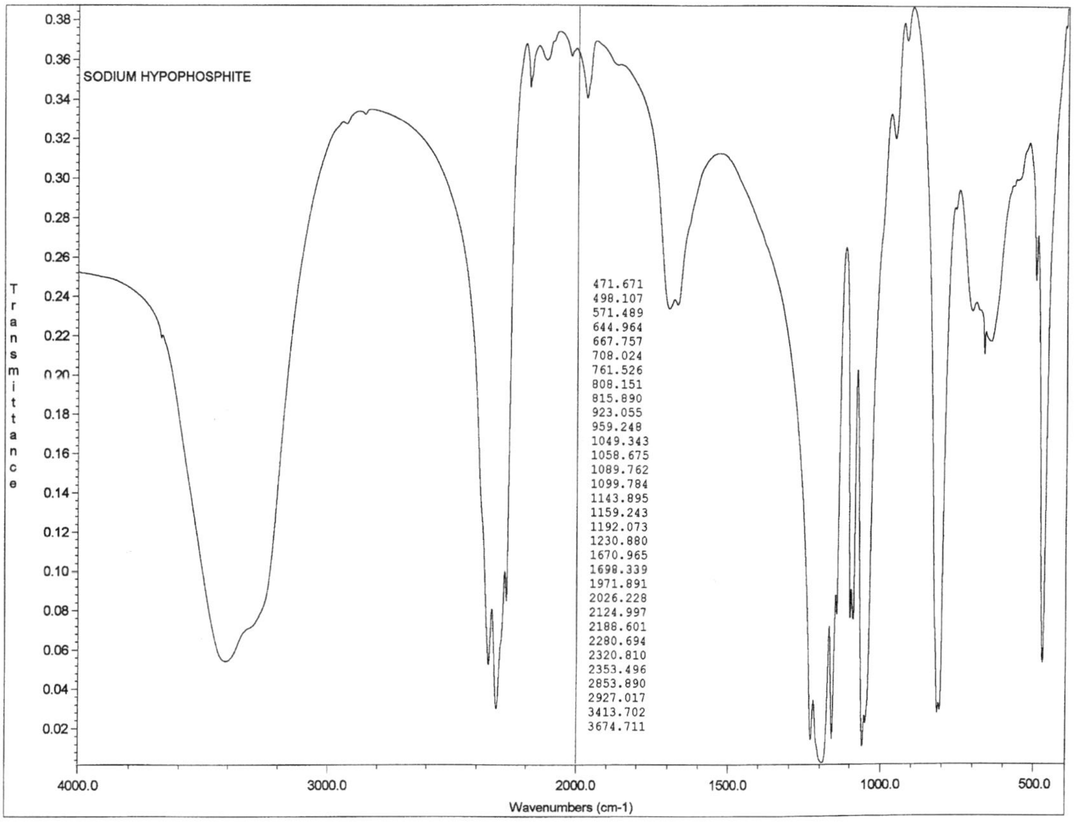

84 Sodium hypophosphite $NaH_2PO_2 \cdot H_2O$

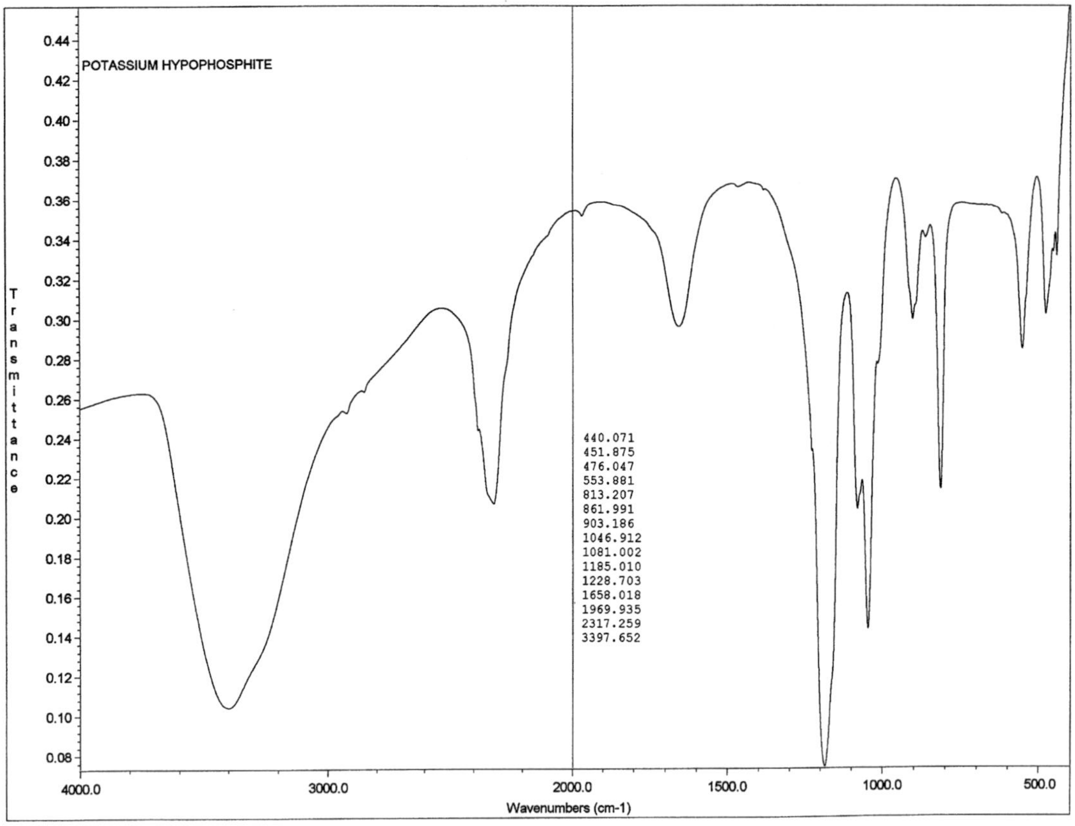

85 Potassium hypophosphite $KH_2PO_2 \cdot xH_2O$

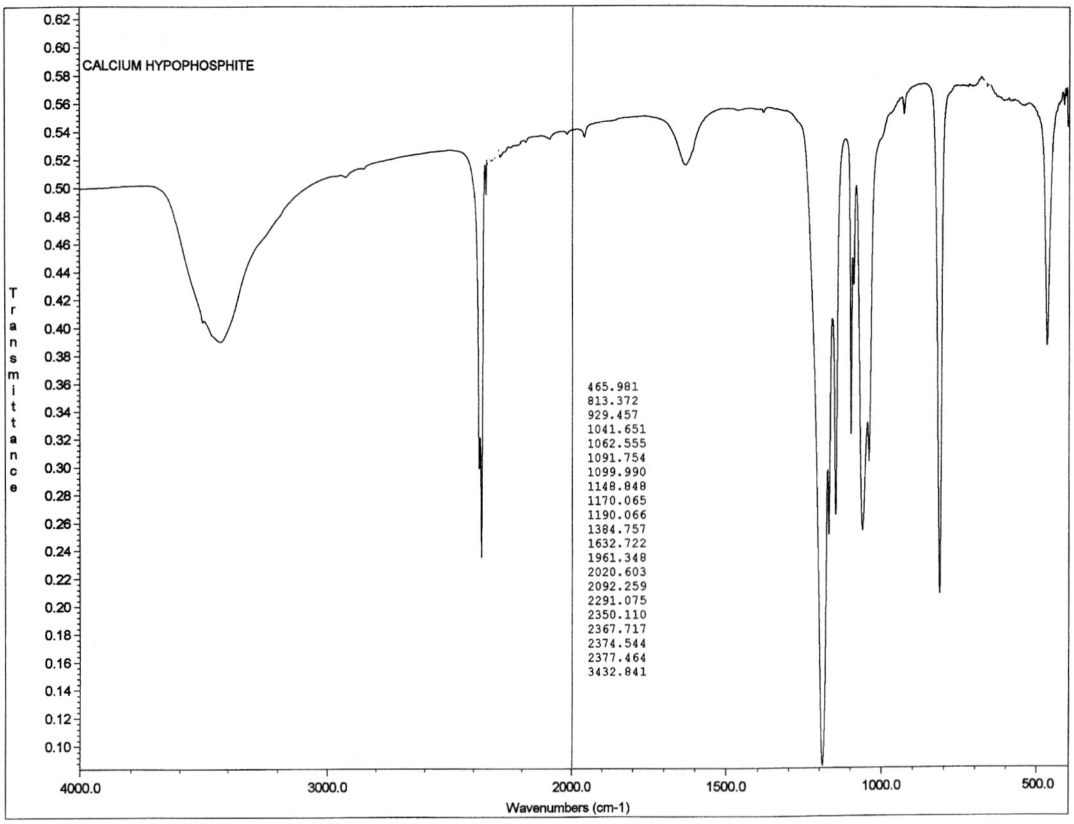

86 Calcium hypophosphite $Ca(H_2PO_2)_2$

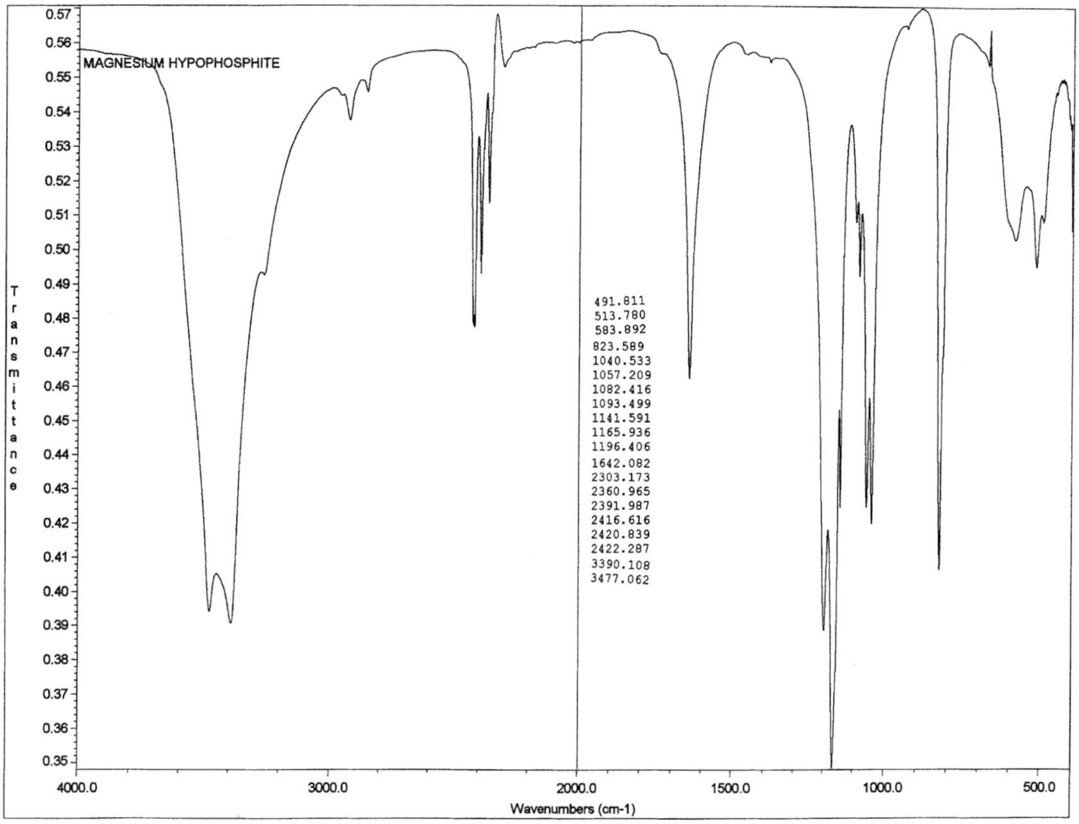

87 Magnesium hypophosphite $Mg(H_2PO_2)_2 \cdot xH_2O$

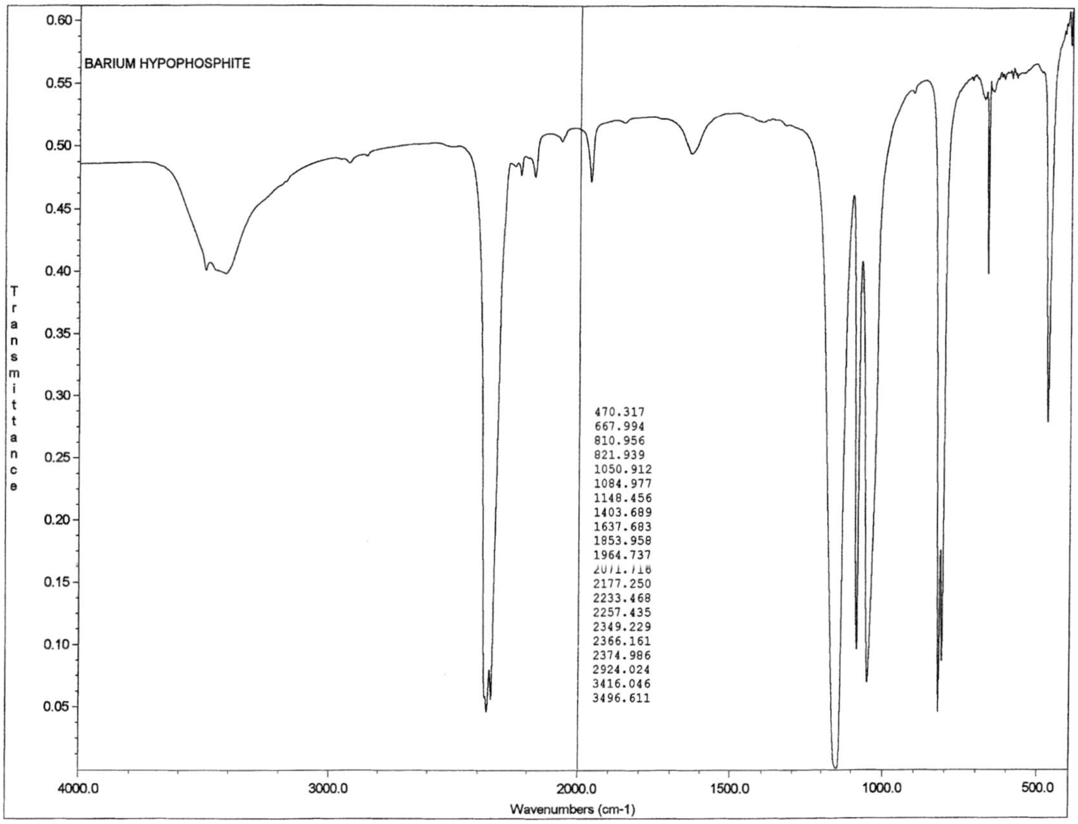

88 Barium hypophosphite $Ba(H_2PO_2)_2$

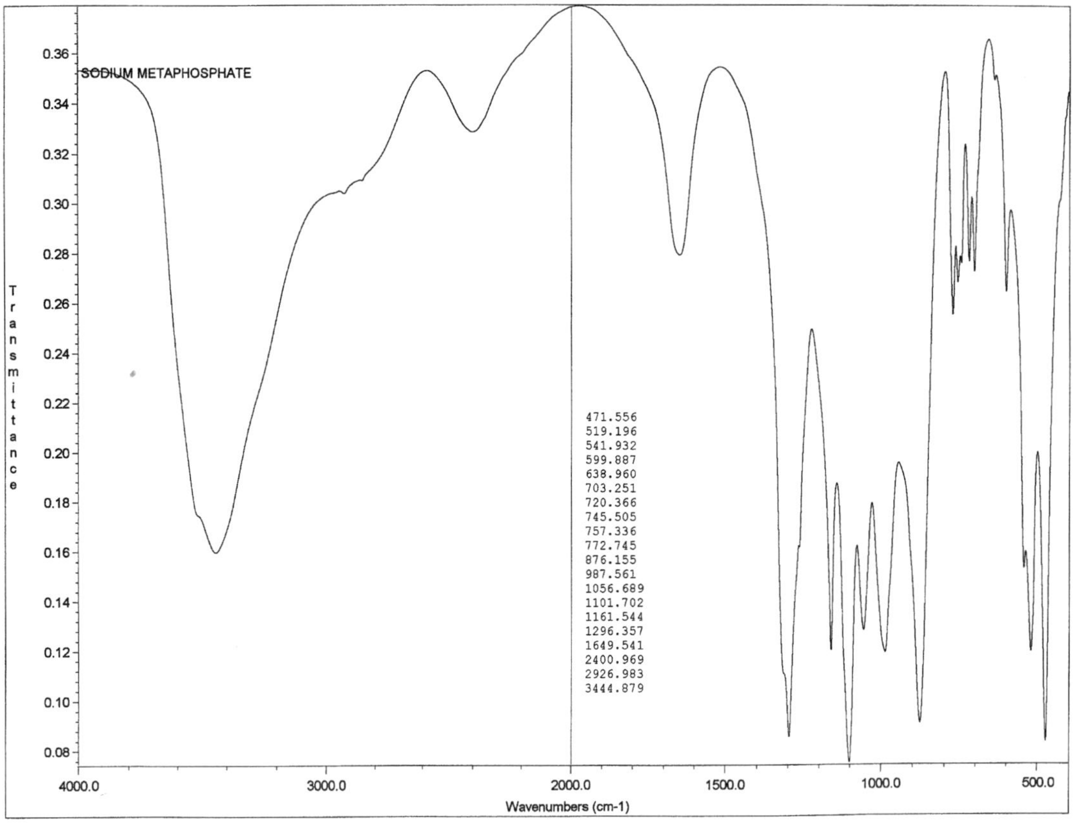

90 Sodium metaphosphate $(NaPO_3)_x \cdot xH_2O$

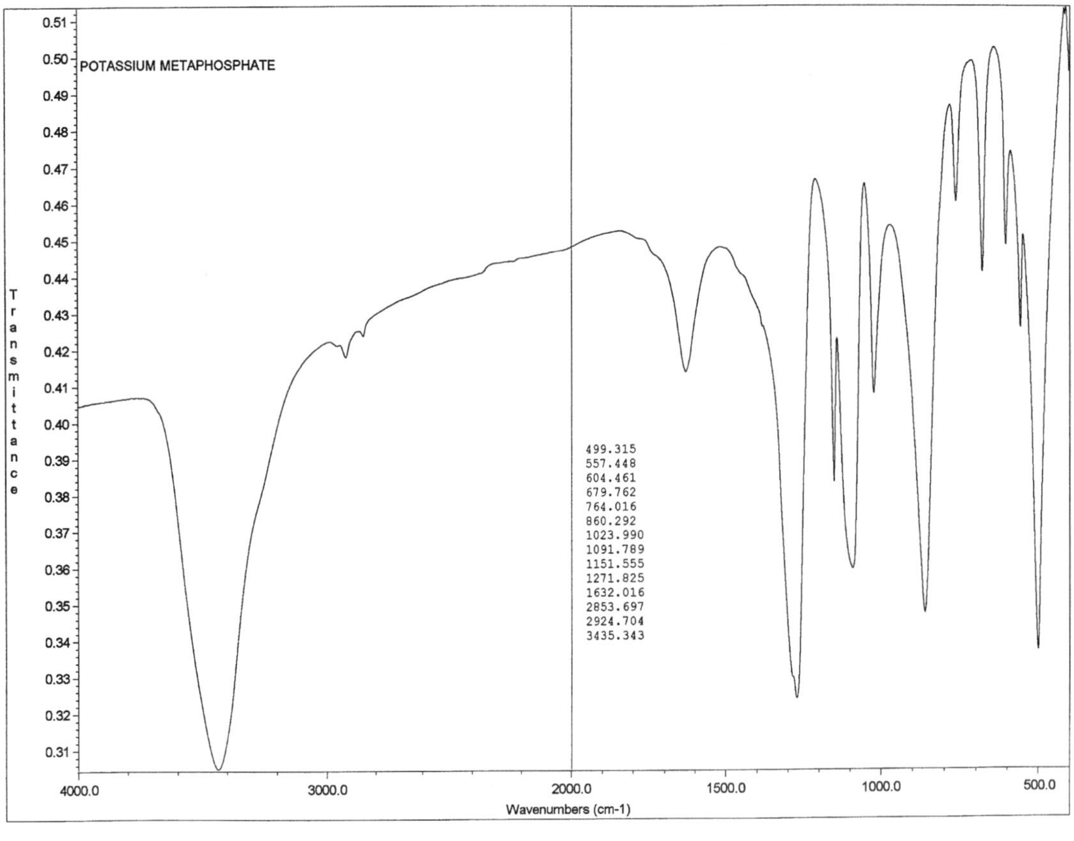

91 Potassium metaphosphate $(KPO_3)_x \cdot xH_2O$

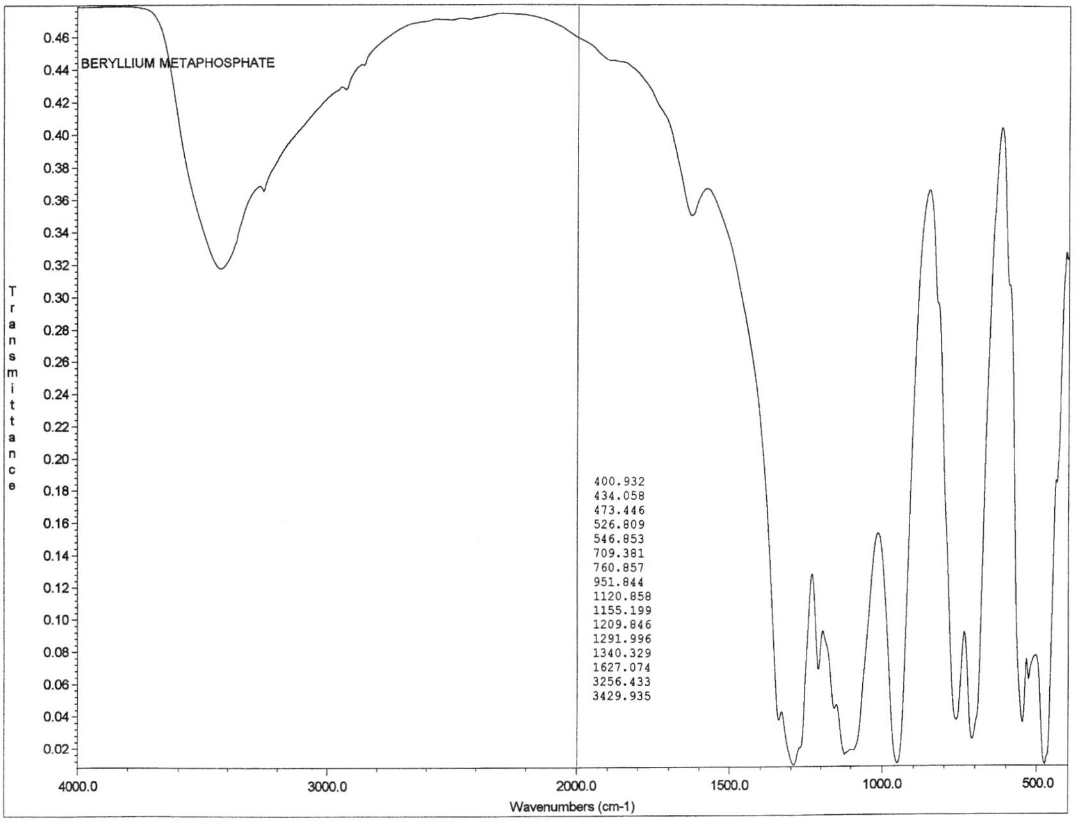

92 Beryllium metaphosphate $[Be(PO_3)_2]_x \cdot xH_2O$

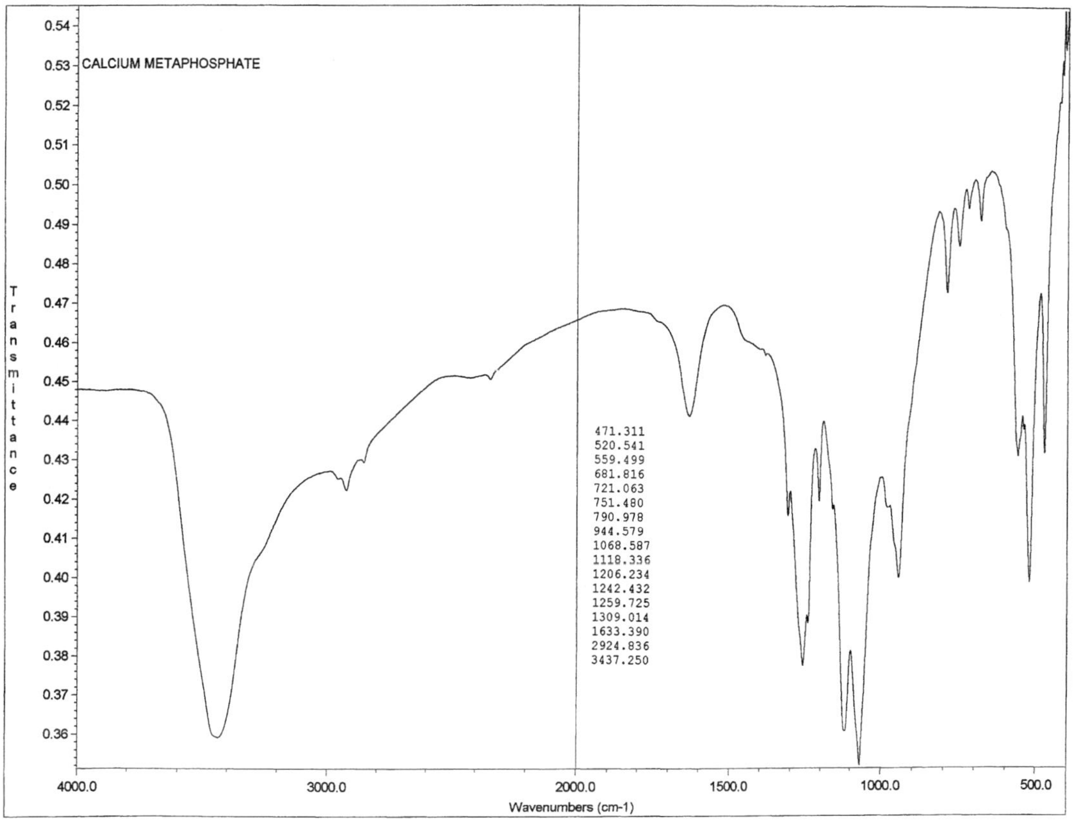

93 Calcium metaphosphate $[Ca(PO_3)_2]_x \cdot xH_2O$

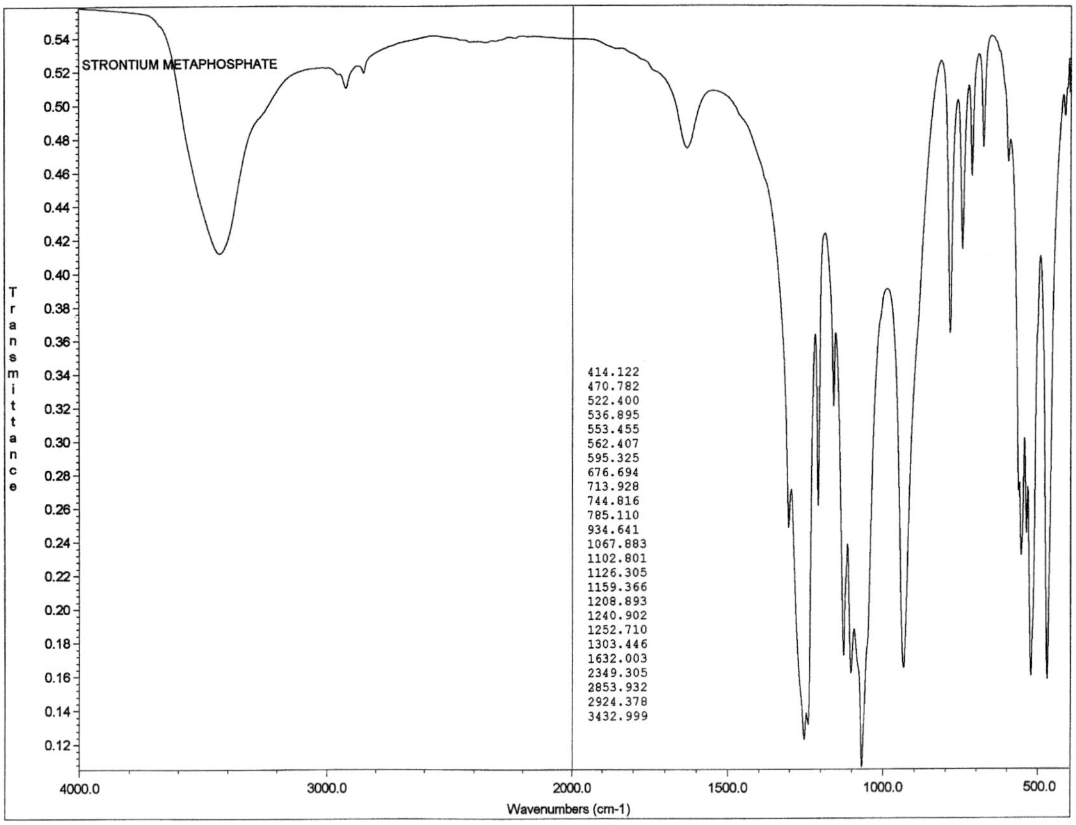

94 Strontium metaphosphate $[Sr(PO_3)_2]_x \cdot xH_2O$

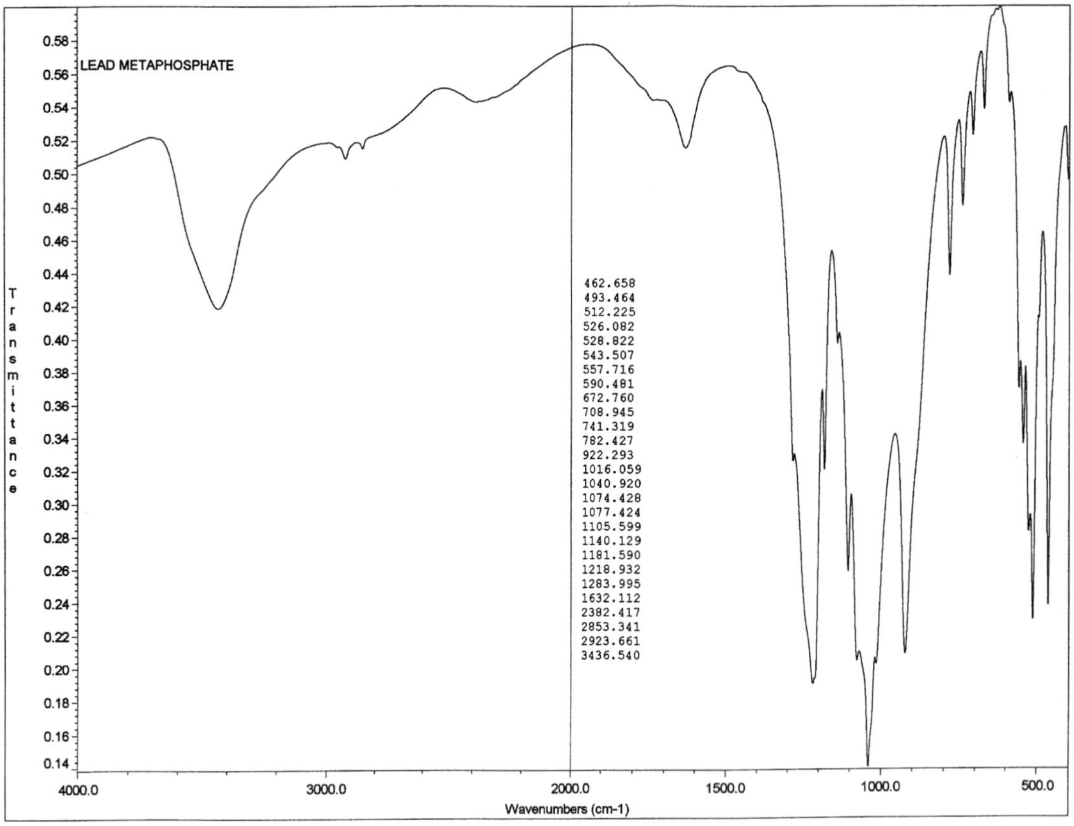

95 Lead metaphosphate $[Pb(PO_3)_2]_x \cdot xH_2O$

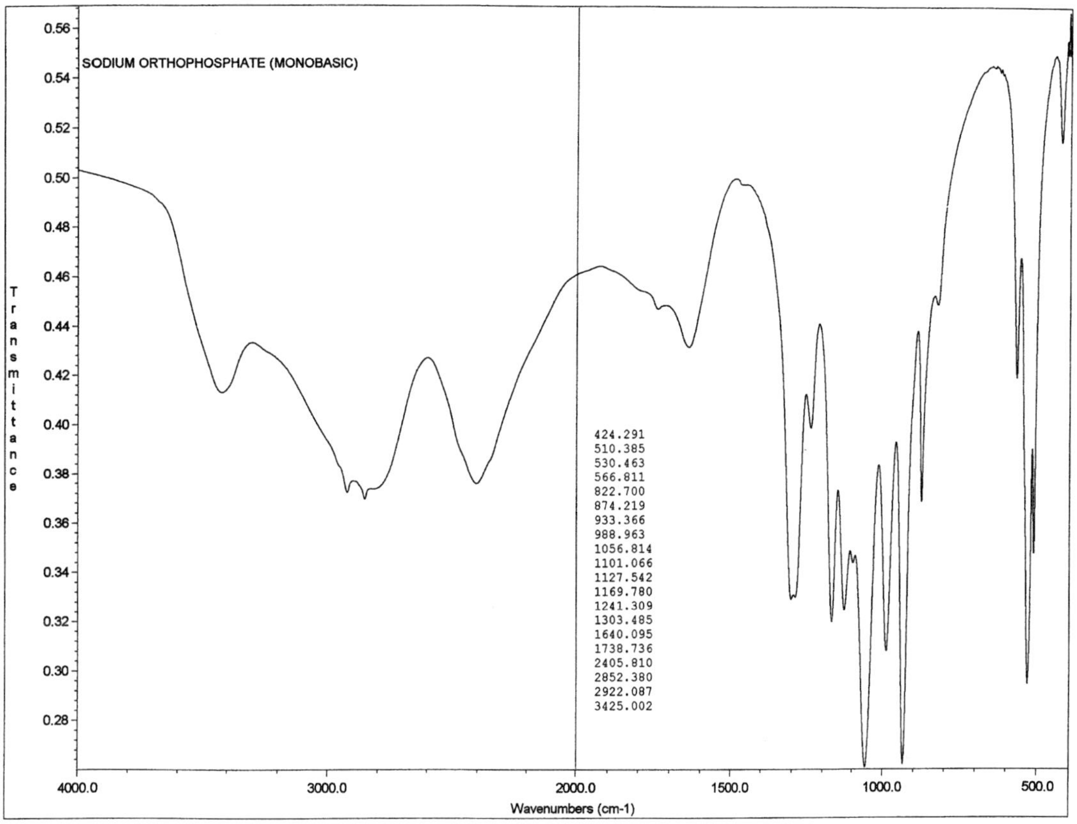

96 Sodium orthophosphate (monobasic) $NaH_2PO_4 \cdot xH_2O$

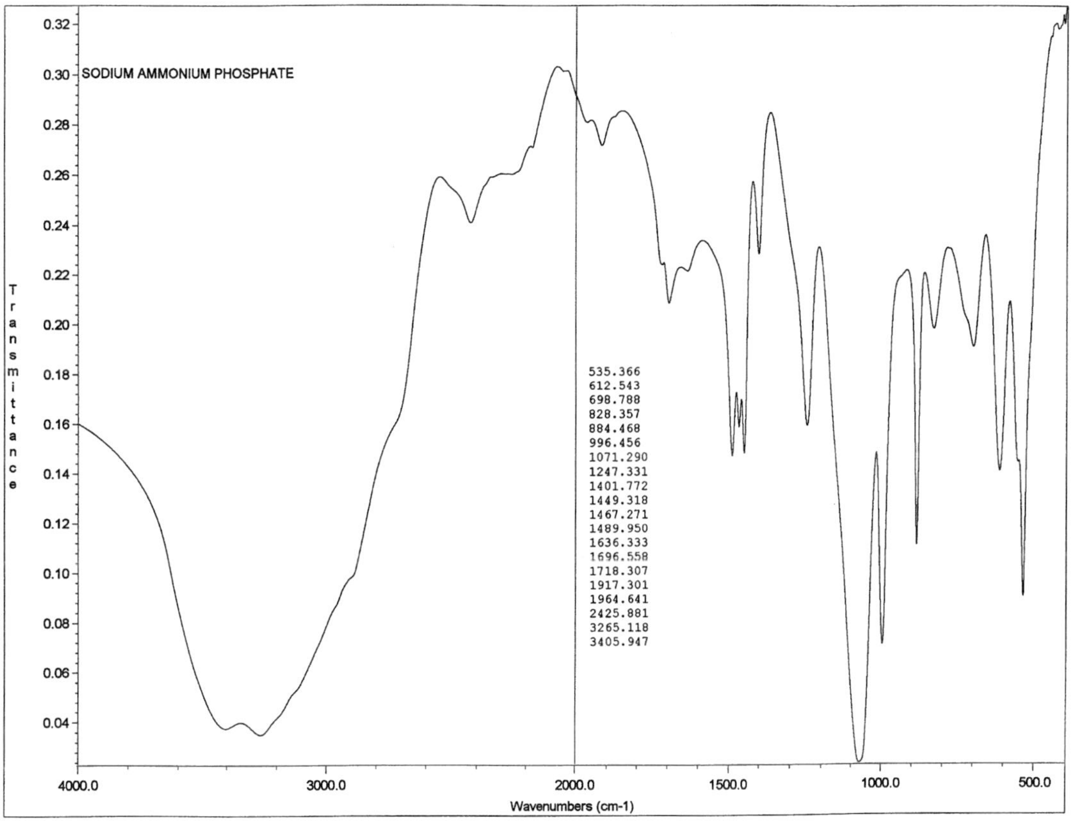

98 Sodium ammonium orthophosphate (dibasic) $NaNH_4HPO_4$

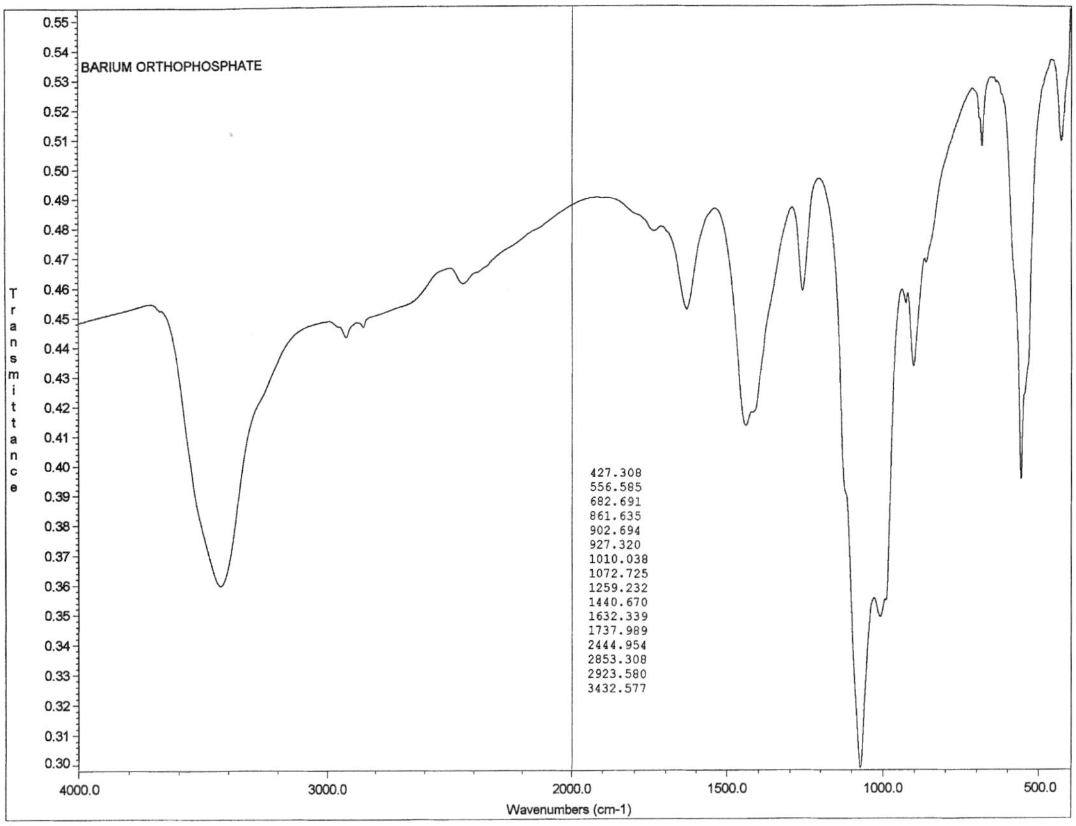

99 Barium orthophosphate (dibasic) $BaHPO_4 \cdot xH_2O$

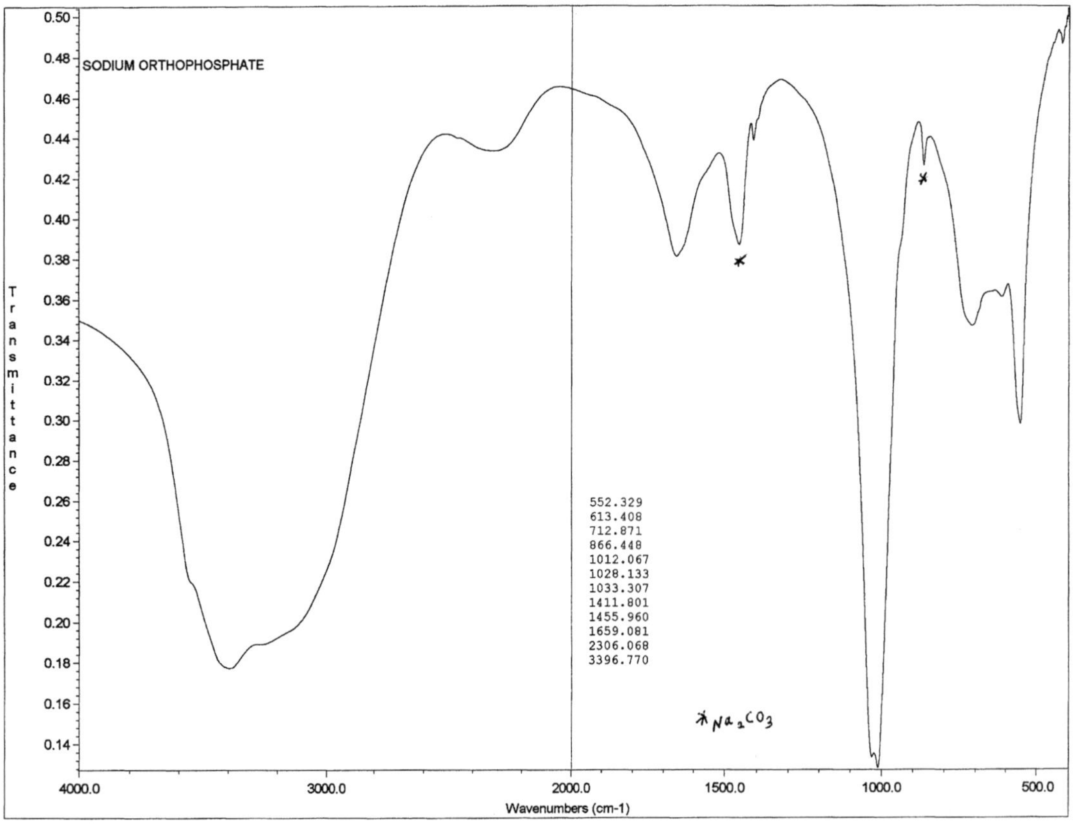

101 Sodium orthophosphate $Na_3PO_4 \cdot H_2O$

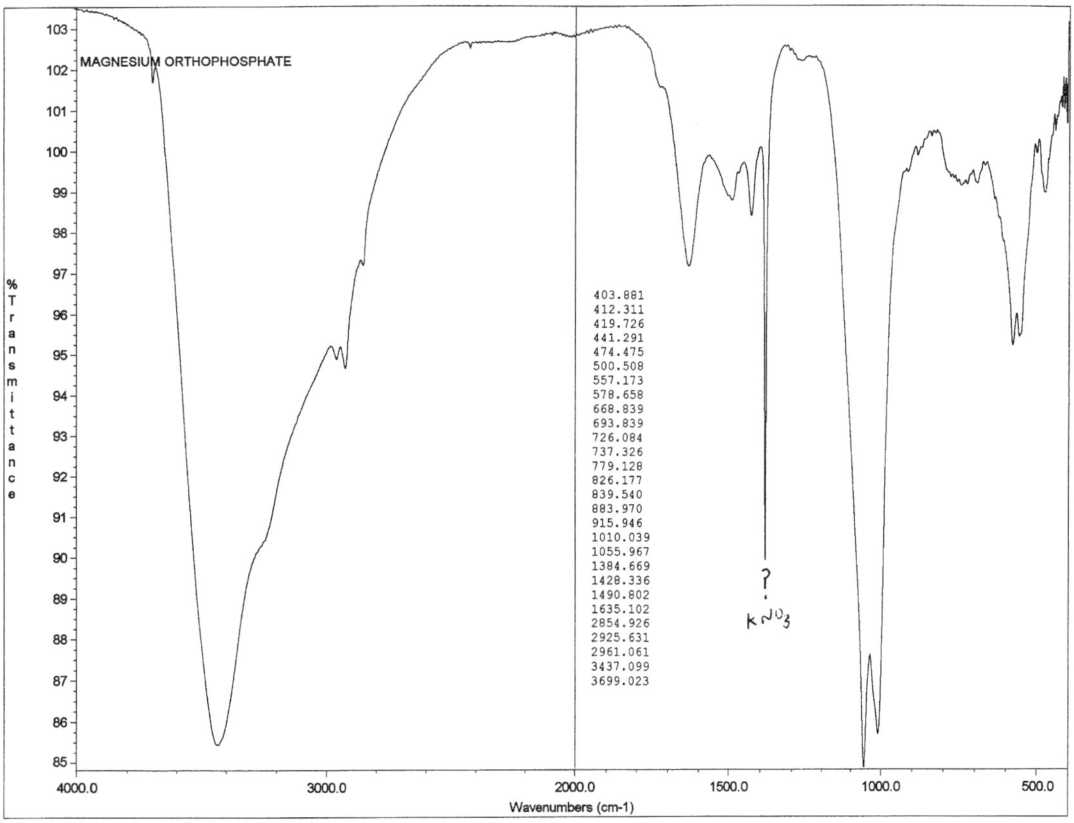

102 Magnesium orthophosphate $Mg_3(PO_4)_2 \cdot 8H_2O$

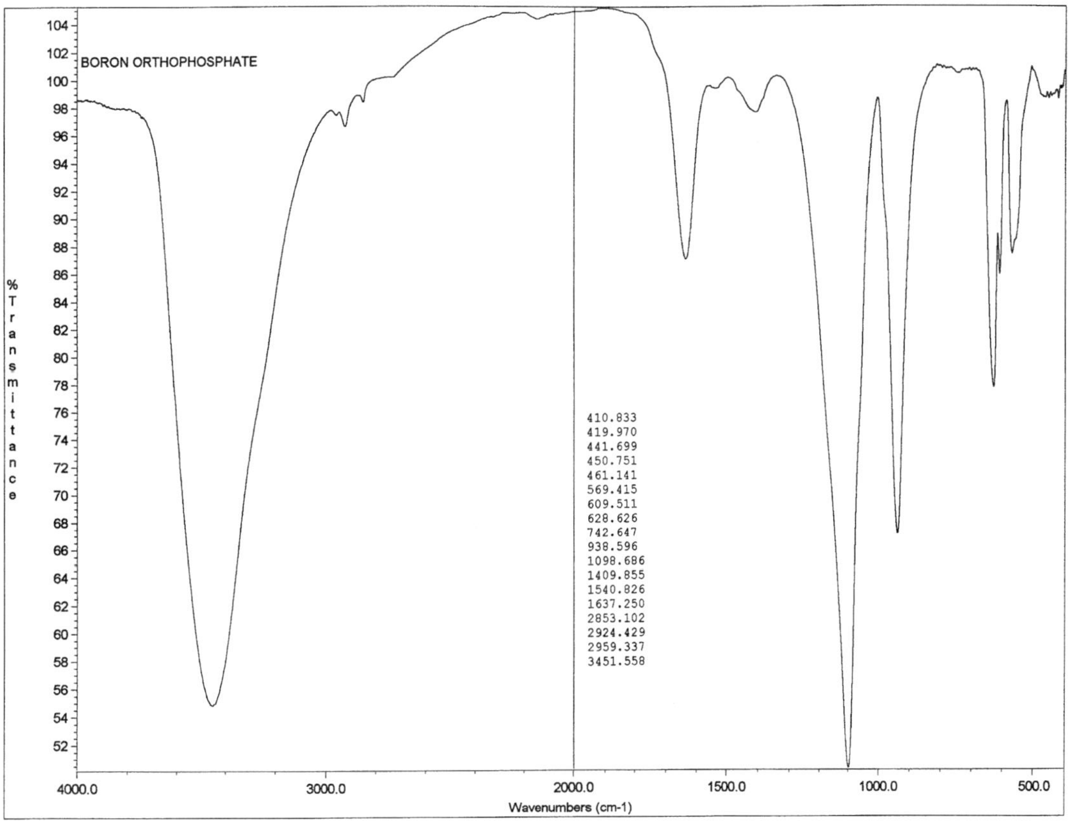

104 Boron orthophosphate (tetragonal) BPO_4

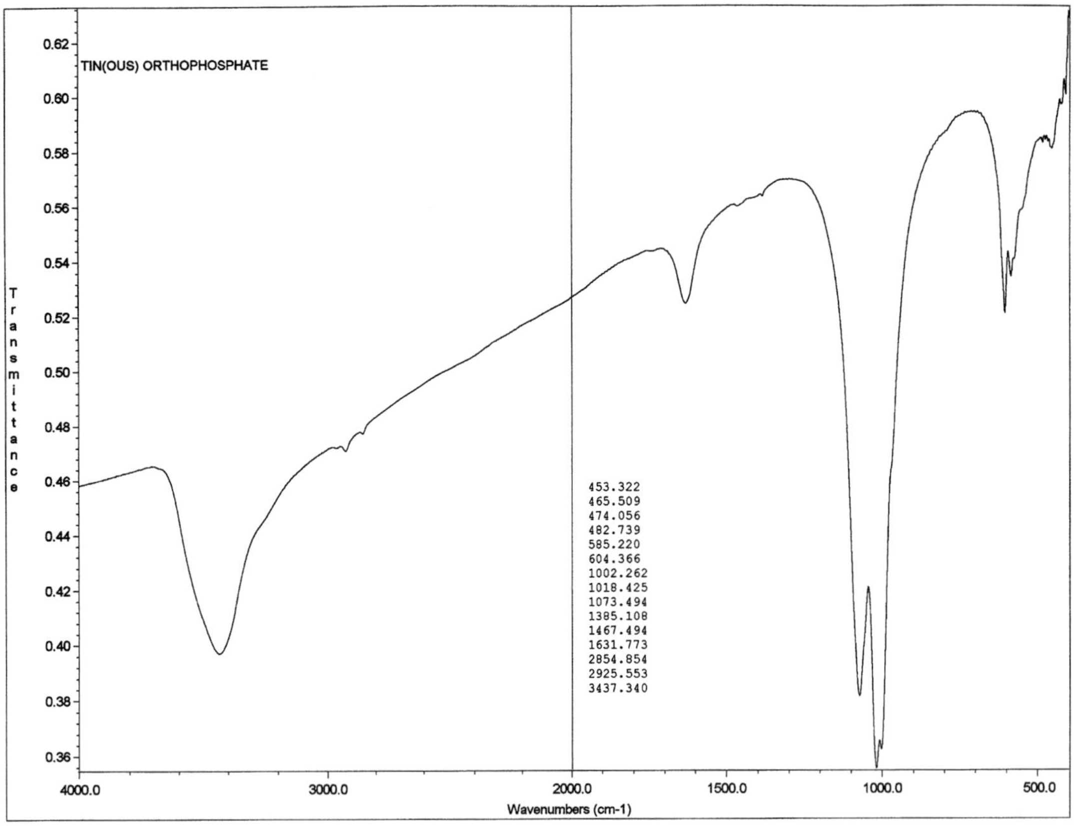

105 Tin (II) orthophosphate $Sn_3(PO_4)_2$ wet

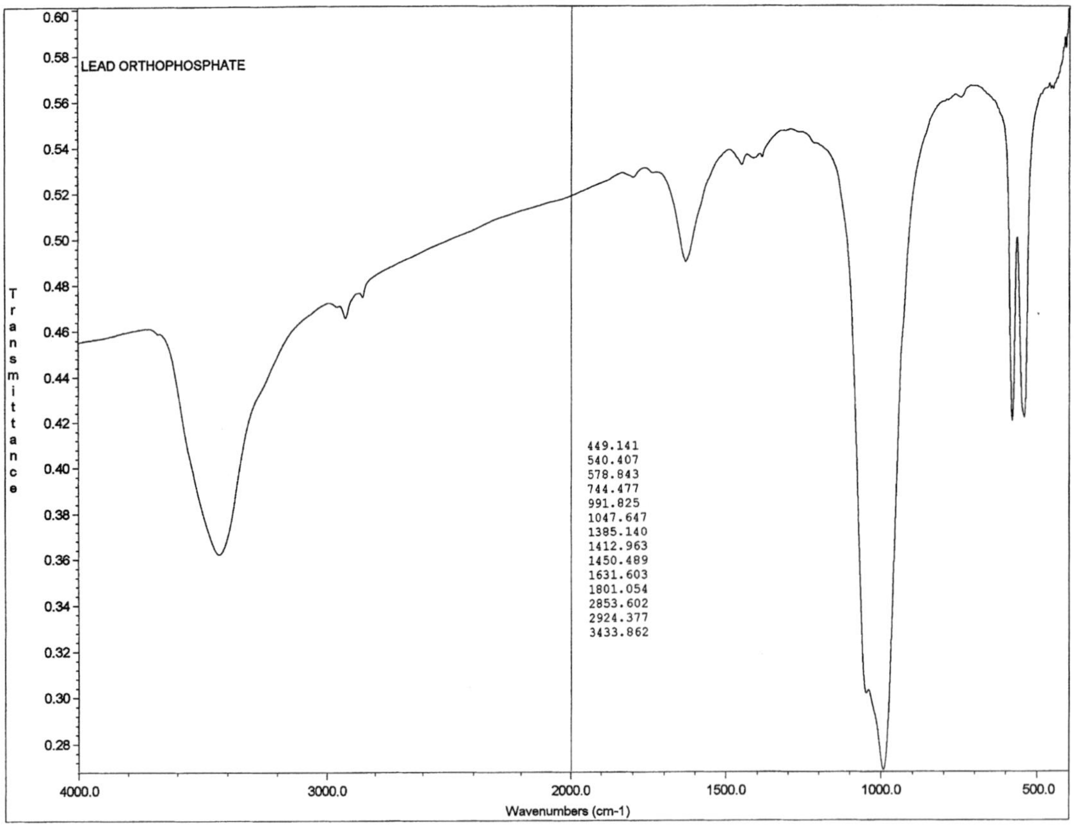

106 Lead orthophosphate $Pb_3(PO_4)_2$ wet

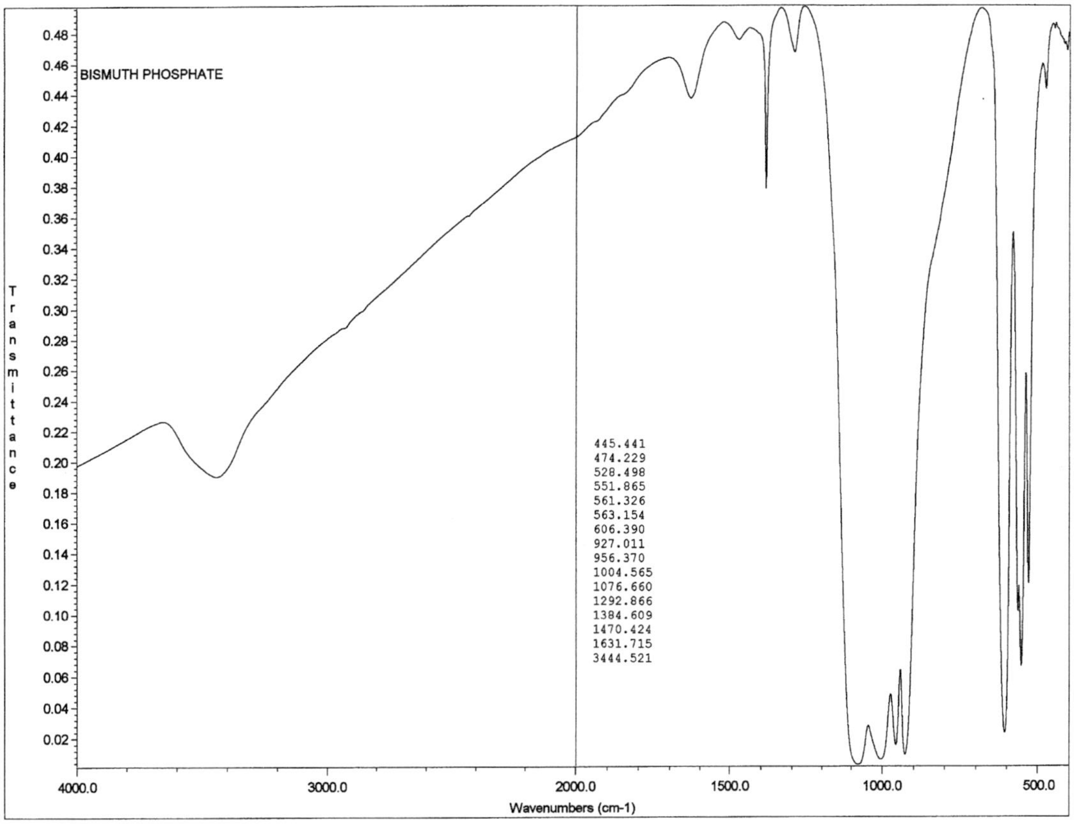

107 Bismuth orthophosphate $BiPO_4$

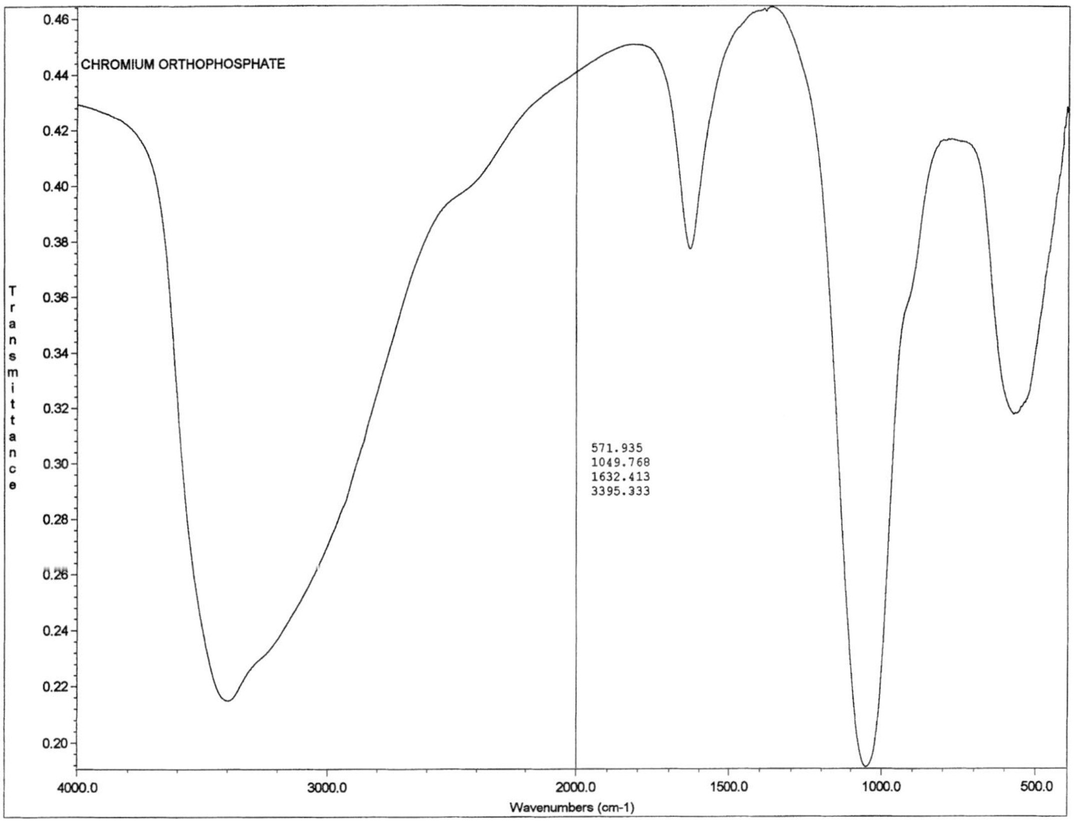

108 Chromium (III) orthophosphate $CrPO_4 \cdot 6H_2O$

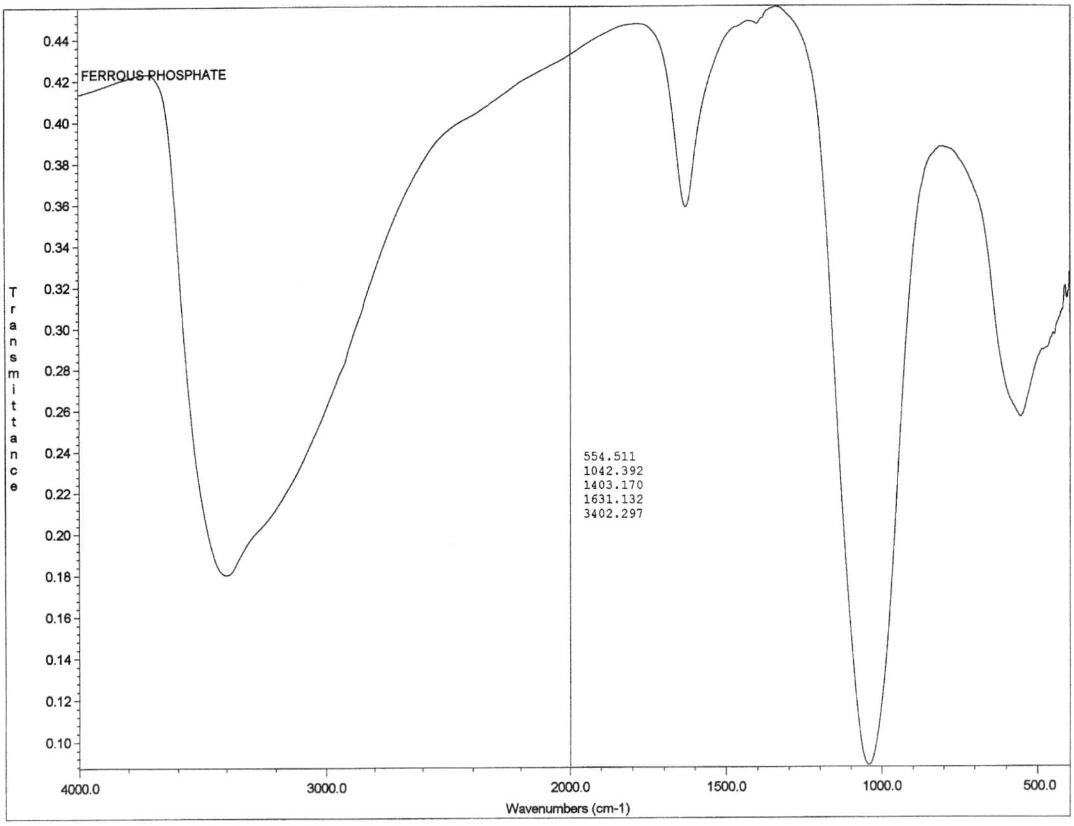

109 Iron (II) orthophosphate $Fe_3(PO_4)_2 \cdot 8H_2O$

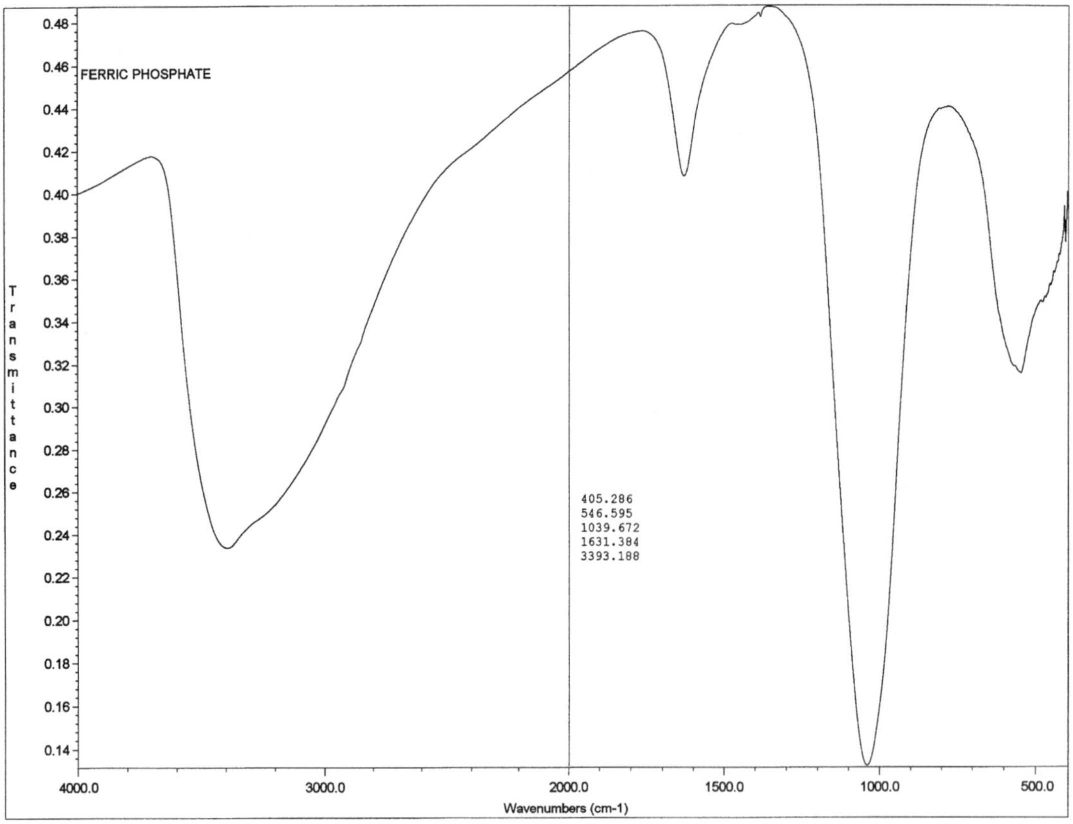

110 Iron (III) orthophosphate $FePO_4 \cdot 2H_2O$

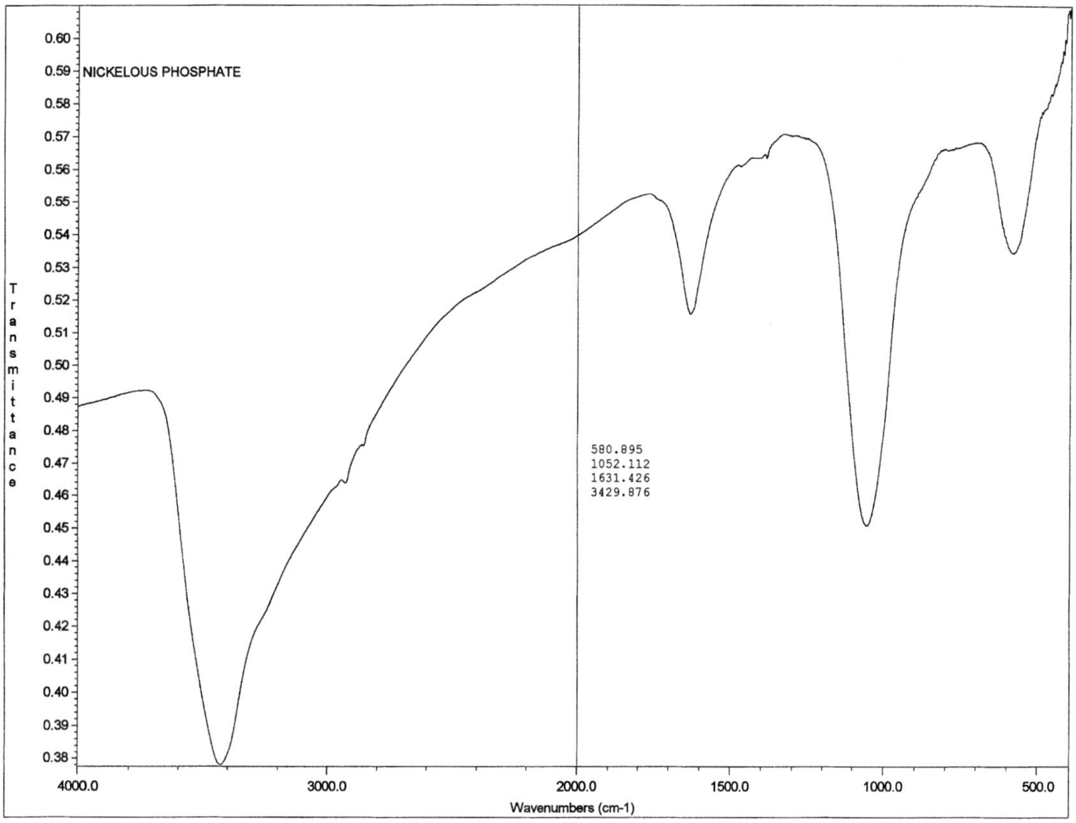

111 Nickel orthophosphate $Ni_3(PO_4)_2 \cdot 8H_2O$

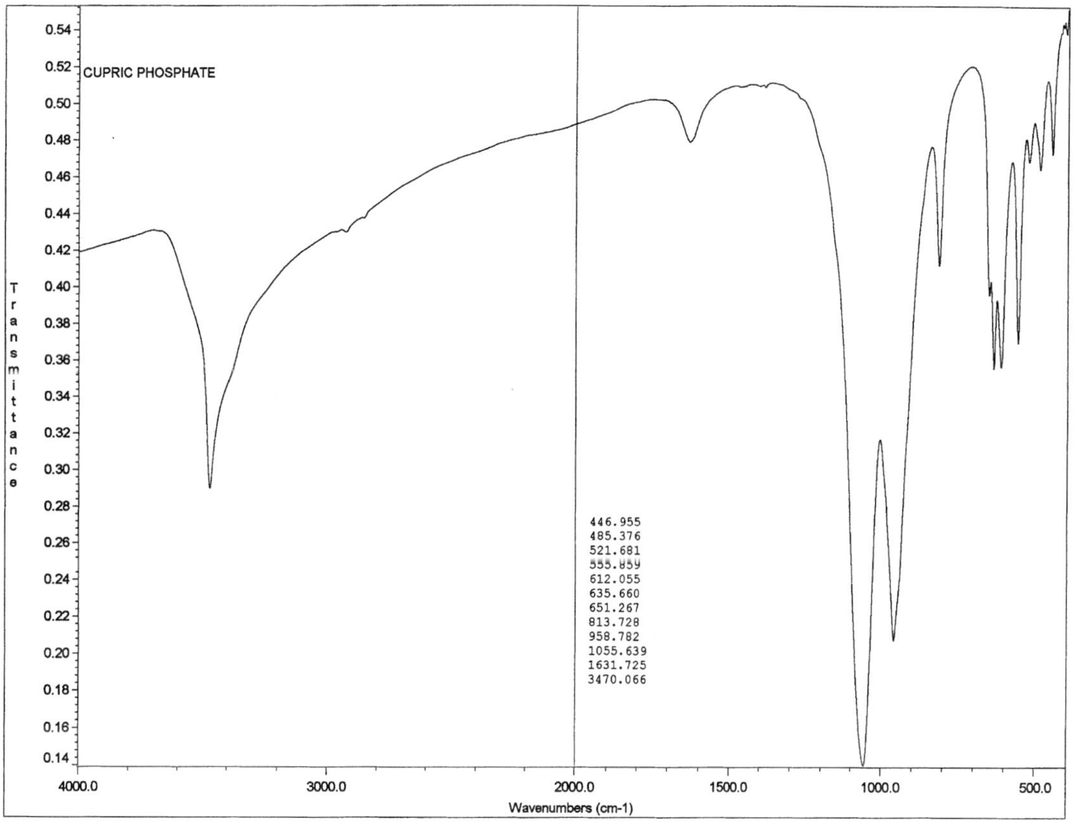

112 Copper (II) orthophosphate $Cu_3(PO_4) \cdot 3H_2O$

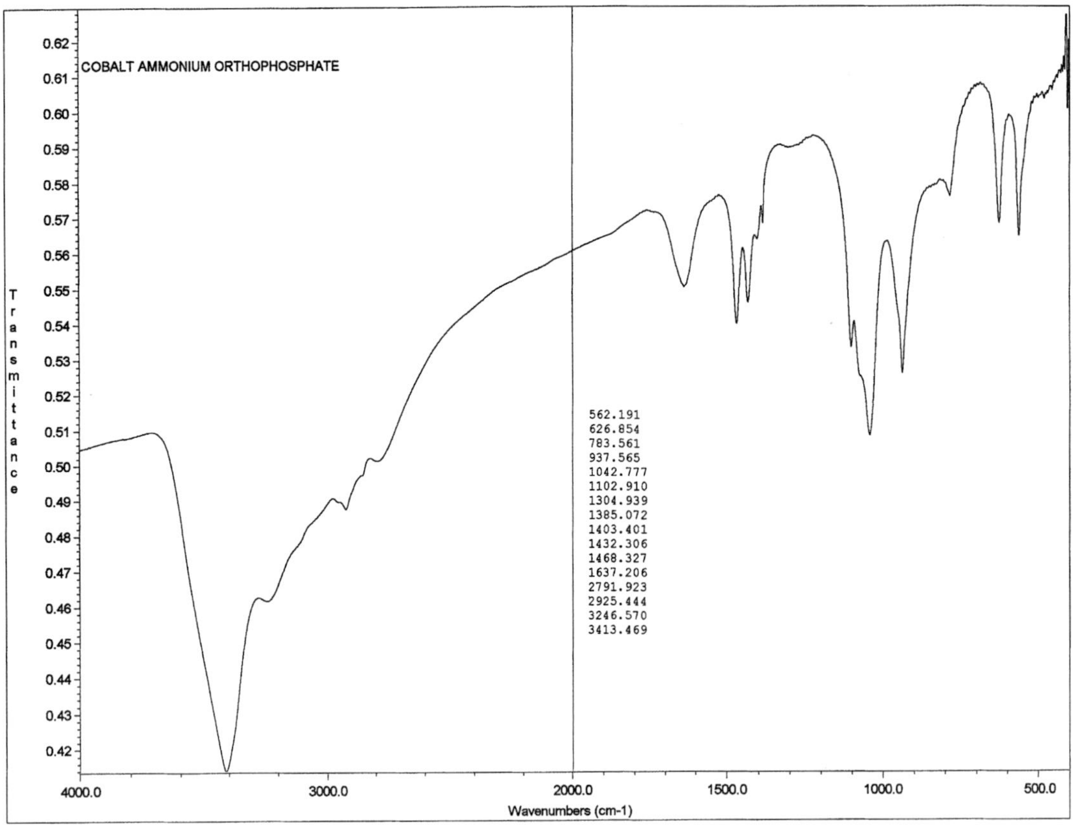

116 Ammonium cobalt orthophosphate $NH_4CoPO_4 \cdot xH_2O$

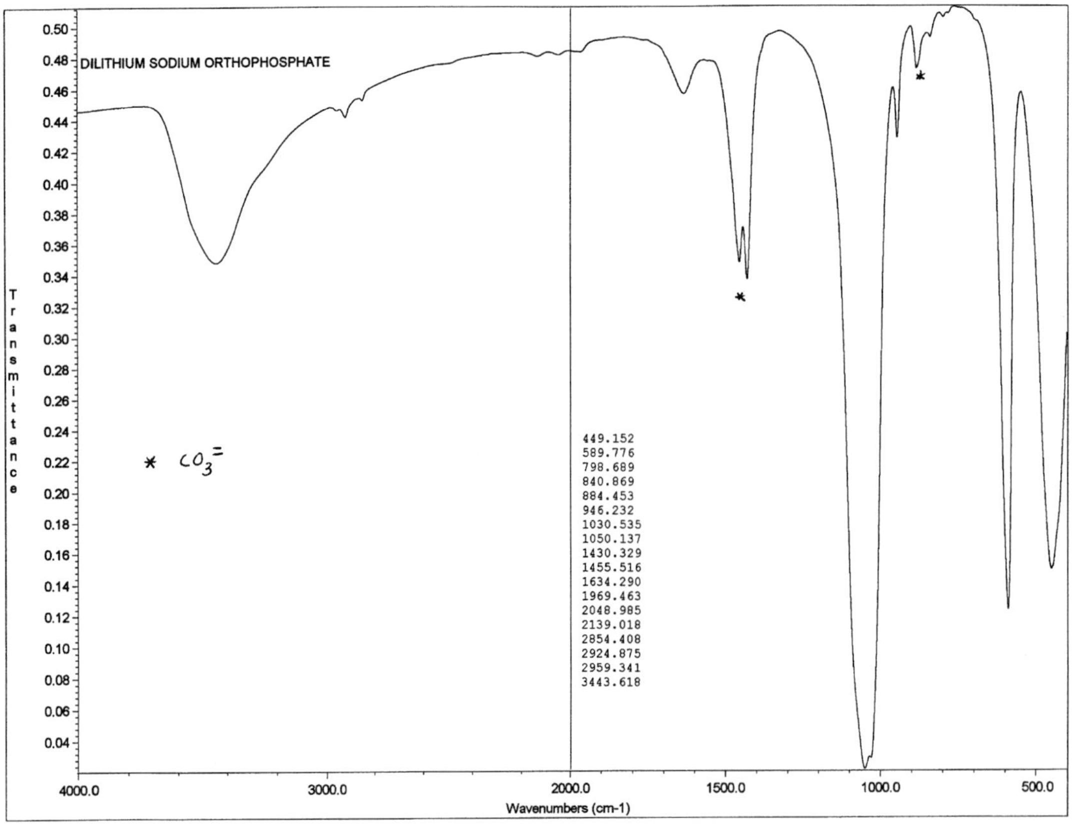

117 Dilithium sodium orthophosphate $Li_2NaPO_4 \cdot xH_22O$

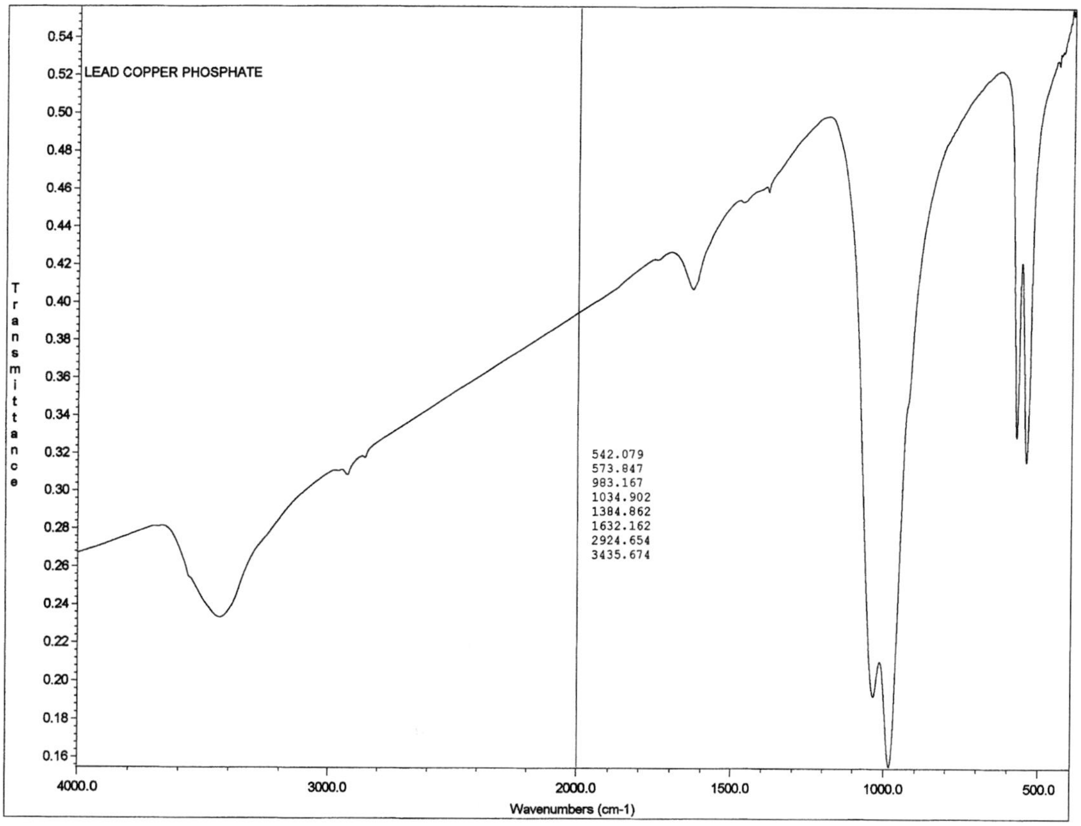

118 Lead copper (I) orthophosphate $PbCuPO_4$

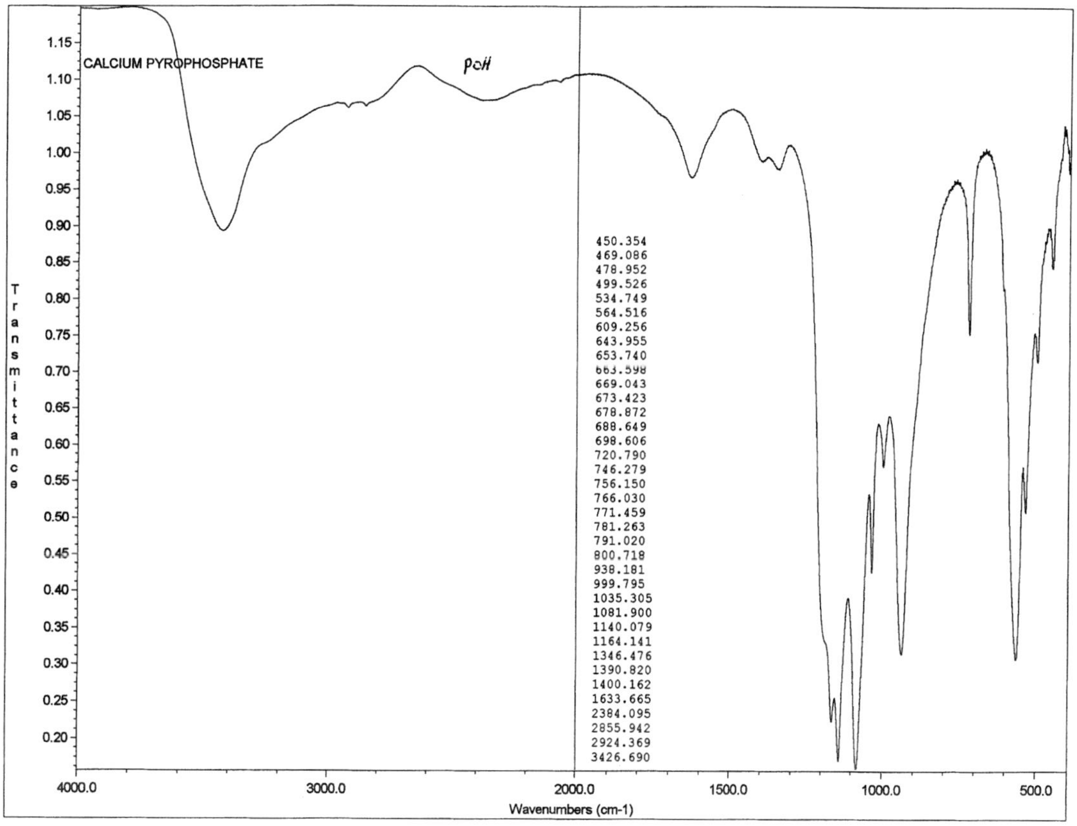

120 Calcium pyrophosphate (δ-form) $Ca_2P_2O_7$ (some POH present)

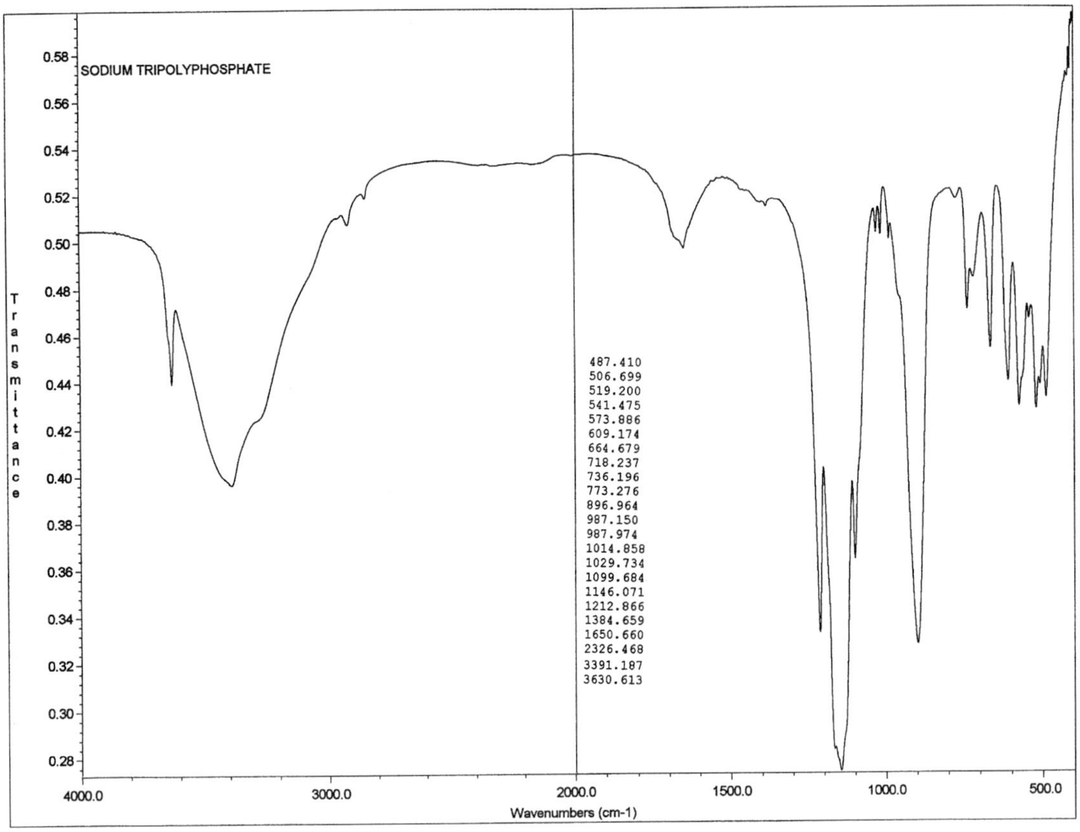

124 Sodium tripolyphosphate $Na_5P_3O_{10} \cdot xH_2O$

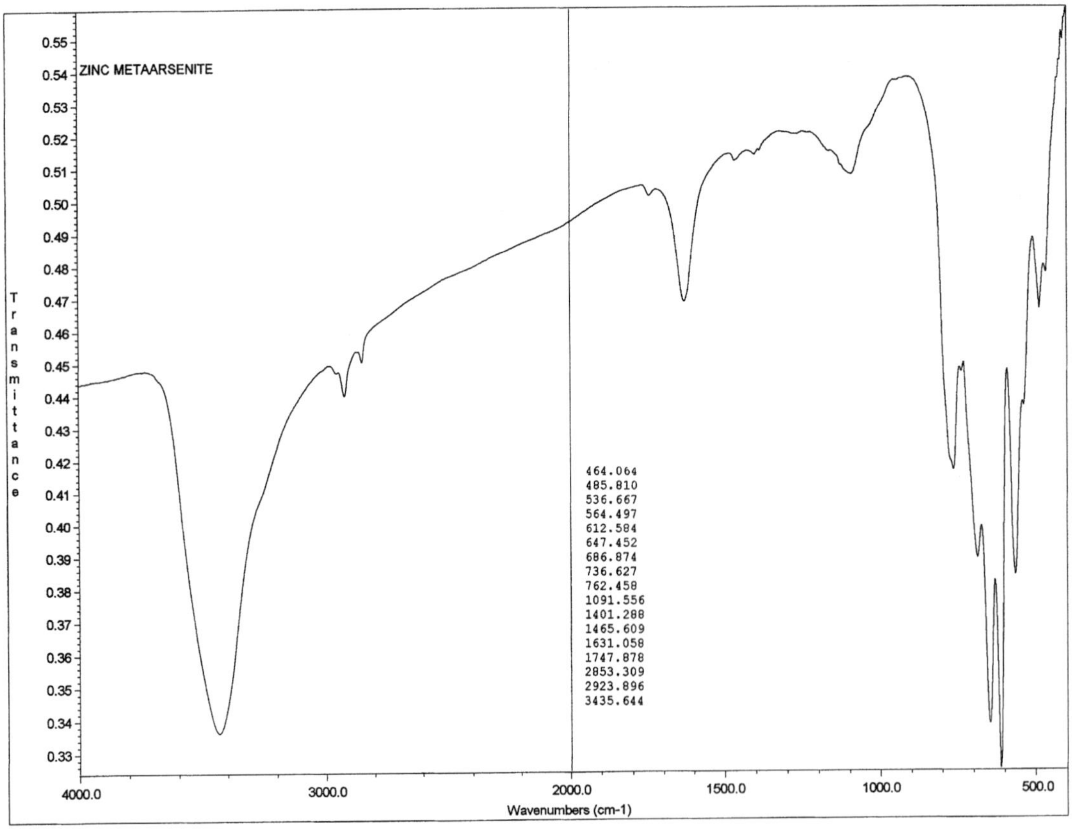

126 Zinc metaarsenite $Zn(AsO_2)_2$

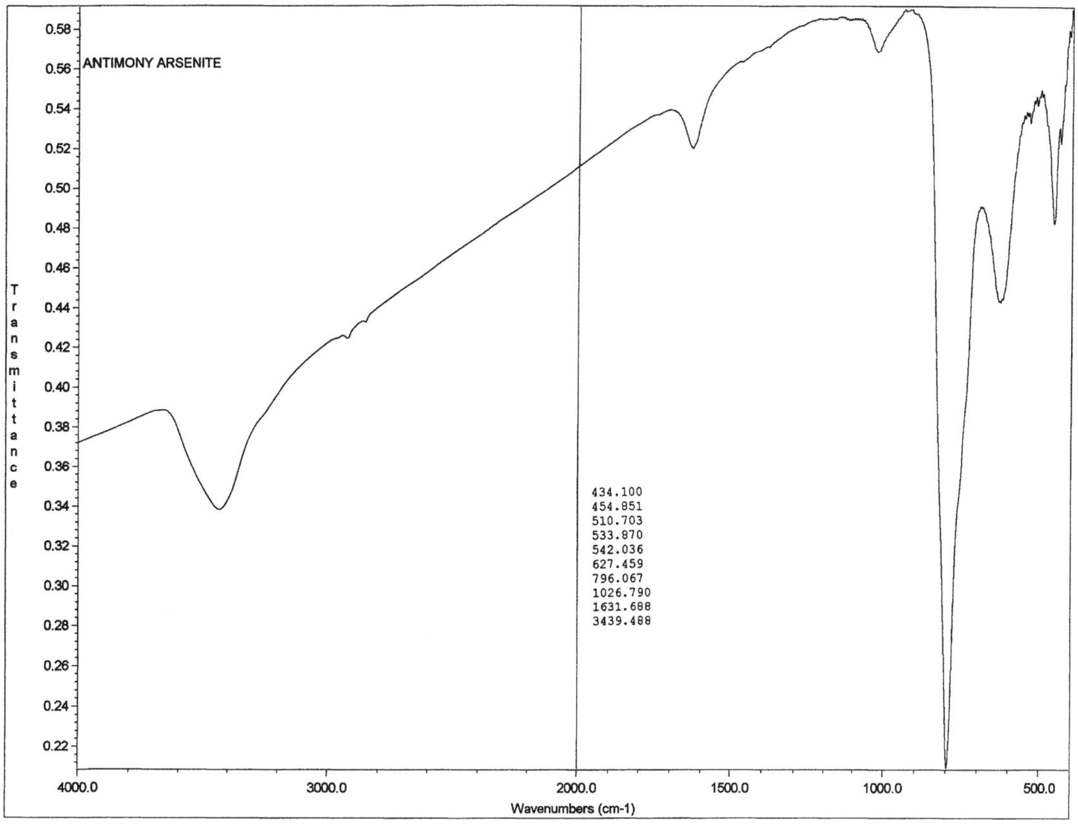

127 Antimony orthoarsenite $SbAsO_3$

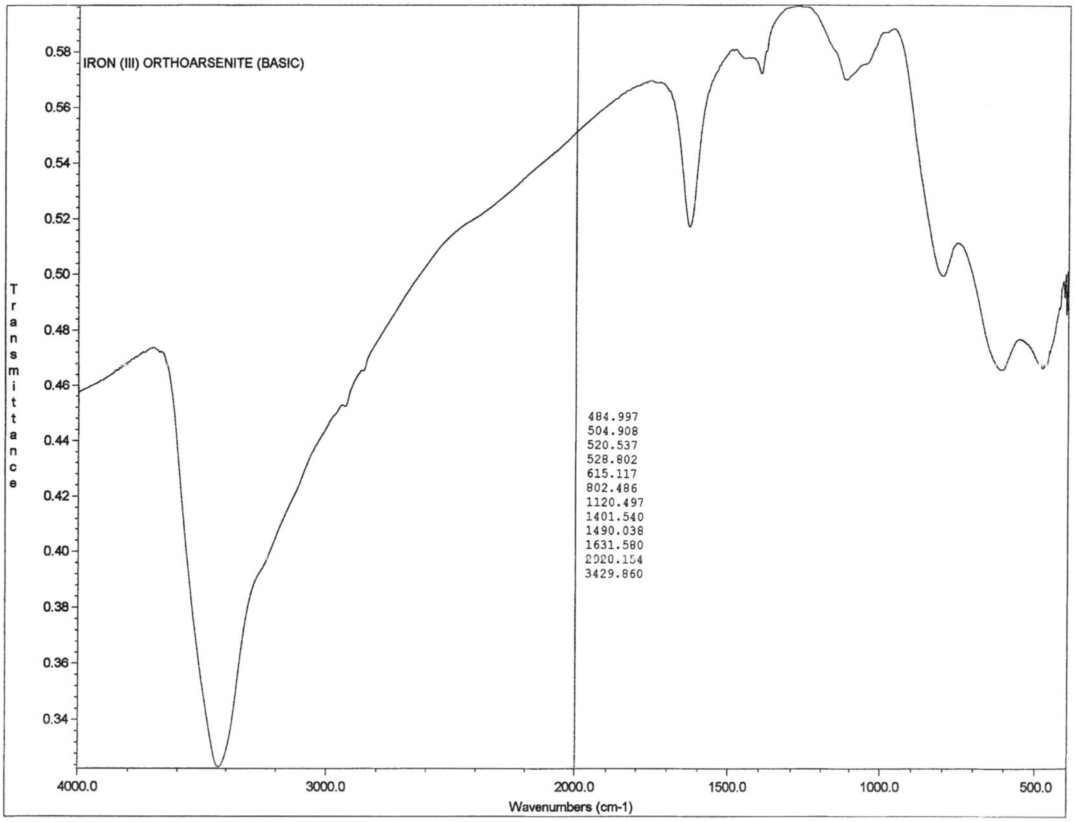

128 Iron (III) orthoarsenite (basic) $2FeAsO_3 \cdot Fe_2O_3 \cdot xH_2O$

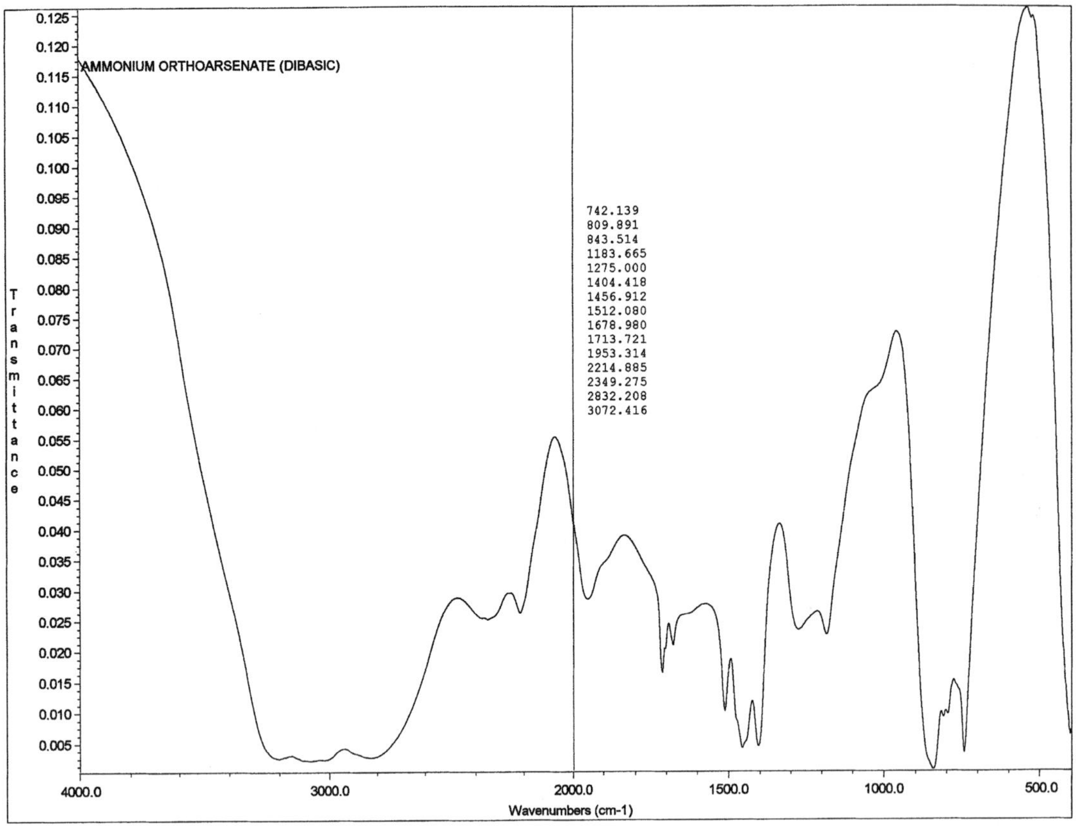

130 Ammonium orthoarsenate (dibasic) $(NH_4)_2HAsO_4$

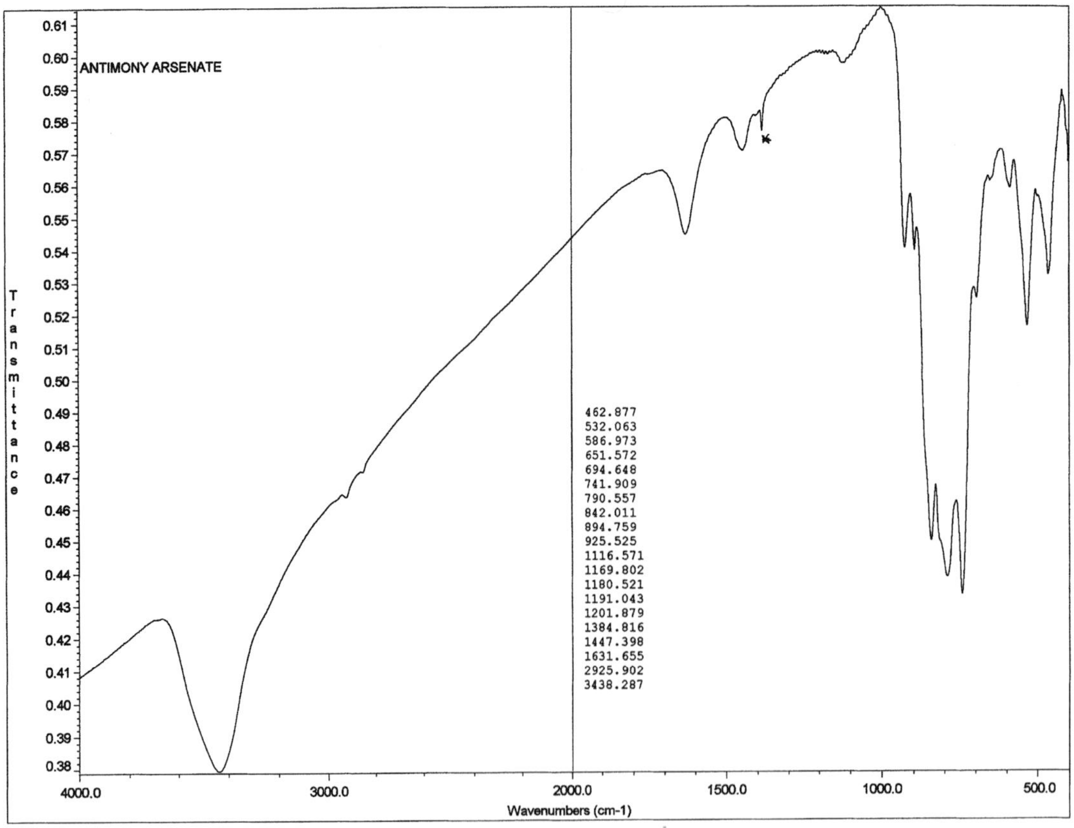

131 Antimony orthoarsenate $SbAsO_4 \cdot xH_2O$

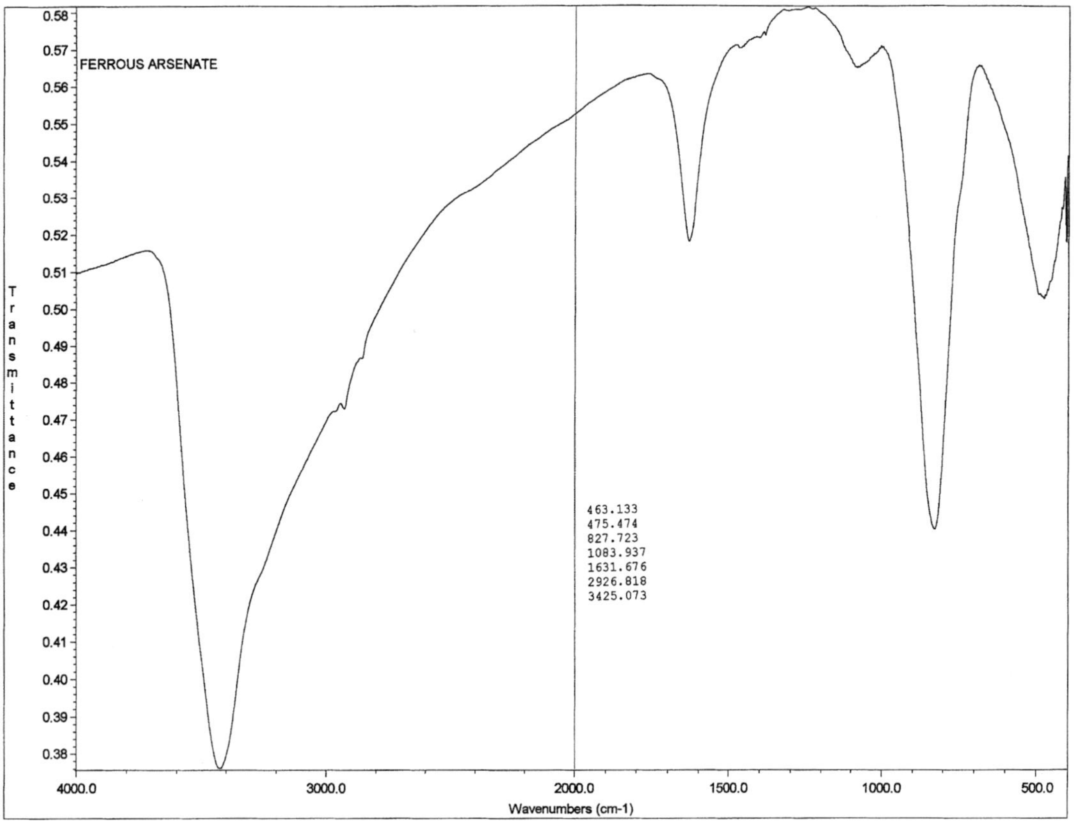

132 Iron (II) orthoarsenate $Fe_3(AsO_4)_2 \cdot 6H_2O$

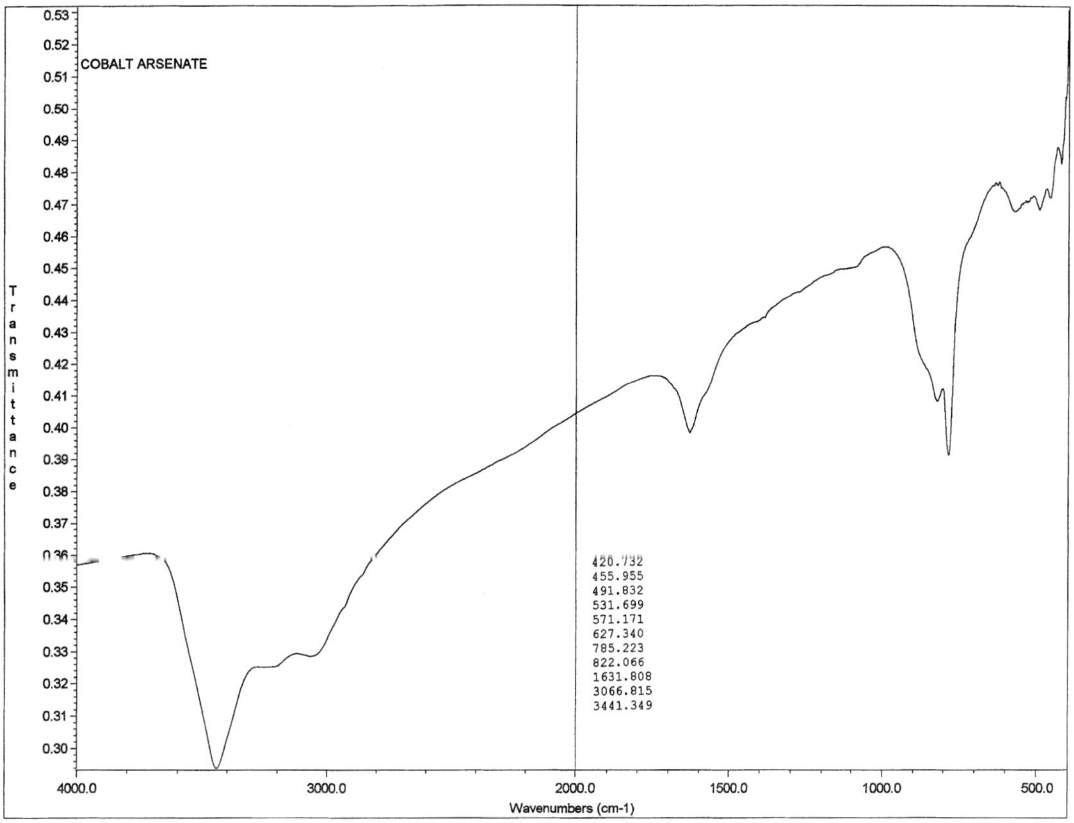

133 Cobalt orthoarsenate $Co(AsO_4)_2 \cdot 8H_2O$

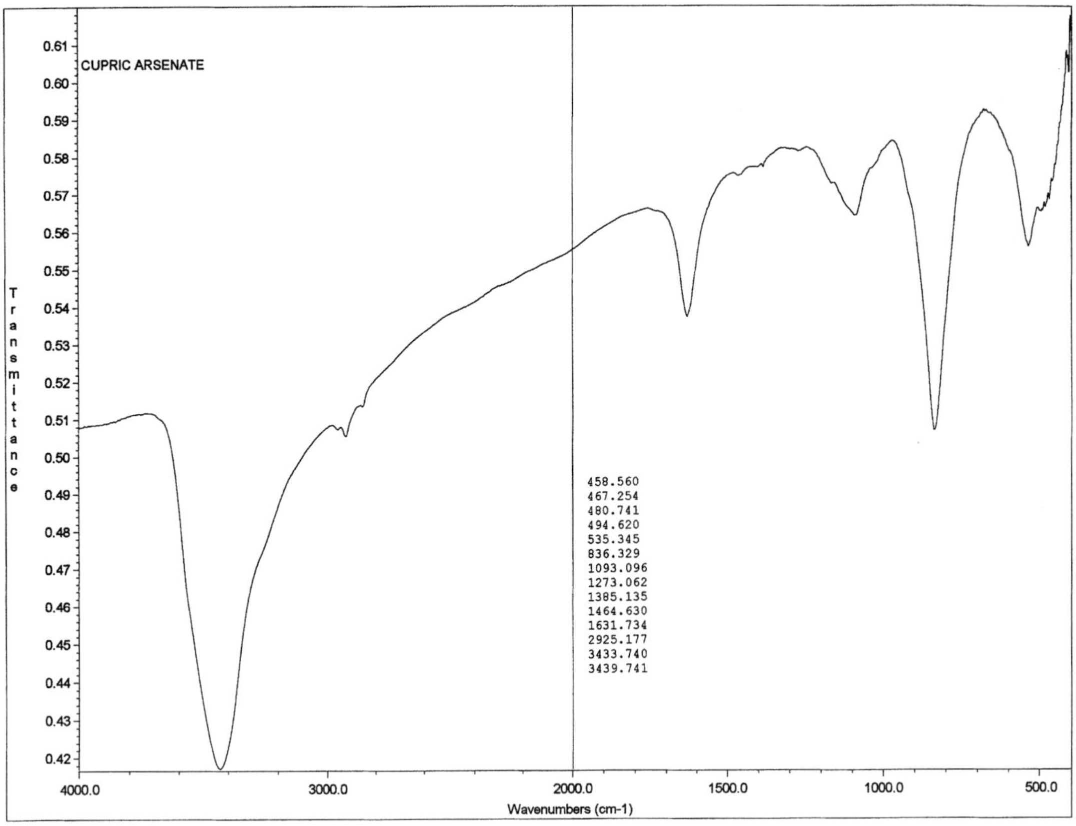

134 Copper (II) orthoarsenate $Cu_3(AsO_4)_2 \cdot 4H_2O$

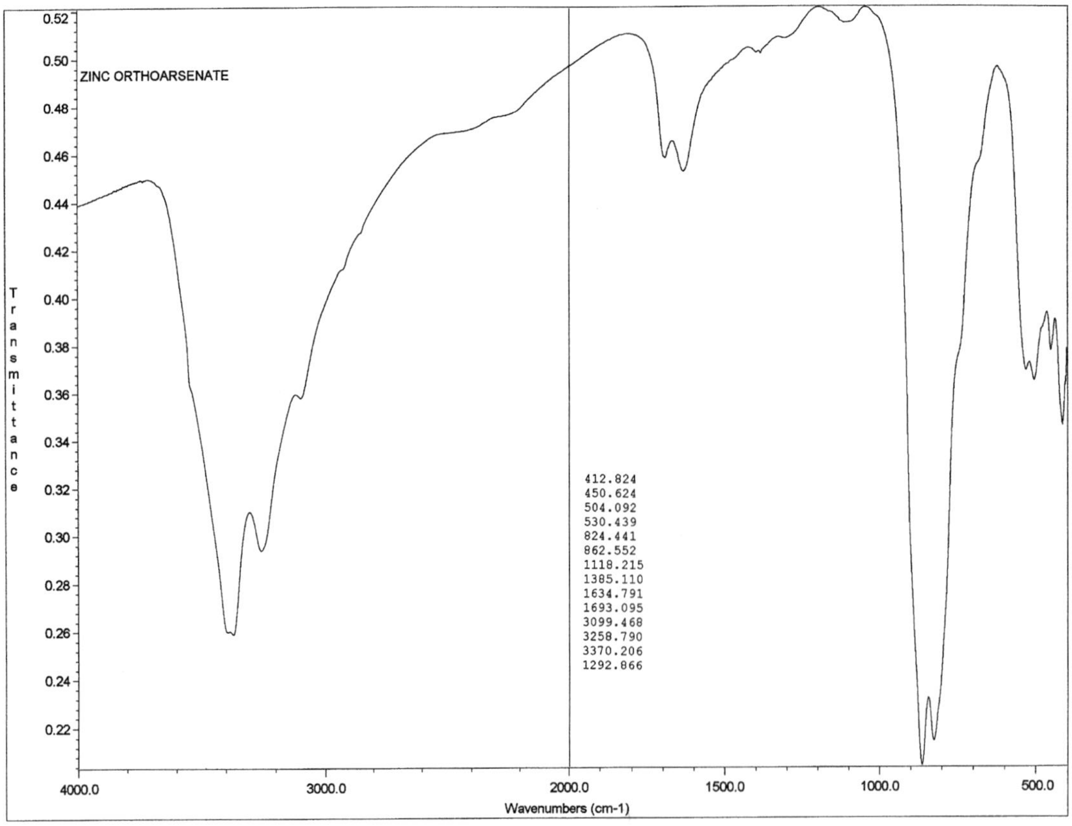

135 Zinc orthoarsenate $Zn_3(AsO_4)_2 \cdot 8H_2O$

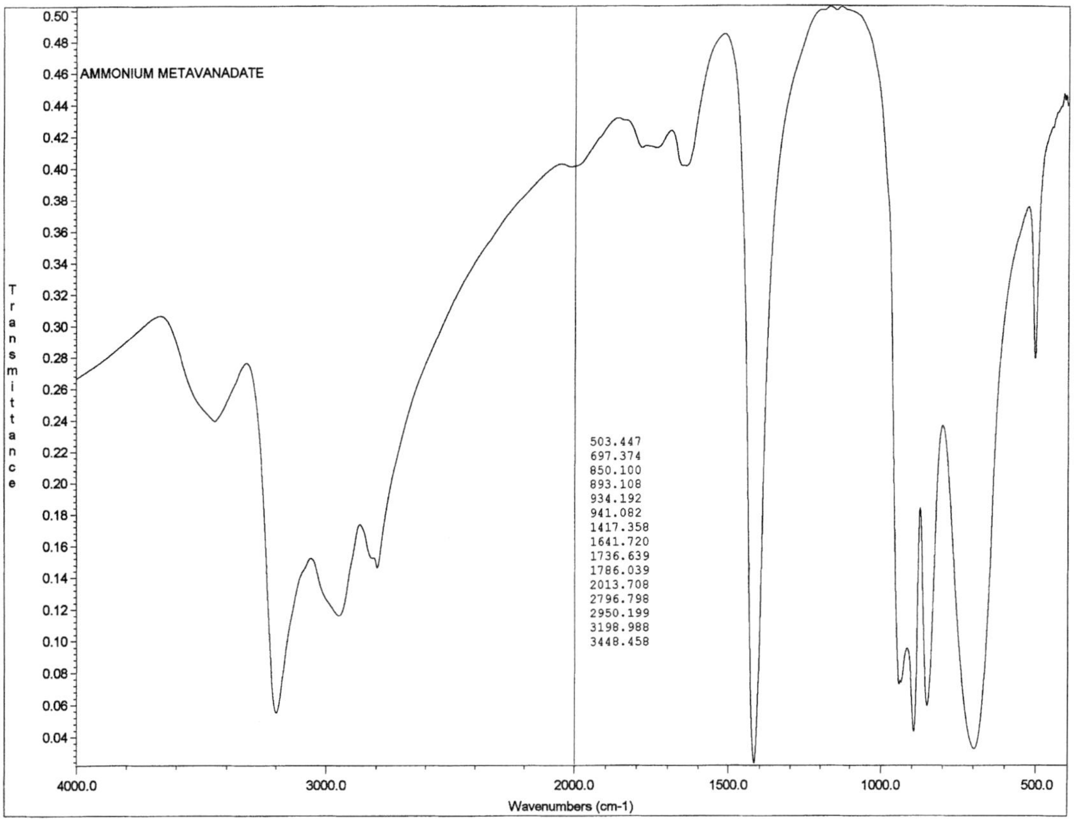

137 Ammonium metavanadate NH_4VO_3

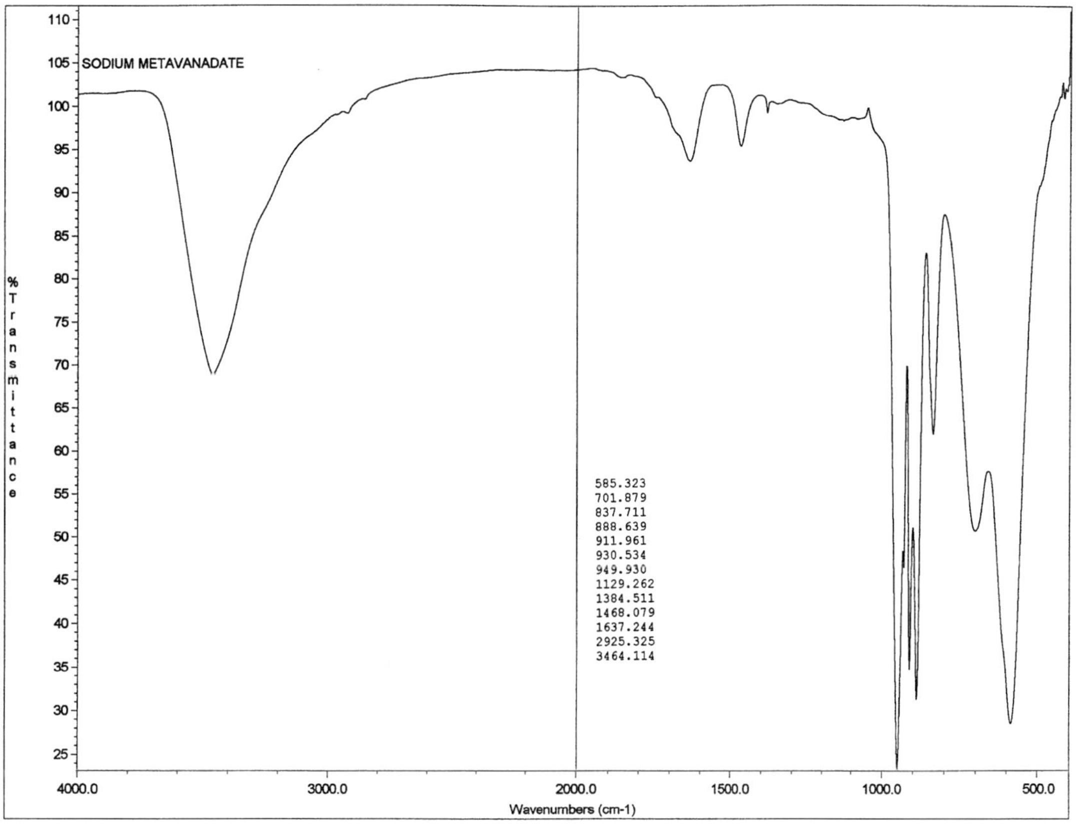

138 Sodium metavanadate $NaVO_3 \cdot xH_2O$

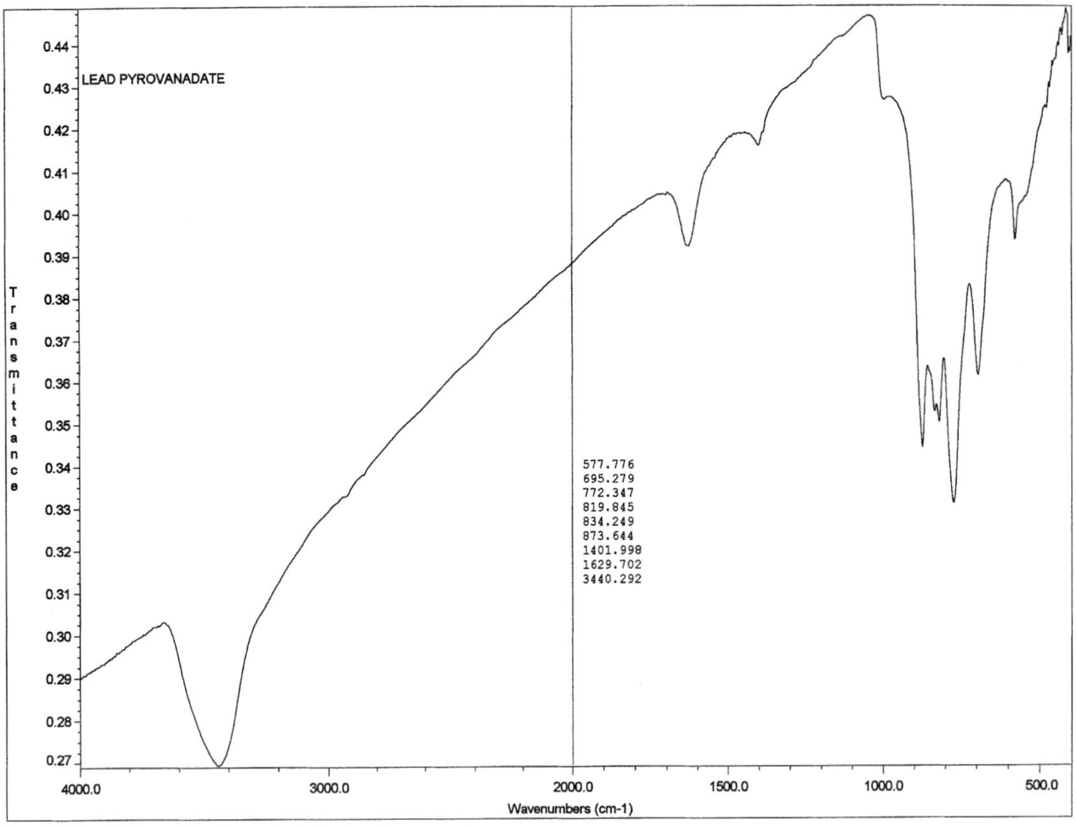

139 Lead pyrovanadate $Pb_2V_2O_7 \cdot xH_2O$

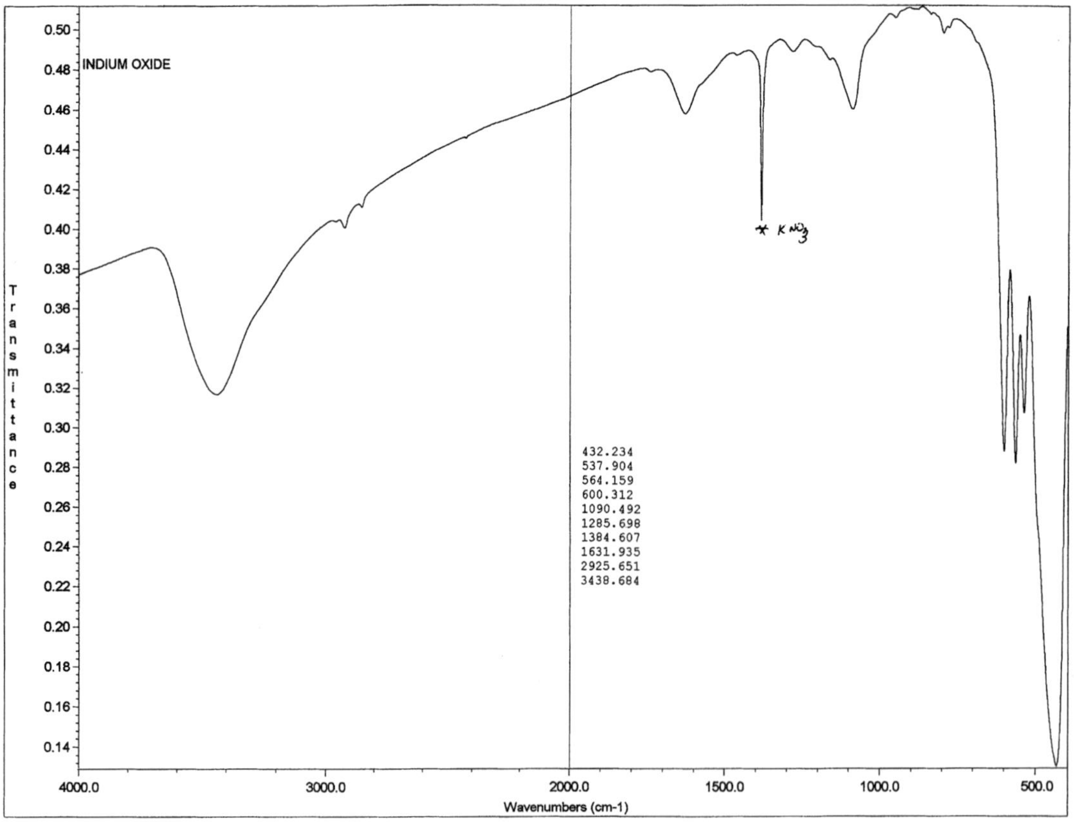

141 Indium sesquioxide In_2O_3

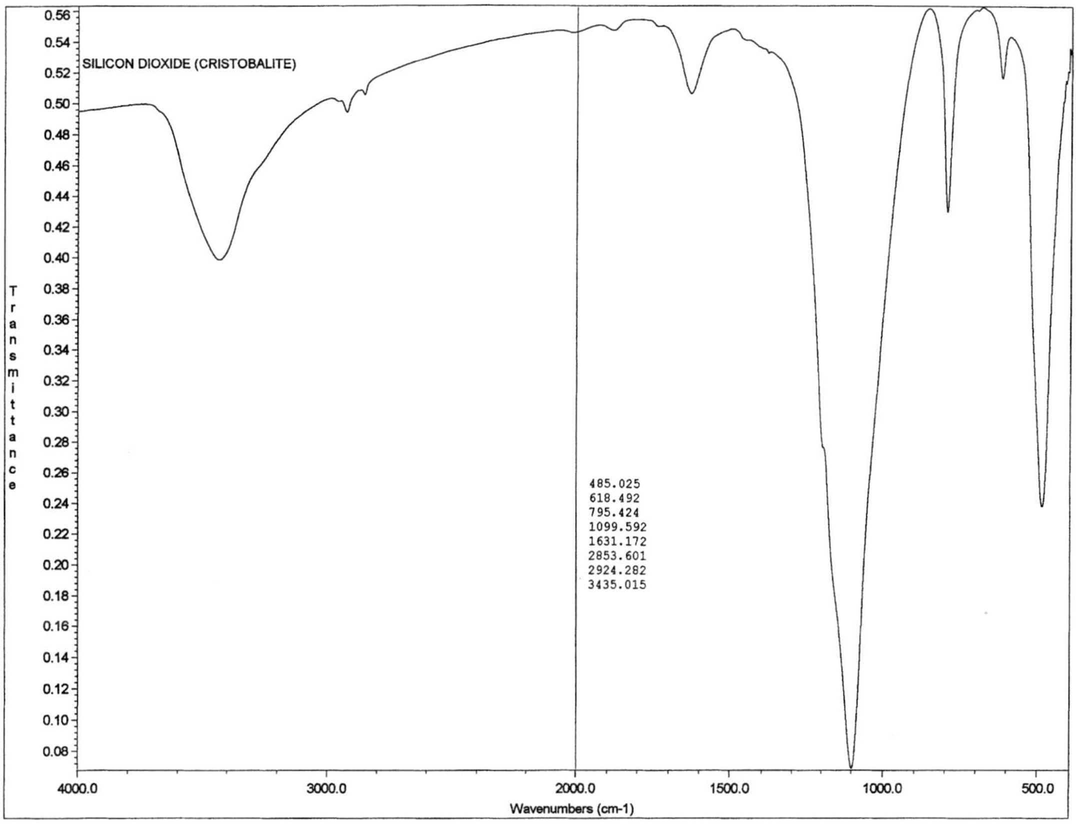

142 Silicon dioxide (cristobalite) SiO_2

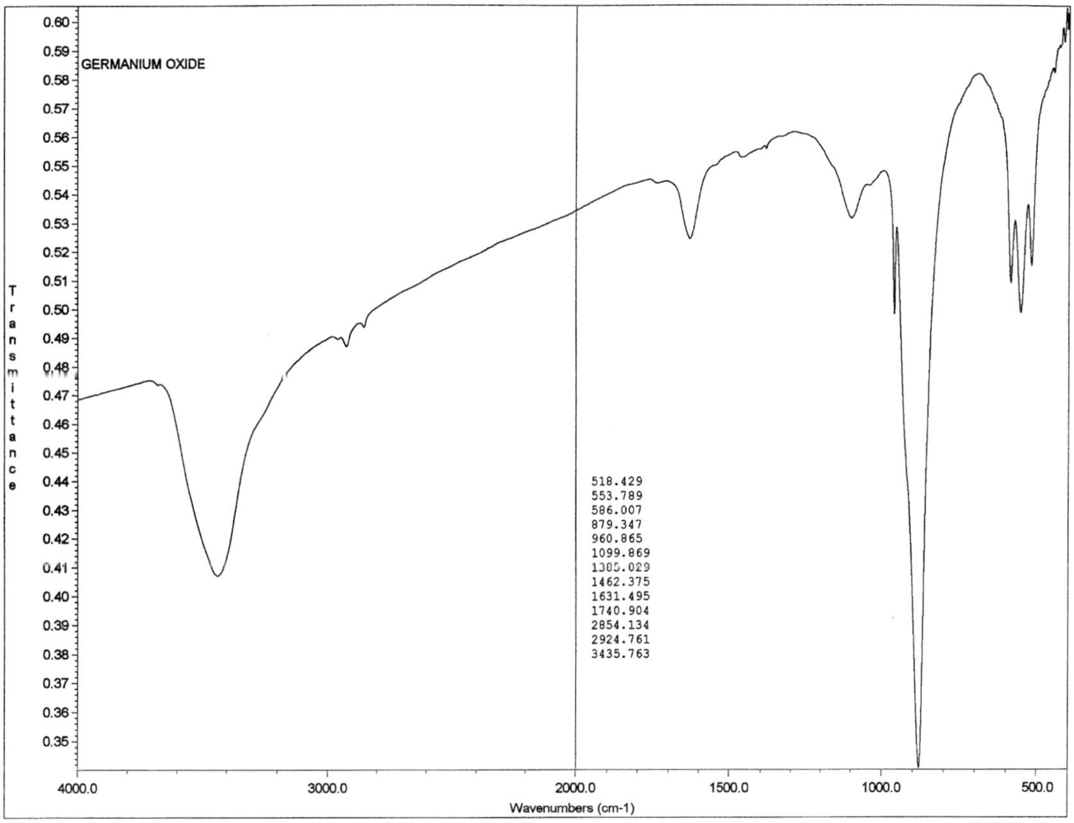

143 Germanium dioxide GeO_2

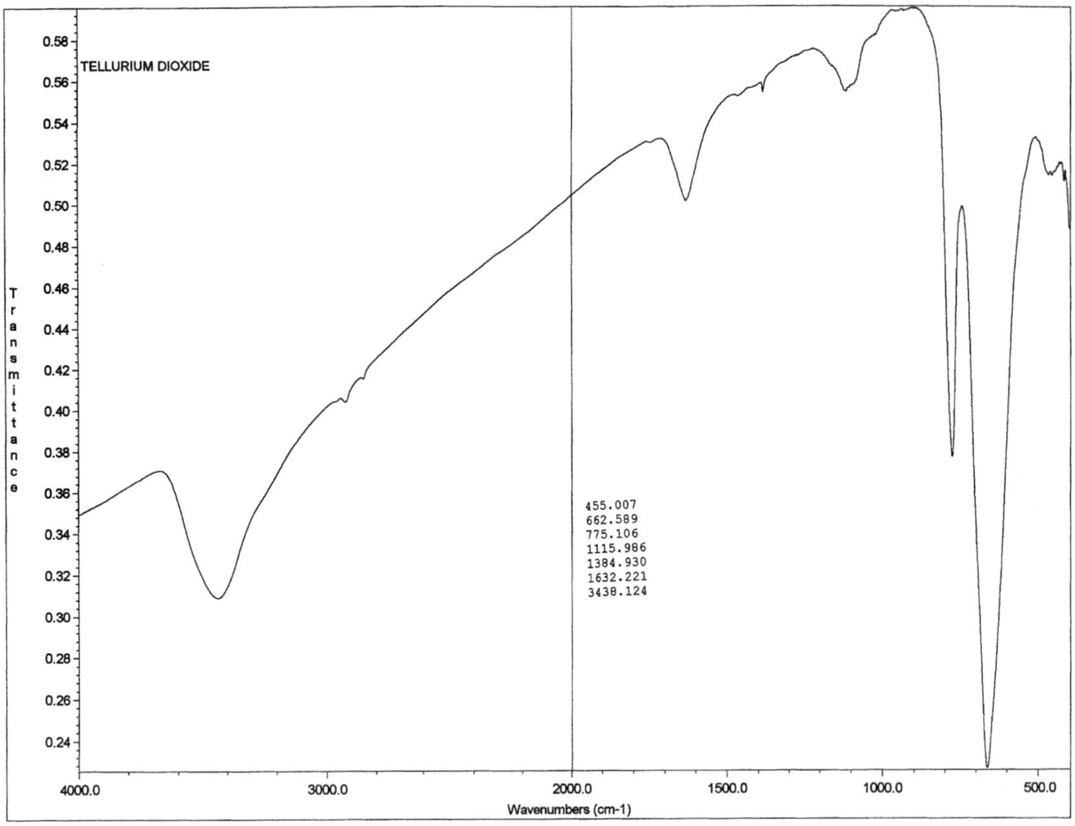

144 Tellurium dioxide TeO_2

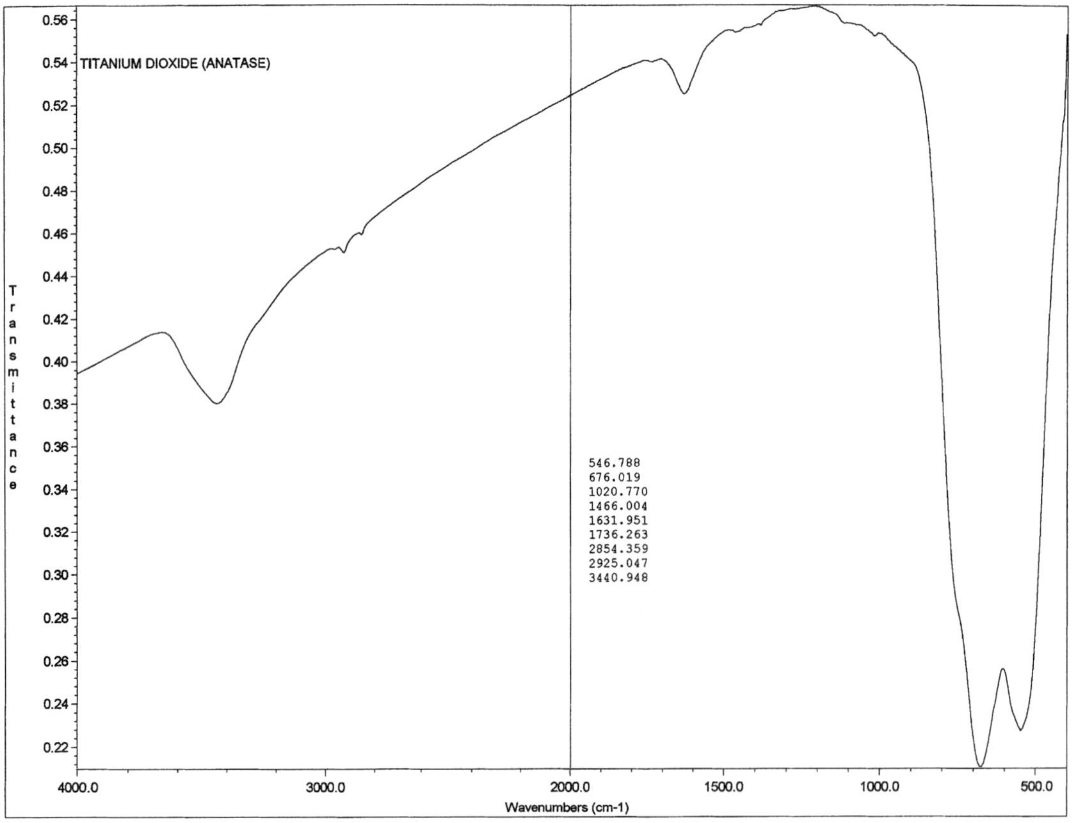

145 Titanium dioxide (anatase) TiO_2

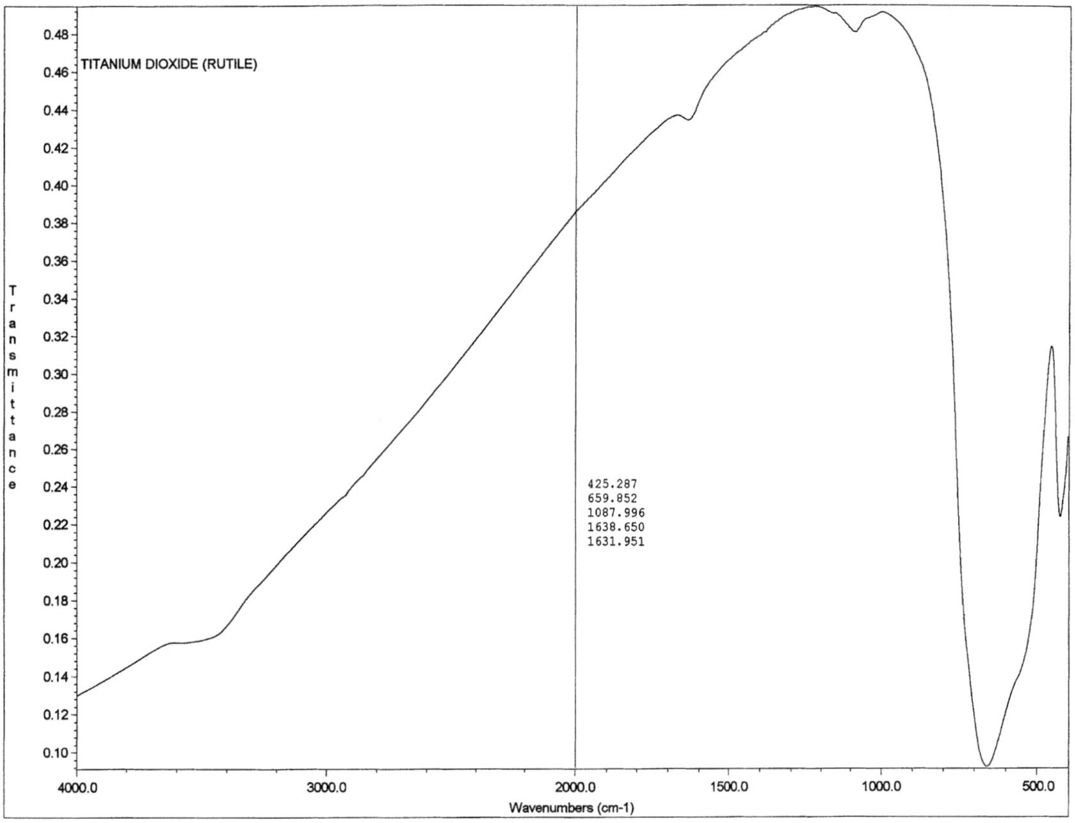

146 Titanium dioxide (rutile) TiO_2

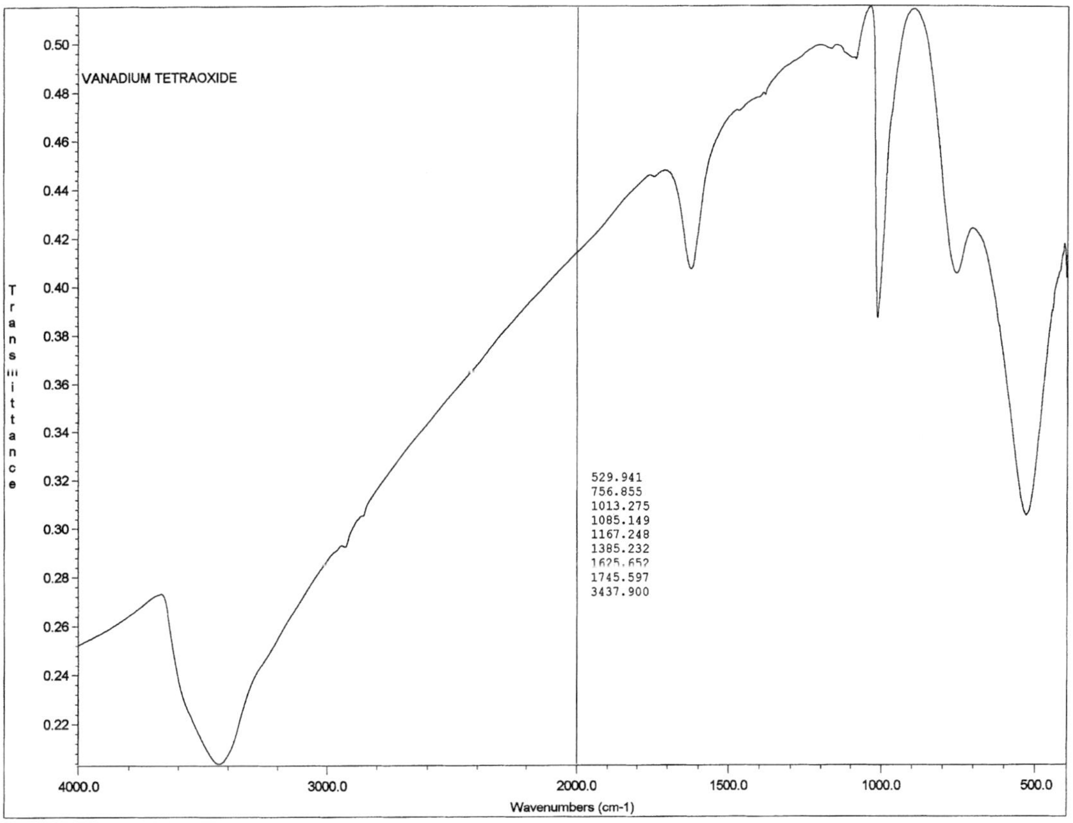

147 Vanadium tetroxide $V_2O_4 \cdot H_2O$

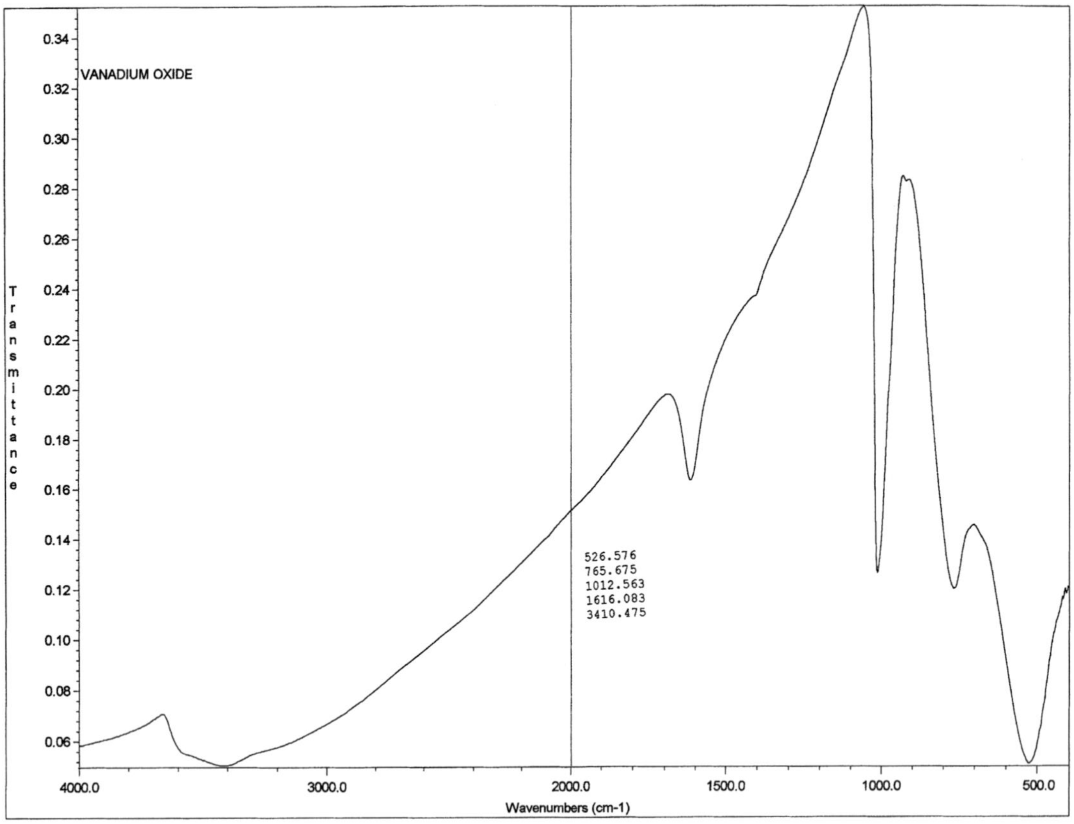

148 Vanadium oxide V_6O_{13} wet

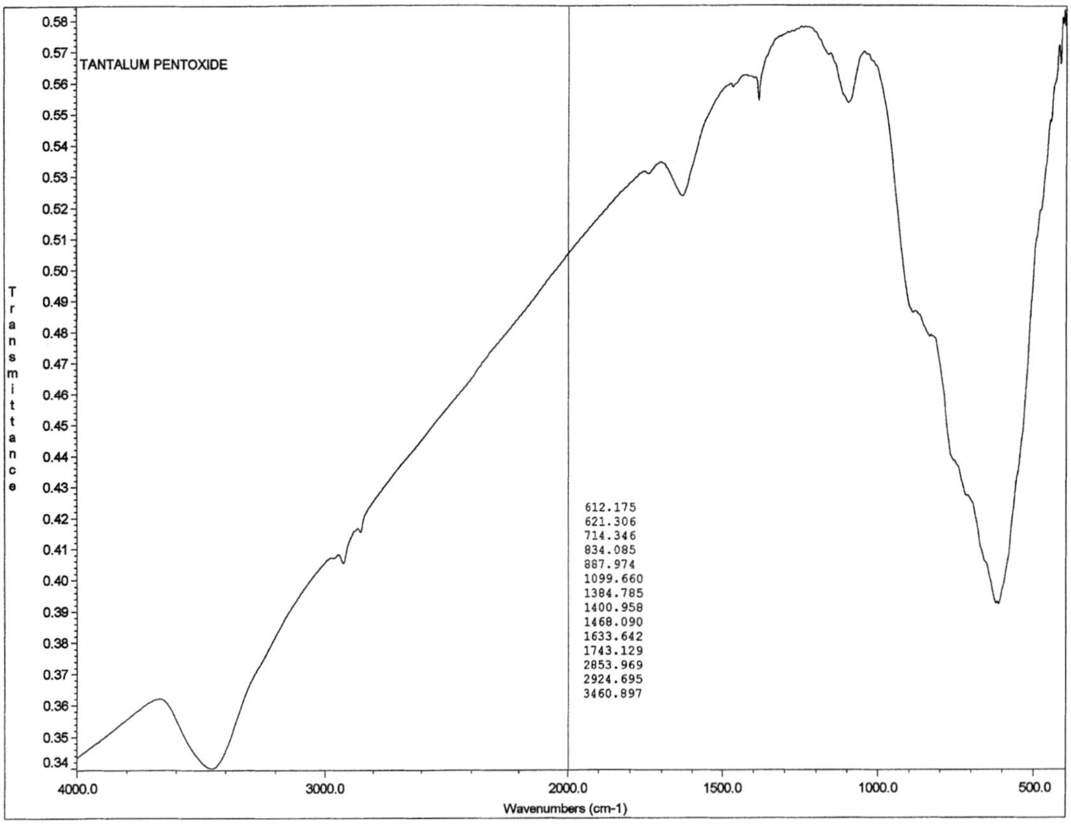

149 Tantalum pentoxide Ta_2O_5 wet

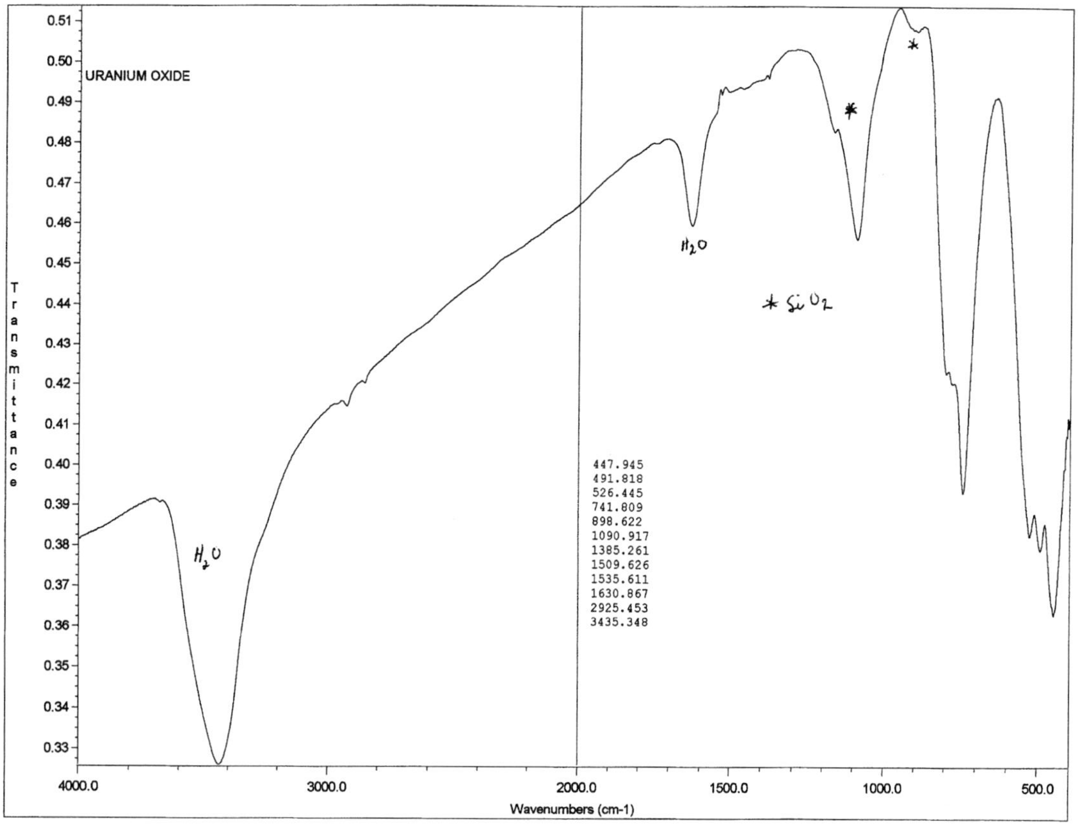

150 Uranium oxide (orthorhomic) U_3O_8

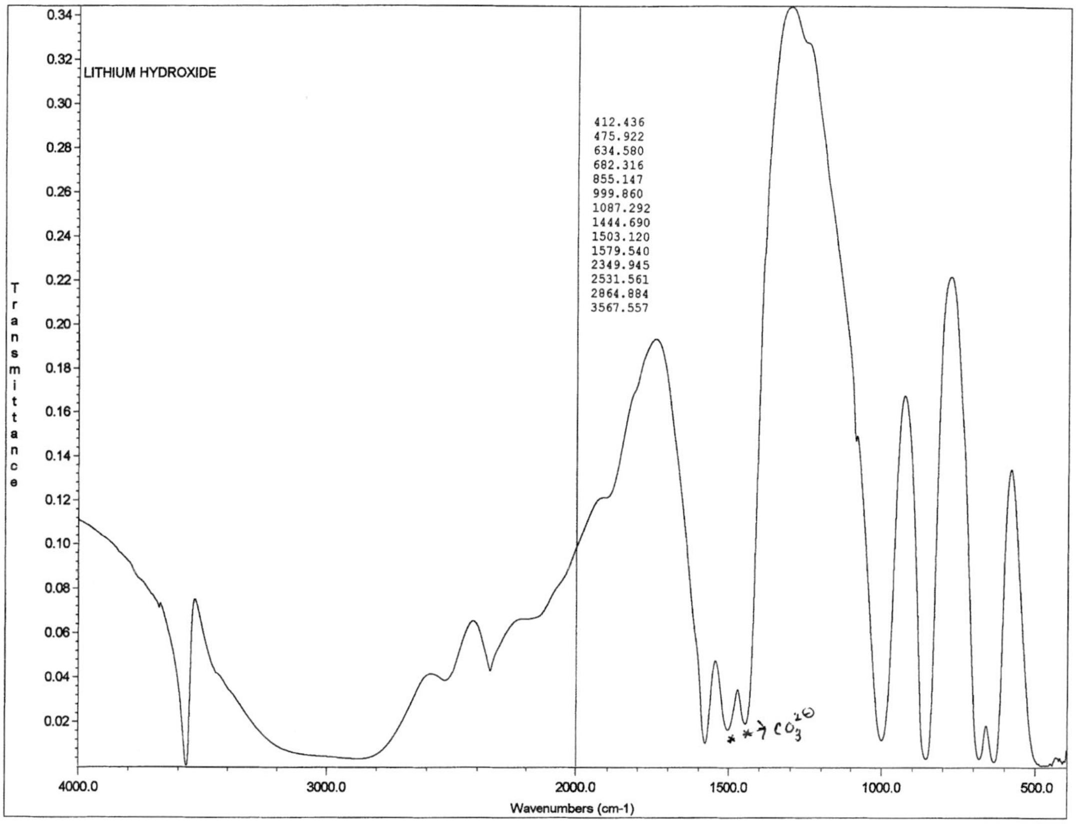

153 Lithium hydroxide $LiOH \cdot H_2O$

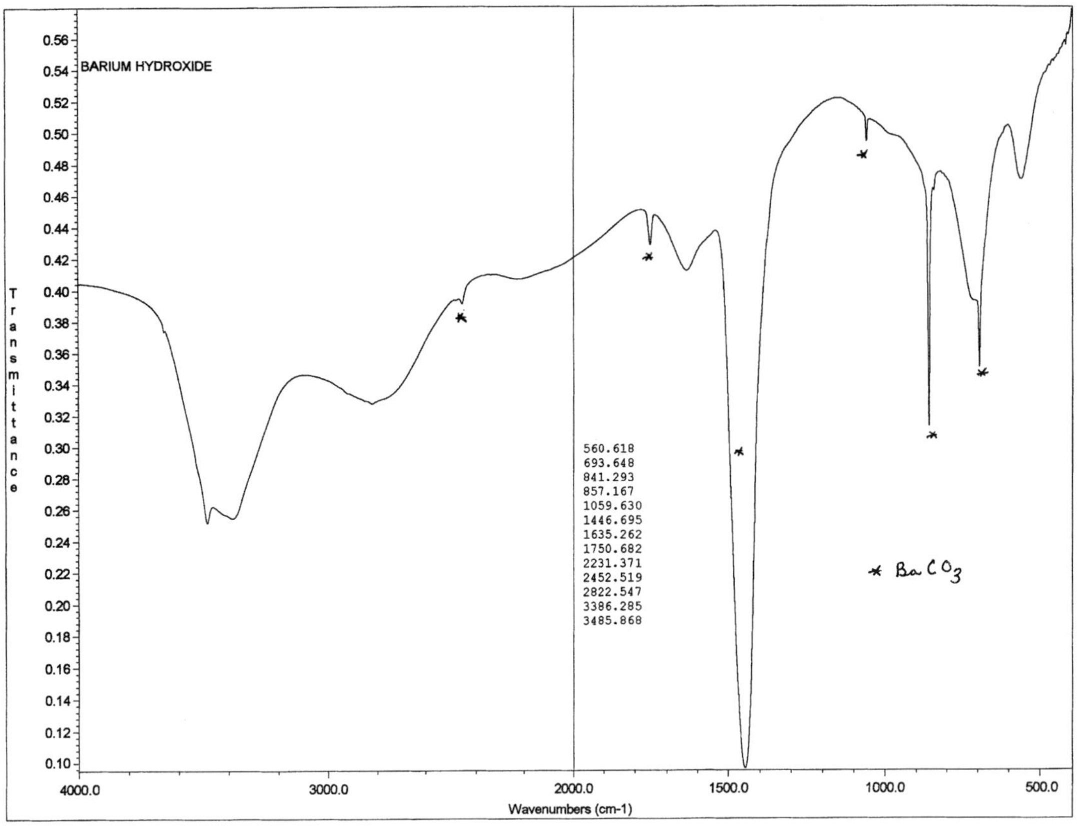

154 Barium hydroxide $Ba(OH)_2 \cdot 8H_2O$

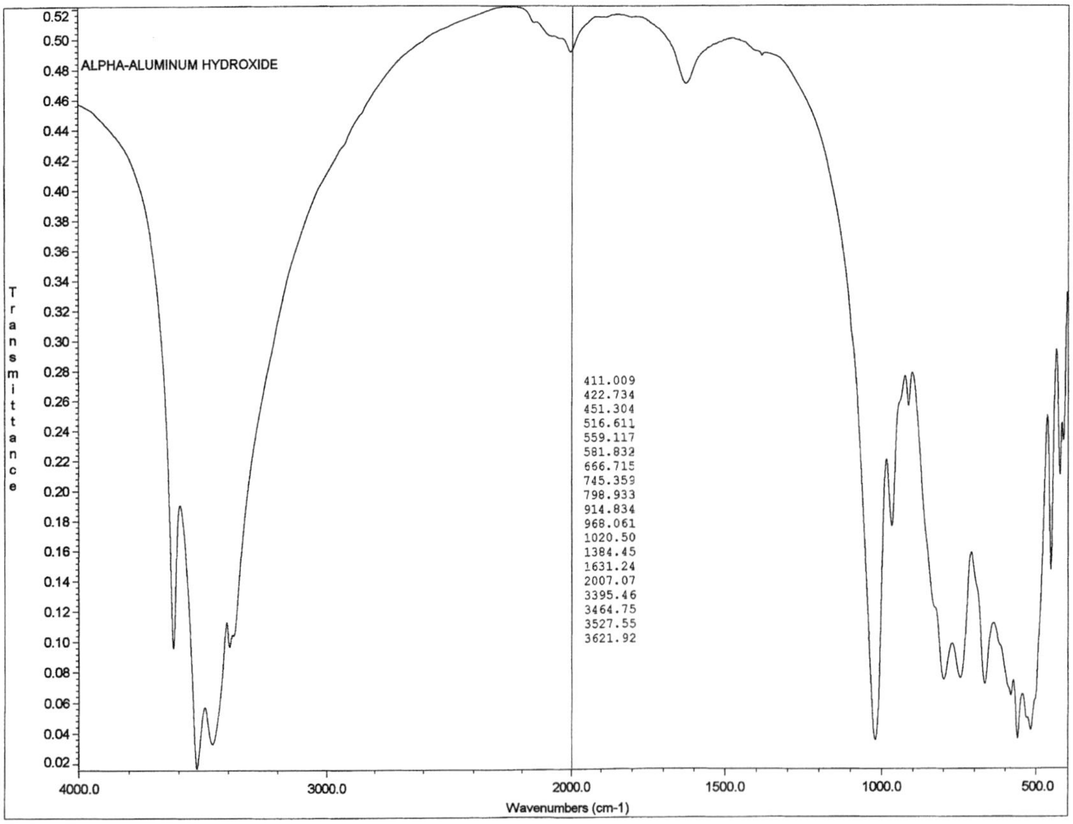

155 α-aluminium hydroxide (gibbsite) $Al(OH)_3$

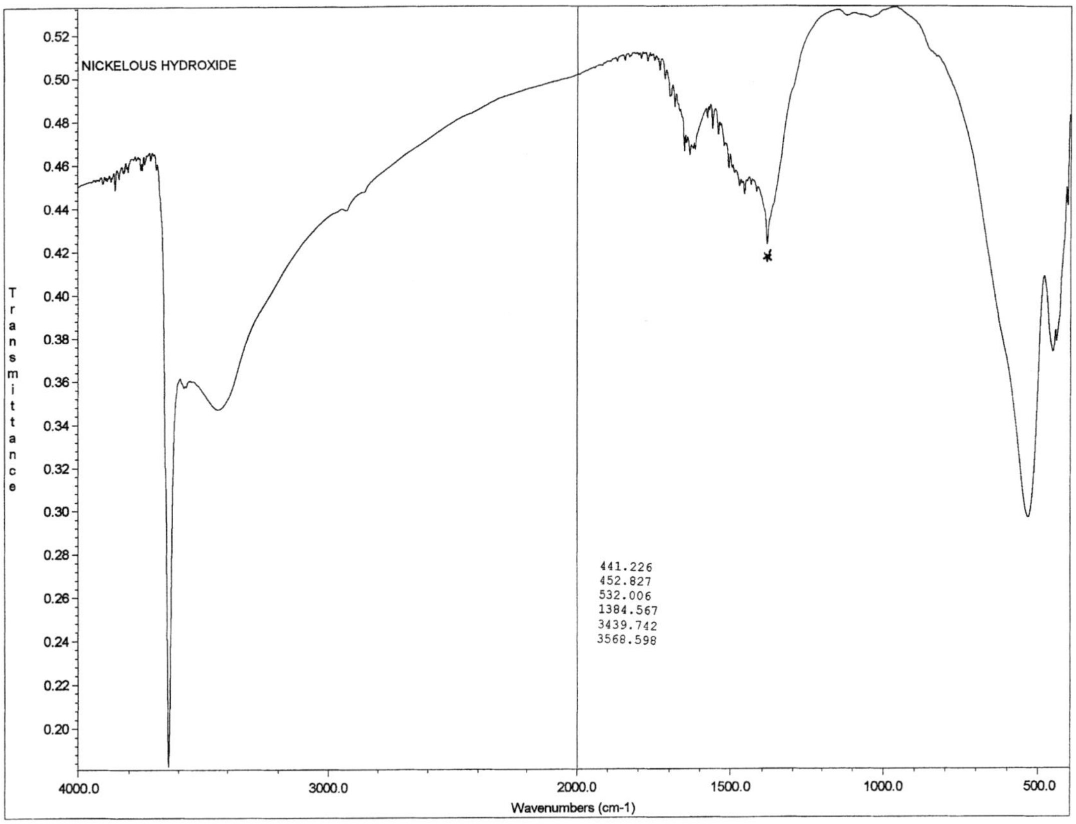

156 Nickel hydroxide $Ni(OH)_2$

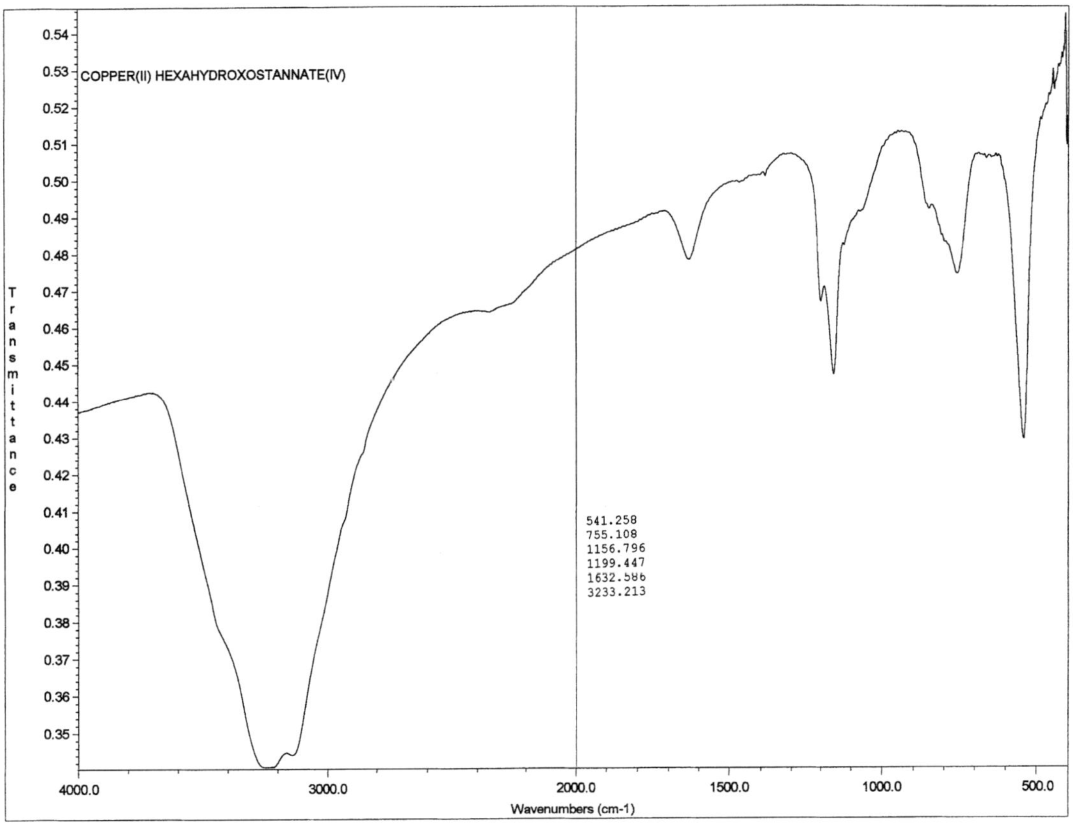

157 Copper (II) hexahydroxostannate (IV) $CuSn(OH)_6$

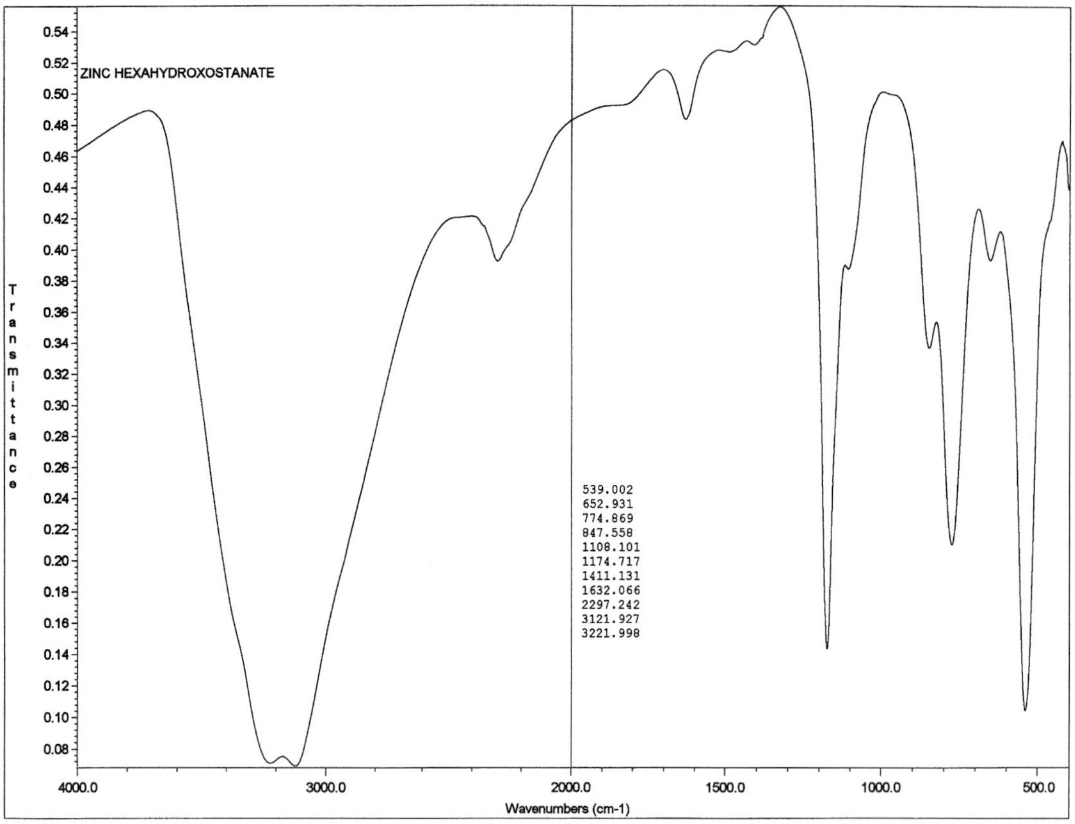

158 Zinc hexahydrostanate (IV) $ZnSn(OH)_6$

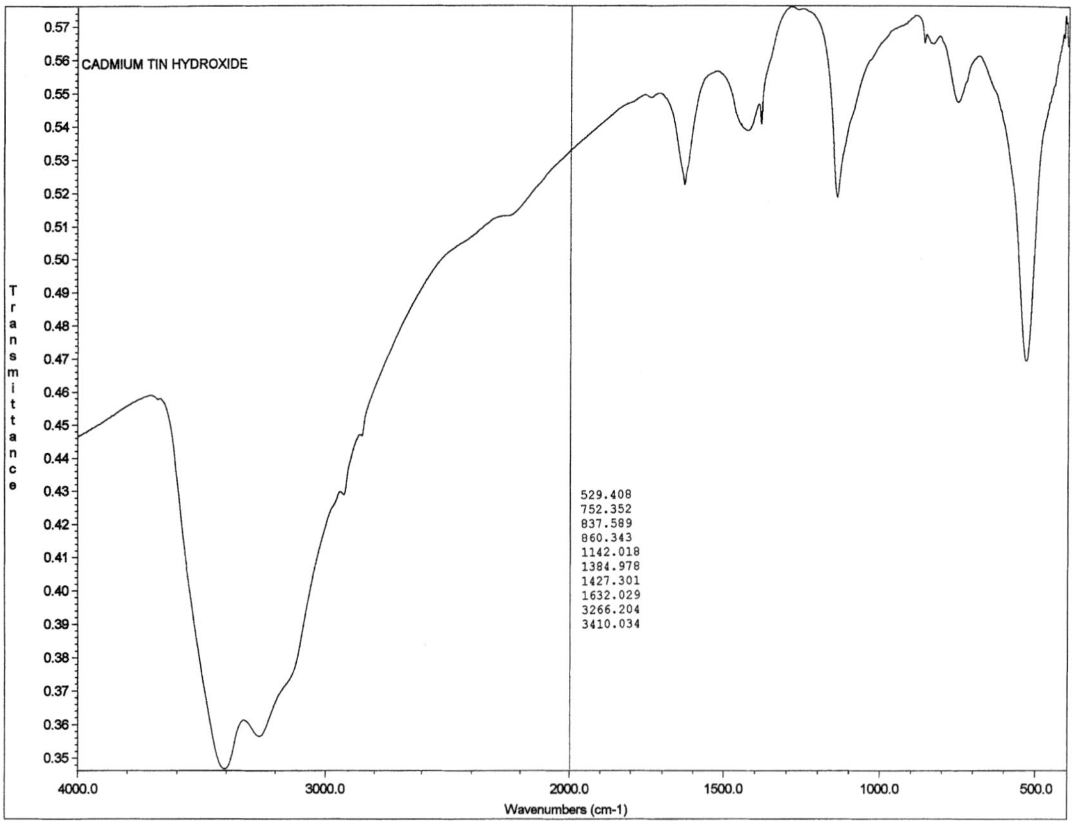

159 Cadmium hexahydrostanate (IV) $CdSn(OH)_6$

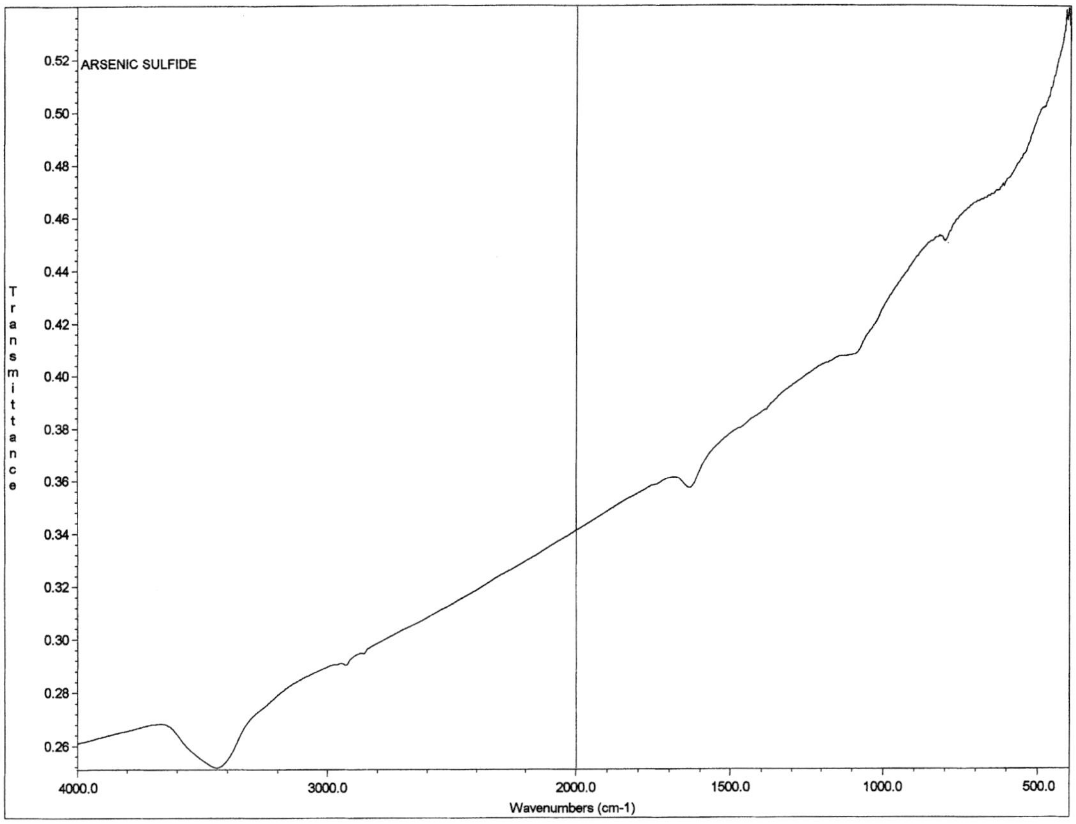

160 Arsenic disulfide As_2S_2

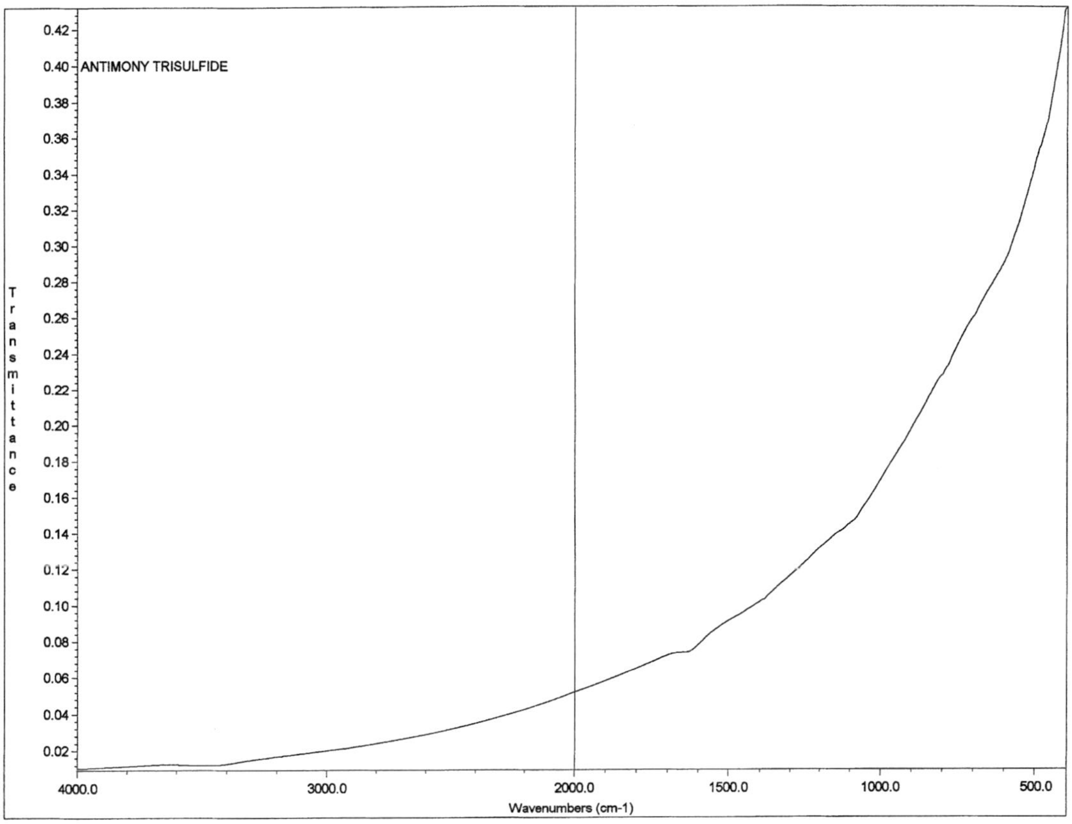

161 Antimony trisulfide Sb_2S_3

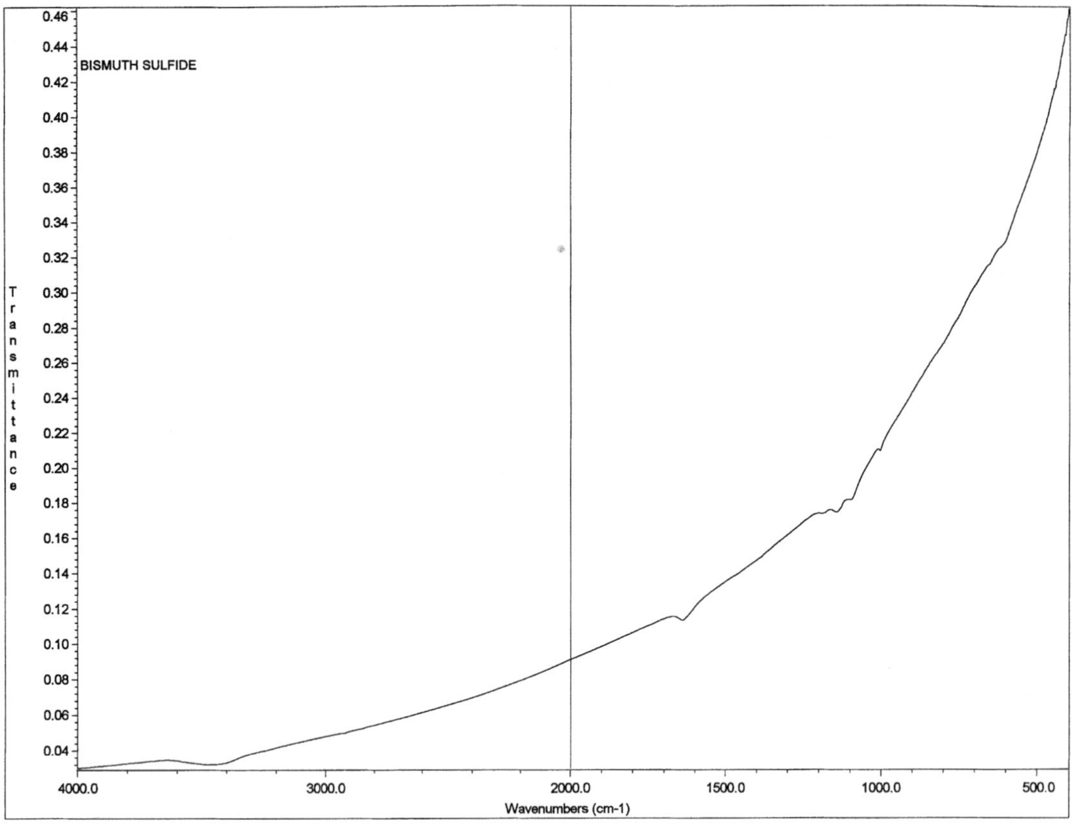

162 Bismuth trisulfide Bi_2S_3

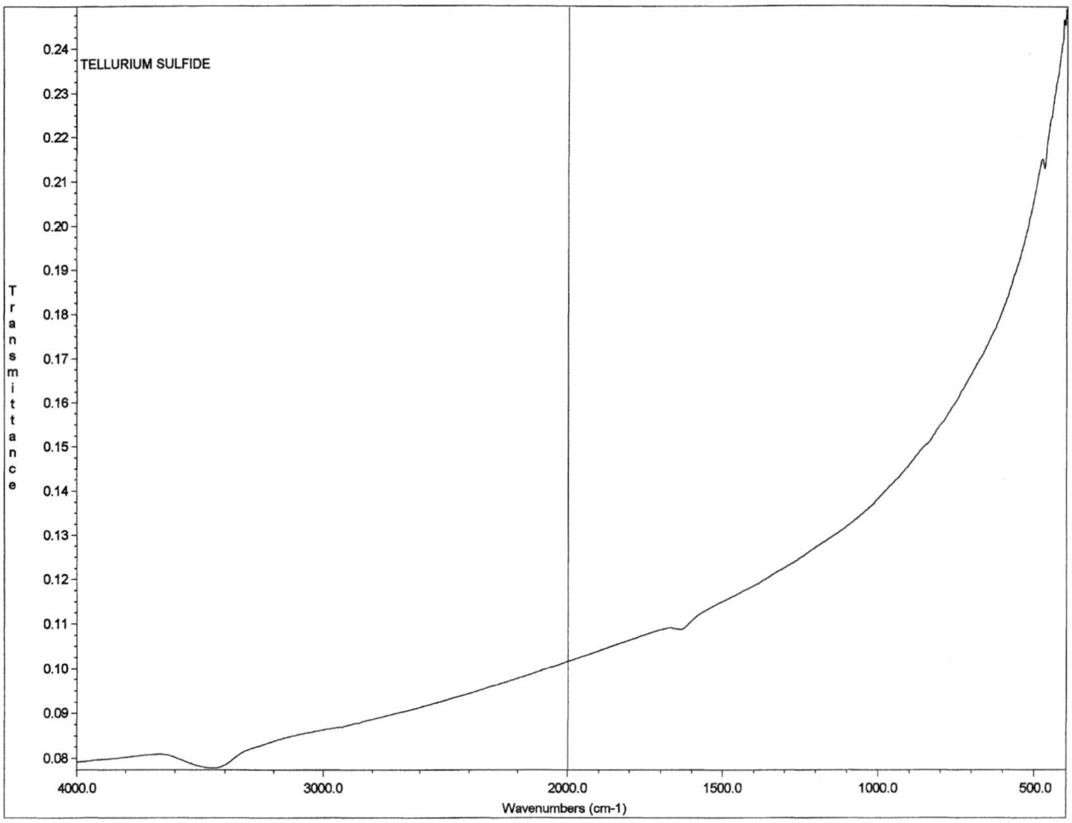

163 Tellurium sulfide TeS_2

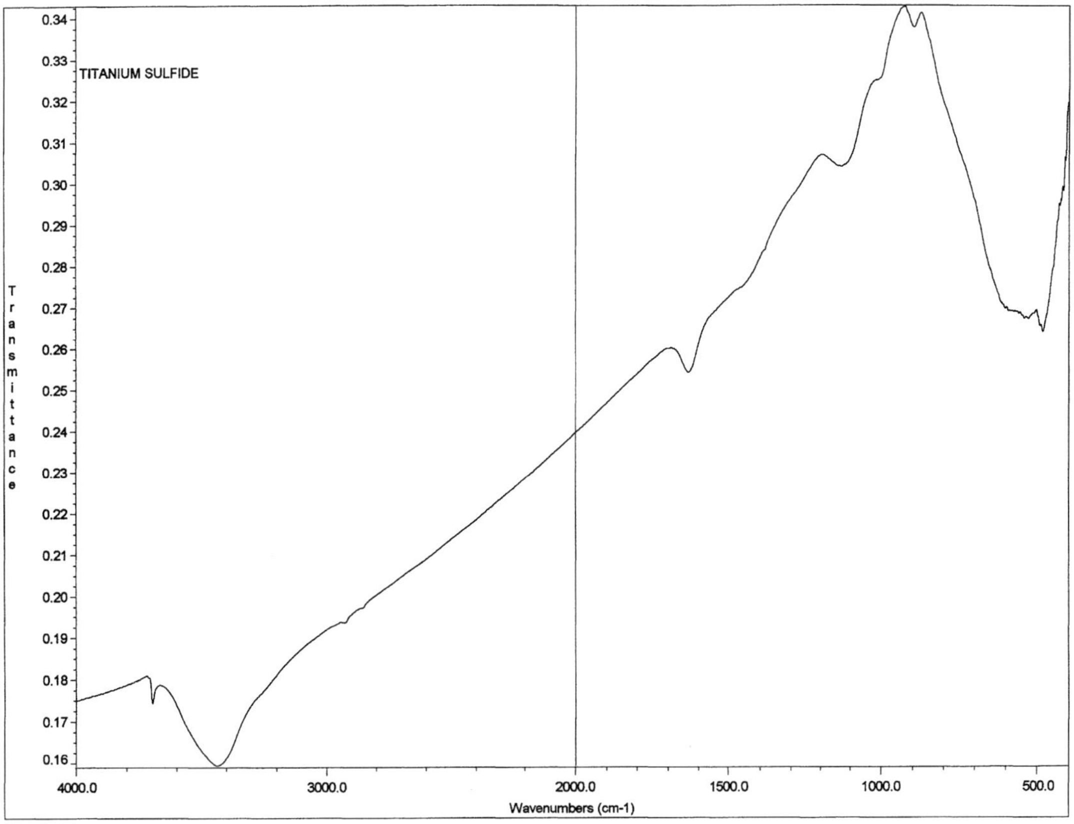

164 Titanium sesquisulfide Ti_2S_3

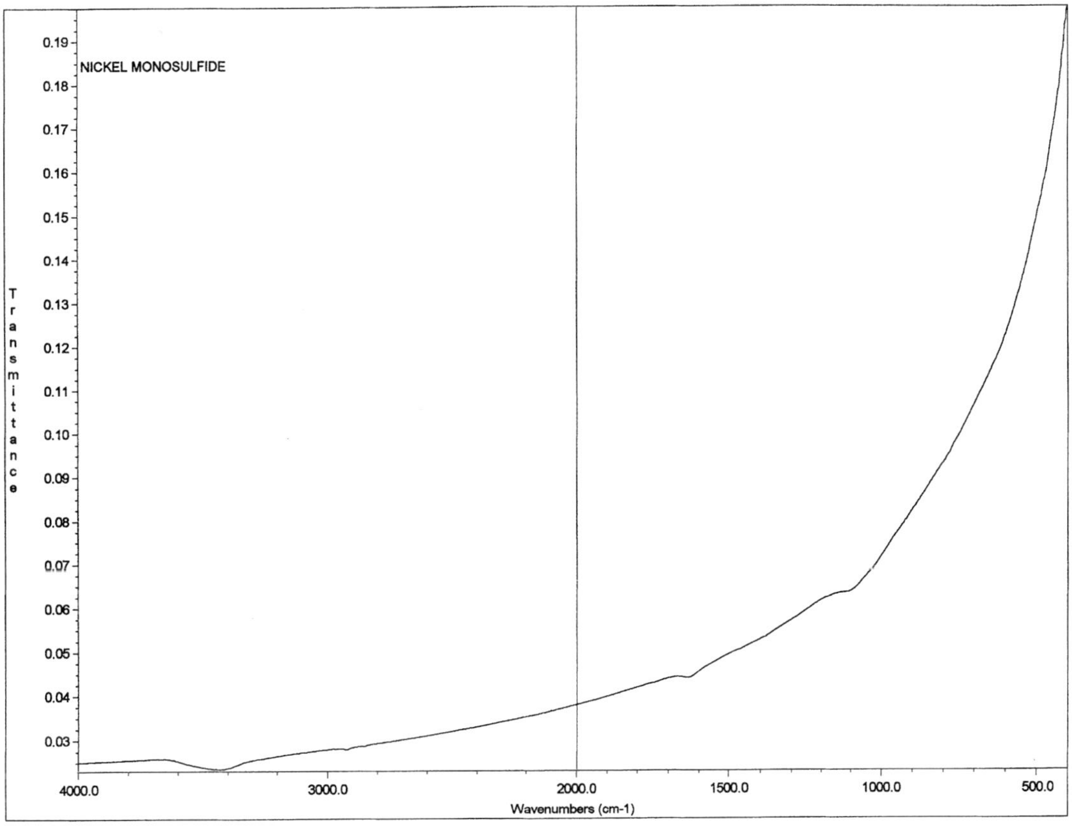

165 Nickel monosulfide NiS

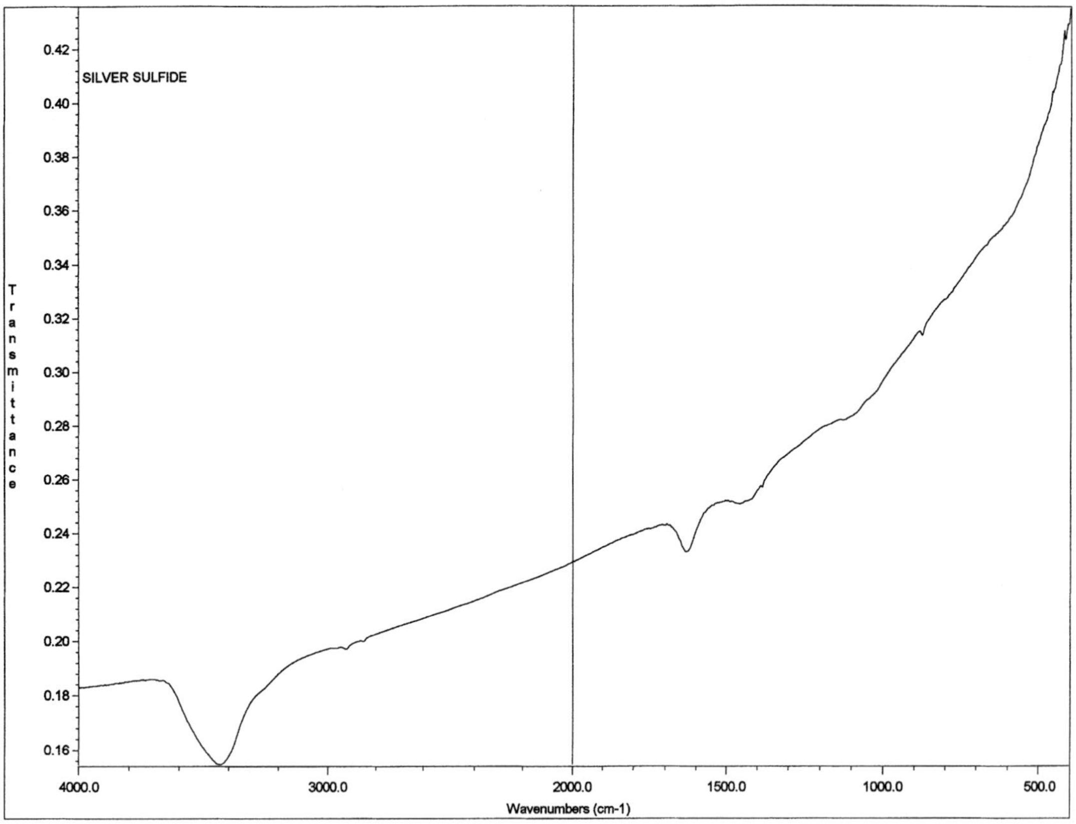

166 Silver sulfide Ag_2S

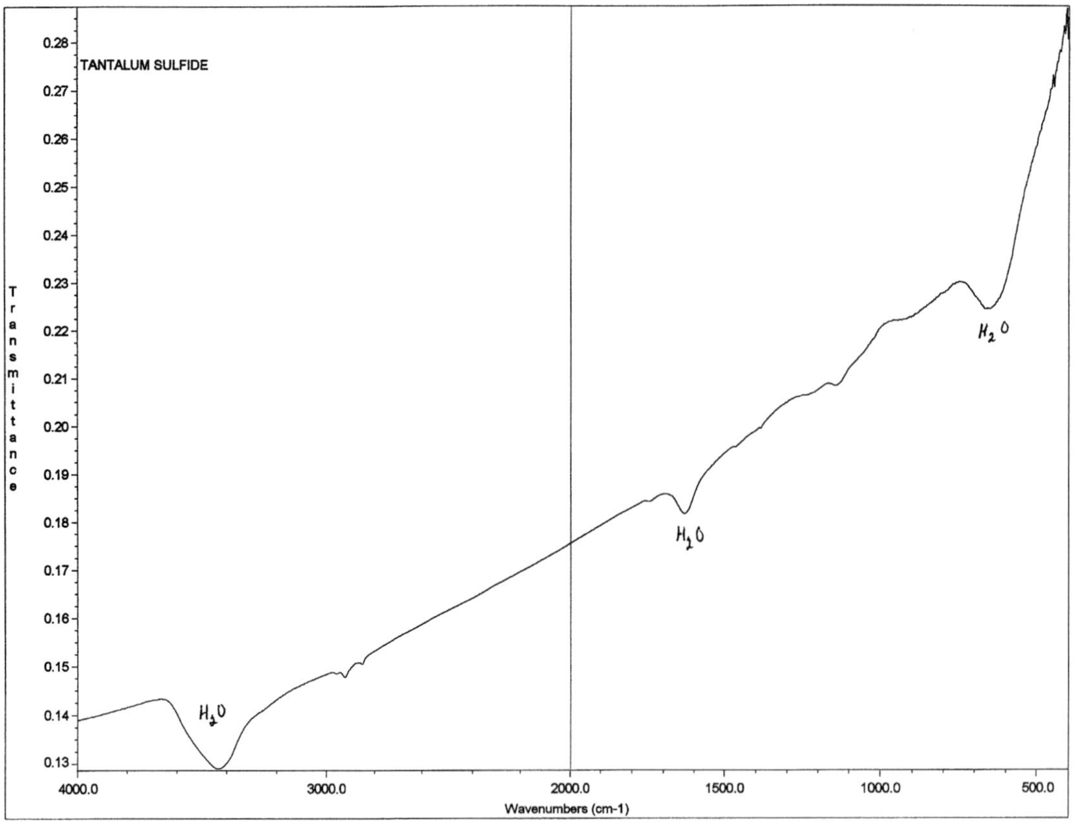

167 Tantalum disulfide TaS_2

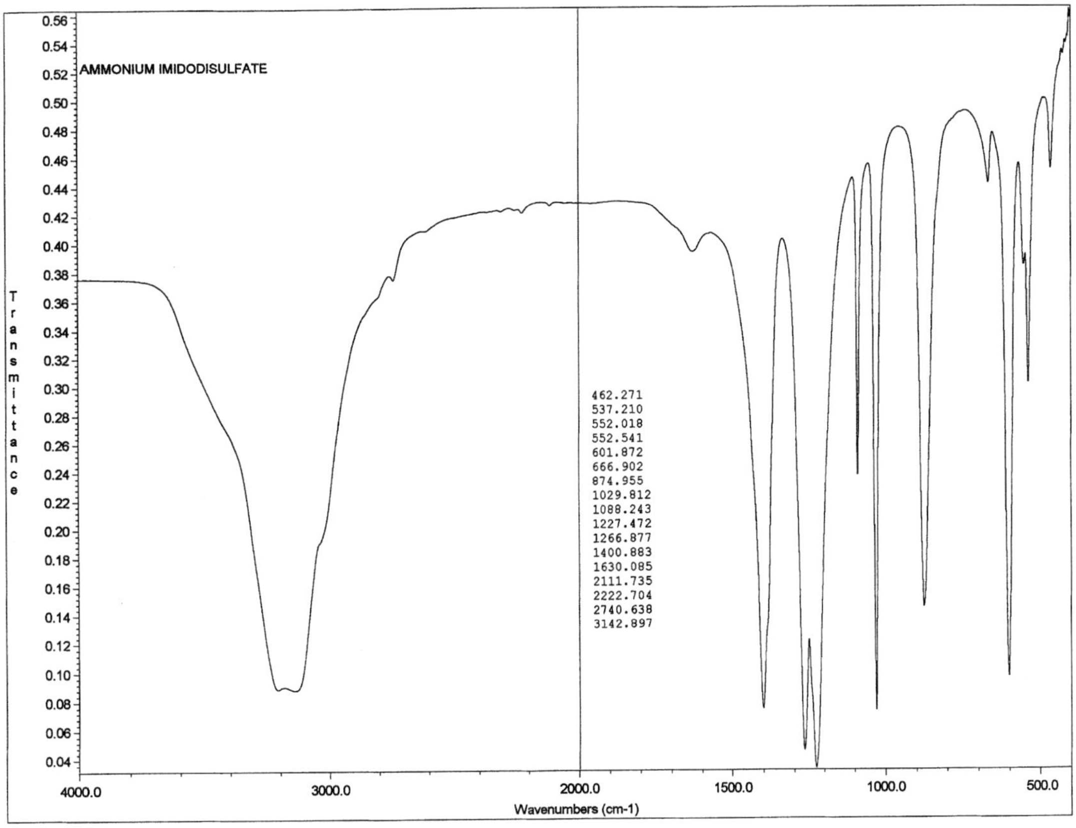

168 Ammonium imidodisulfate $(NH_4)_2S_2NHO_6$

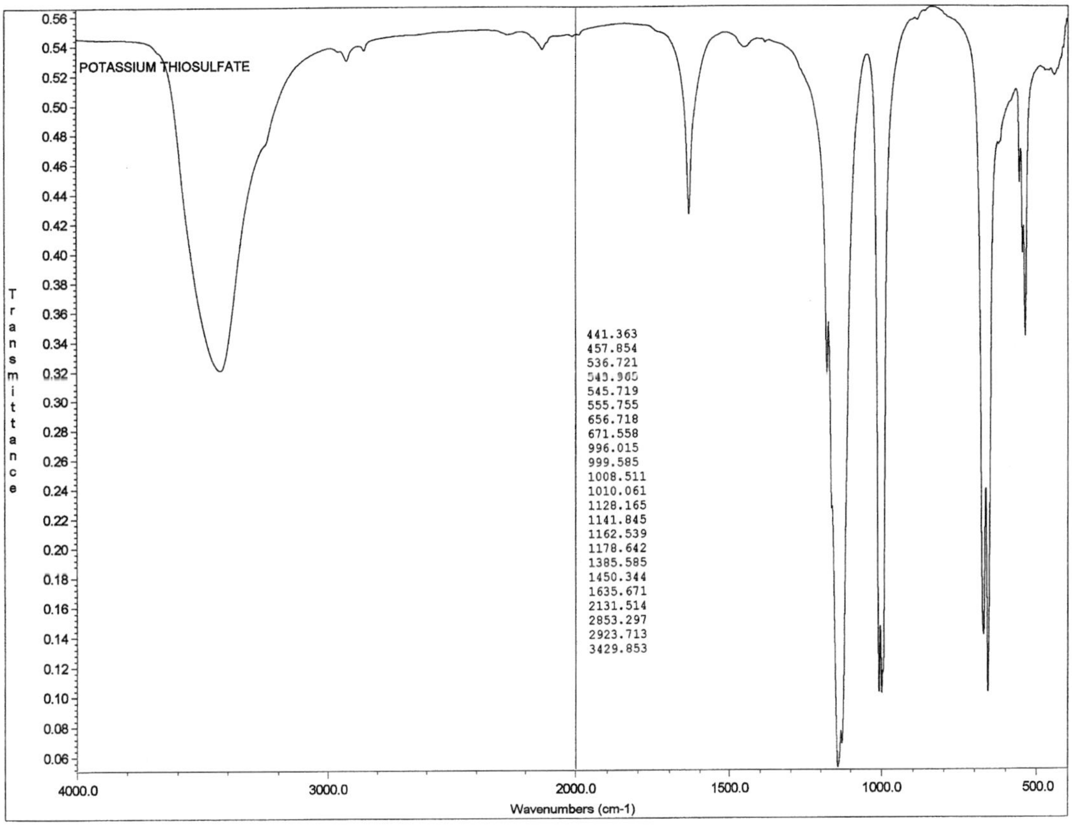

171 Potassium thiosulfate $K_2S_2O_3 \cdot {}^1/_3\ H_2O$

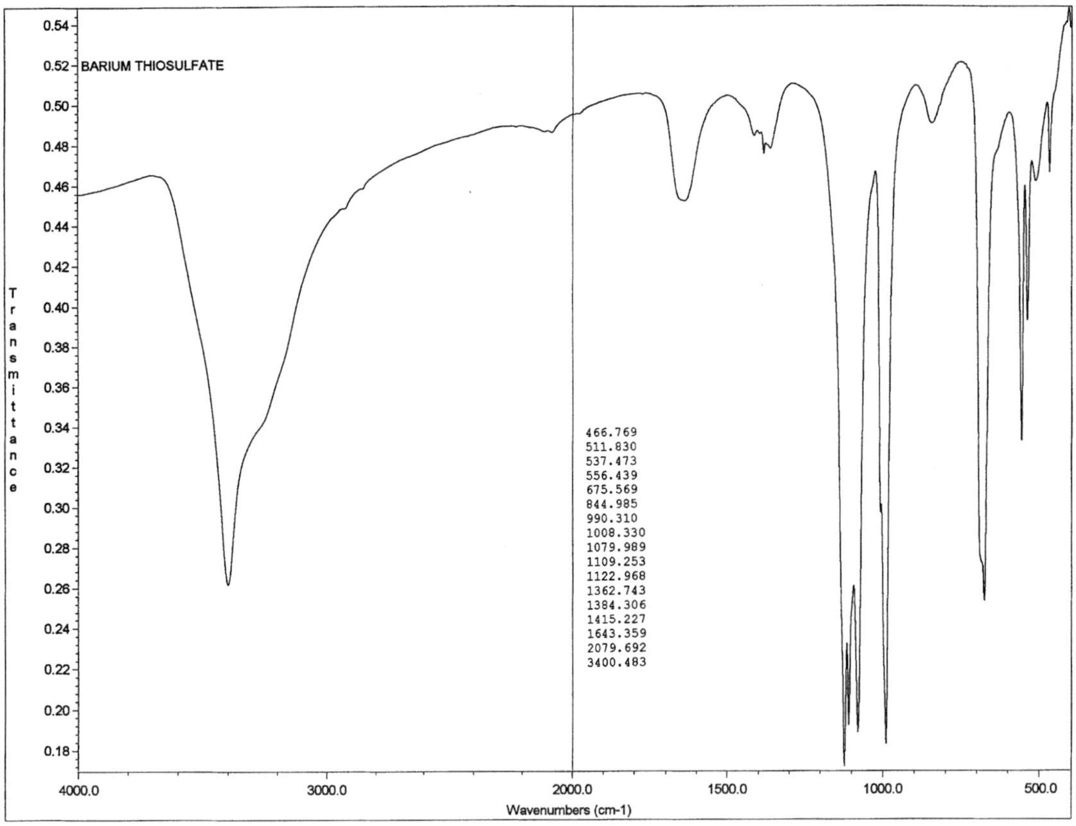

172 Barium thiosulfate $BaS_2O_3 \cdot H_2O$

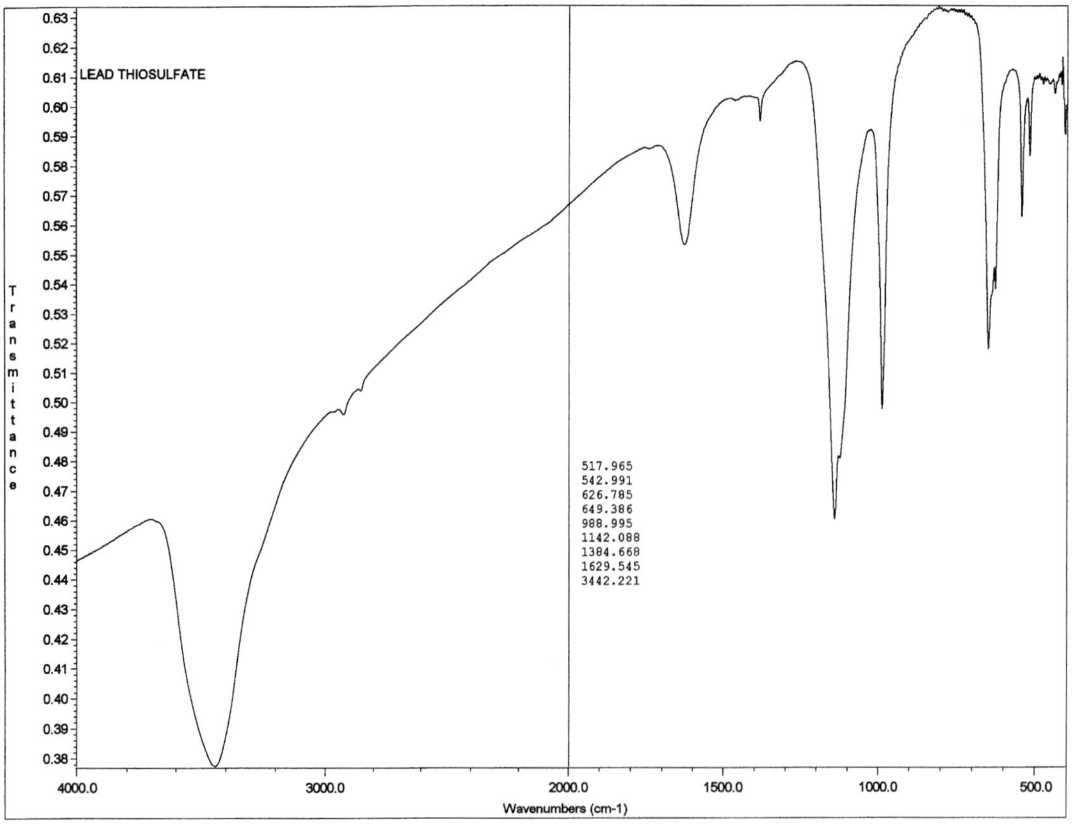

173 Lead thiosulfate $PbS_2O_3 \cdot xH_2O$ or wet

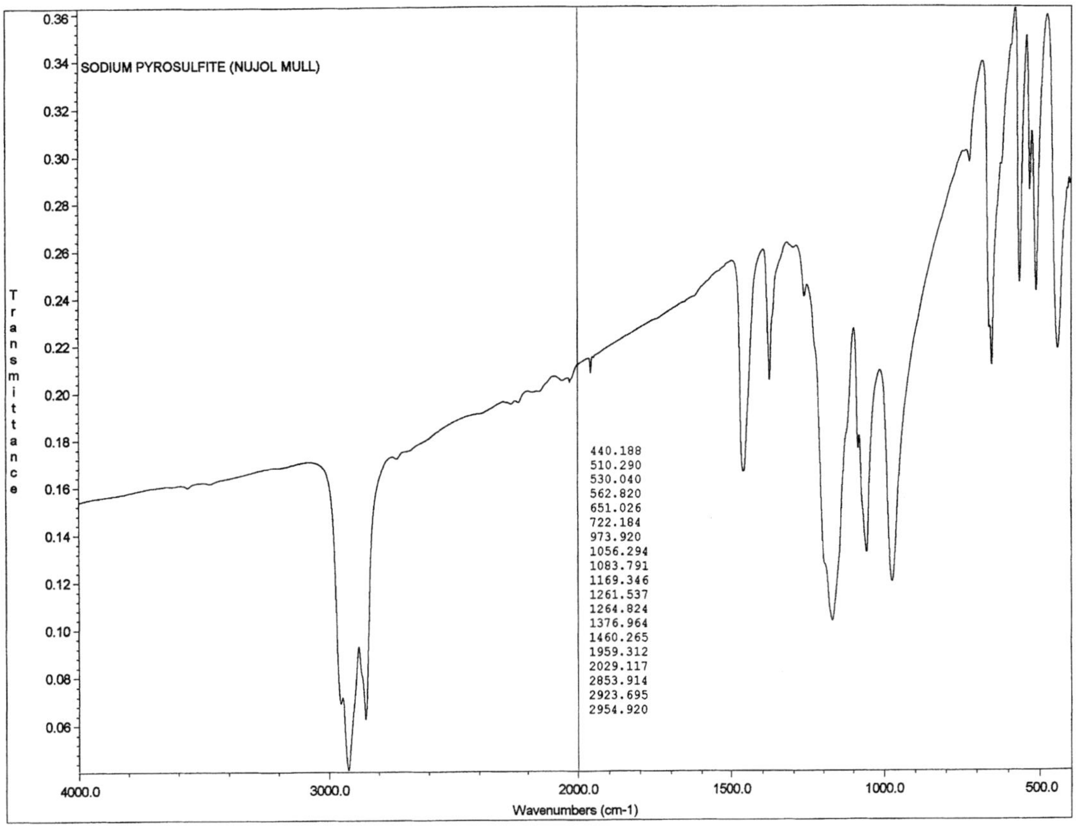

174 Sodium pyrosulfite $Na_2S_2O_5$

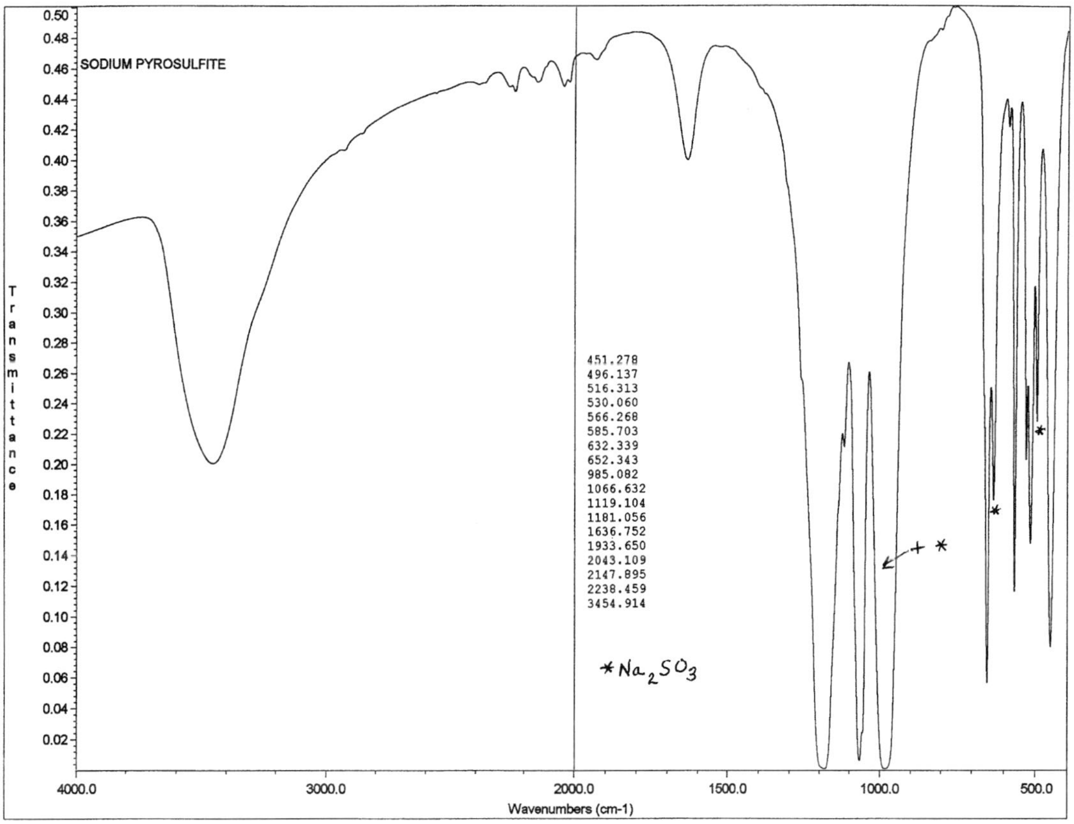

174a Sodium pyrosulfite $Na_2S_2O_5$

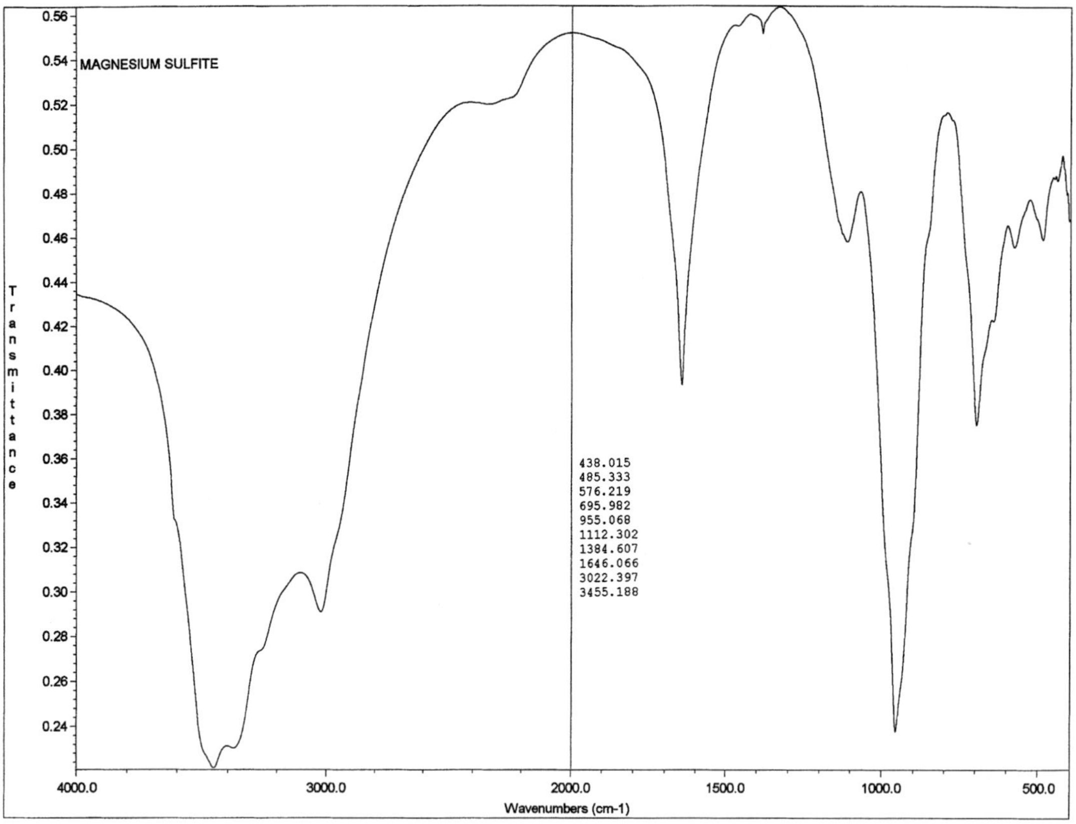

179 Magnesium sulfite $MgSO_3 \cdot xH_2O$

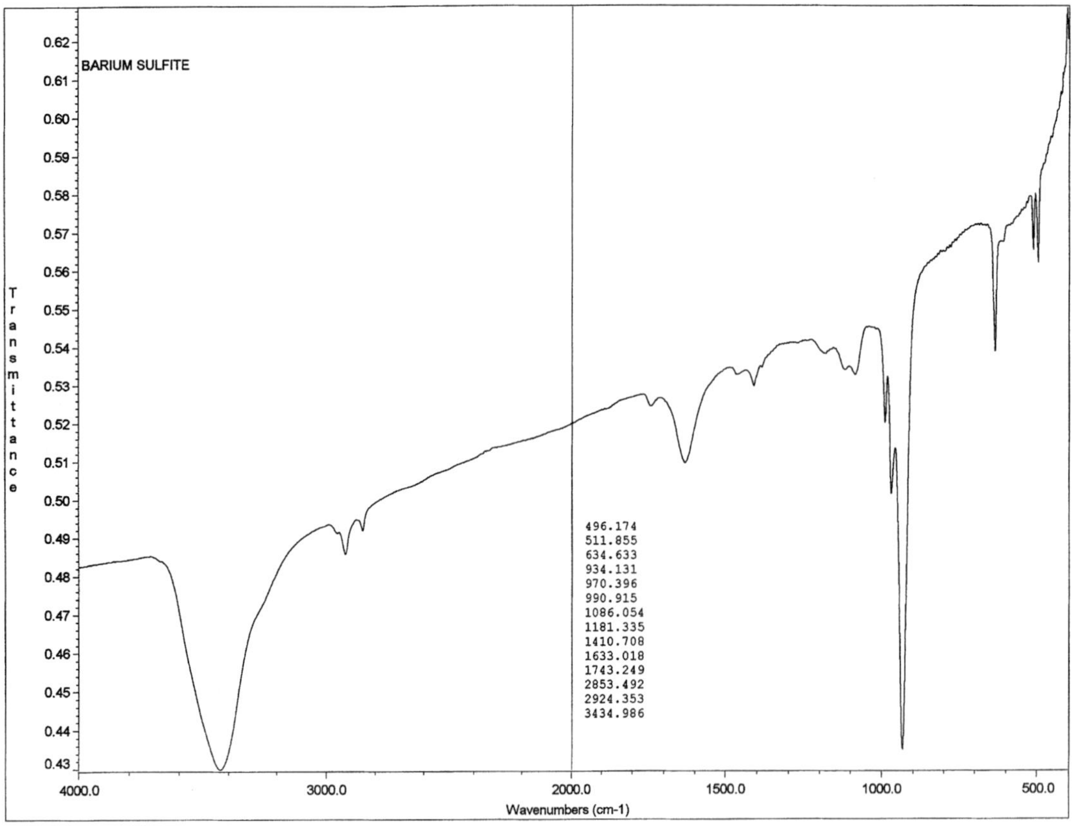

181 Barium sulfite $BaSO_3 \cdot xH_2O$ or wet

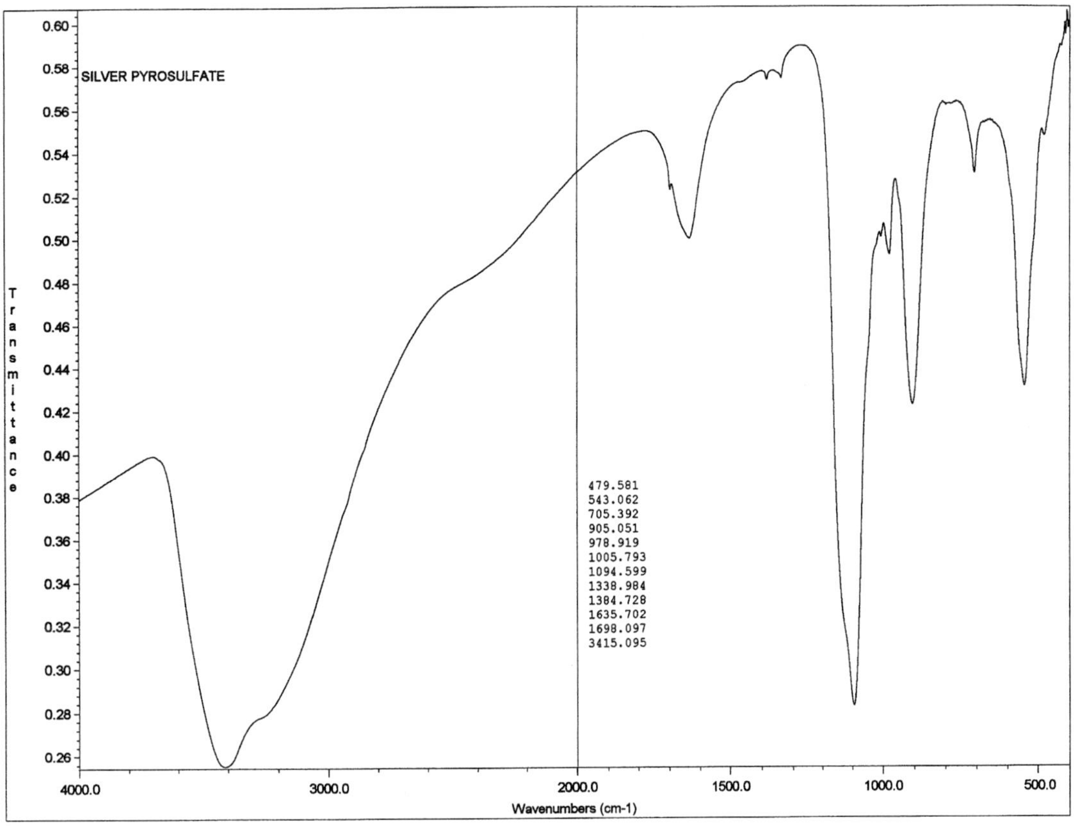

184 Silver pyrosulfite $Ag_2S_2O_7 \cdot xH_2O$

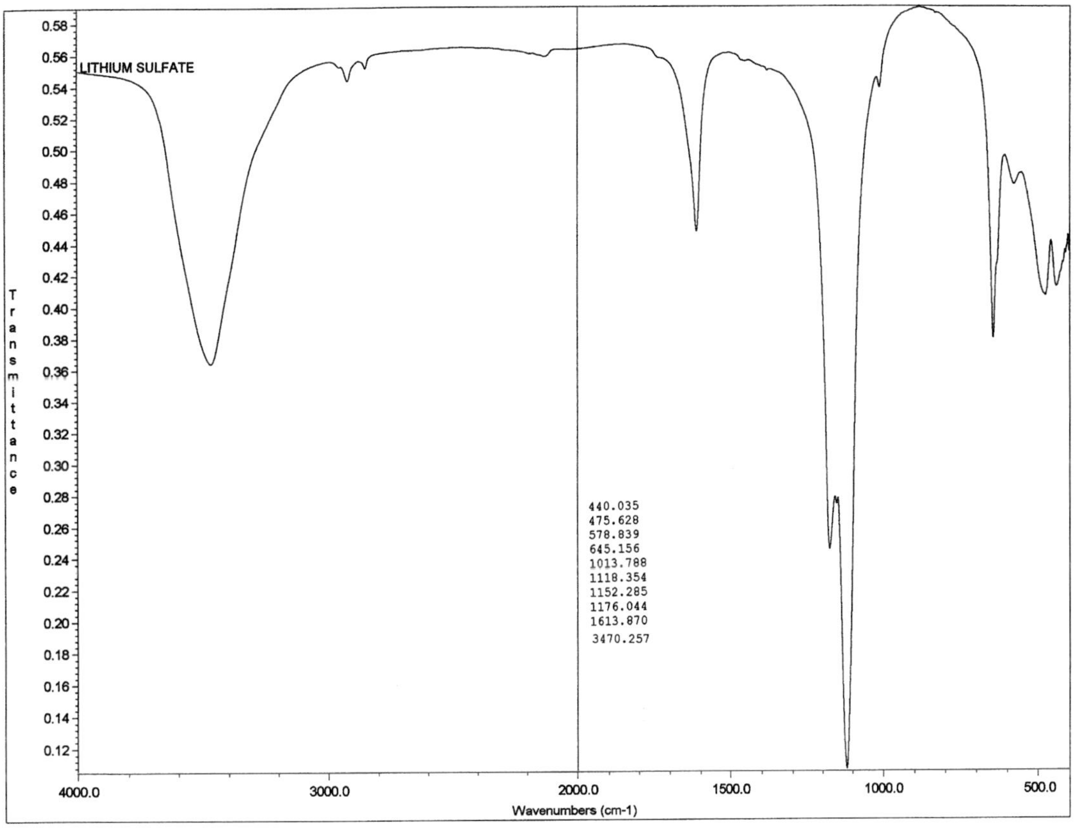

185 Lithium sulfate $Li_2SO_4 \cdot H_2O$

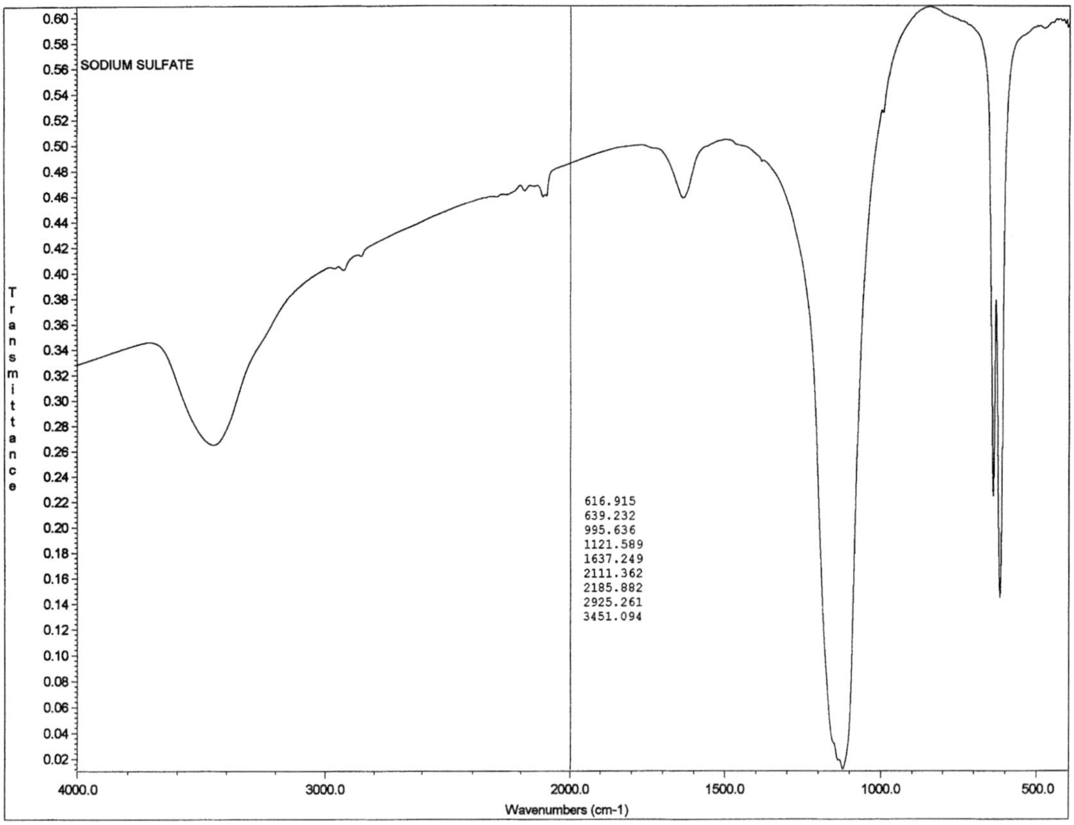

186 Sodium sulfate Na_2SO_4

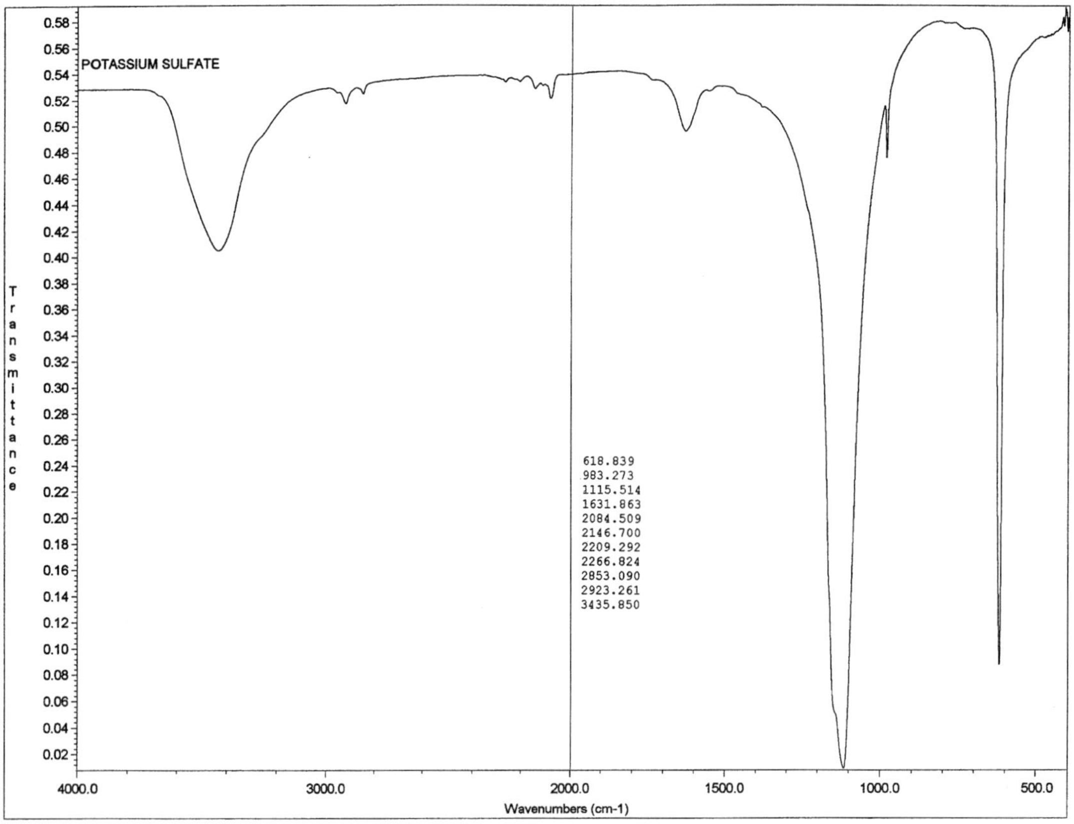

187 Potassium sulfate K_2SO_4

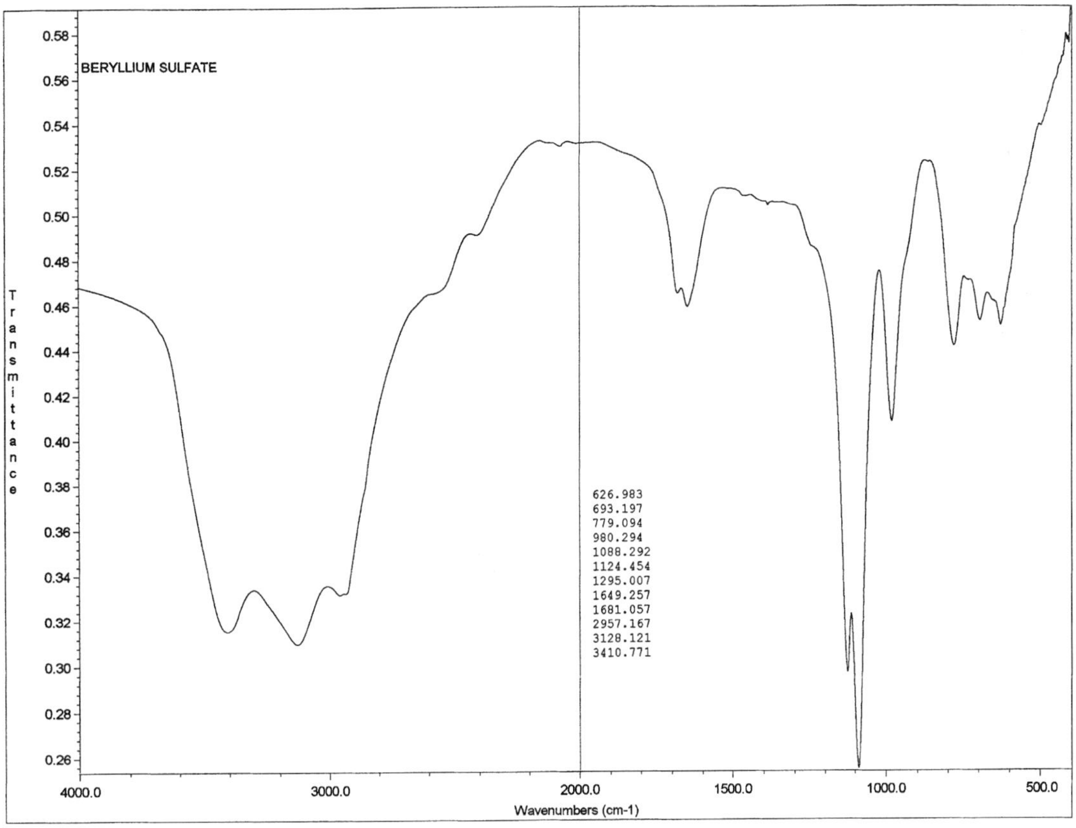

188 Beryllium sulfate $BeSo_4 \cdot 4H_2O$

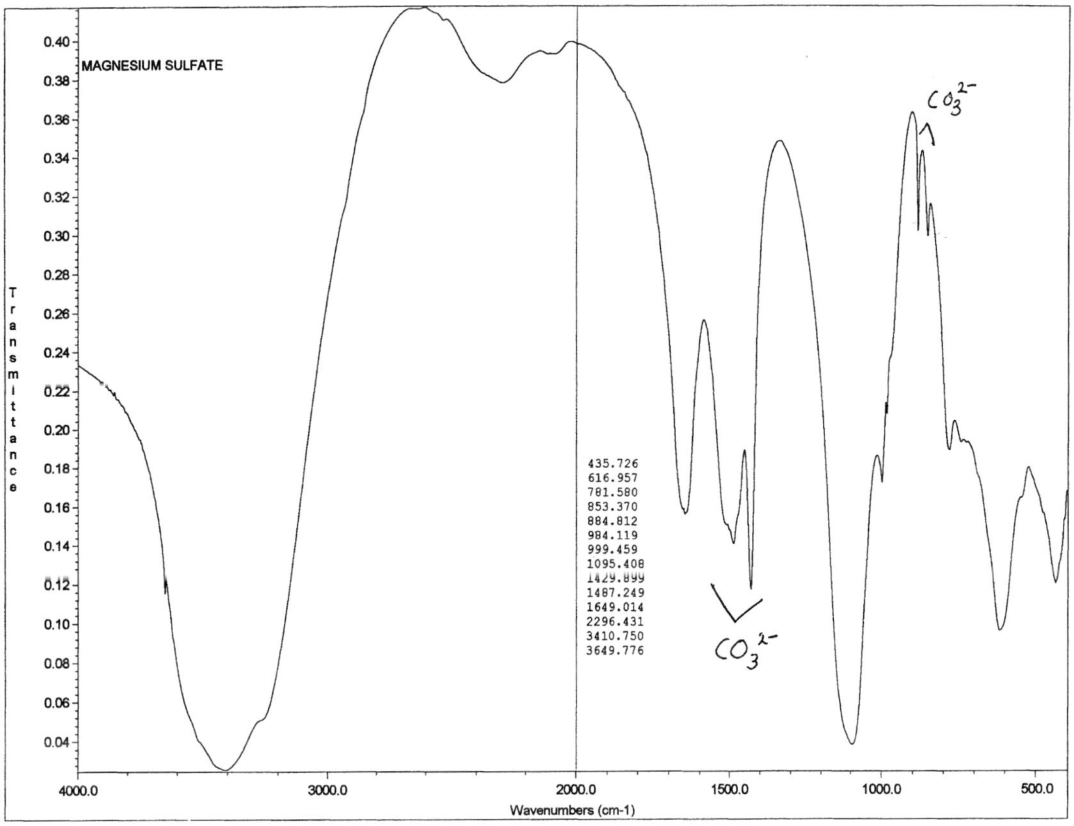

189 Magnesium sulfate $MgSO_4 \cdot 7H_2O$

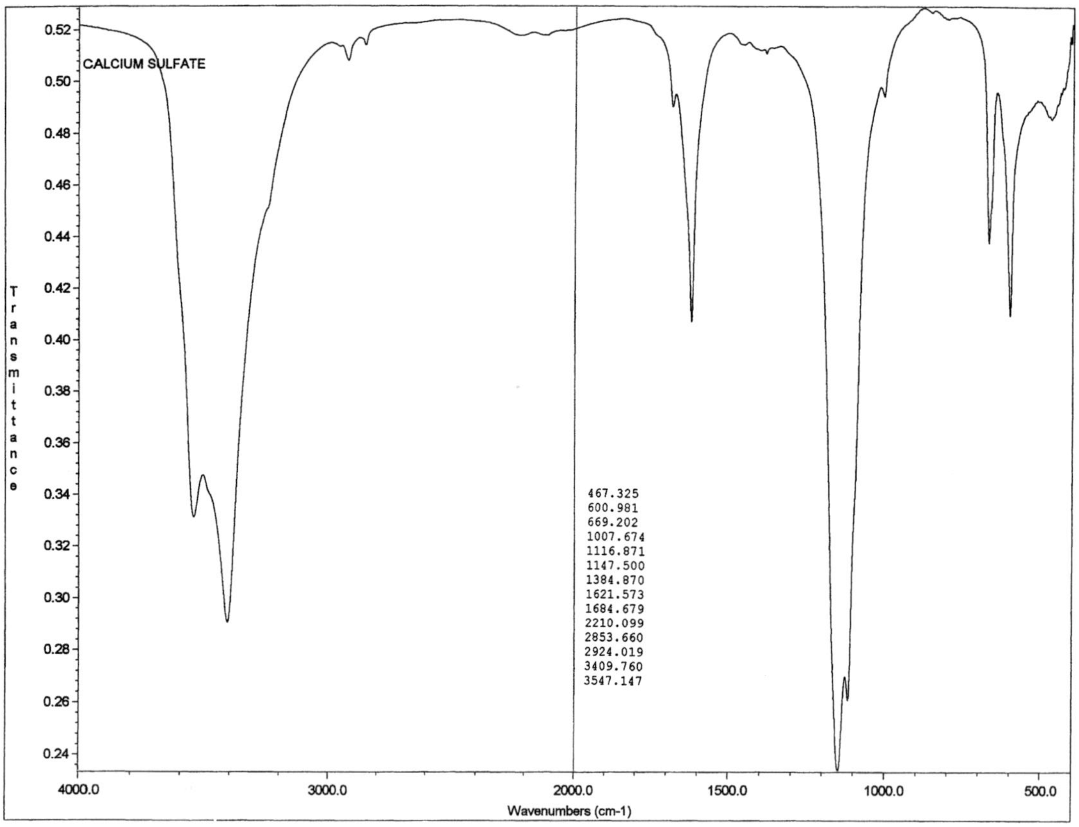

190 Calcium sulfate $CaSO_4 \cdot 2H_2O$

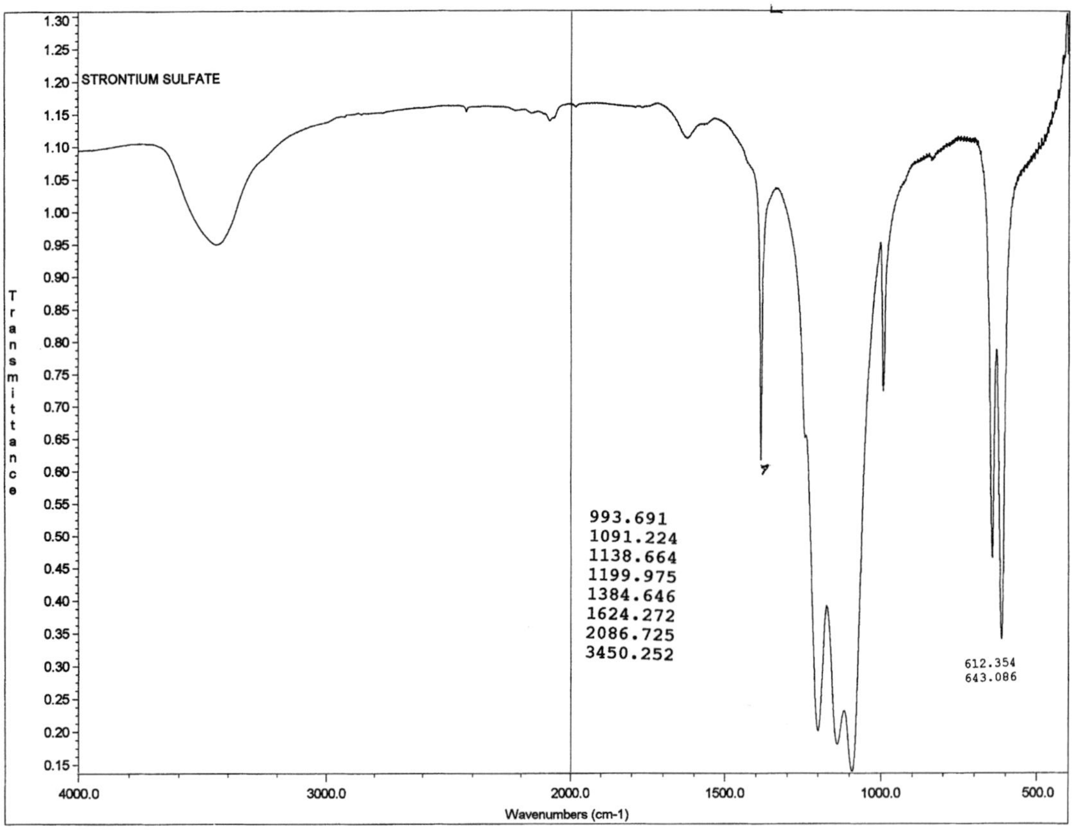

191 Strontium sulfate $SrSO_4$

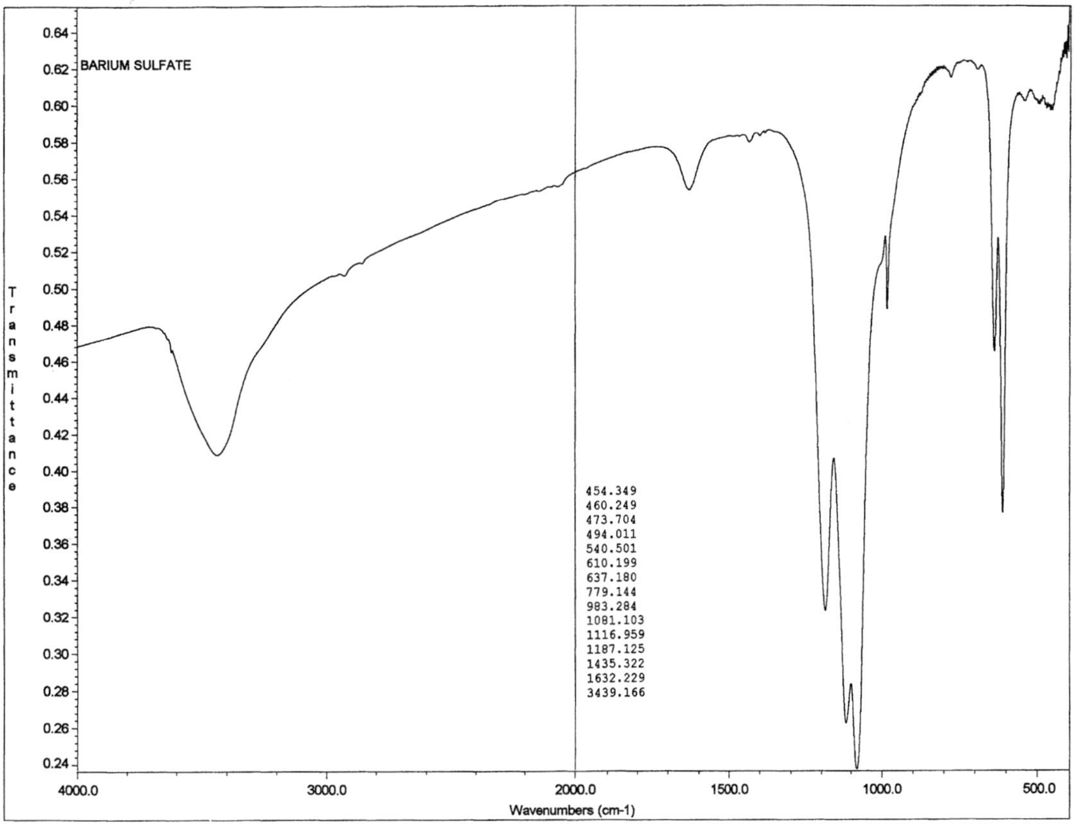

192 Barium sulfate $BaSO_4$

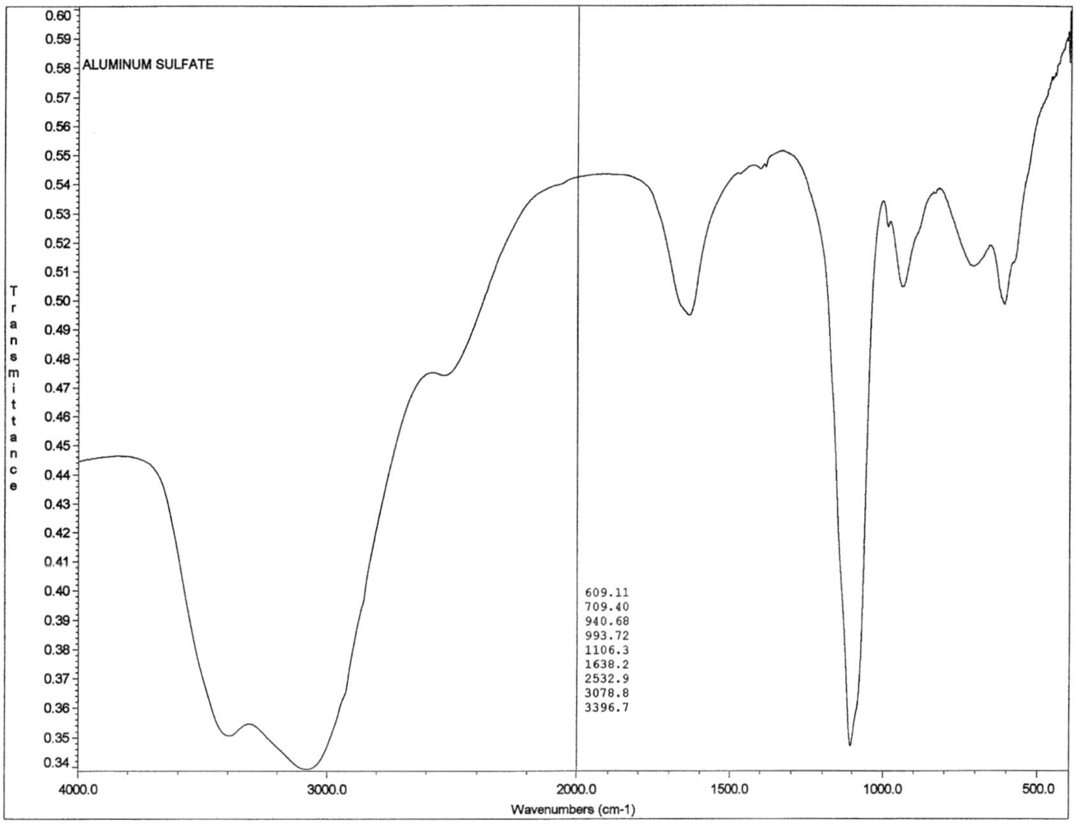

193 Aluminum sulfate $Al_2(SO_4)_3 \cdot 18H_2O$

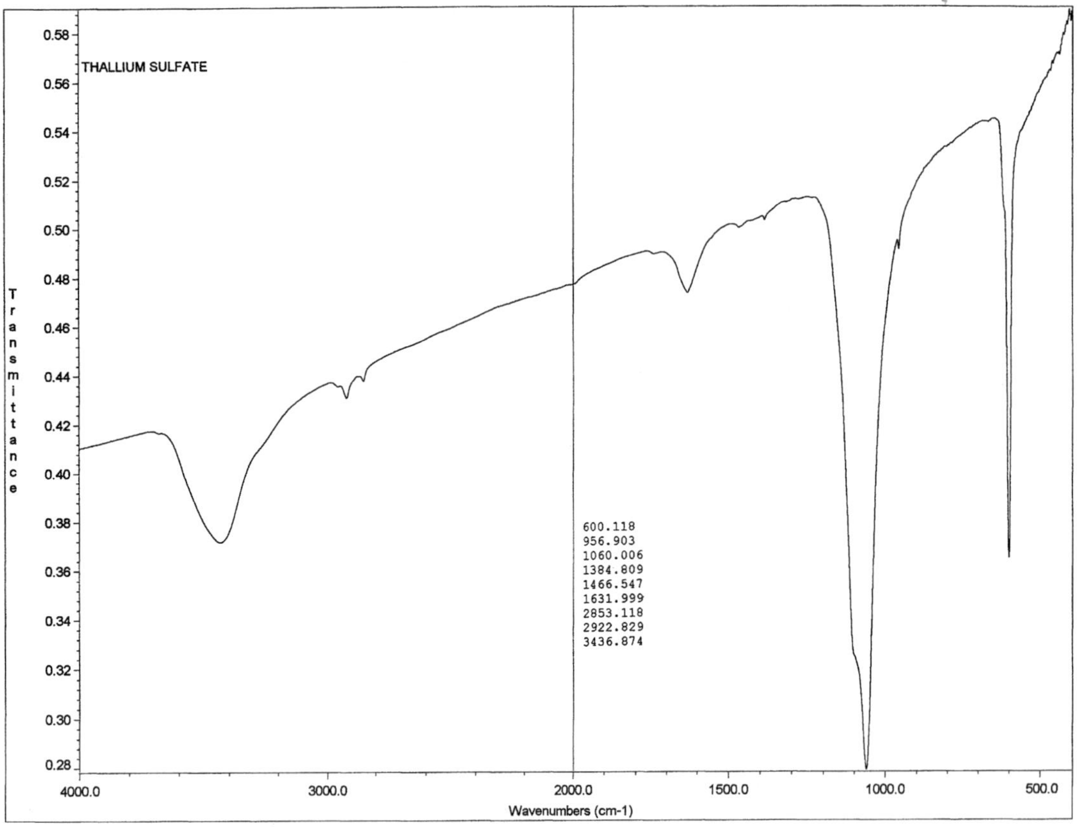

194 Thallium sulfate $Tl(SO_4)_3$

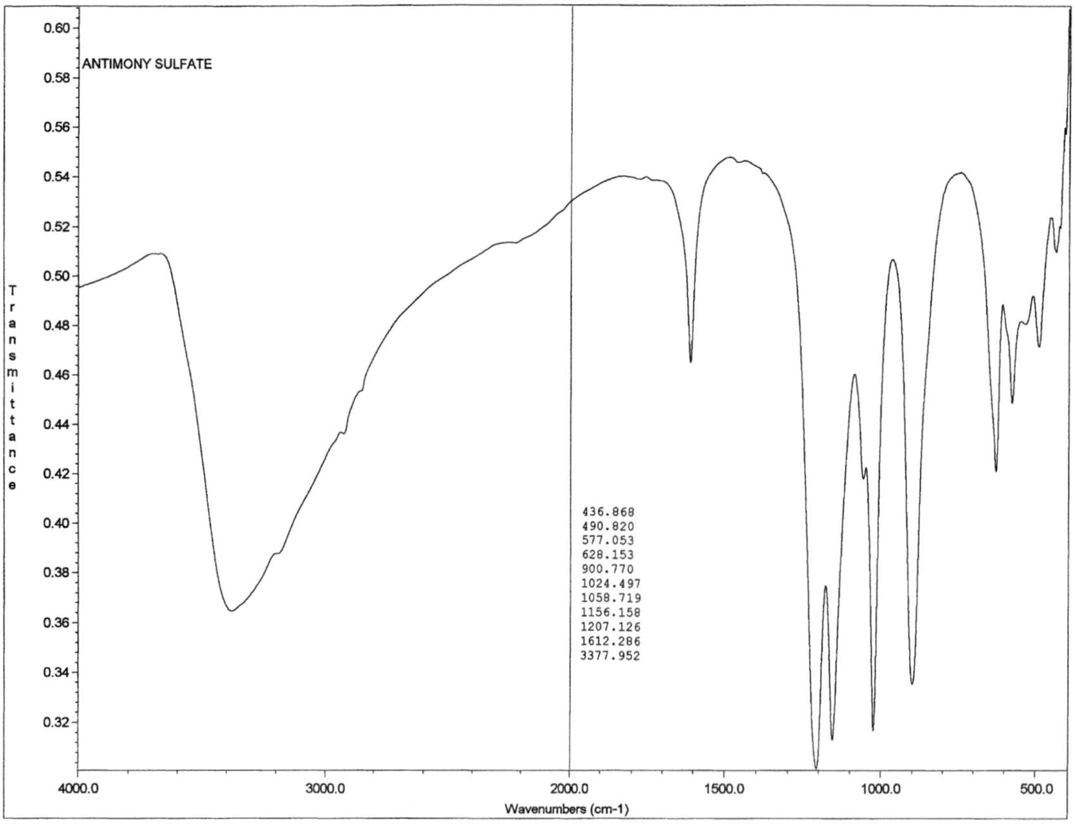

196 Antimony sulfate $Sb_2(SO_4)_3 \cdot xH_2O$

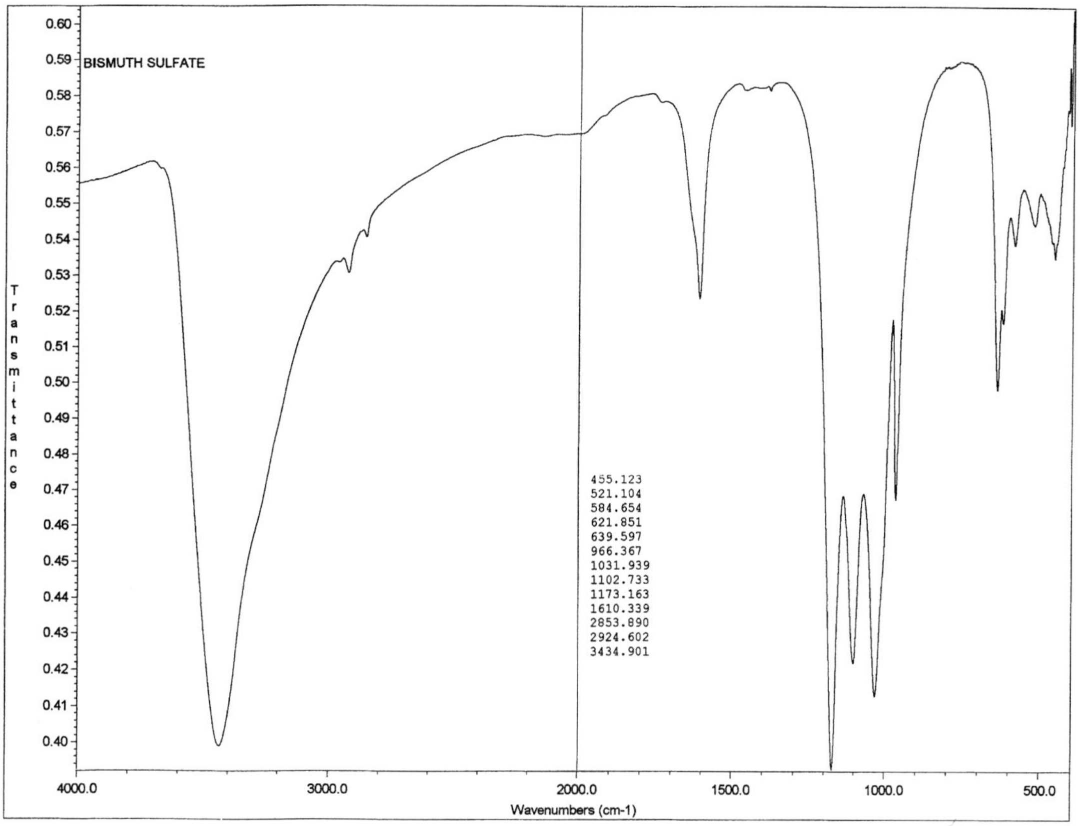

197 Bismuth sulfate $Bi_2(SO_4)_3 \cdot xH_2O$

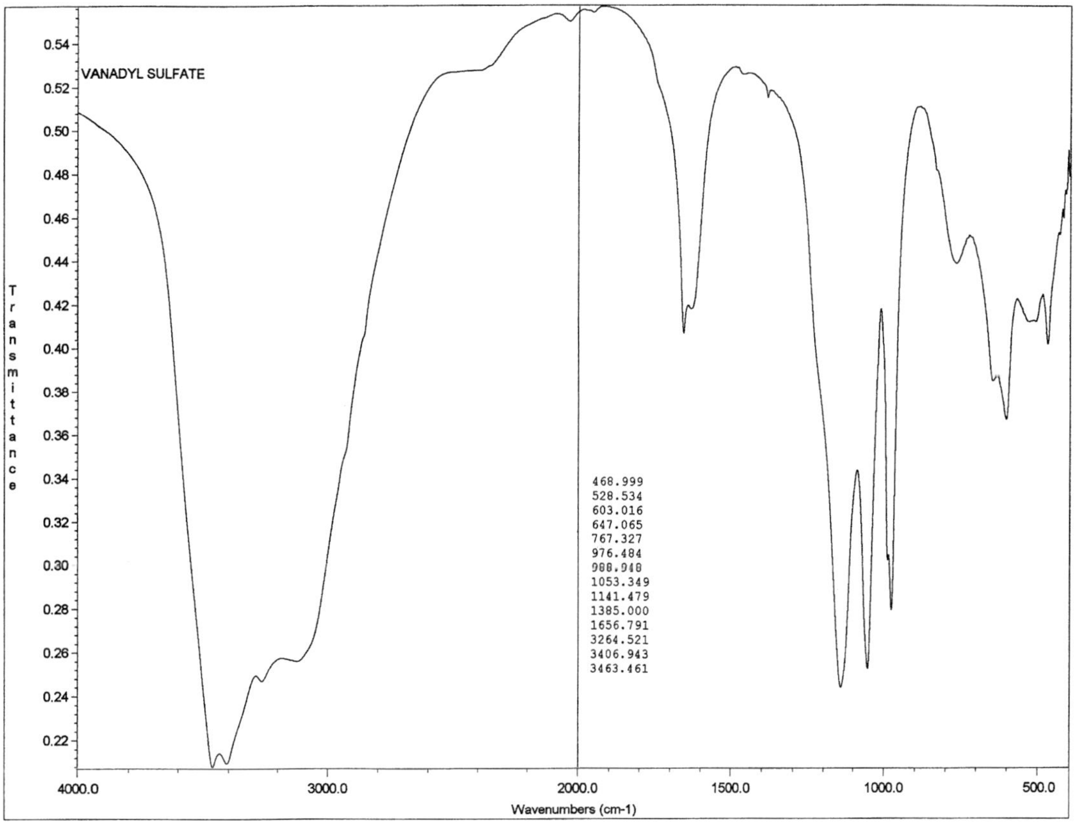

198 Vanadyl sulfate $VSO_4 \cdot xH_2O$

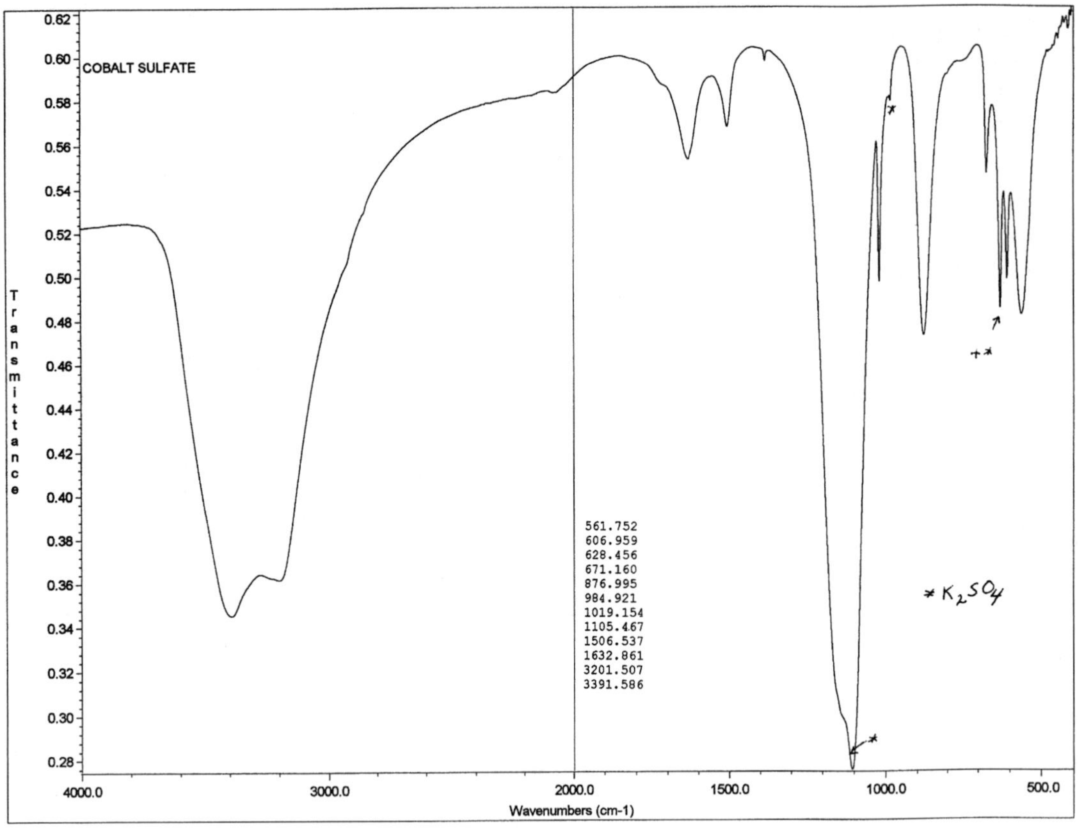

200 Cobalt (II) sulfate $CoSO_4 \cdot 7H_2O$

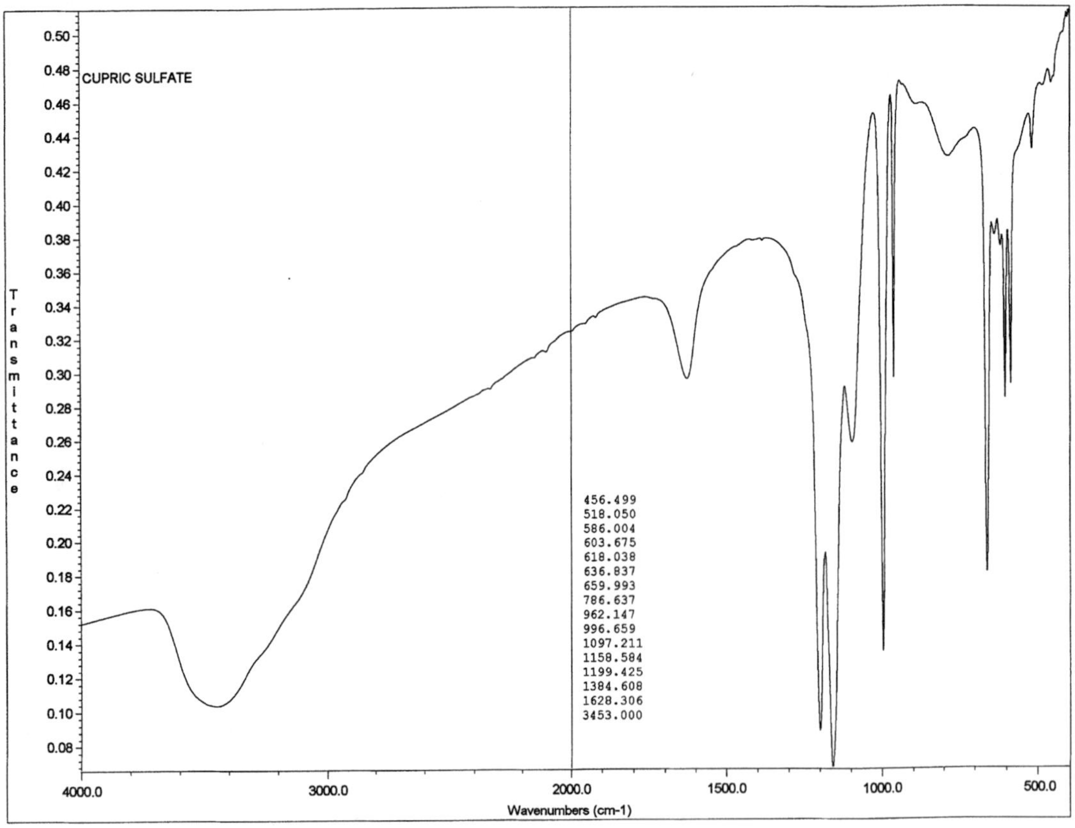

201 Copper (II) sulfate $CuSO_4 \cdot 5H_2O$

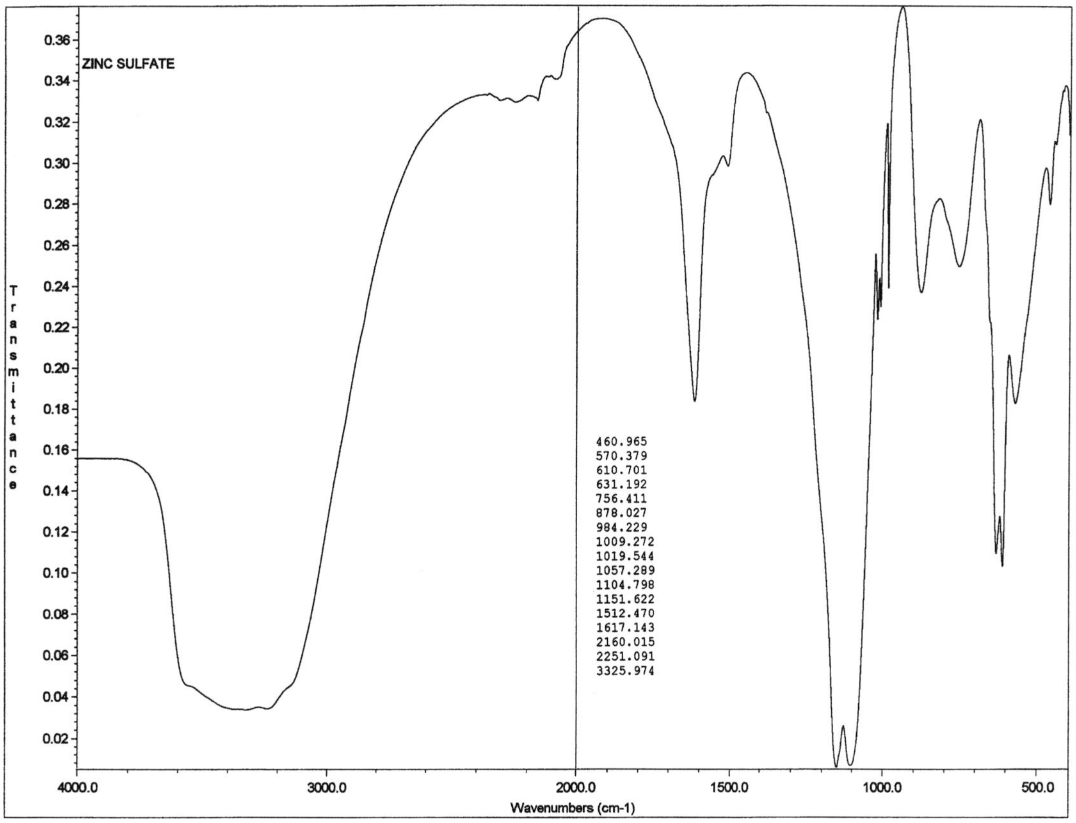

202 Zinc sulfate $ZnSO_4 \cdot 6H_2O$

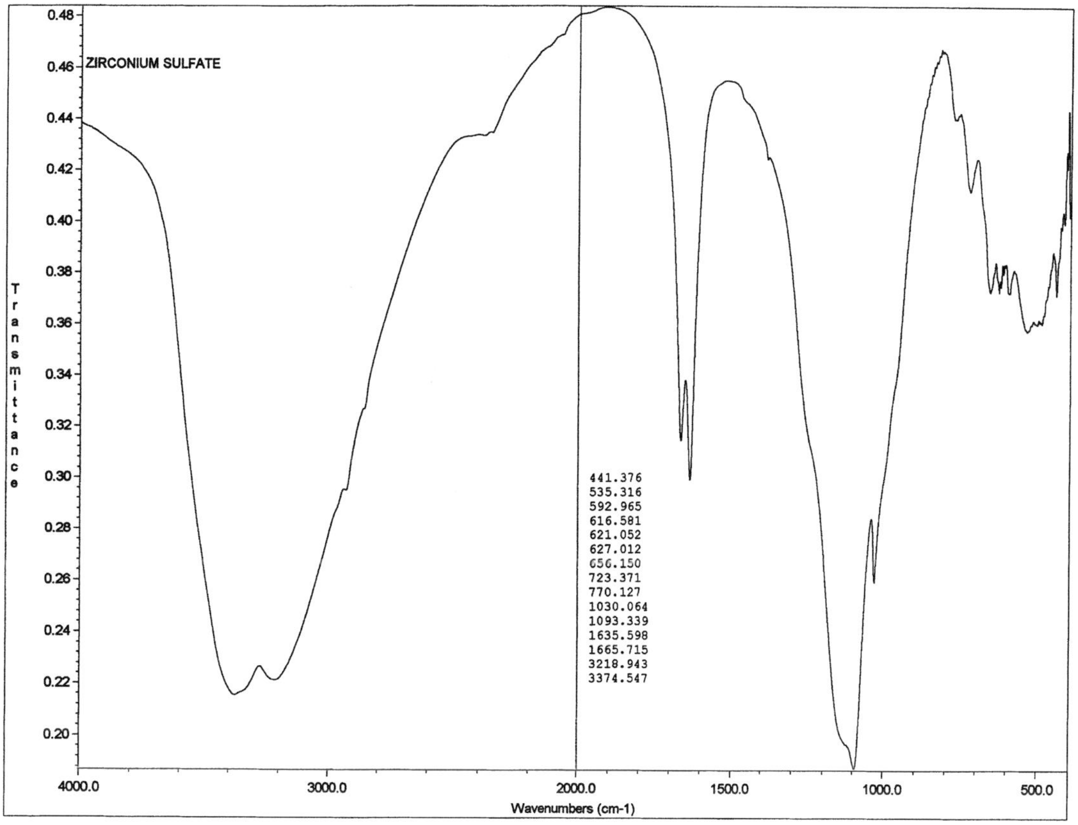

203 Zirconium sulfate $Zr(SO_4)_2 \cdot 4H_2O$

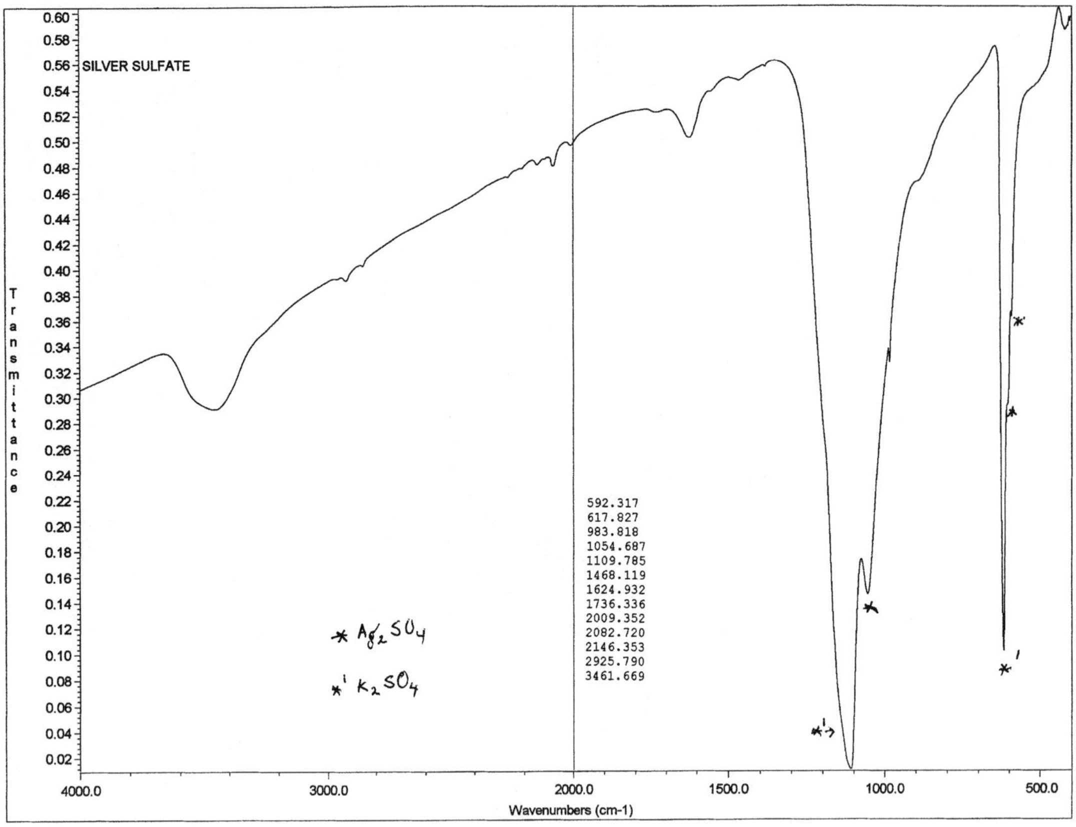

204 Silver sulfate Ag_2SO_4

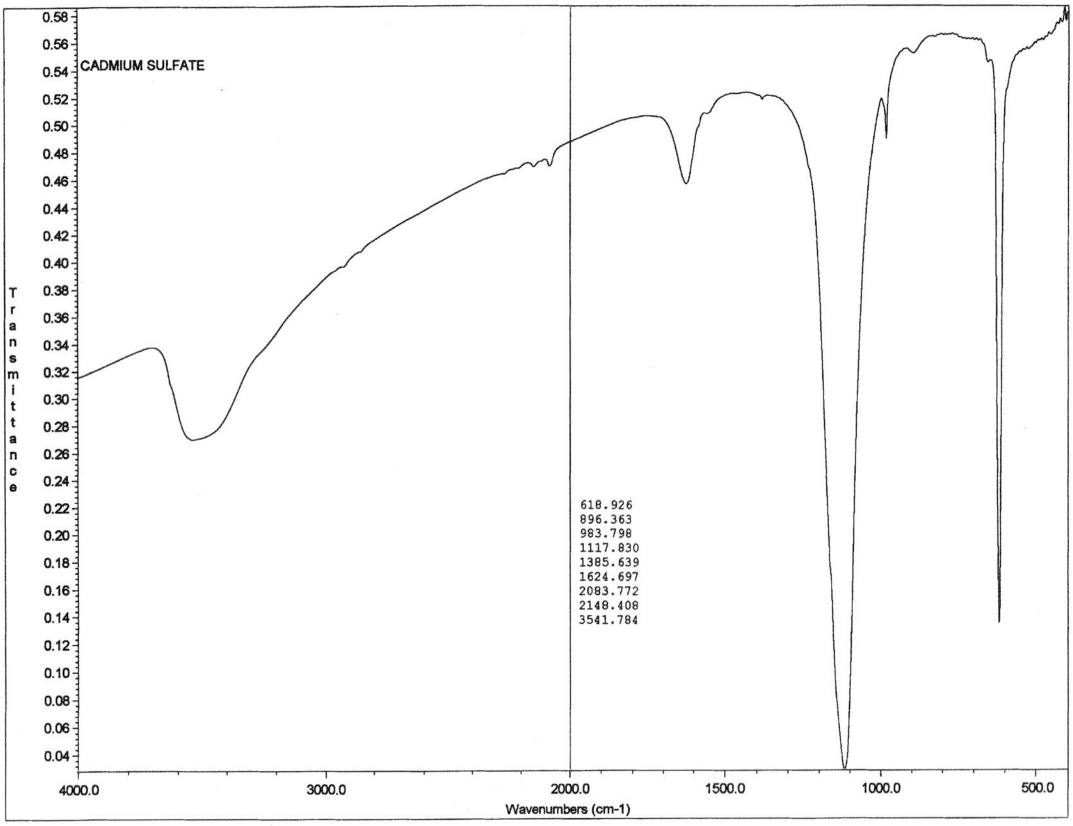

205 Cadmium sulfate $CdSO_4 \cdot 7H_2O$

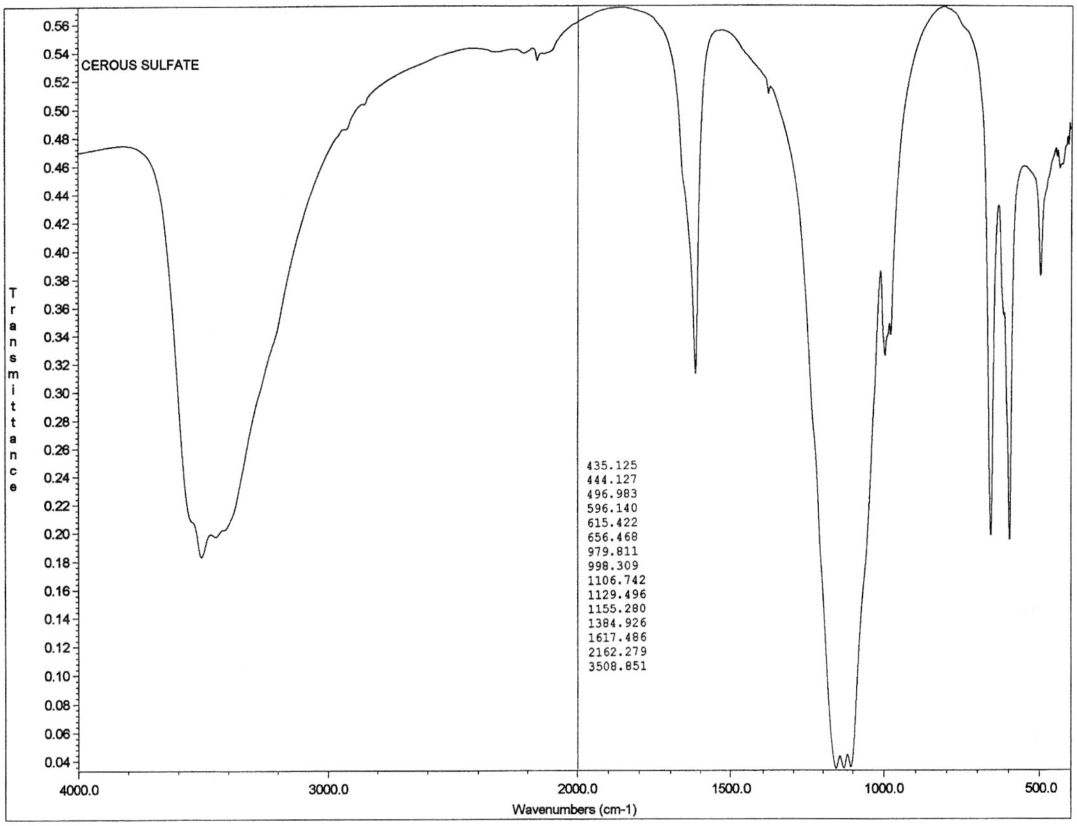

206 Cerium (III) sulfate $Ce_2(SO_4)_3 \cdot 4H_2O$

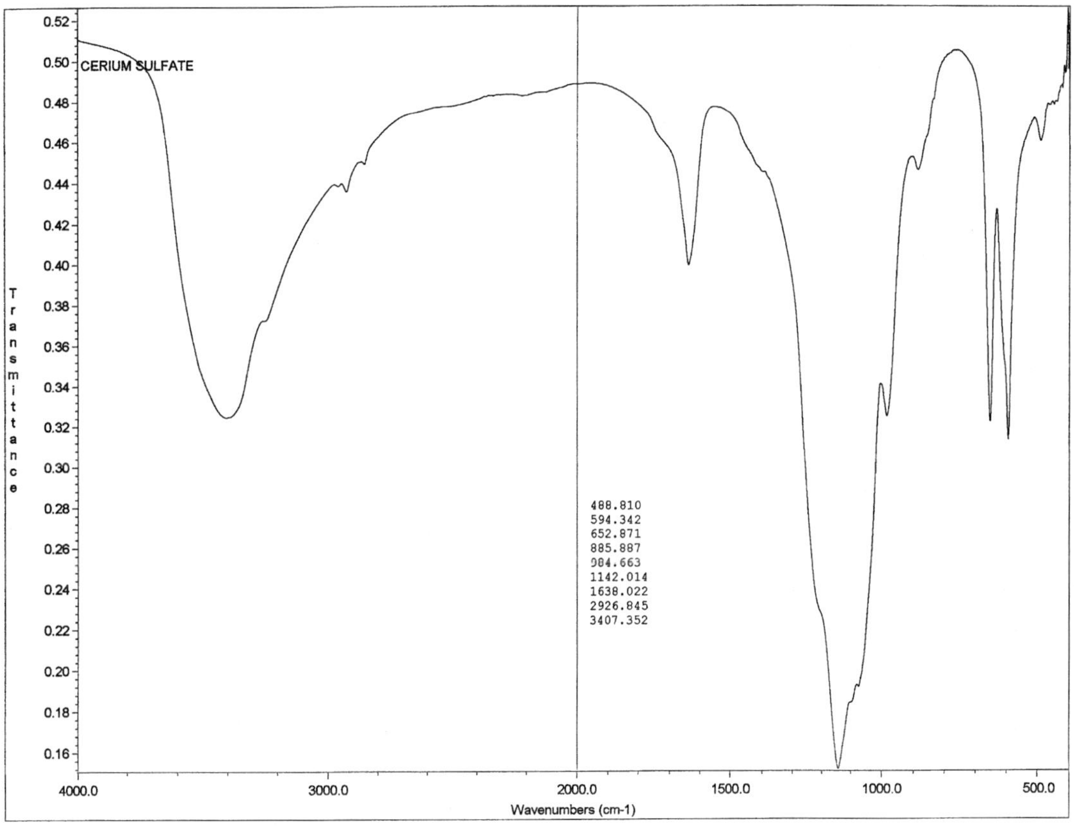

207 Cerium (IV) sulfate $Ce(SO_4)_2 \cdot 4H_2O$

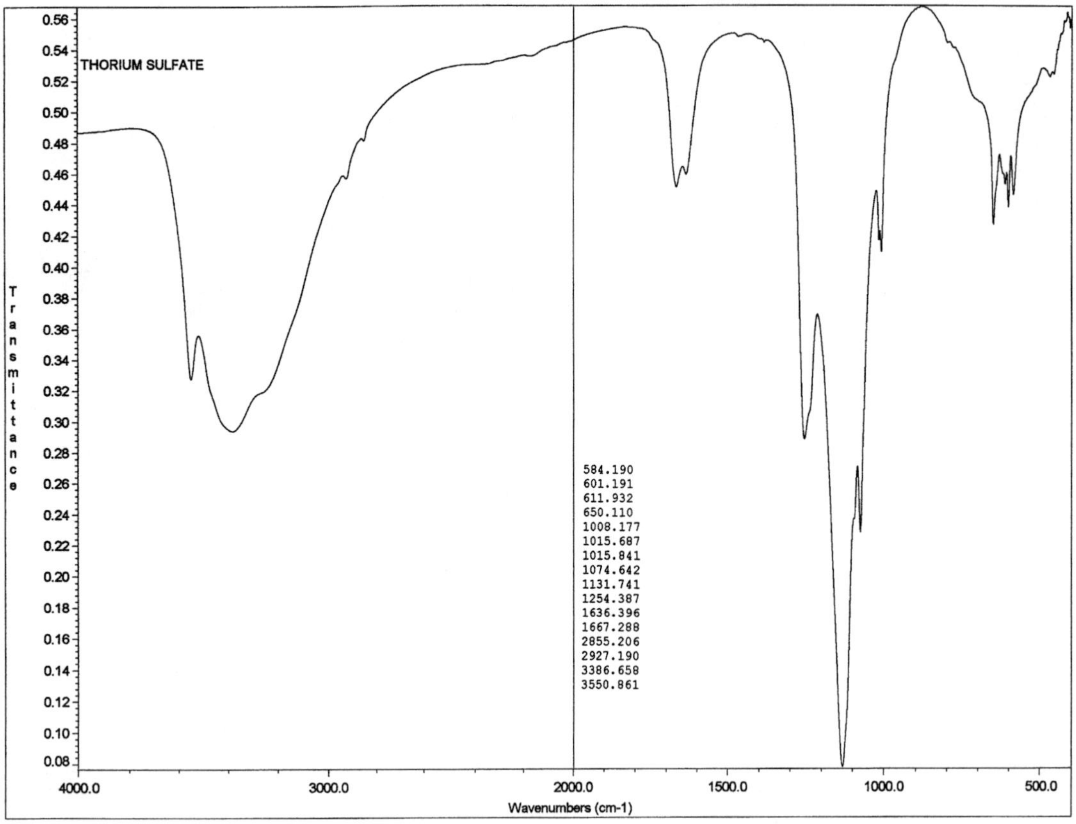

208 Thorium sulfate $Th(SO_4)_2 \cdot xH_2O$

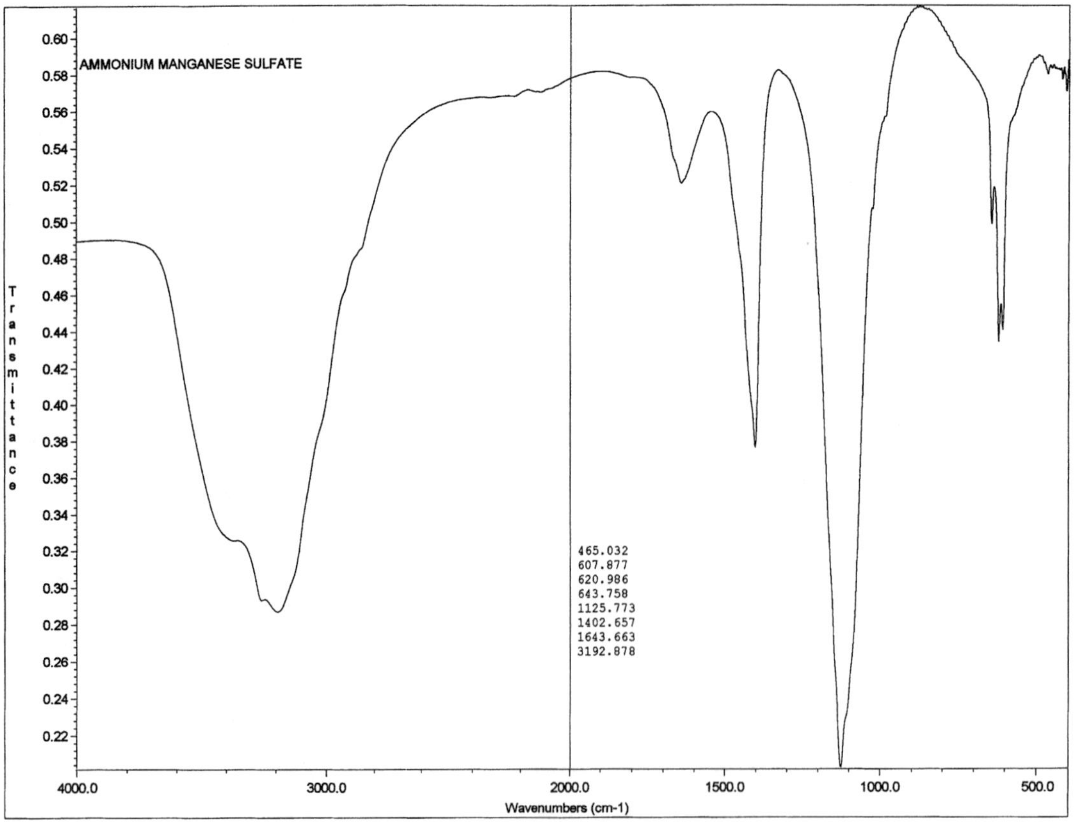

209 Ammonium manganese sulfate $(NH_4)_2MnSO_4 \cdot xH_2O$

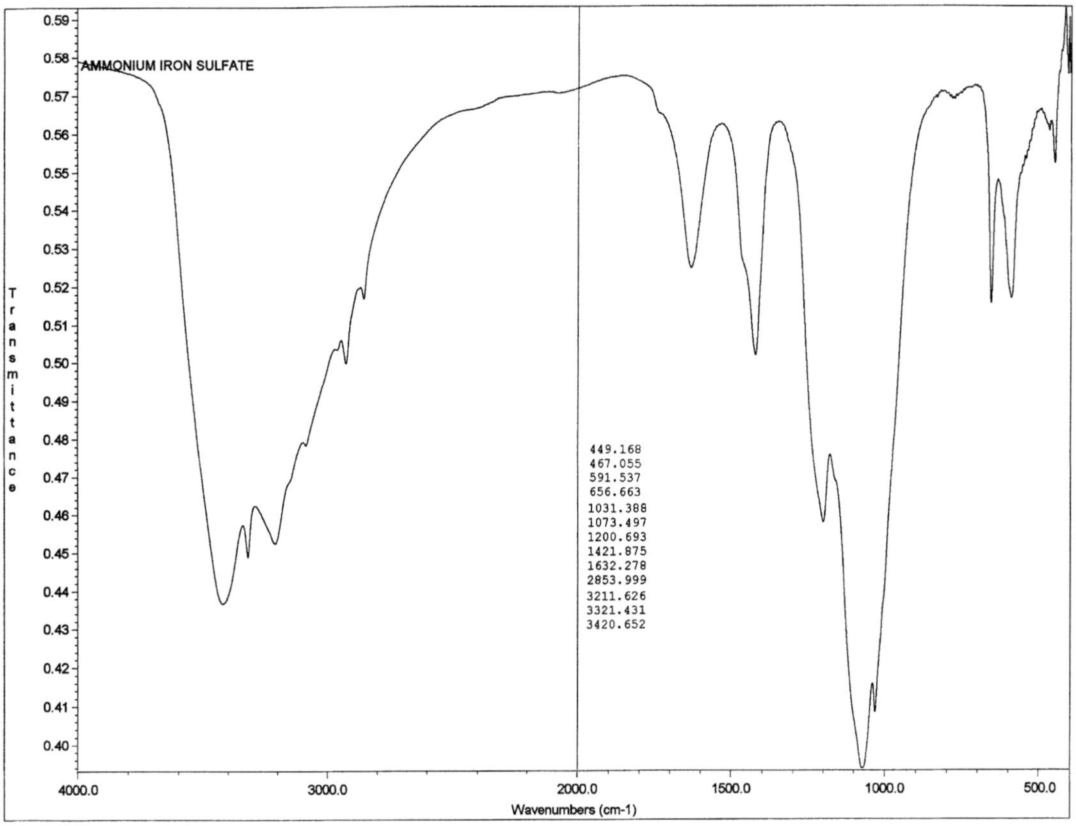

210 Ammonium iron (III) sulfate $(NH_4)Fe(SO_4)_2 \cdot 3H_2O$

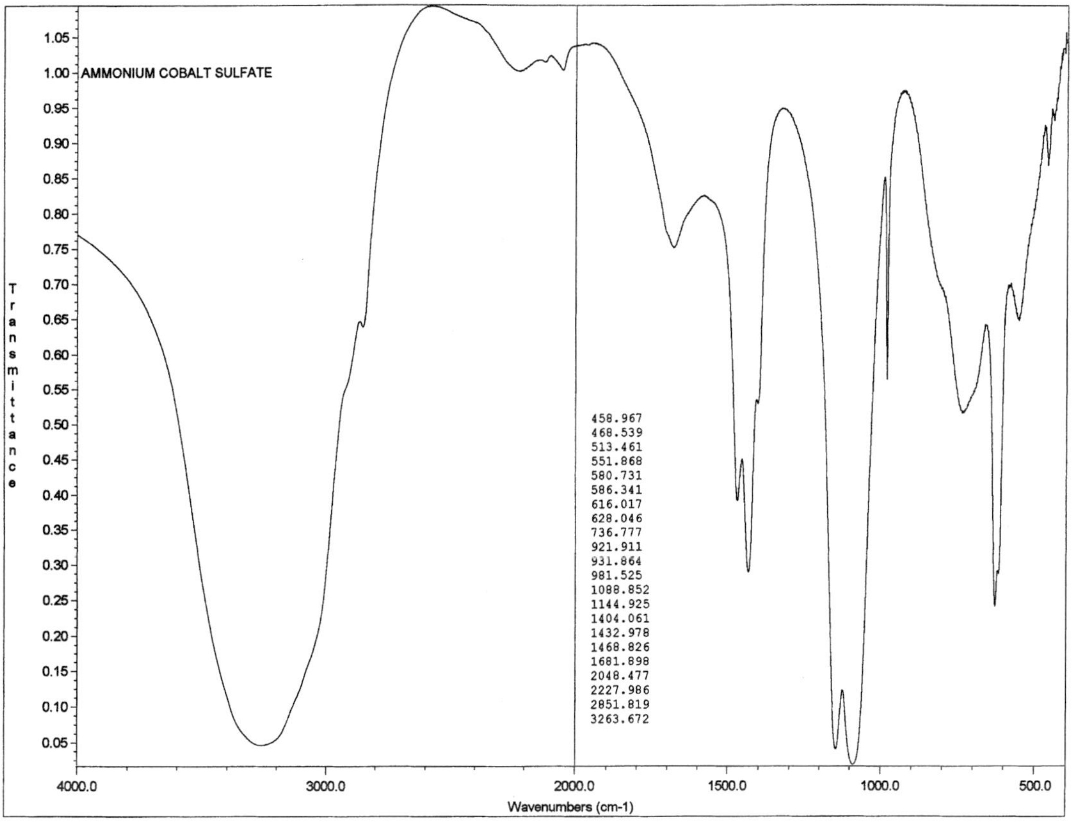

212 Ammonium cobalt sulfate $(NH_4)_2Co(SO_4)_2 \cdot 6H_2O$

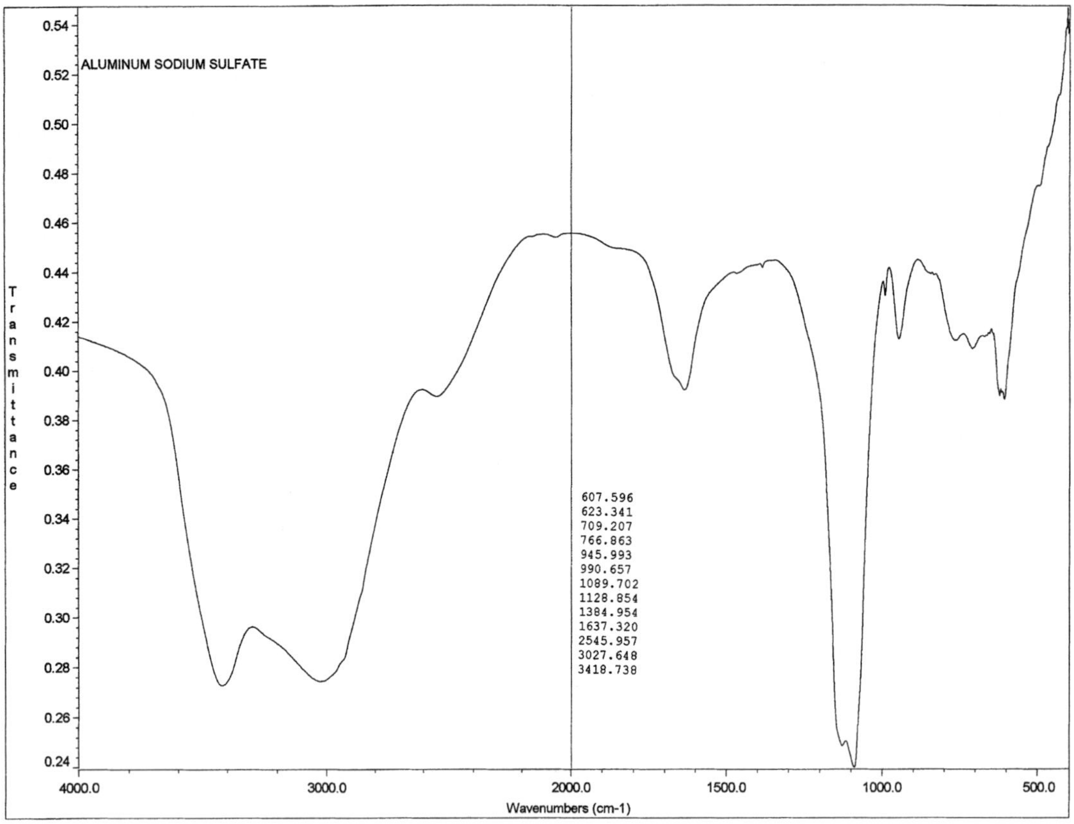

214 Aluminum sodium sulfate $NaAl(SO_4)_2 \cdot xH_2O$

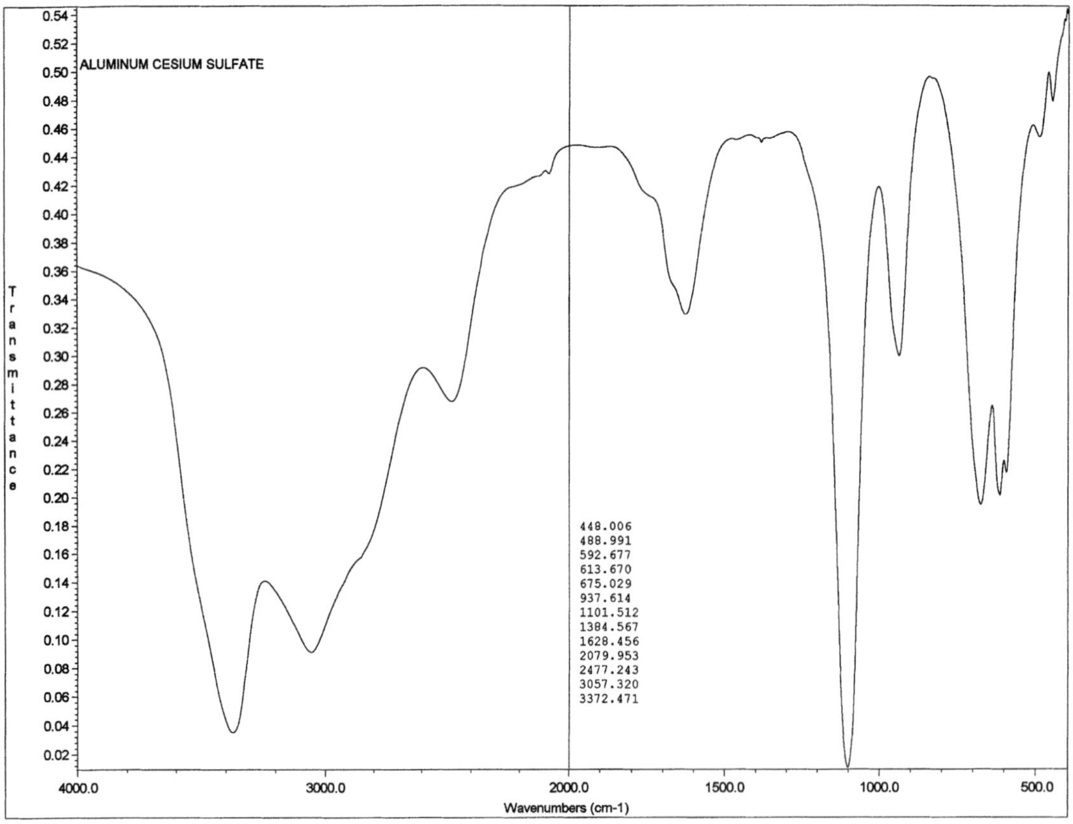

215 Cesium aluminum sulfate $CsAl(SO_4)_2 \cdot 12H_2O$

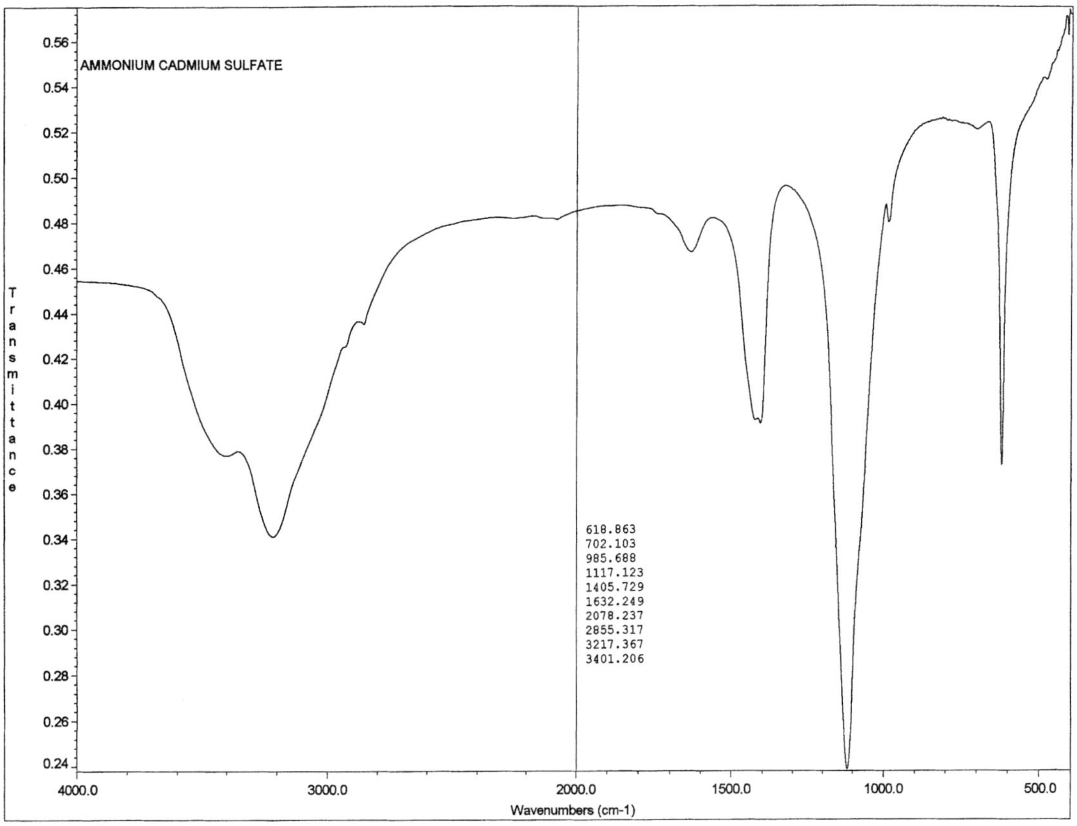

216 Ammonium cadmium sulfate $(NH_4)Cd(SO_4)_2 \cdot 6H_2O$

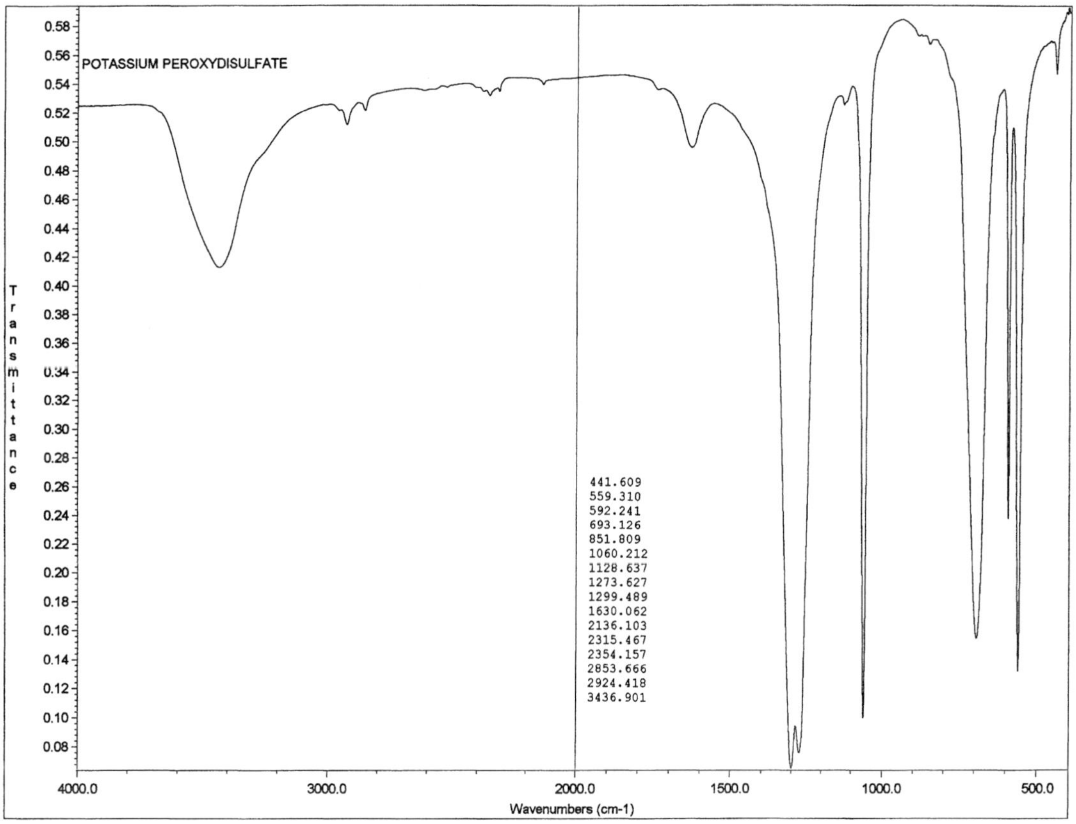

217 Potassium peroxydisulfate $K_2S_2O_8$

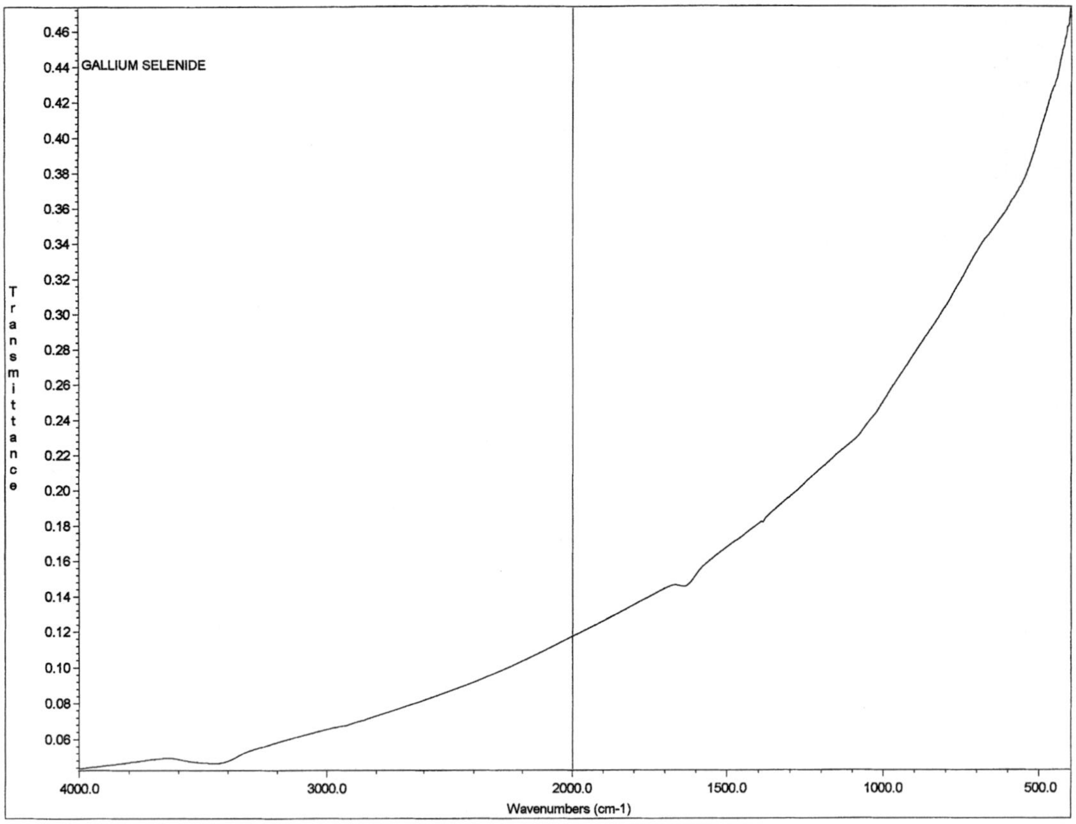

218 Gallium monselenide GaSe

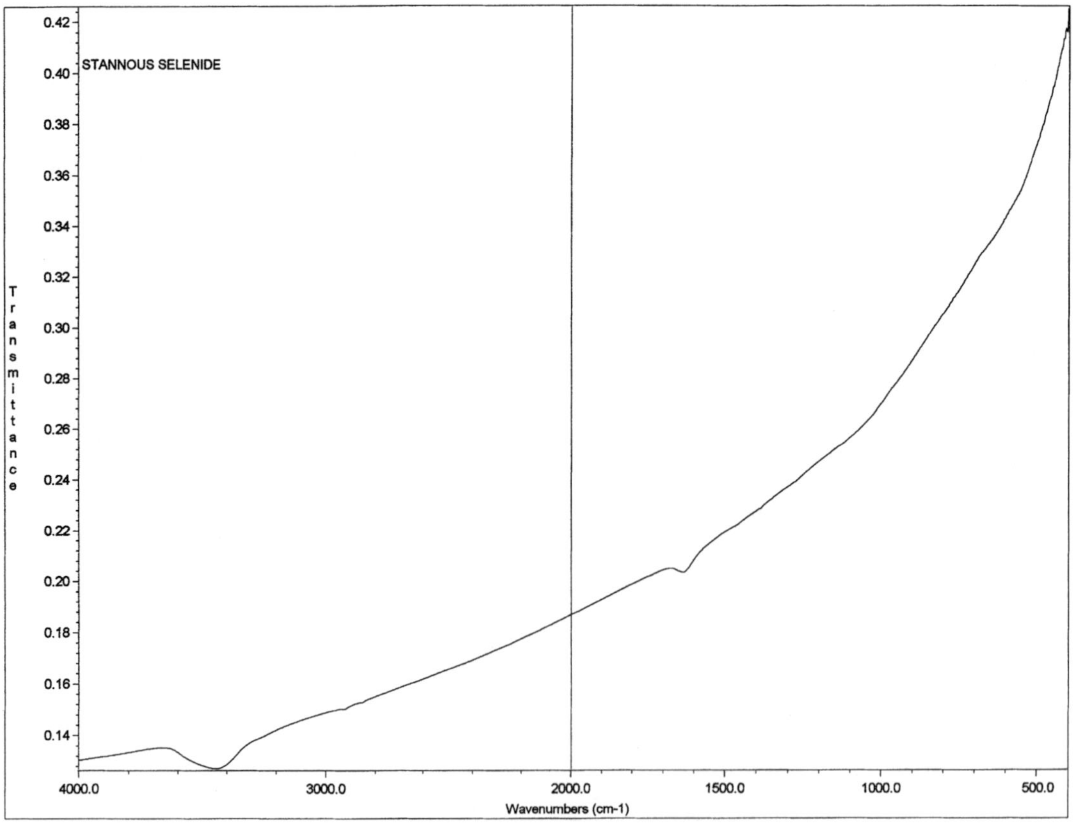

219 Tin (II) selenide SnSe

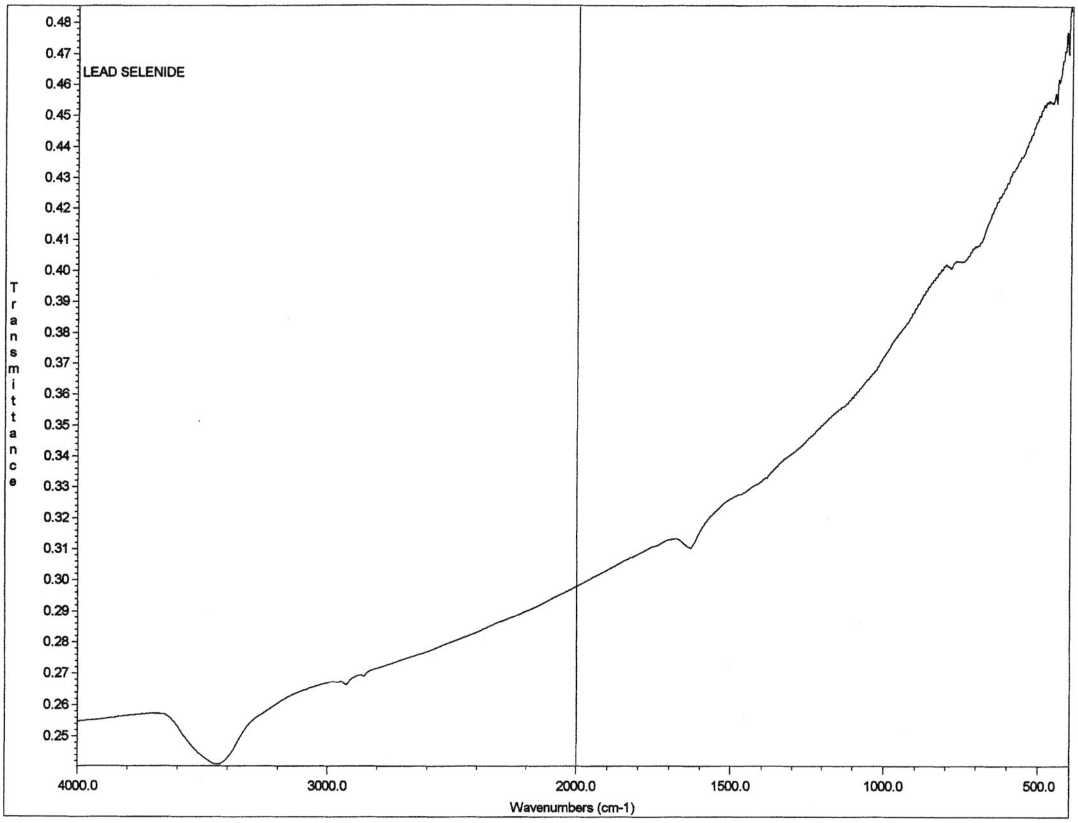

220 Lead selenide PbSe

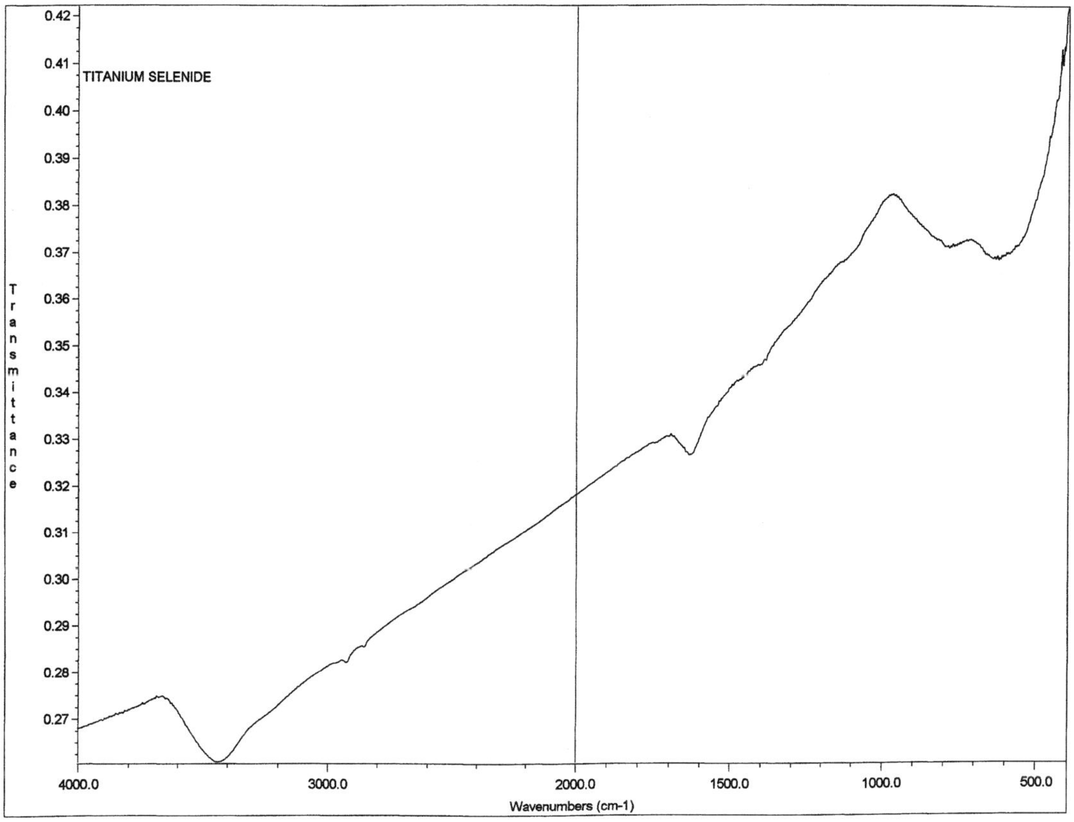

221 Titanium diselenide $TiSe_2$

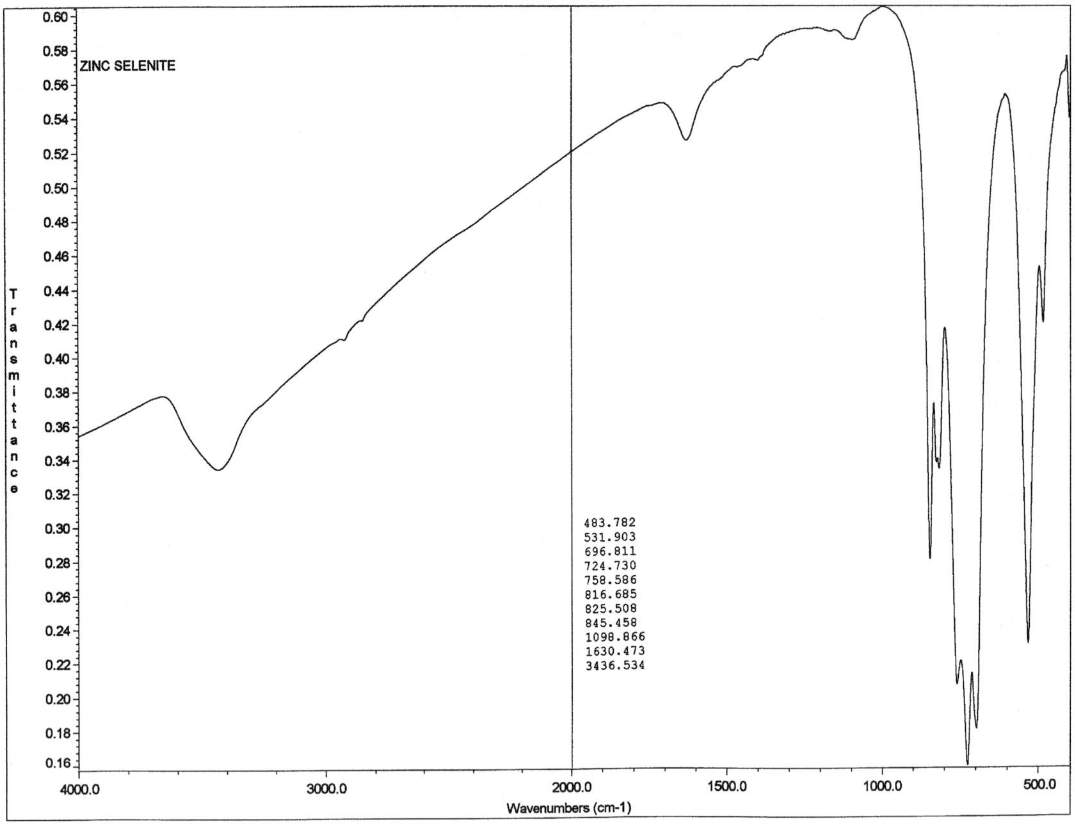

222 Zinc selenite $ZnSeO_3$

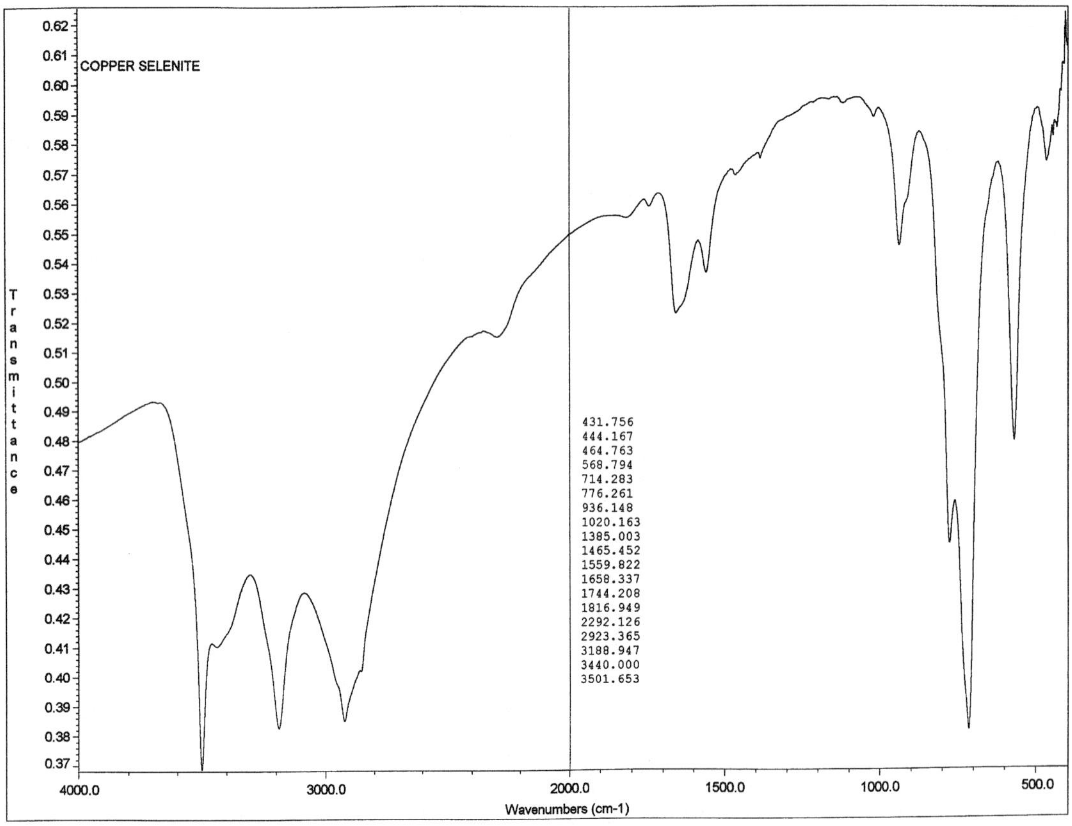

223 Copper selenite $Cu(OH)SeO_3H \cdot H_2O$

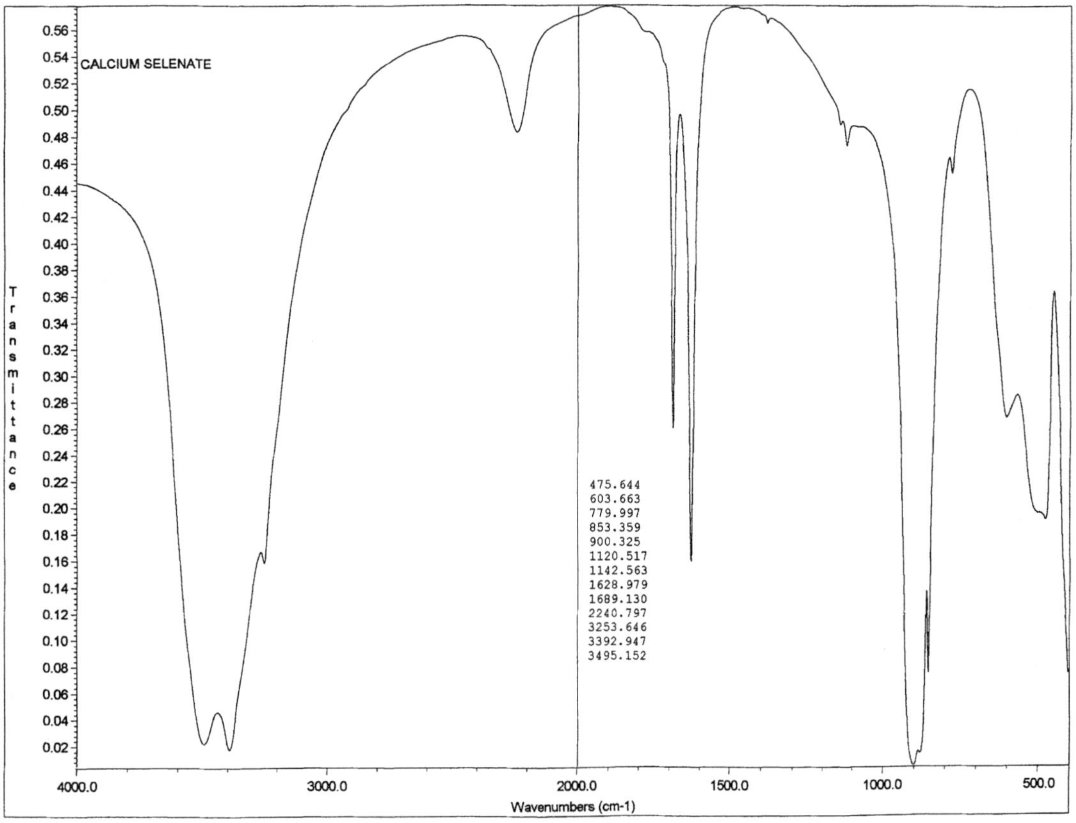

225 Calcium selenate $CaSeO_4 \cdot 2H_2O$

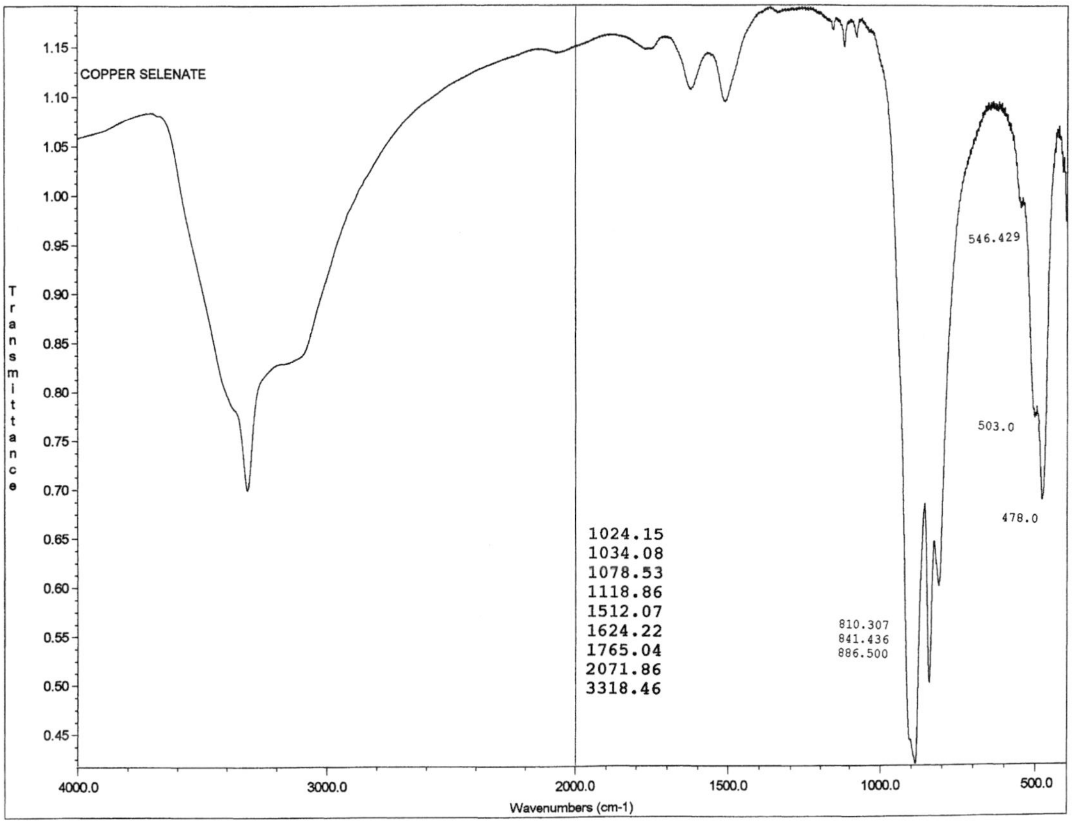

226 Copper (II) selenate $CuSeO_4 \cdot 5H_2O$

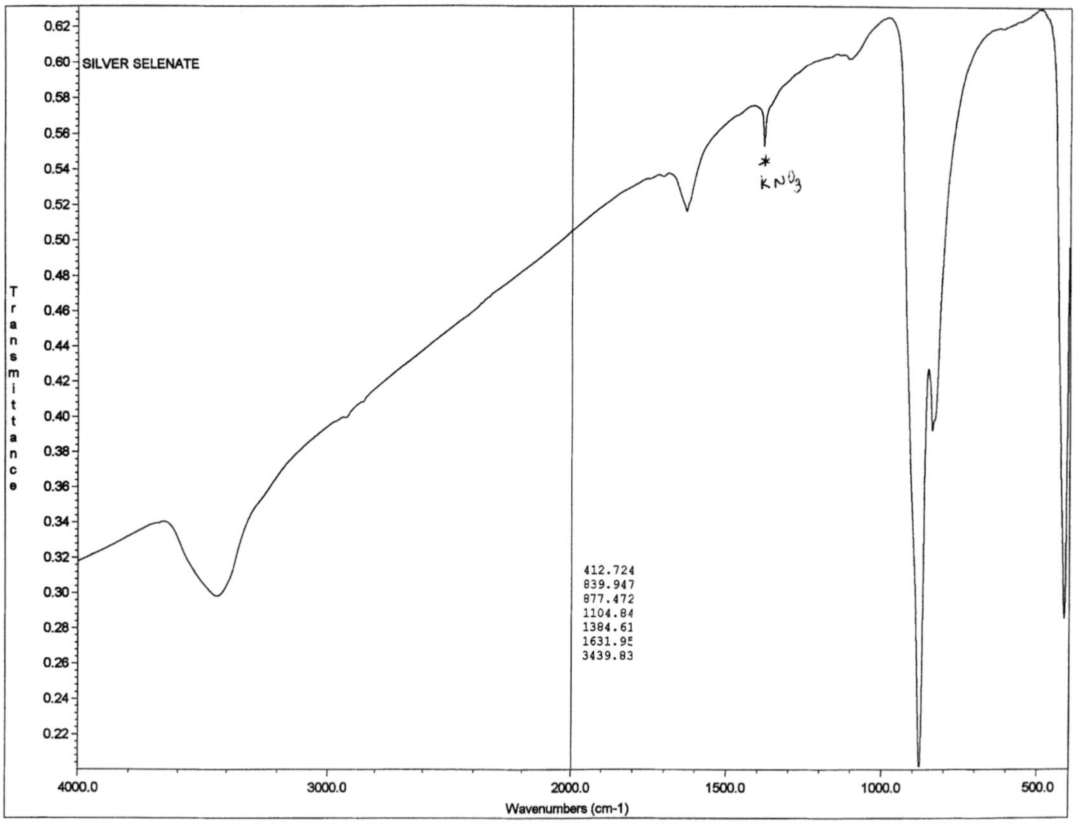

228 Silver selenate $Ag_2SeO_4 \cdot xH_2O$ or wet

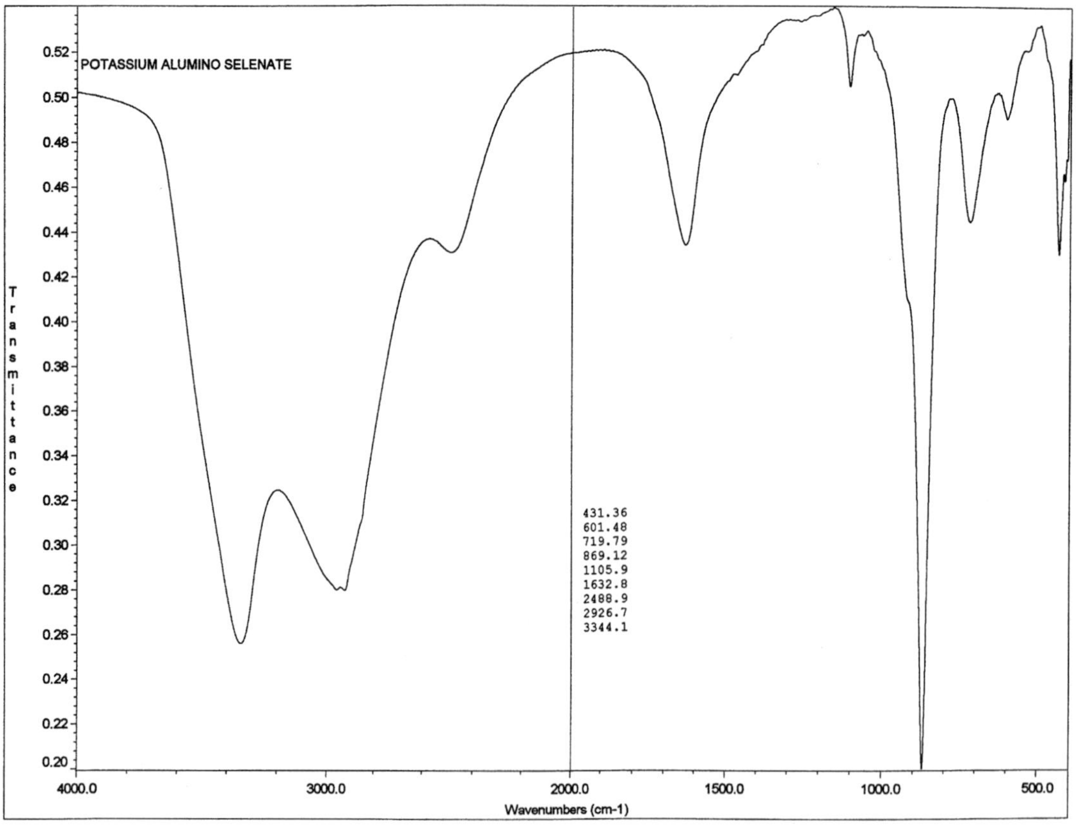

229 Potassium alumino selenate $KAl(SeO_4)_2 \cdot 8H_2O$

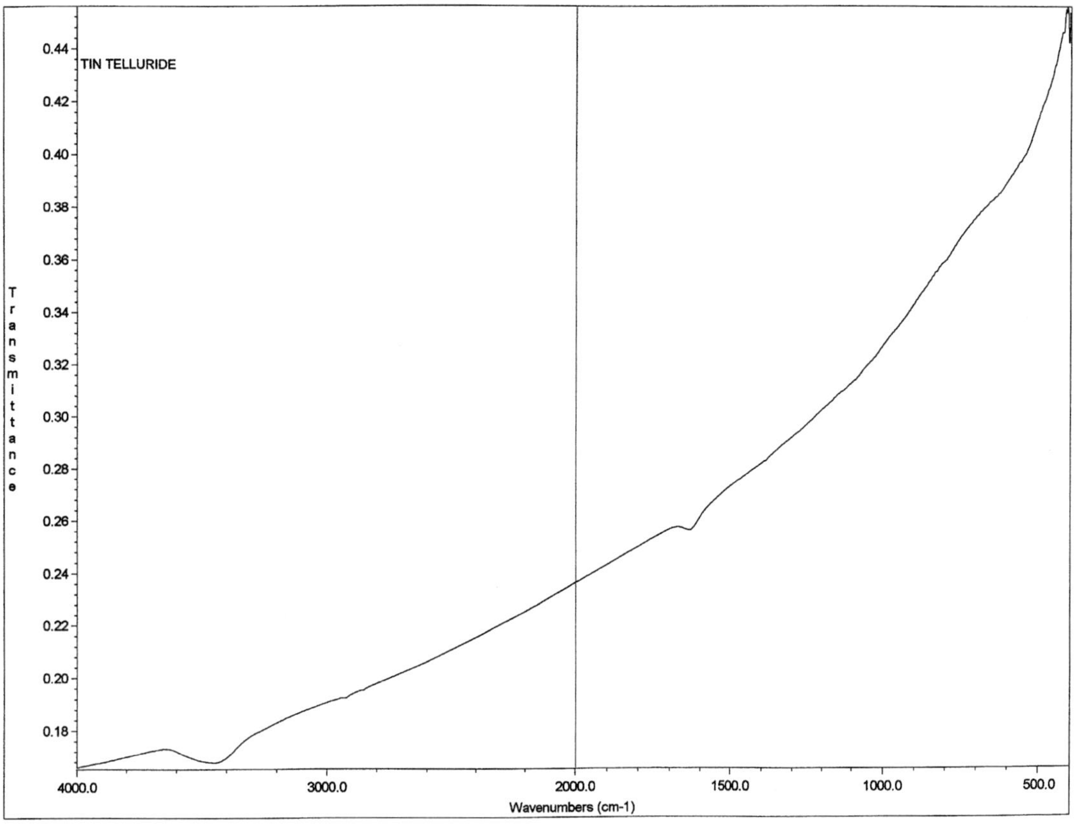

230 Tin (II) telluride SnTe

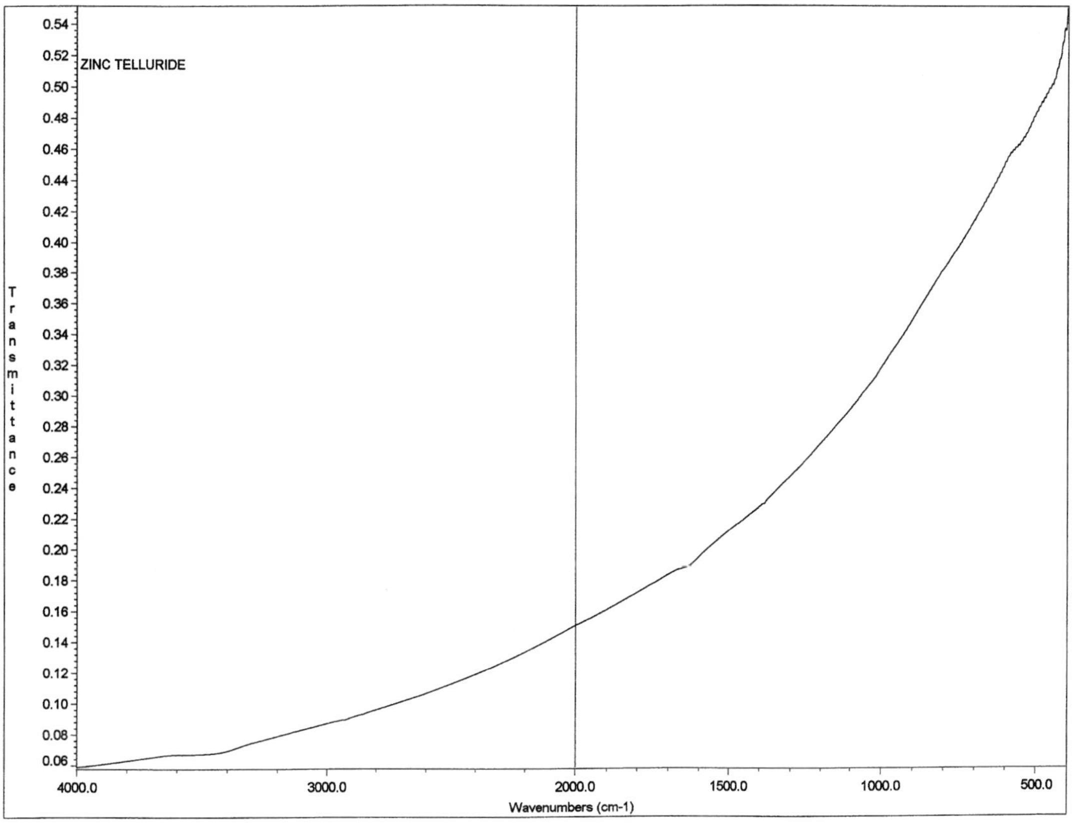

230a Zinc telluride ZnTe

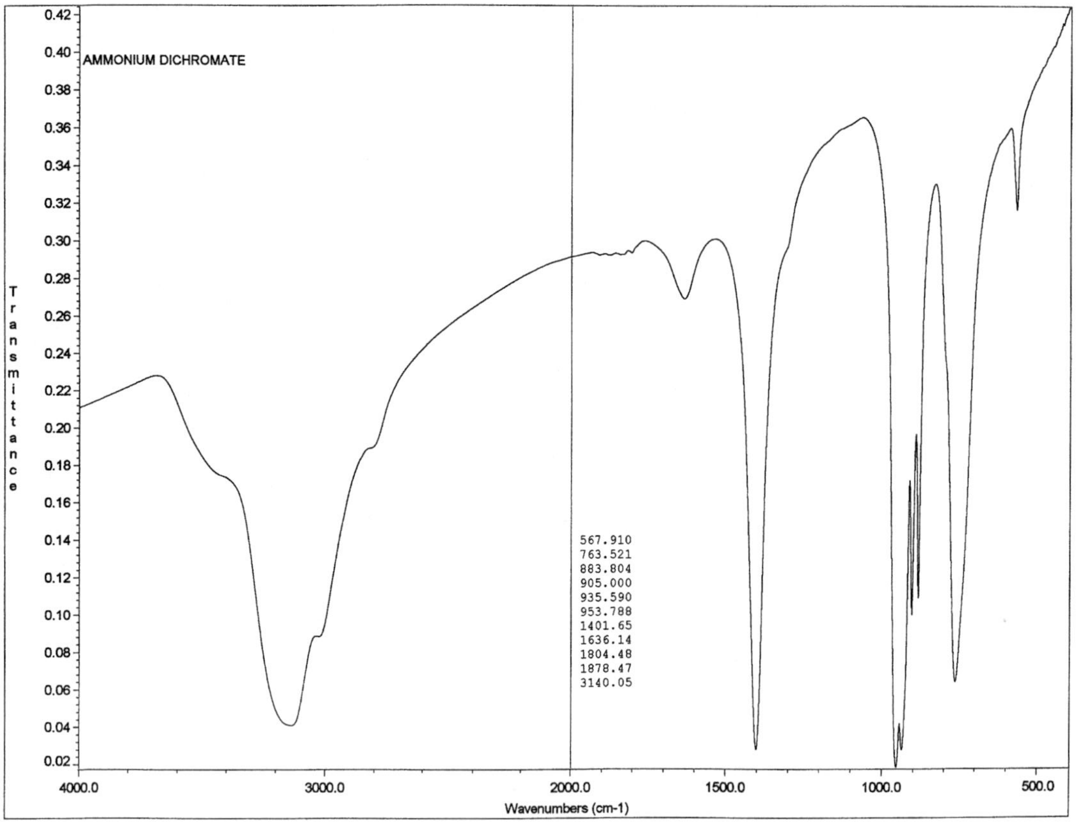

231 Ammonium dichromate $(NH_4)_2Cr_2O_7$

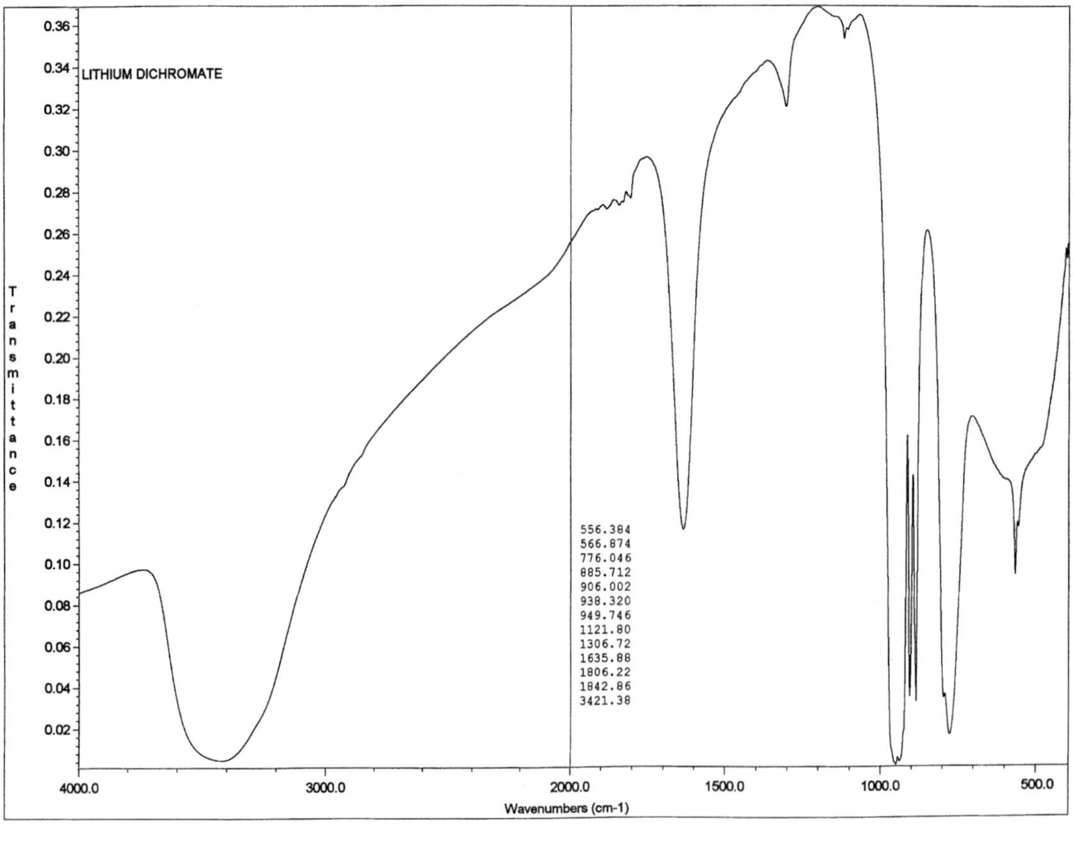

232 Lithium dichromate $Li_2Cr_2O_7 \cdot 2H_2O$

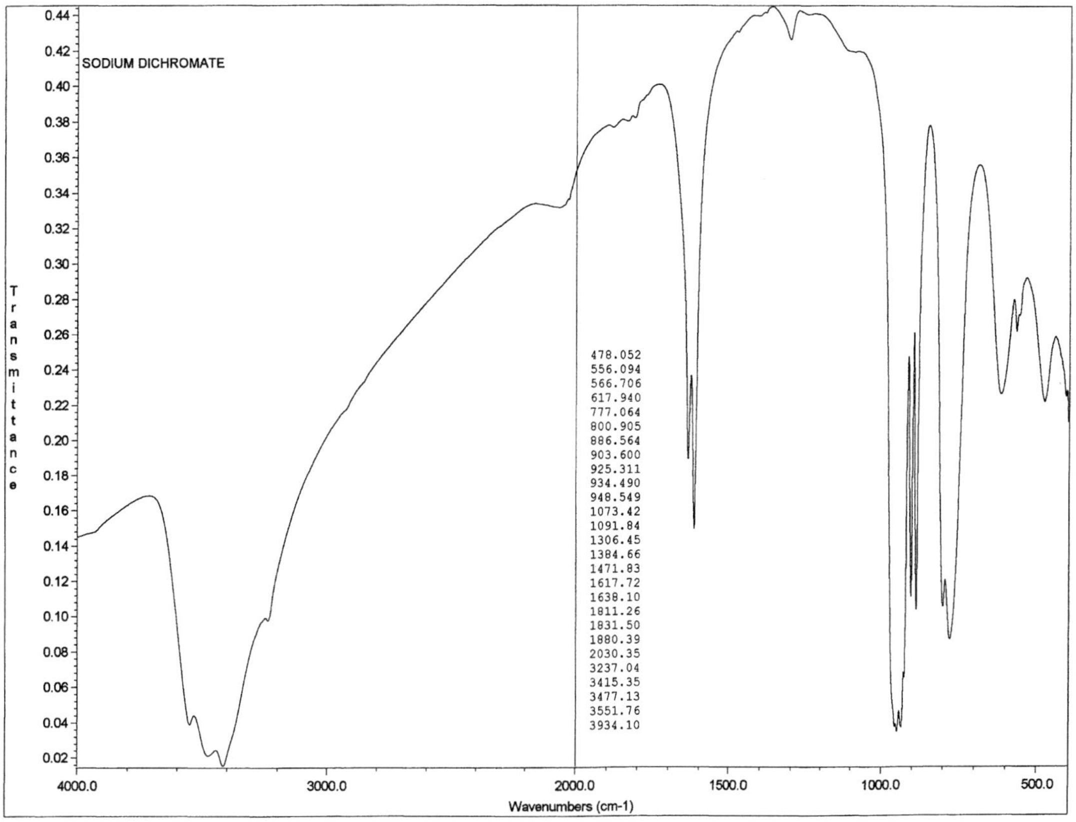

233 Sodium dichromate $Na_2Cr_2O_7 \cdot 2H_2O$

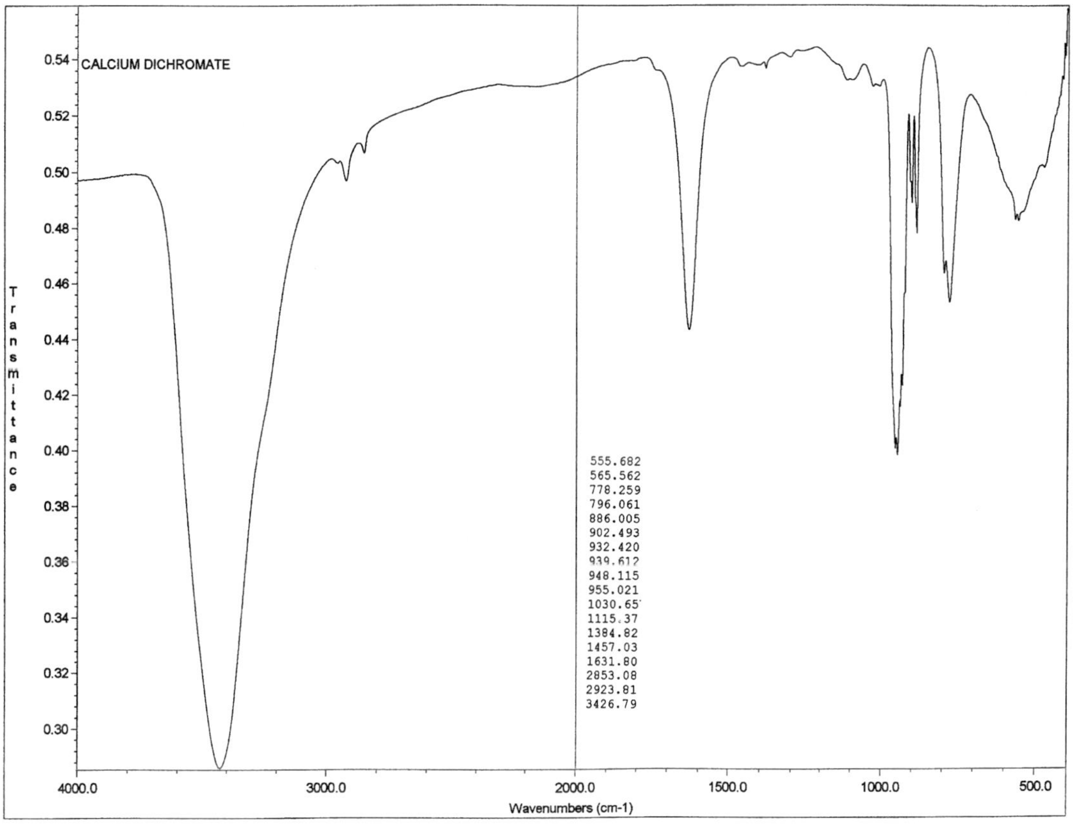

235 Calcium dichromate $CaCr_2O_7 \cdot xH_2O$

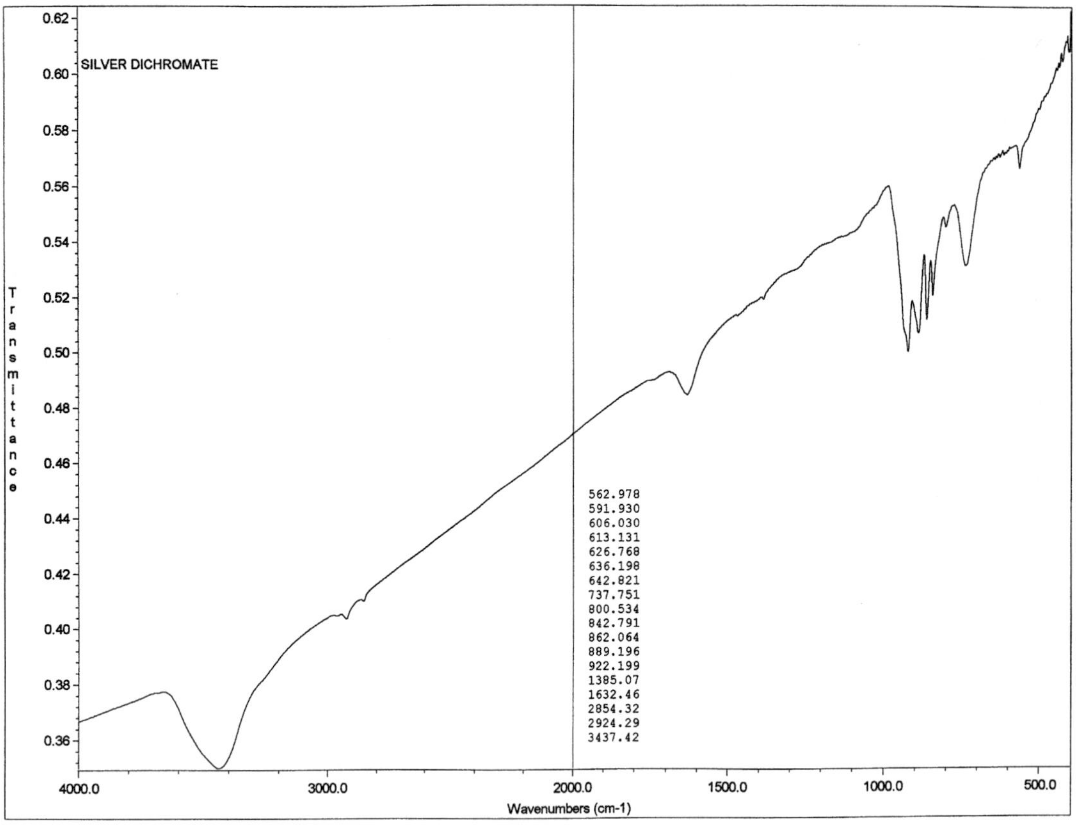

236 Silver dichromate $Ag_2Cr_2O_7 \cdot xH_2O$ or wet

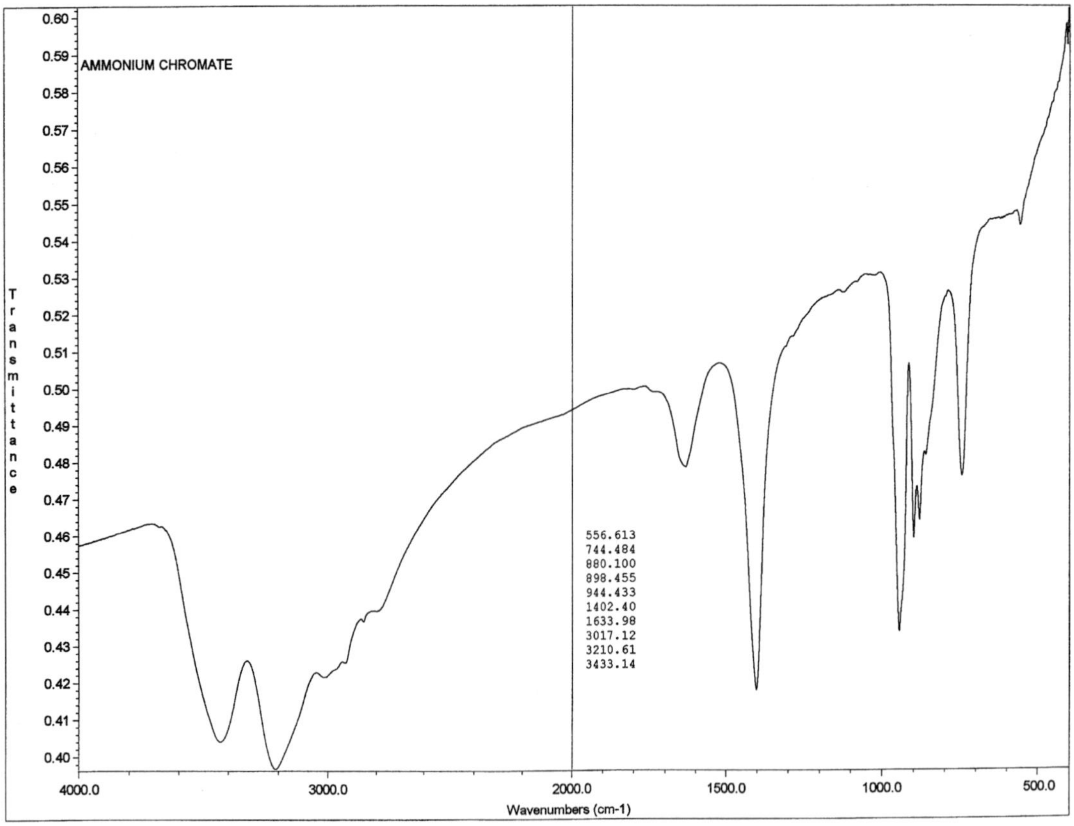

237 Ammonium chromate $(NH_4)_2CrO_4 \cdot xH_2O$

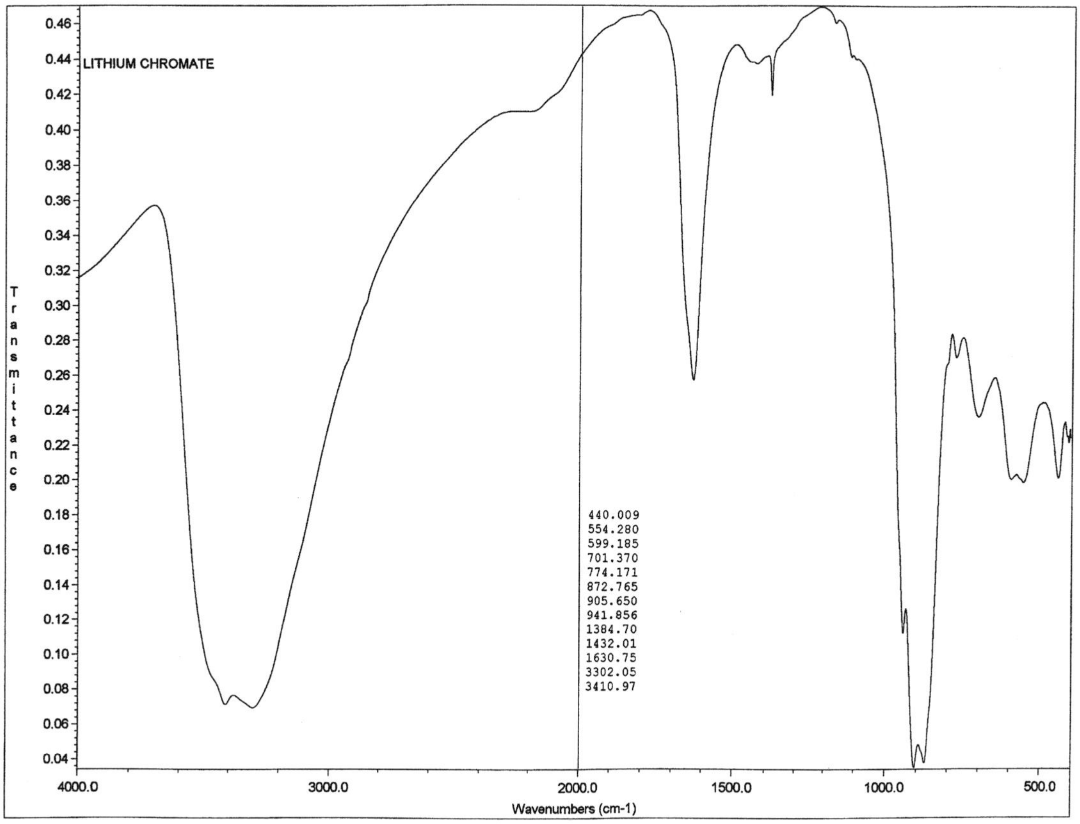

238 Lithium chromate $Li_2CrO_4 \cdot xH_2O$

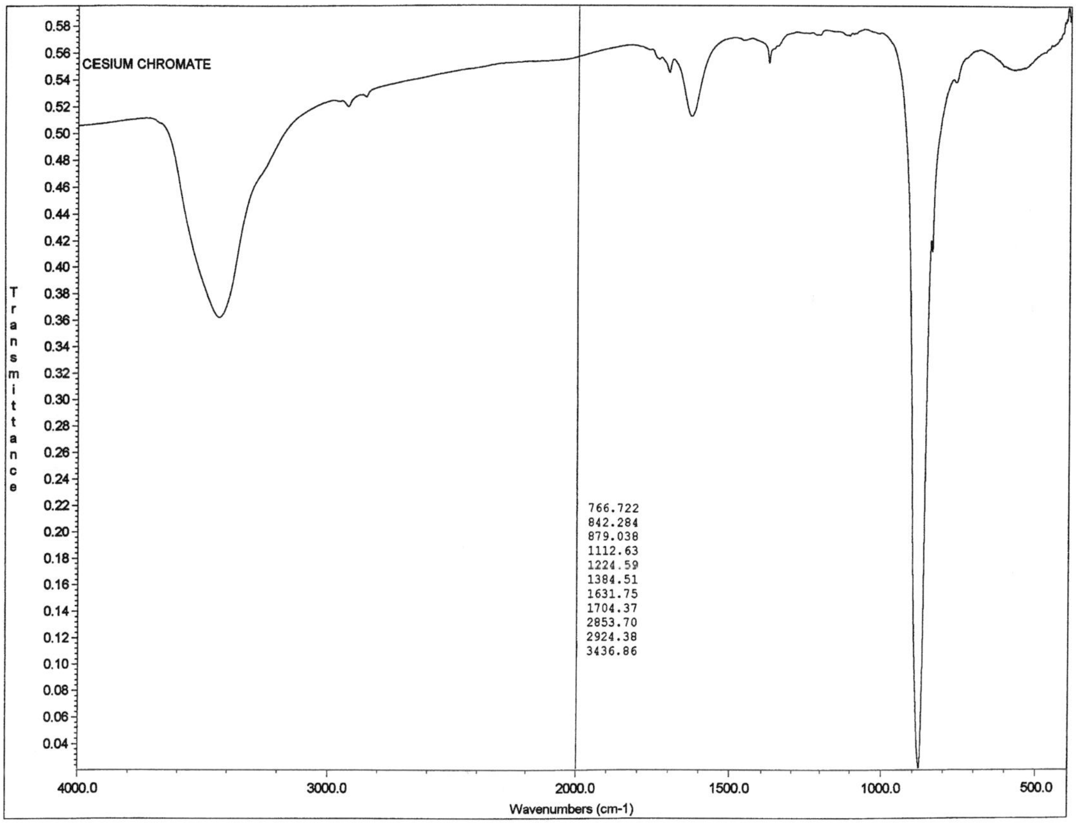

241 Cesium chromate Cs_2CrO_4

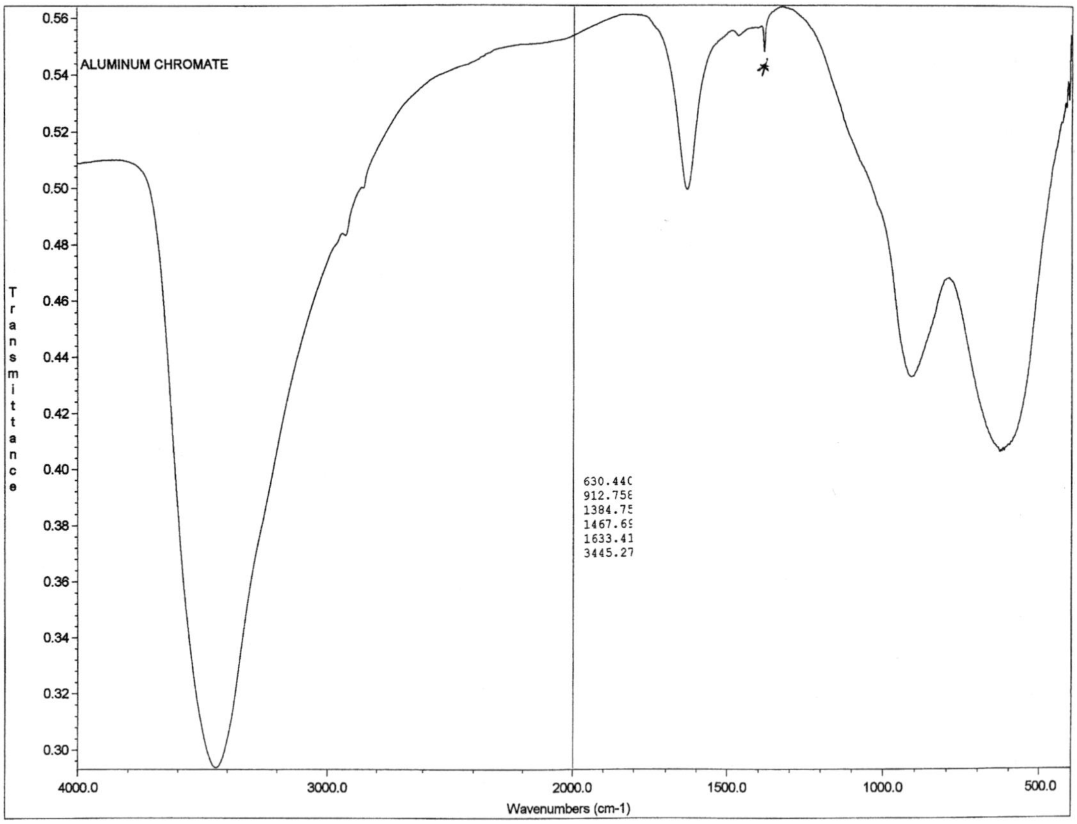

244 Aluminum chromate $Al_2(CrO_4)_3 \cdot xH_2O$

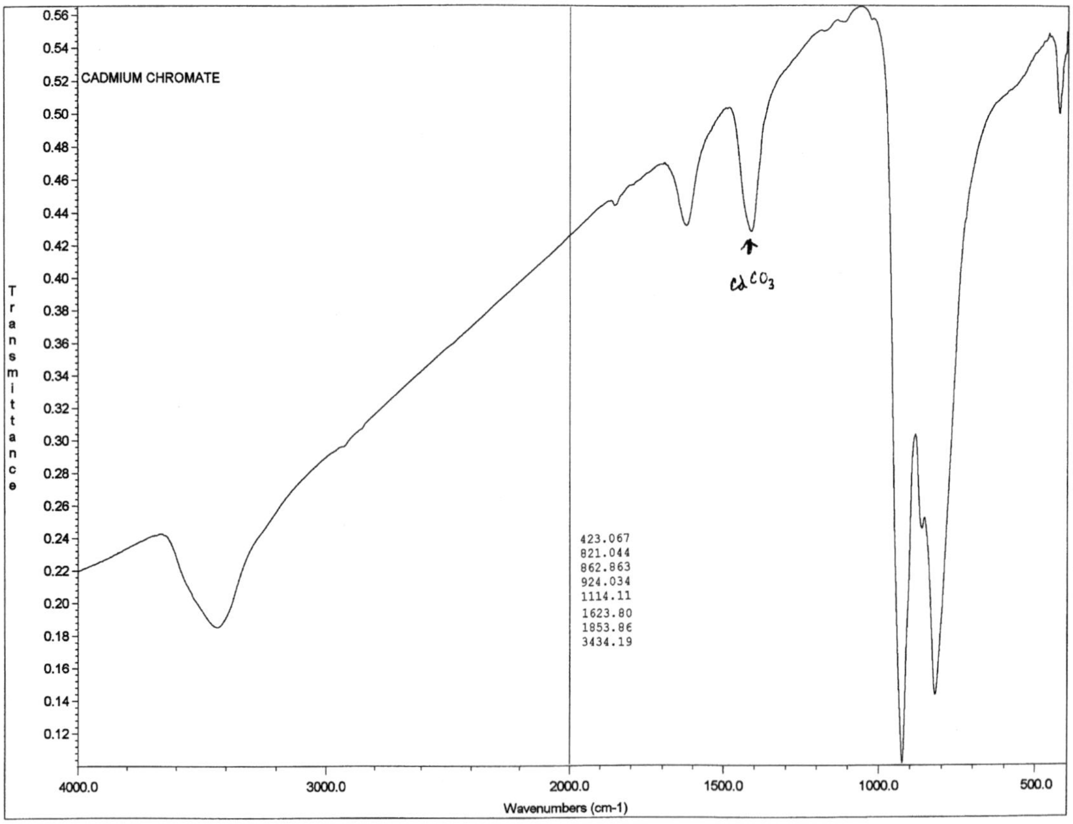

246 Cadmium chromate (carbonate imp) $CdCrO_4$

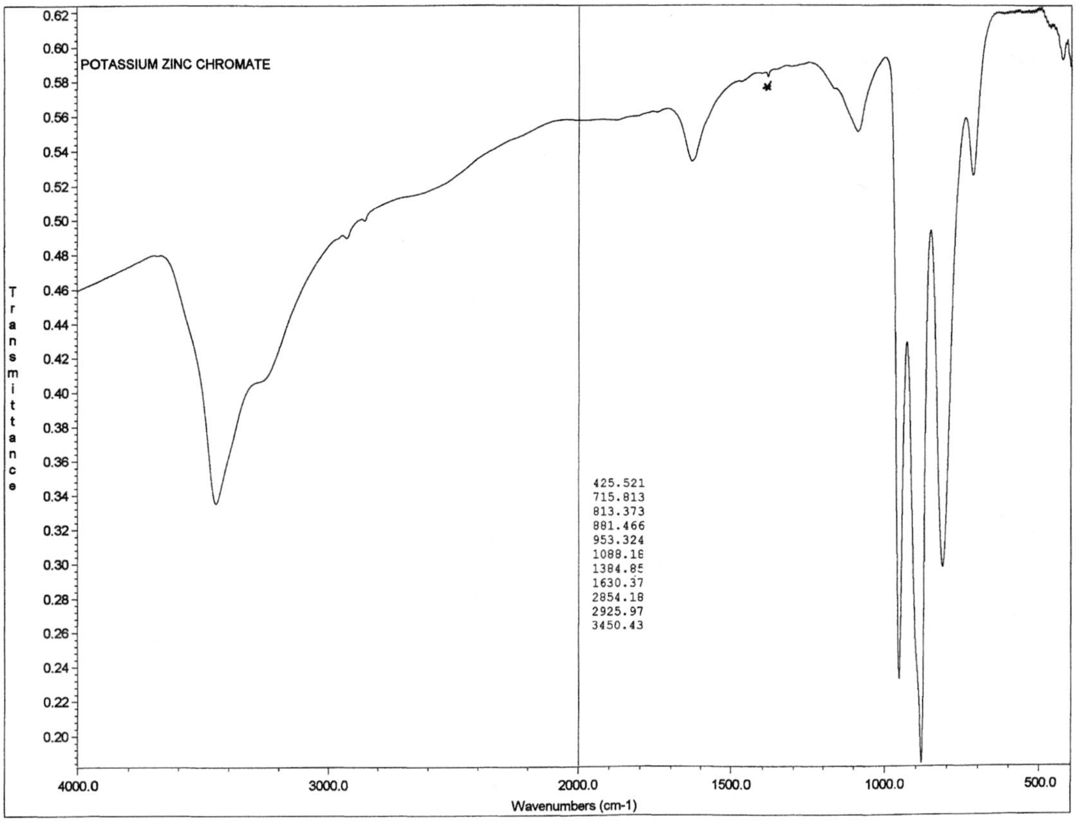

247 Potassium zinc chromate $K_2CrO_4 \cdot 3ZnCrO_4 \cdot Zn(OH)_2$

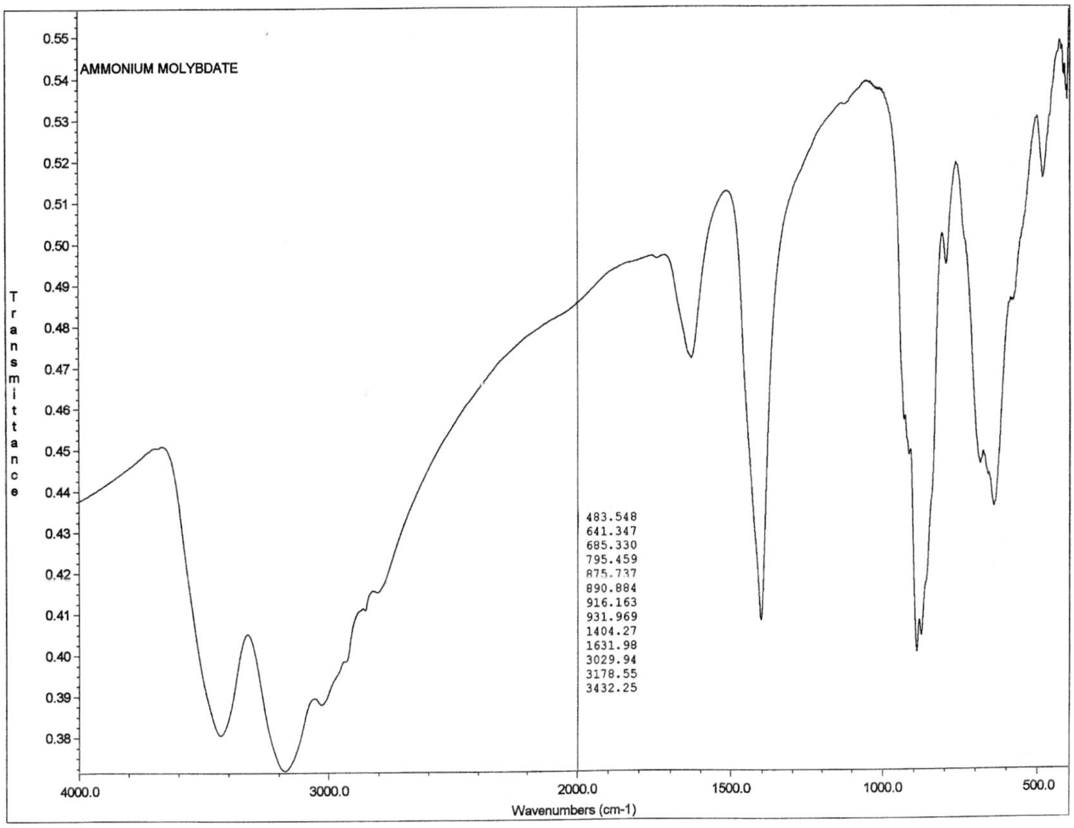

248 Ammonium molybdate (VI) $(NH_4)_2MoO_4$

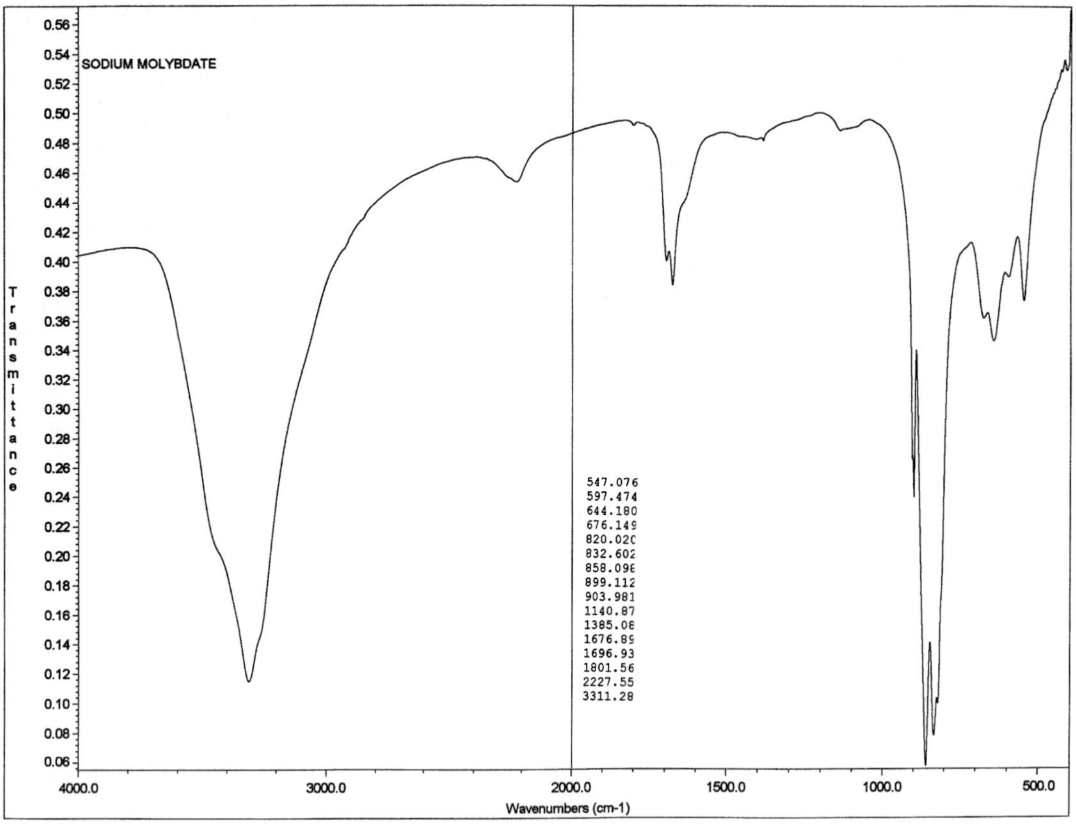

249 Sodium molybdate (VI) $Na_2MoO_4 \cdot 2H_2O$

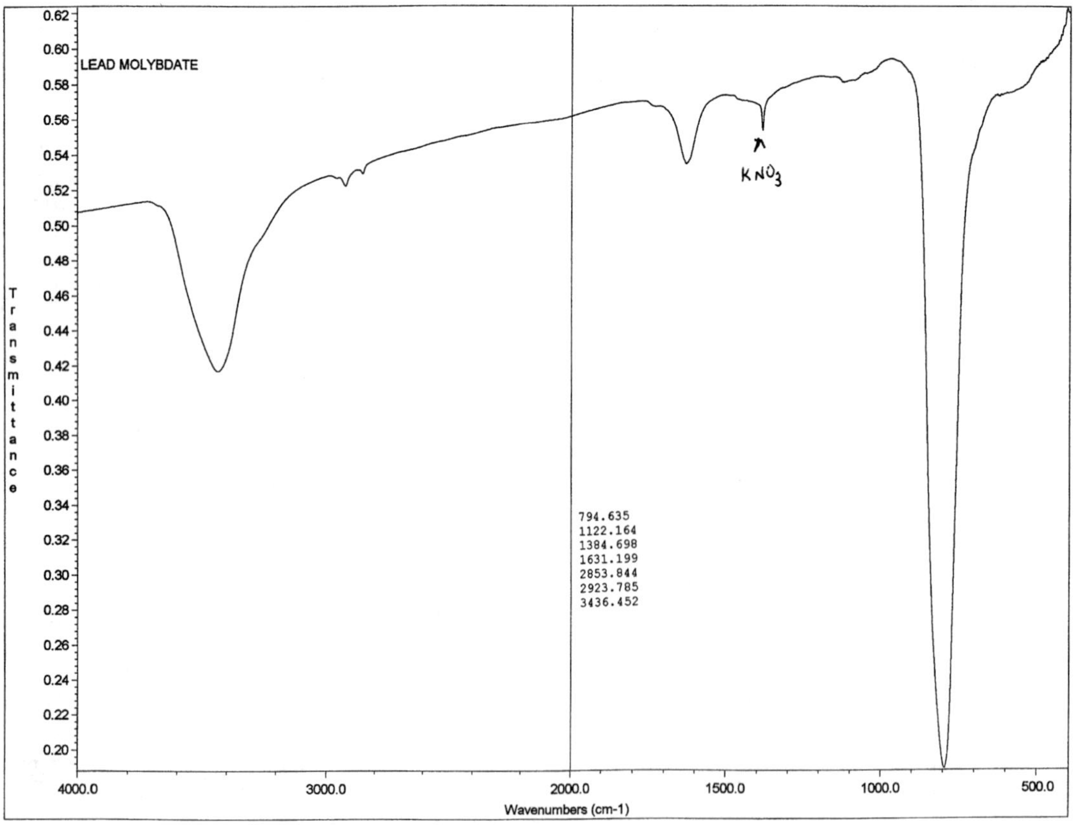

250 Lead molybdate (VI) $PbMoO_4 \cdot xH_2O$ or wet

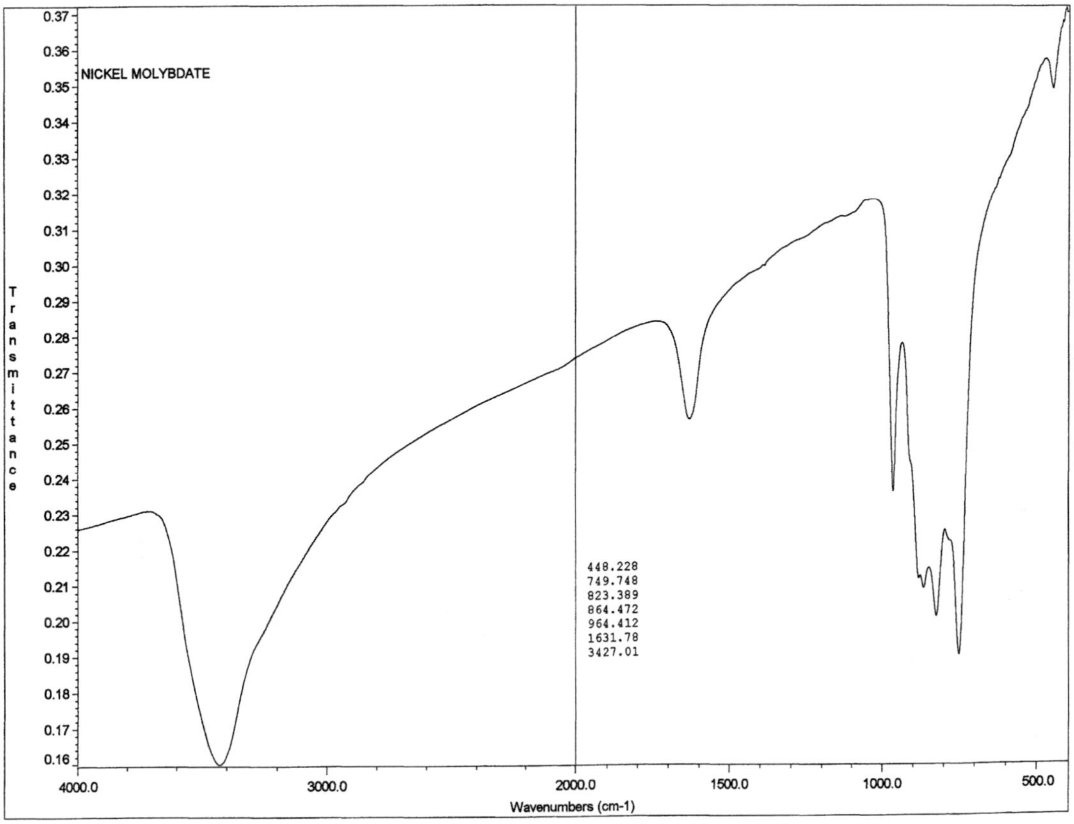

251 Nickel molybdate (VI) $NiMoO_4 \cdot H_2O$ or wet

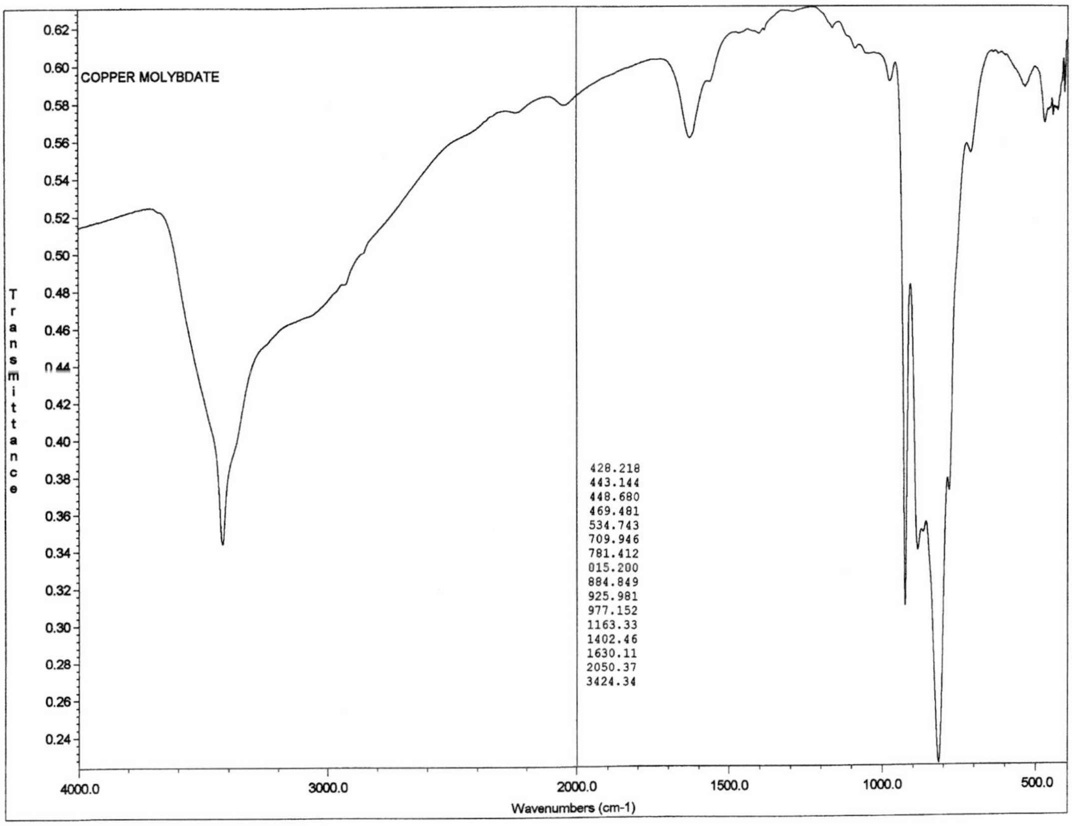

252 Copper (II) molybdate (VI) $CuMoO_4 \cdot xH_2O$

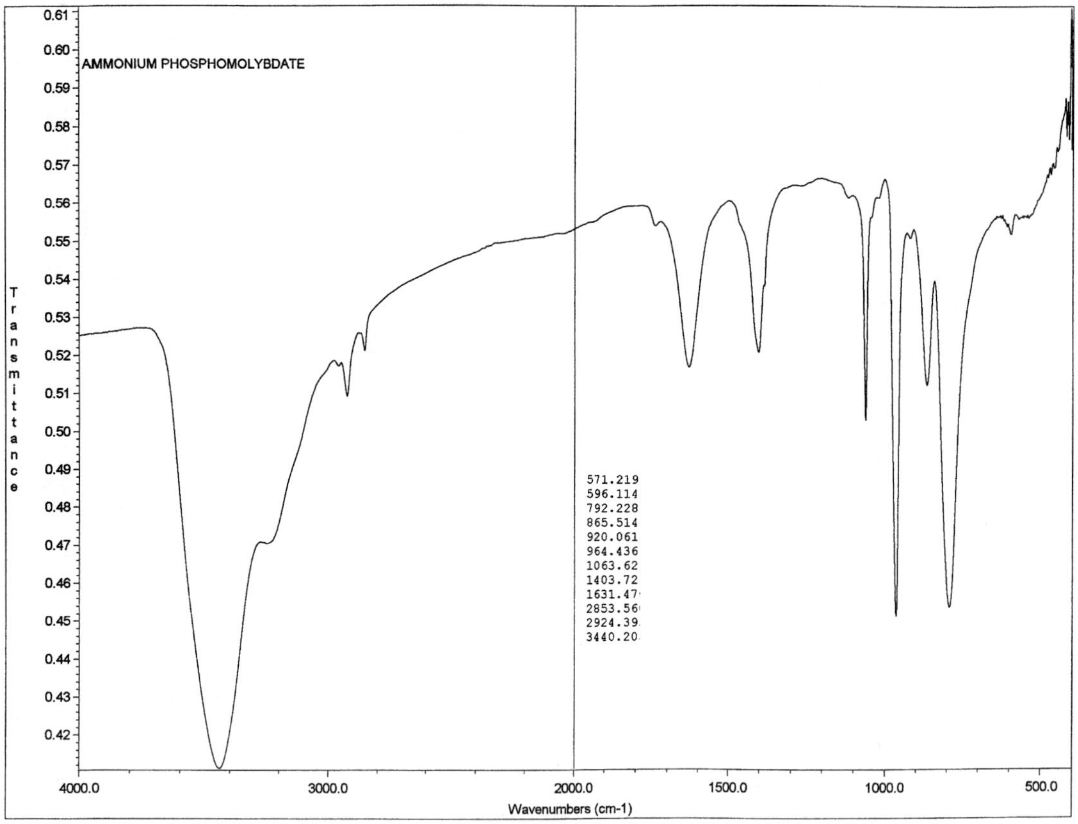

253 Ammonium phosphomolybdate $(NH_4)_3PMo_{12}O_{40}$

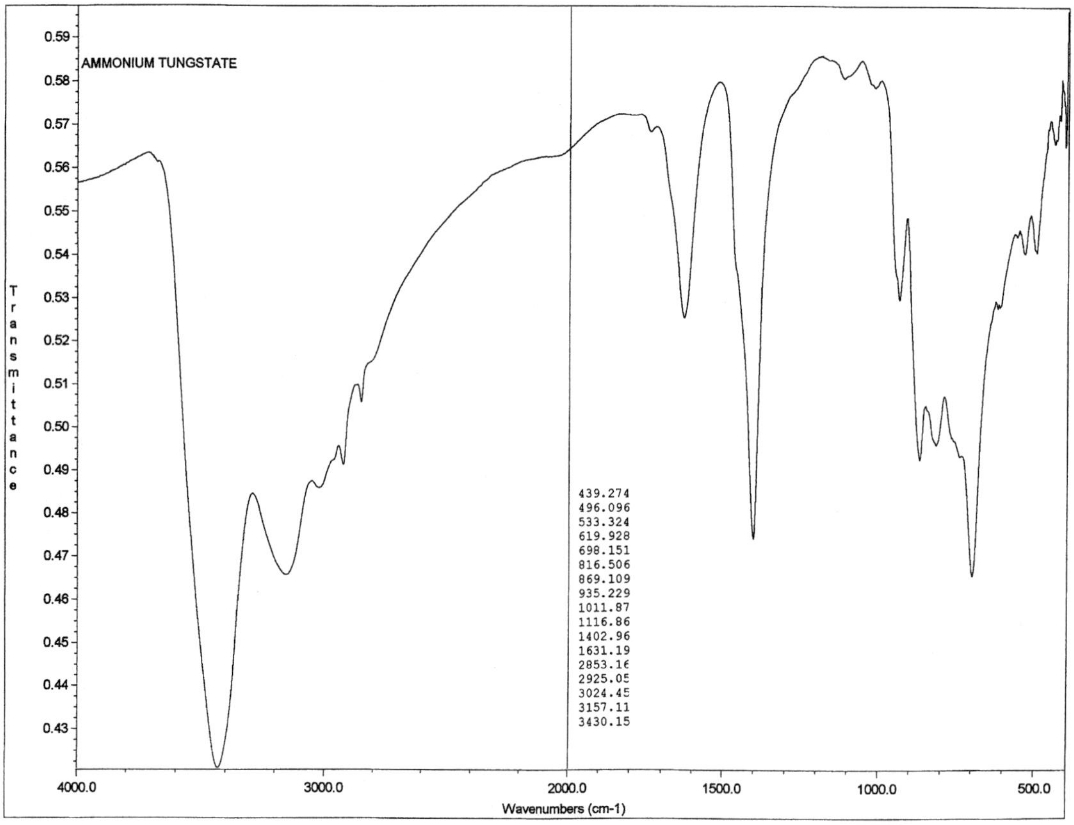

255 Ammonium tungstate $(NH_4)_2WO_4$

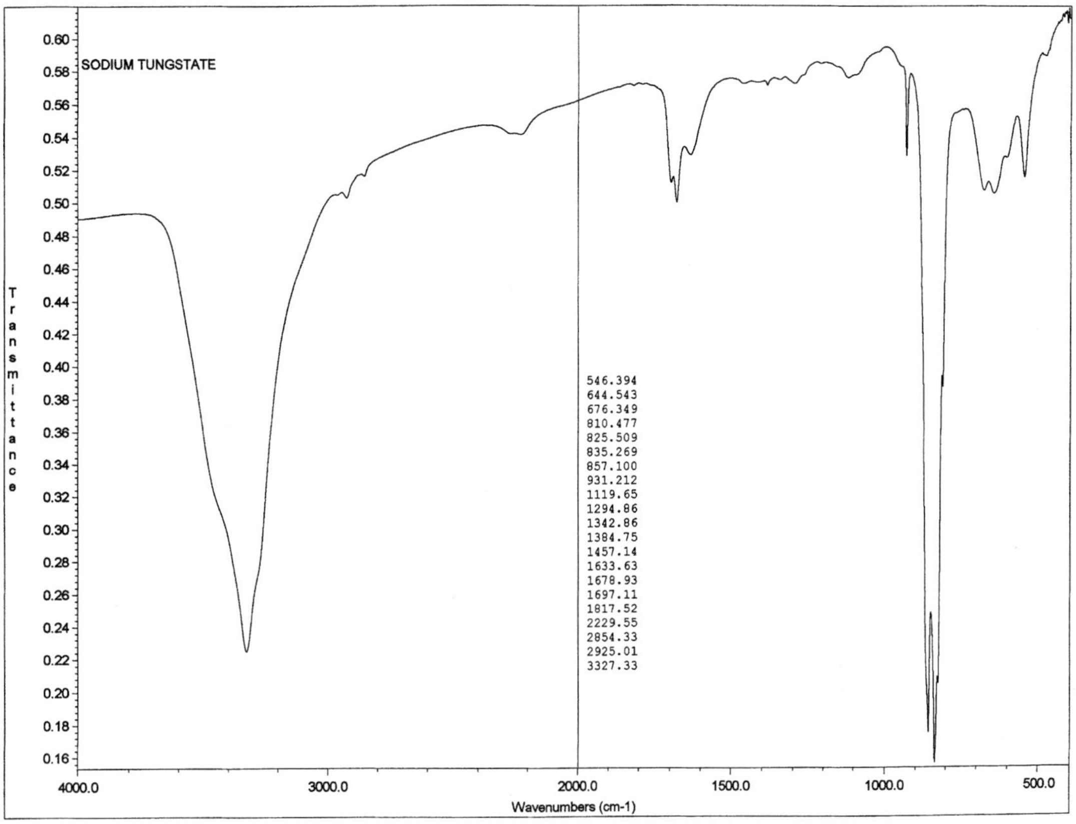

256 Sodium tungstate $Na_2WO_4 \cdot 2H_2O$

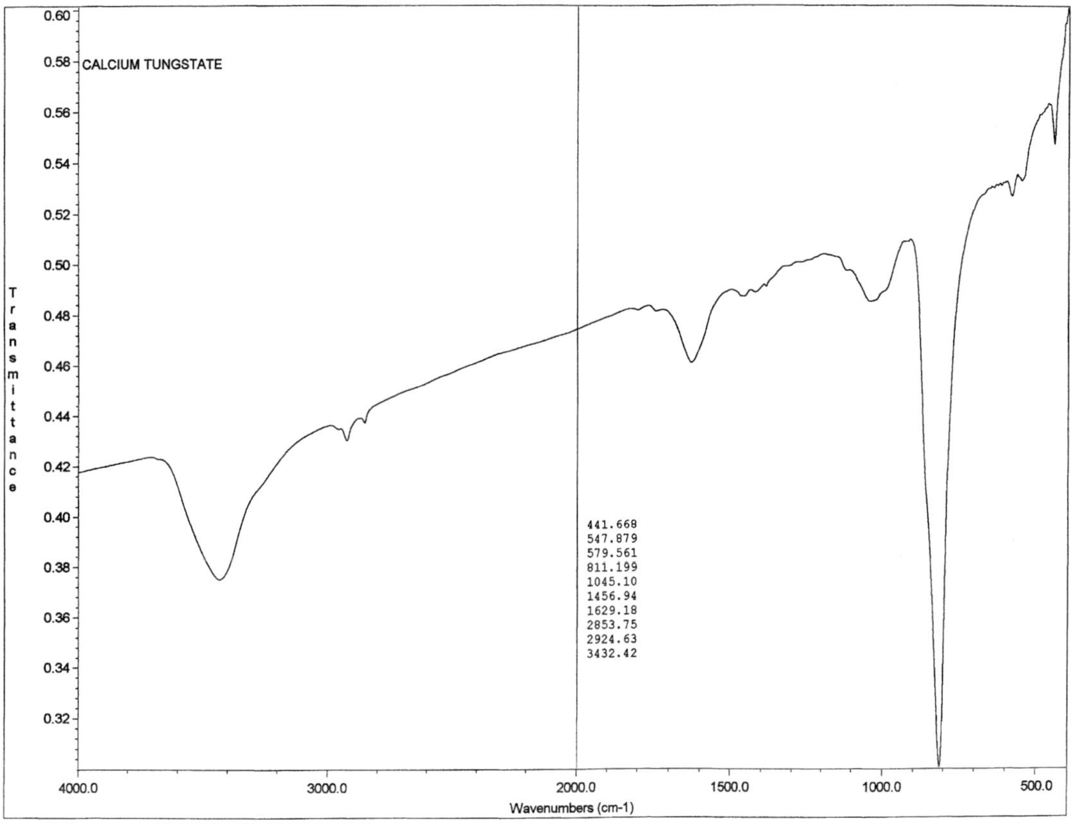

257 Calcium tungstate $CaWO_4$

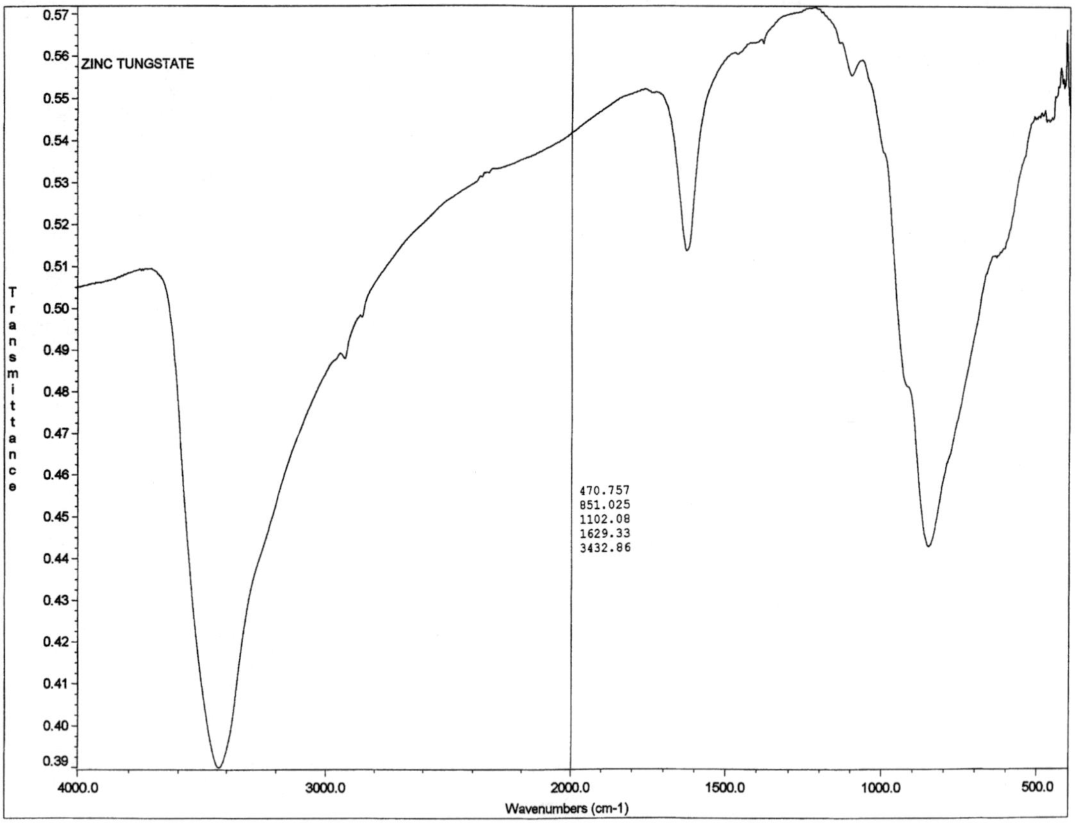

258 Zinc tungstate $ZnWO_4 \cdot xH_2O$

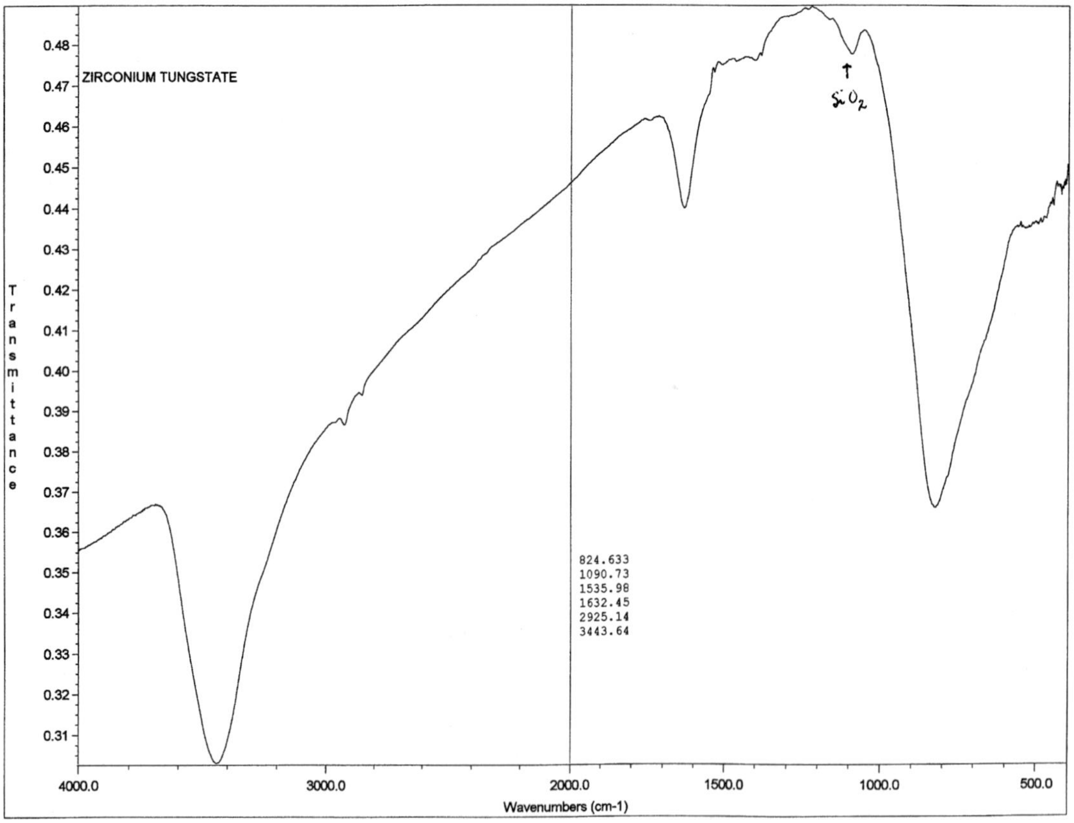

259 Zirconium tungstate $Zr(WO_4)_2 \cdot xH_2O$ or wet

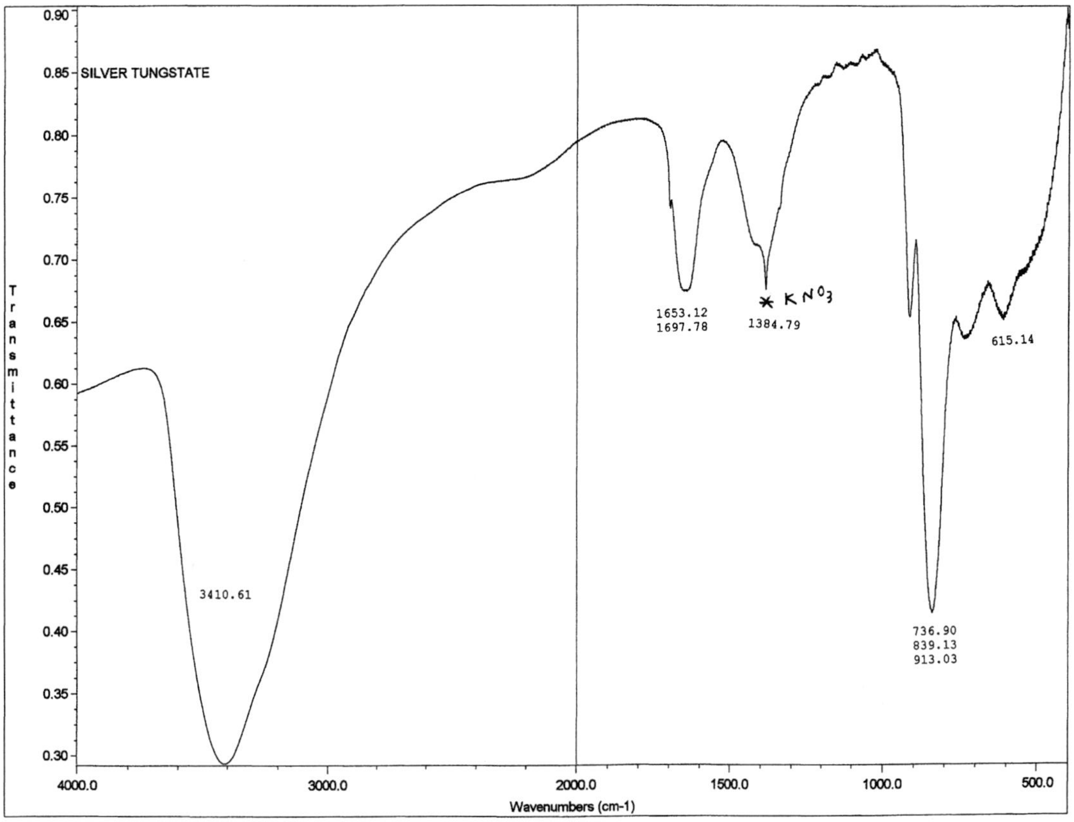

260 Silver tungstate Ag_2WO_4

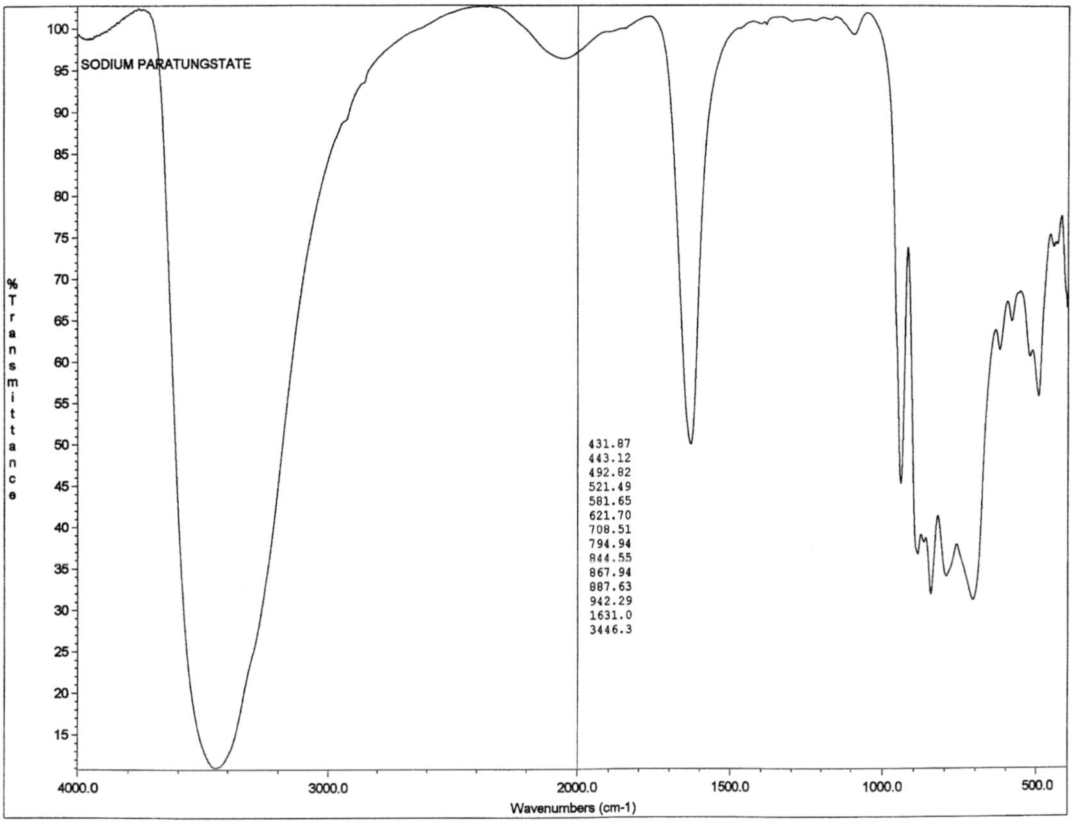

261 Sodium paratungstate $Na_6W_7O_{24} \cdot 16H_2O$

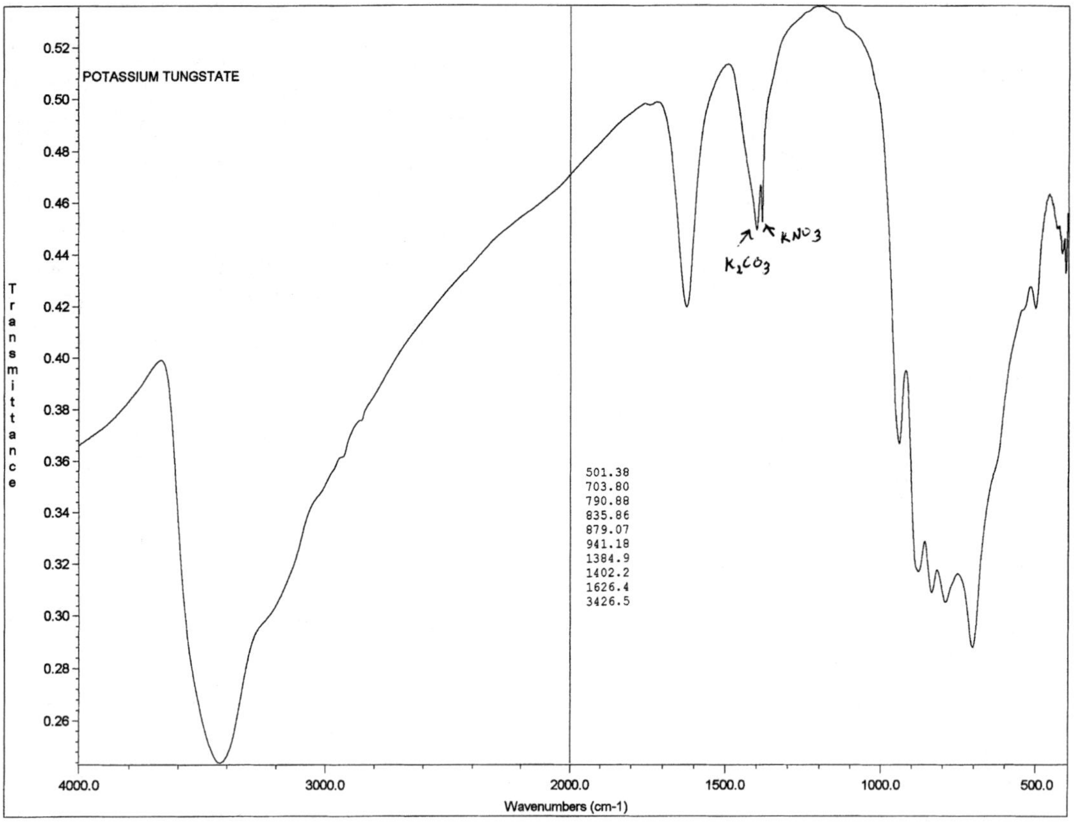

262 Potassium tungstate $K_6W_7O_{24} \cdot xH_2O$

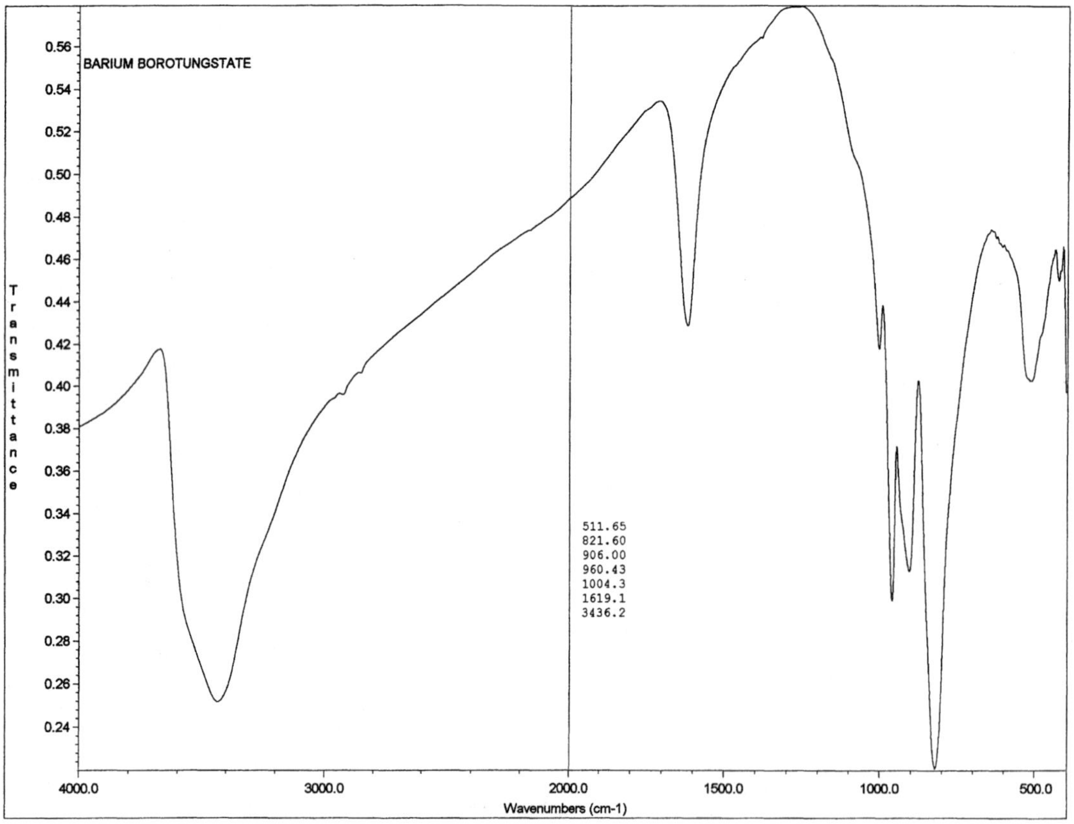

263 Barium borotungstate $Ba_3(BW_{12}O_{40})_2 \cdot xH_2O$

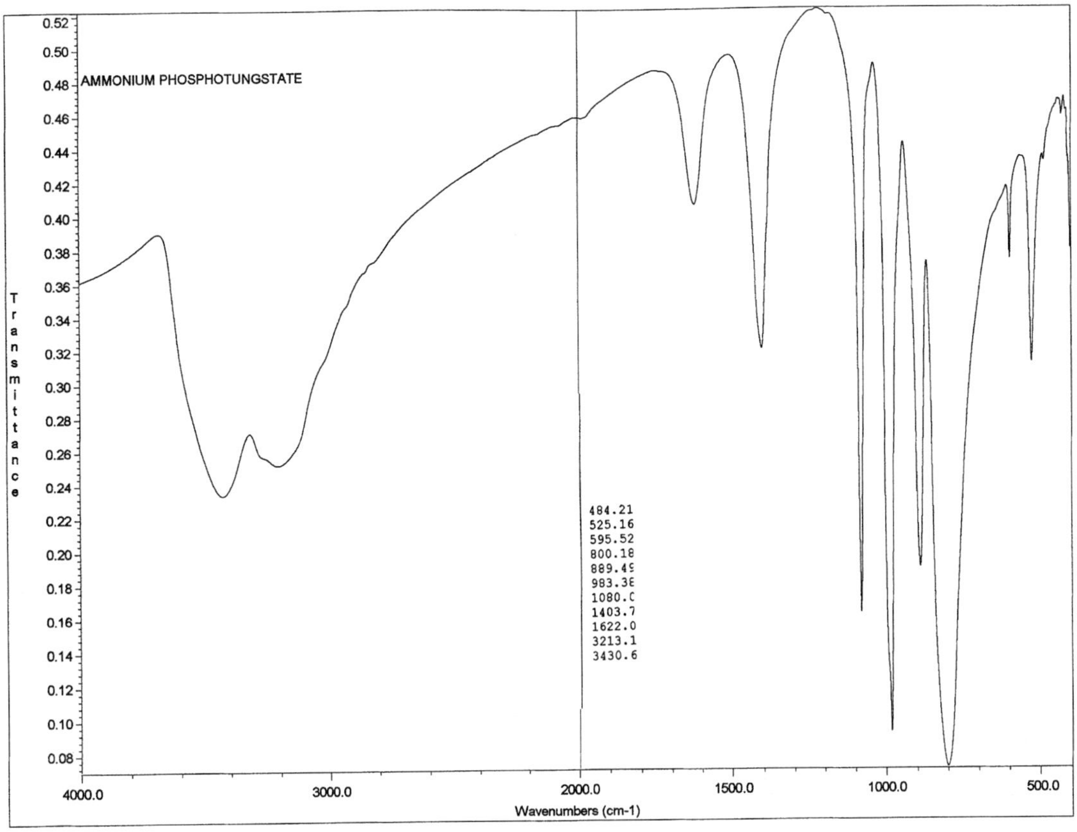

264 Ammonium phosphotungstate $(NH_4)_3PW_{12}O_{40} \cdot 4H_2O$

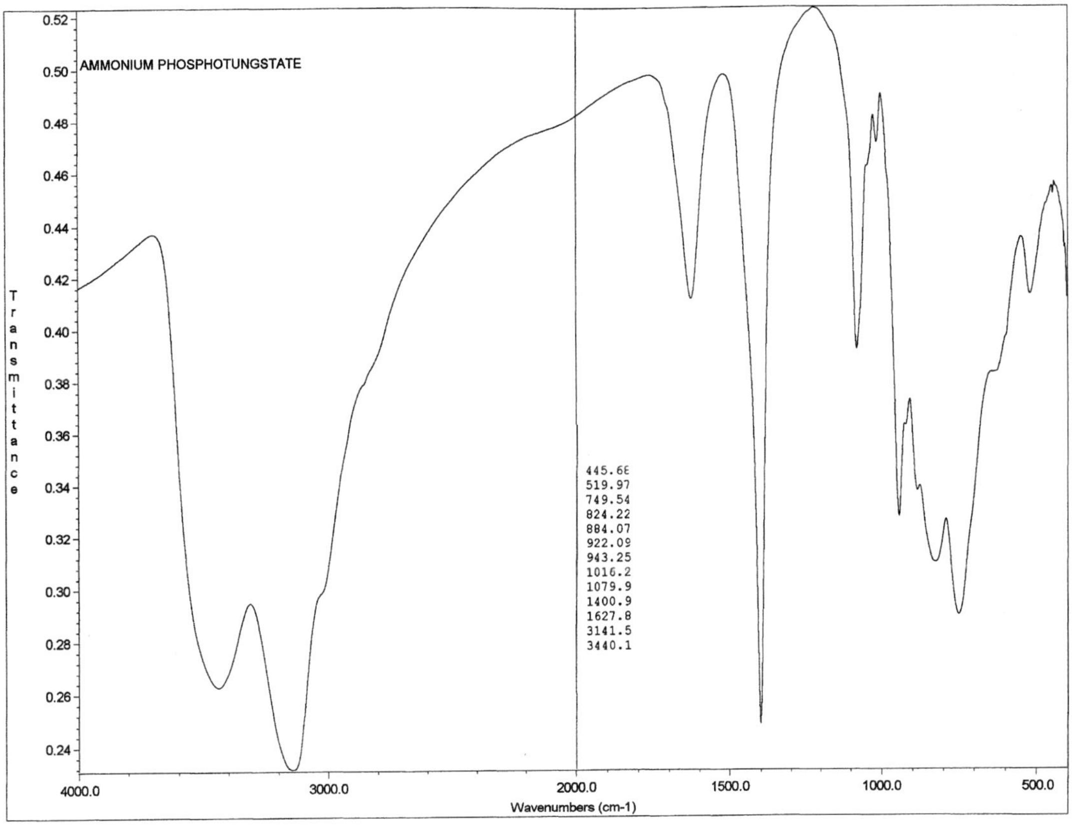

264 Ammonium phosphotungstate $(NH_4)_3PW_{12}O_{40} \cdot 4H_2O$

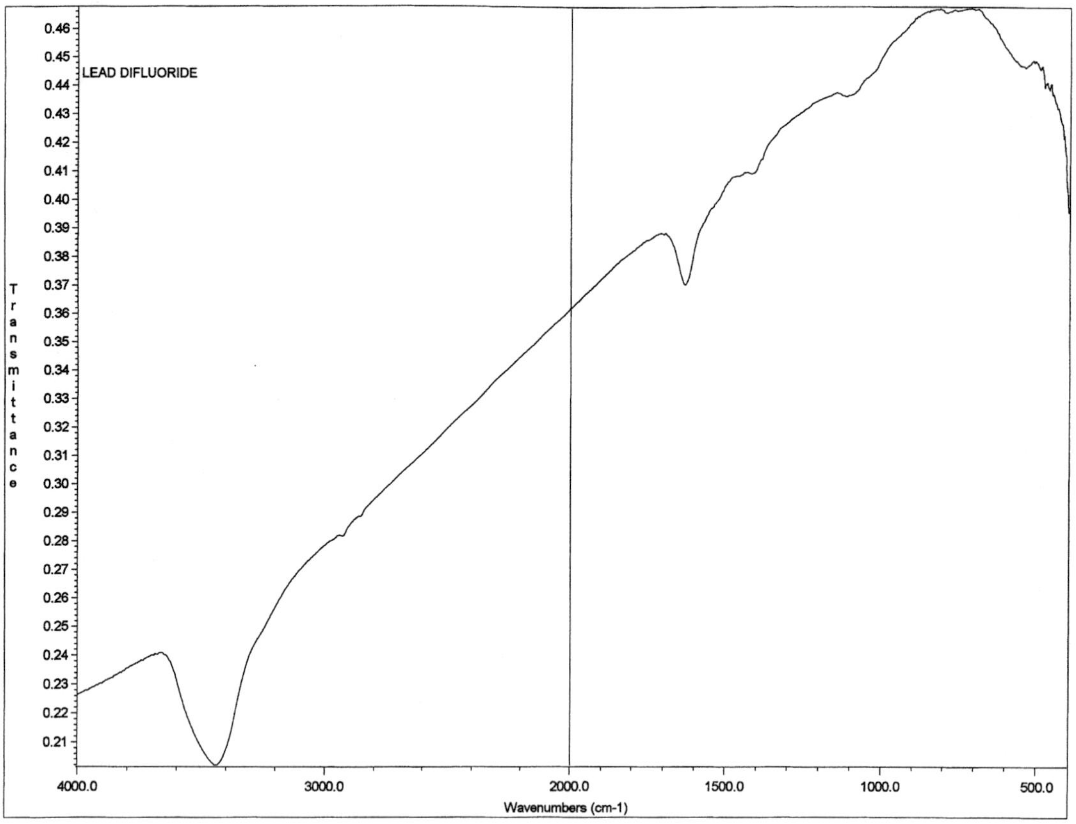

266 Lead difluoride PbF_2

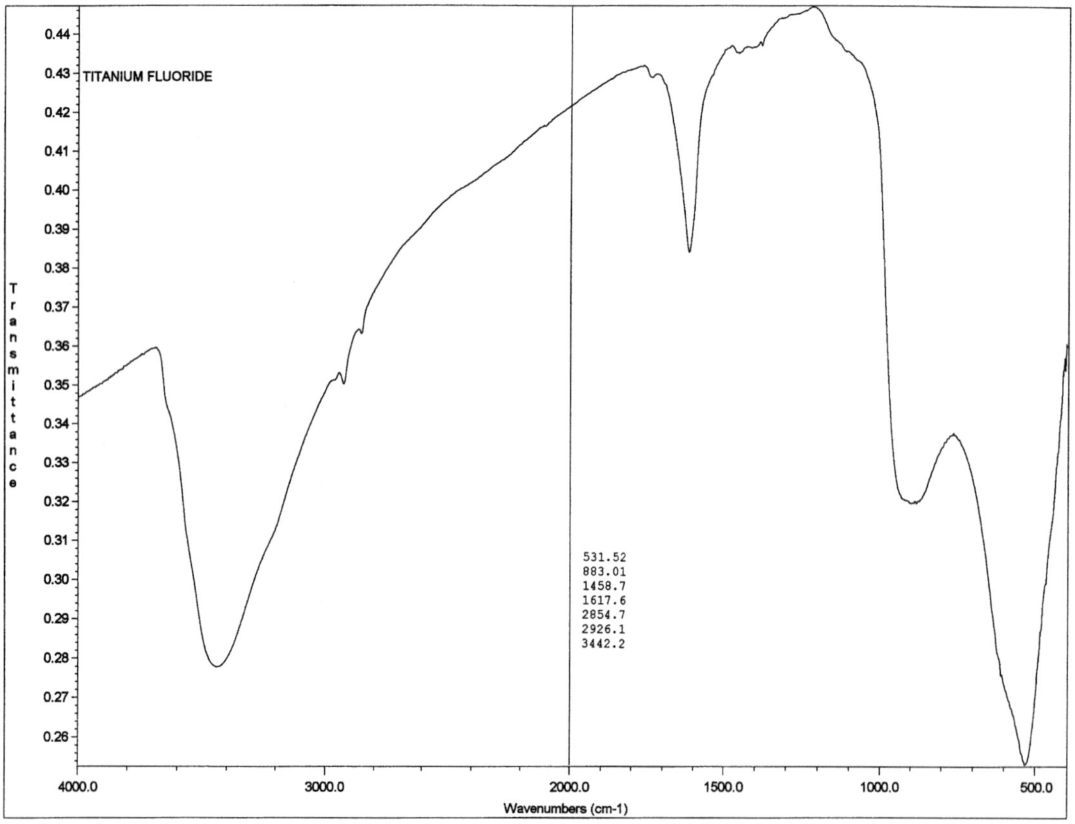

267 Titanium tetrafluoride $TiF_4 \cdot xH_2O$

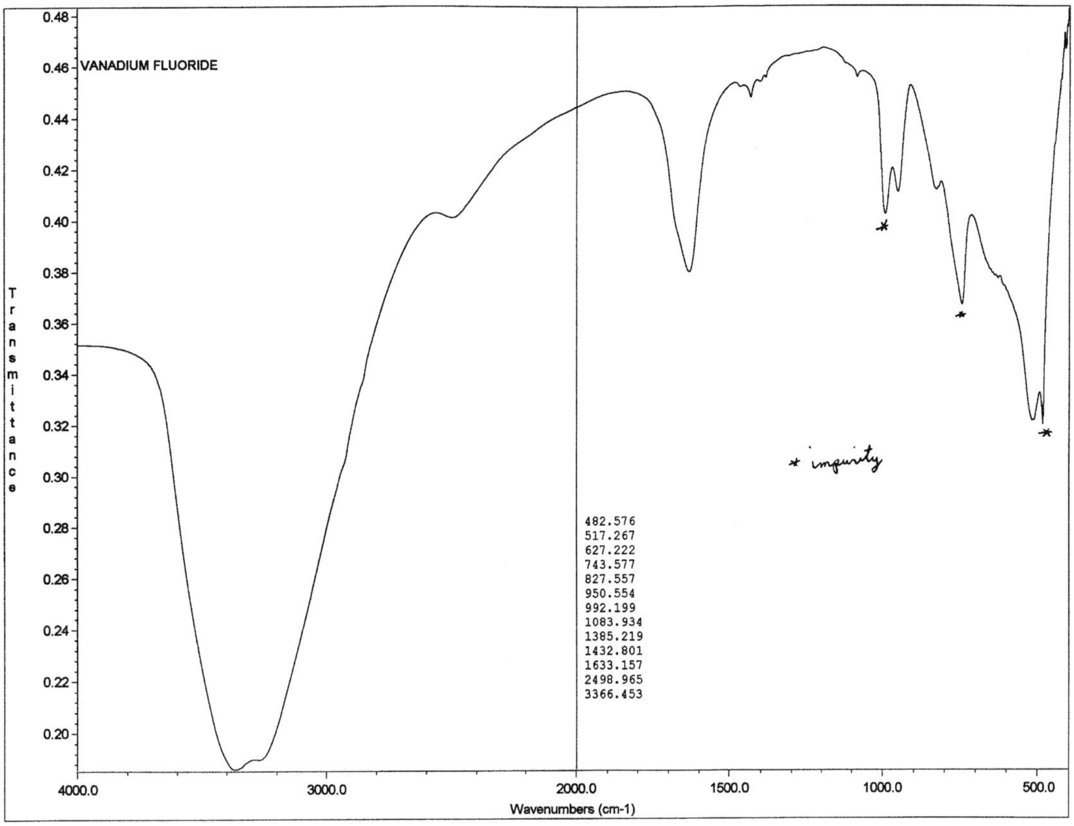

268 Vanadium trifluoride $VF_3 \cdot 3H_2O$

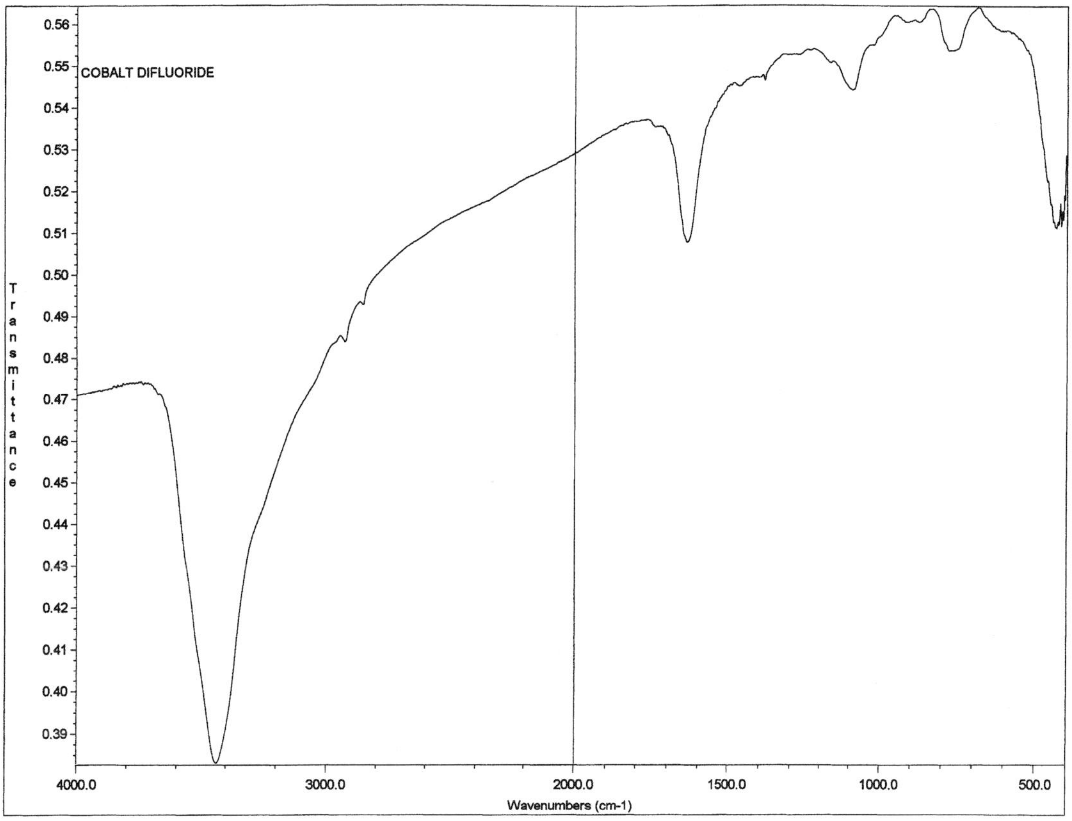

269 Cobalt (II) fluoride $CoF_2 \cdot xH_2O$

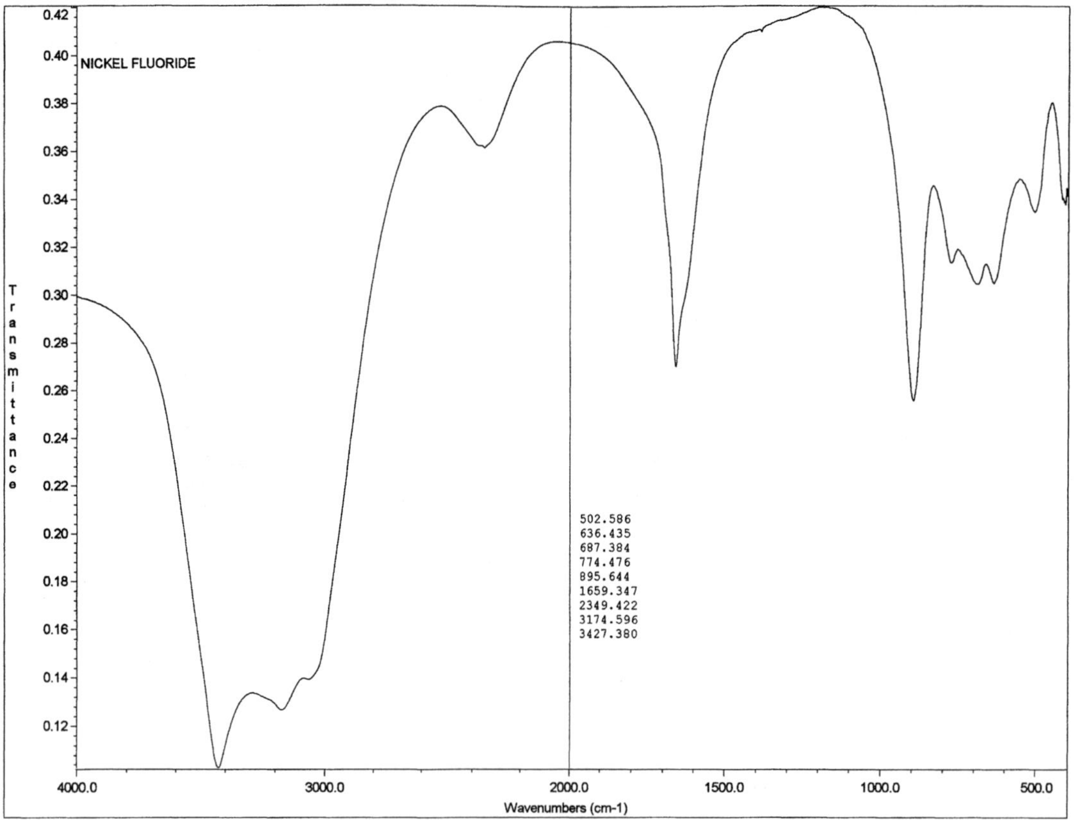

270 Nickel fluoride $NiF_2 \cdot xH_2O$

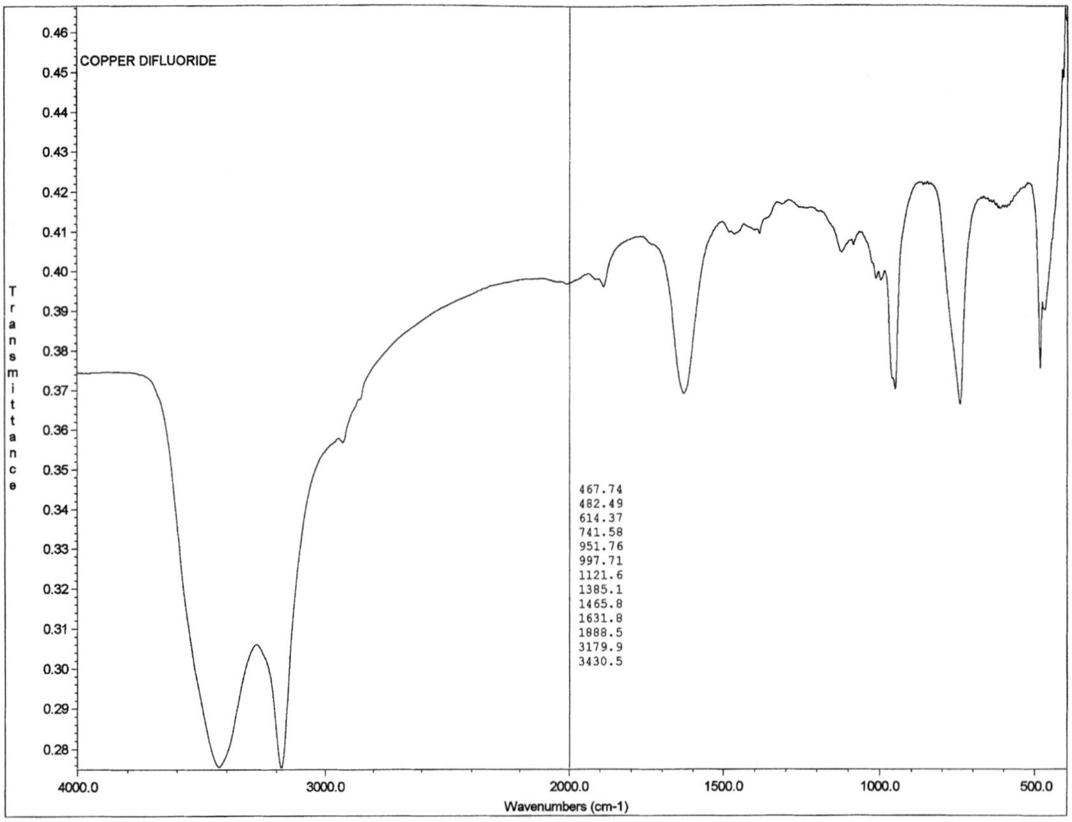

271 Copper (II) fluoride $CuF_2 \cdot 2H_2O$

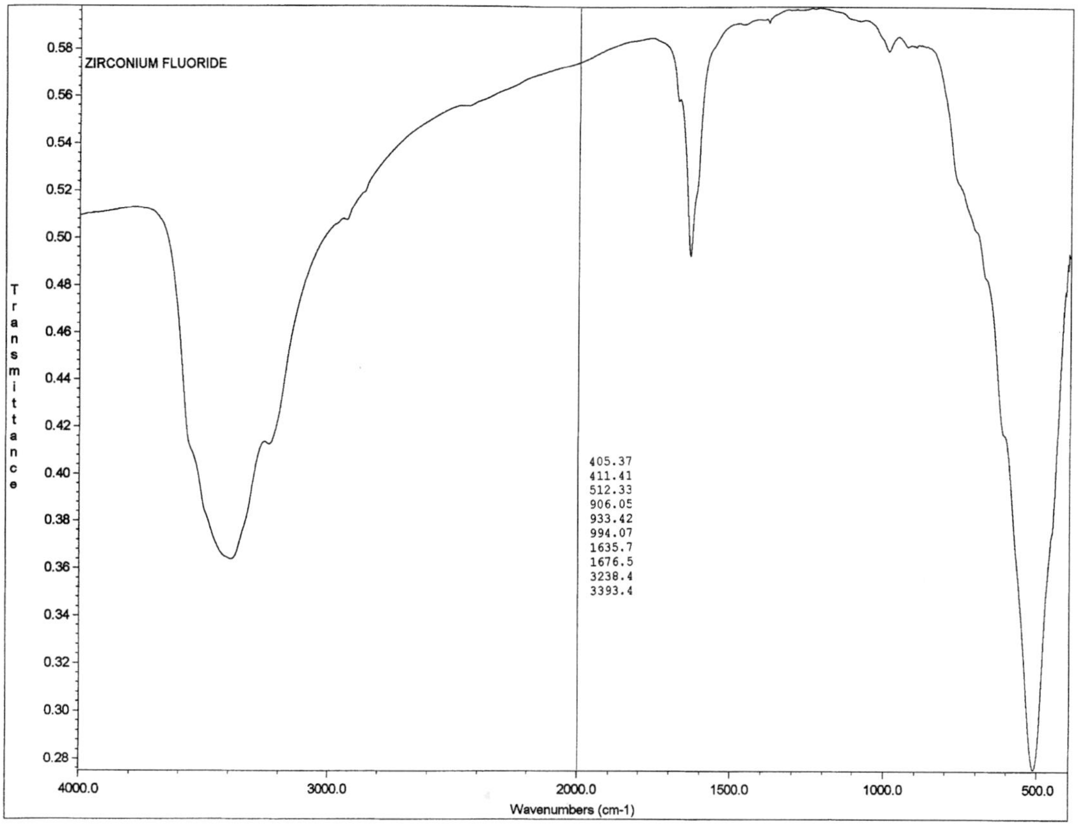

272 Zirconium fluoride $ZrF_4 \cdot xH_2O$

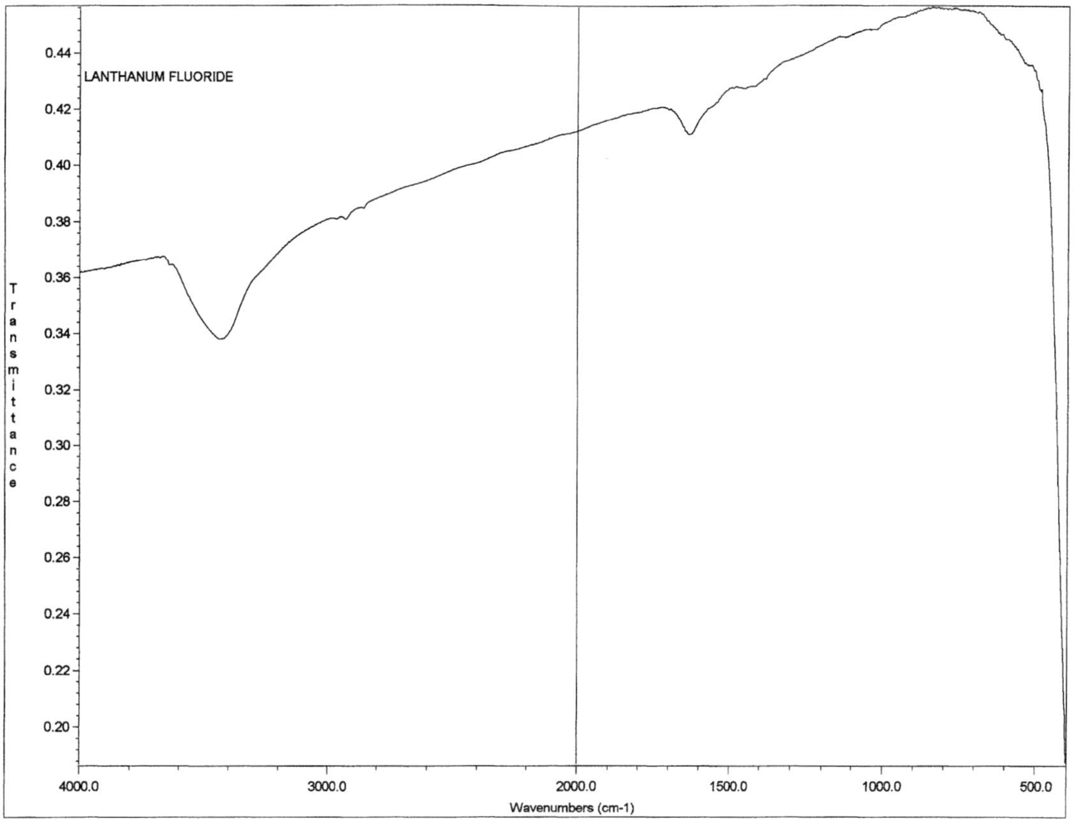

273 Lanthanum fluoride LaF_3

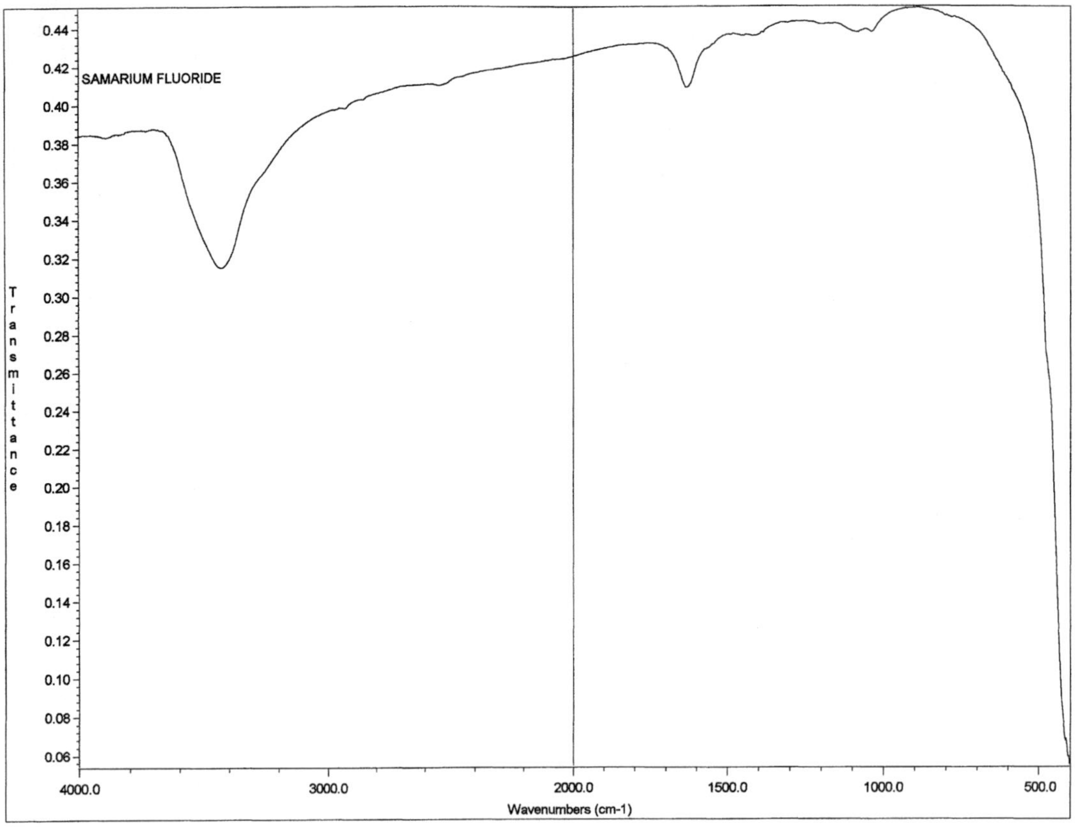

274 Samarium fluoride SmF_3

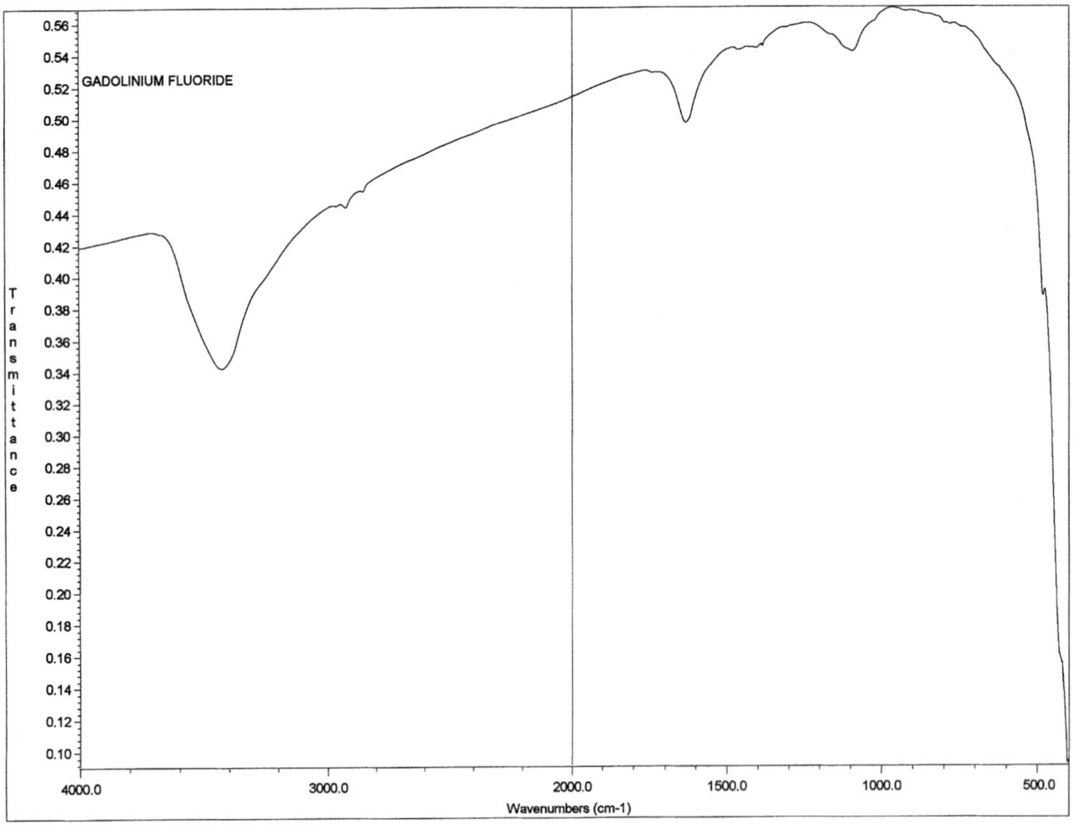

275 Gadolinium fluoride GdF_3

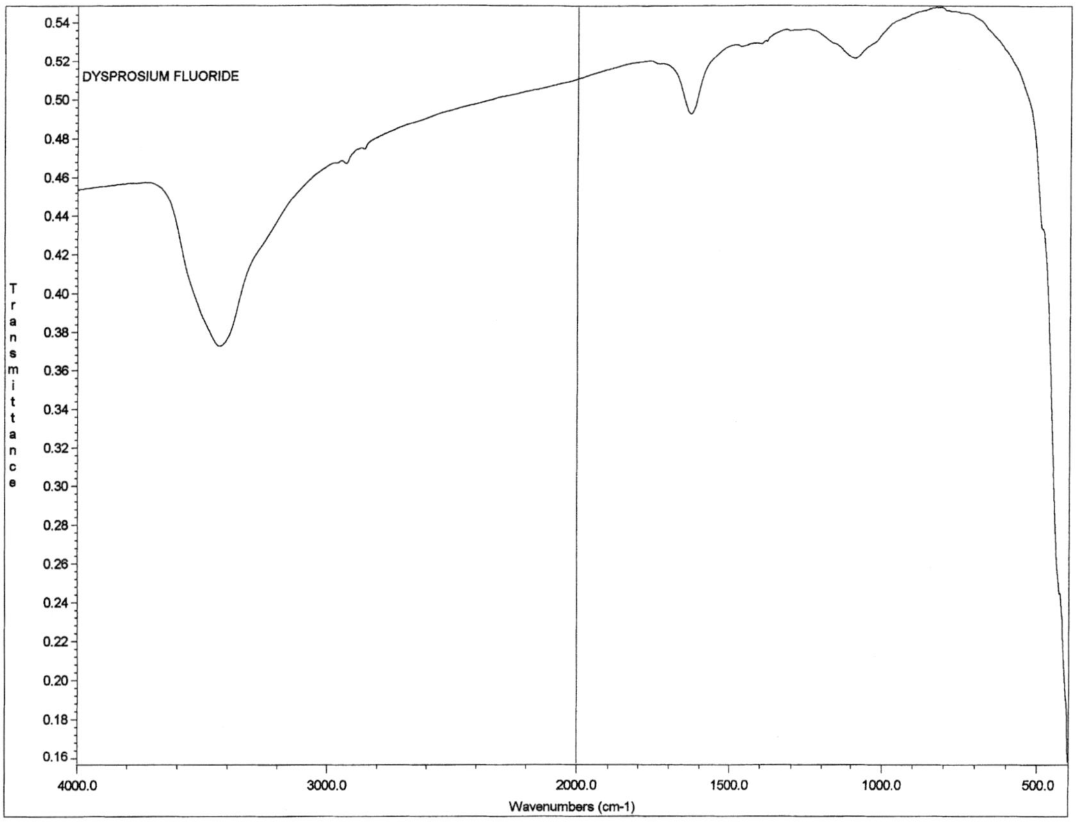

276 Dysprosium fluoride DyF_3

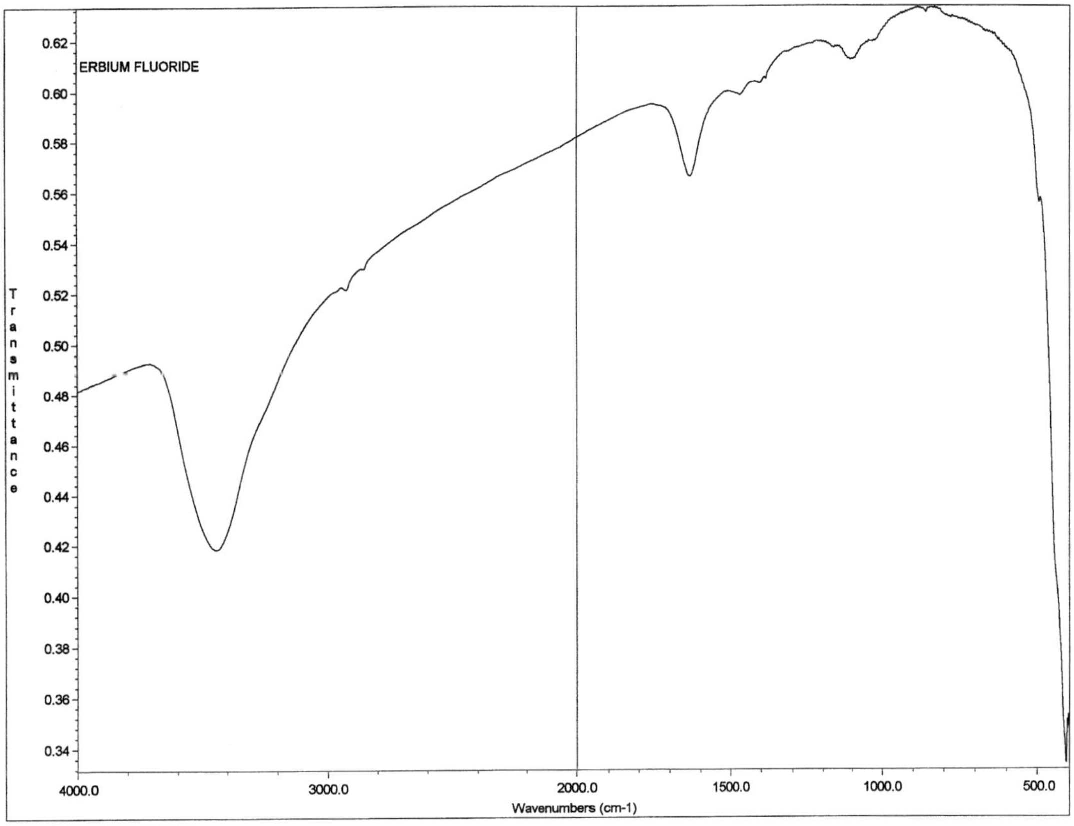

278 Erbium fluoride ErF_3

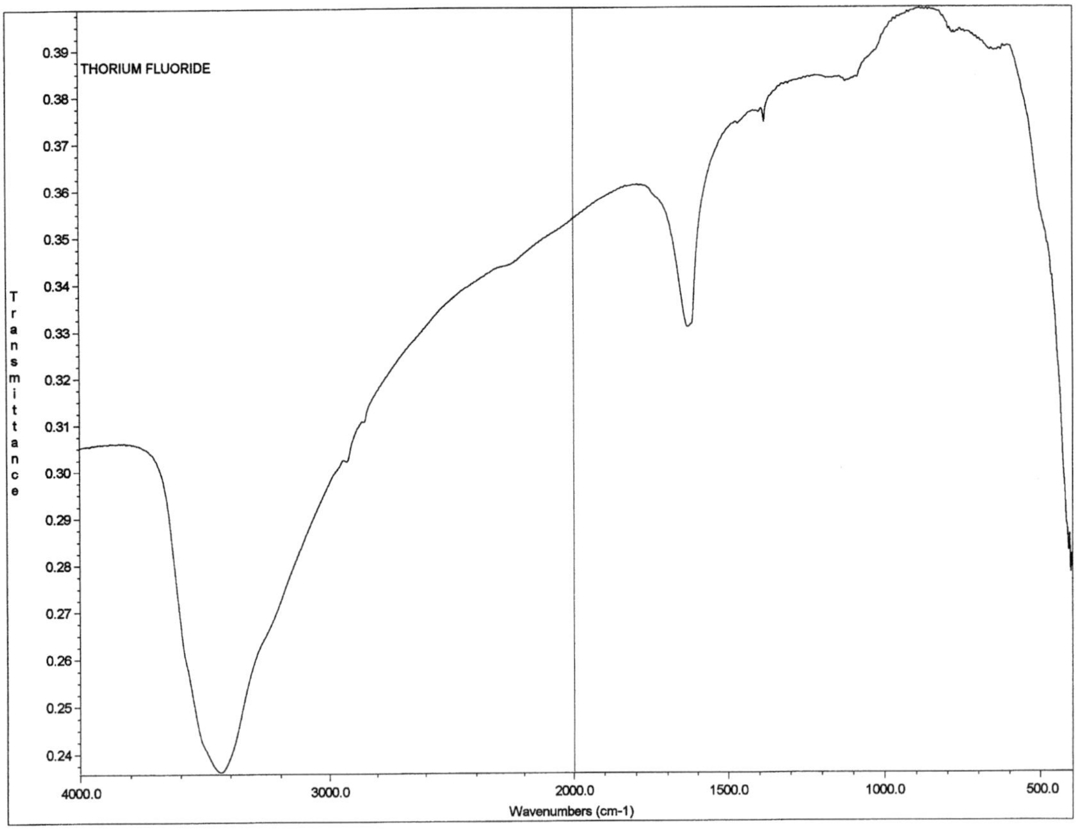

279 Thorium fluoride $ThF_4 \cdot 4H_2O$

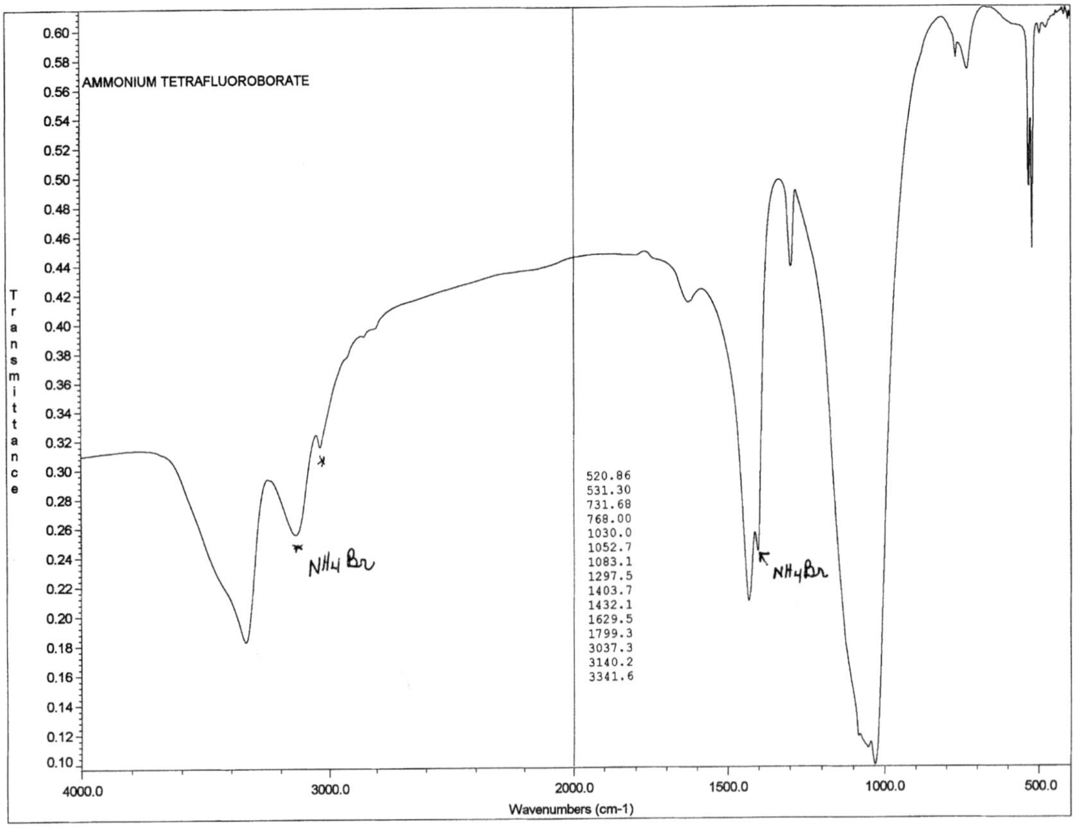

280 Ammonium tetrafluoroborate NH_4BF_4

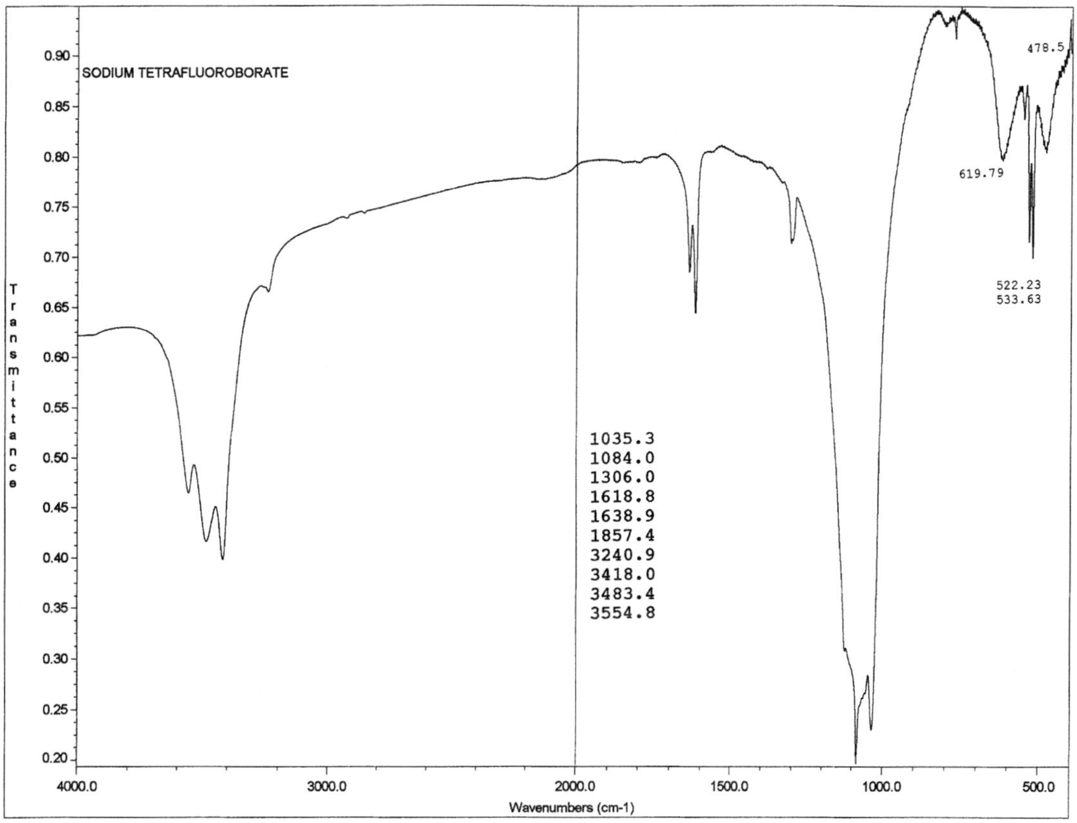

281 Sodium tetrafluoroborate $NaBF_4 \cdot xH_2O$

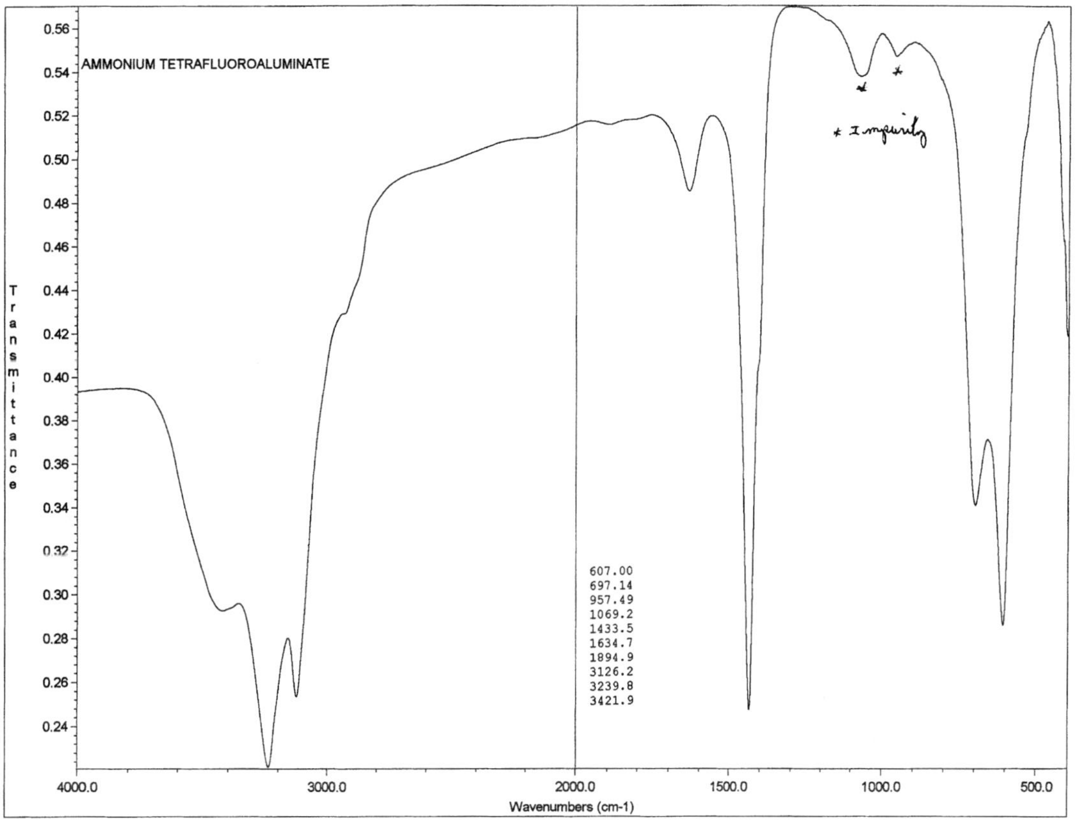

282 Ammonium tetrafluoroaluminate NH_4AlF_4

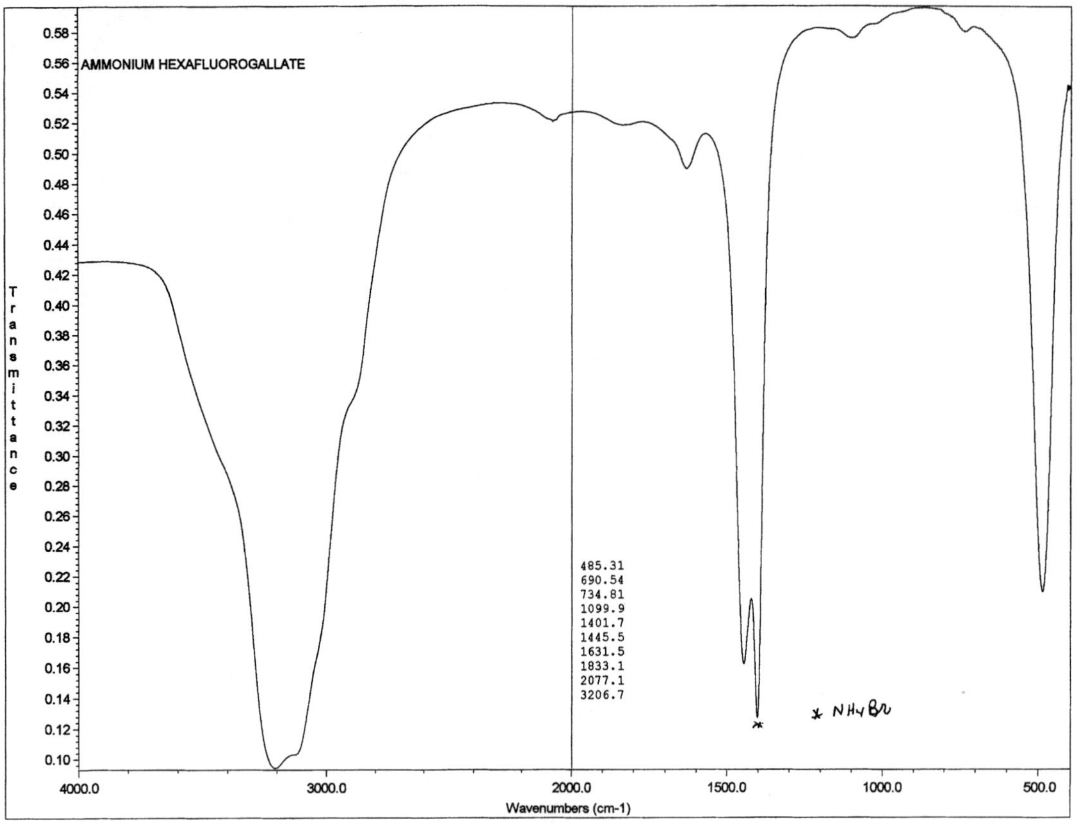

283 Ammonium hexafluorogallate $(NH_4)_3GaF_6$

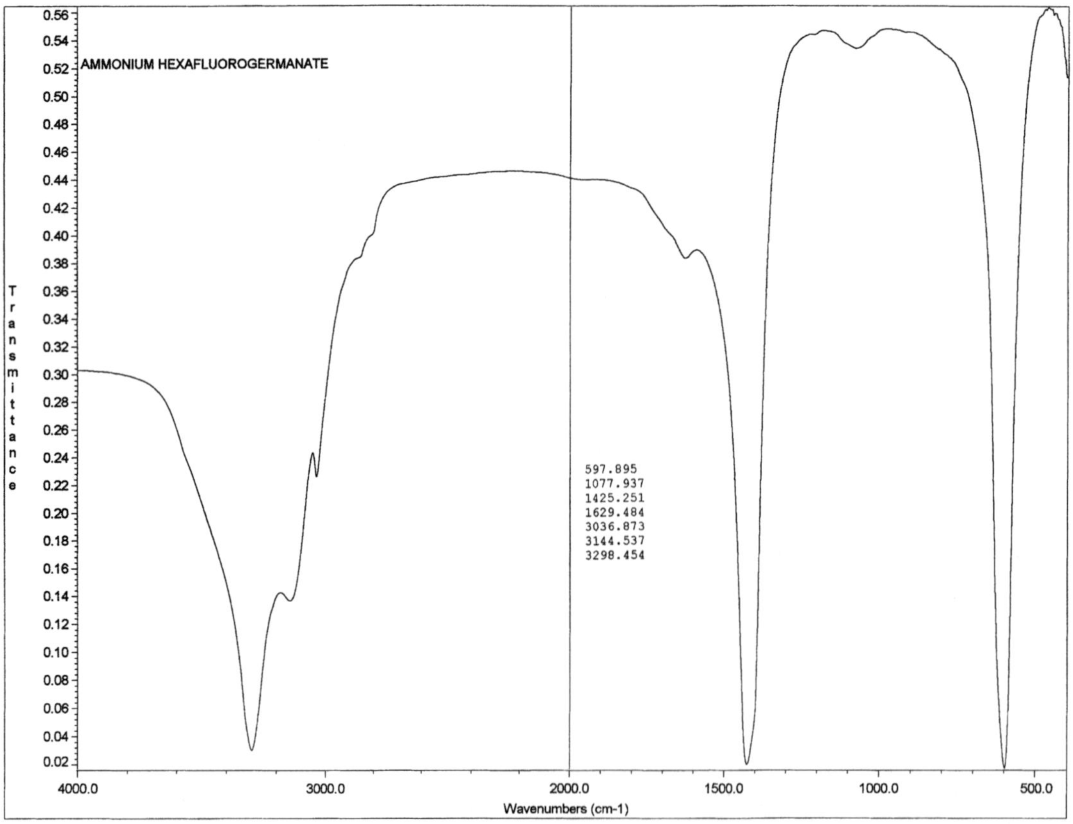

286 Ammonium hexafluorogermanate $(NH_4)_2GeF_6$

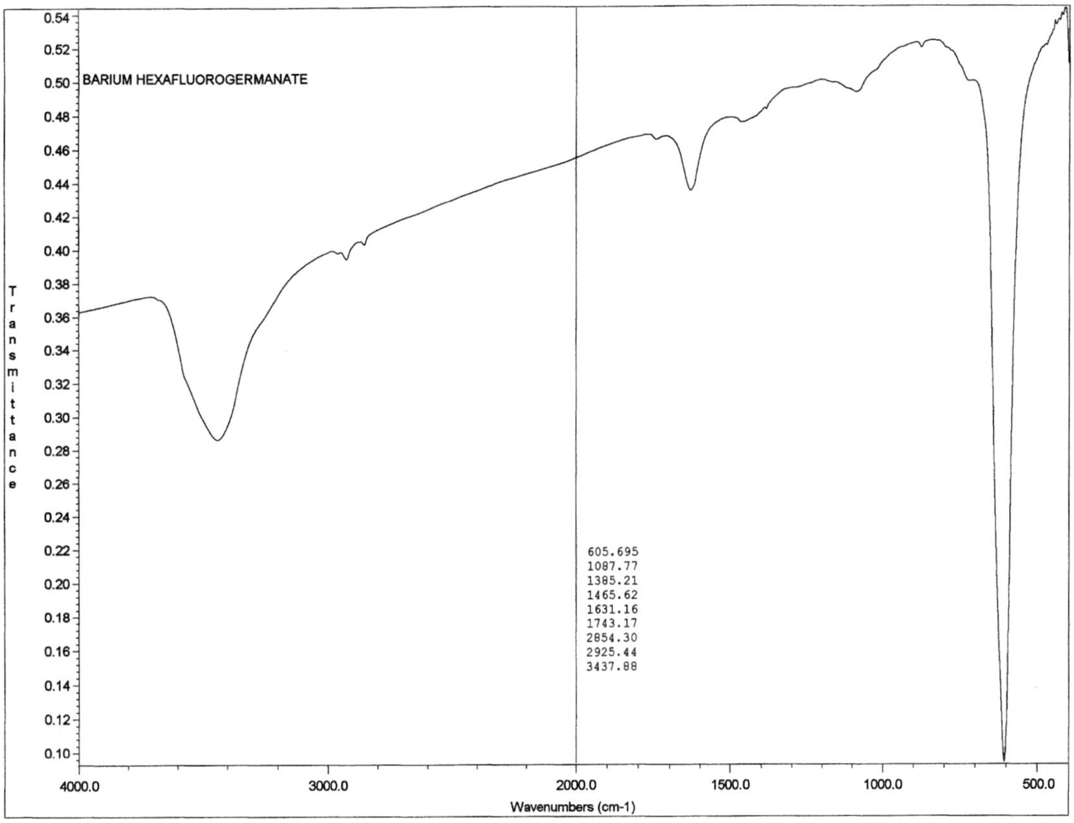

287 Barium hexafluorogermanate $BaGeF_6$

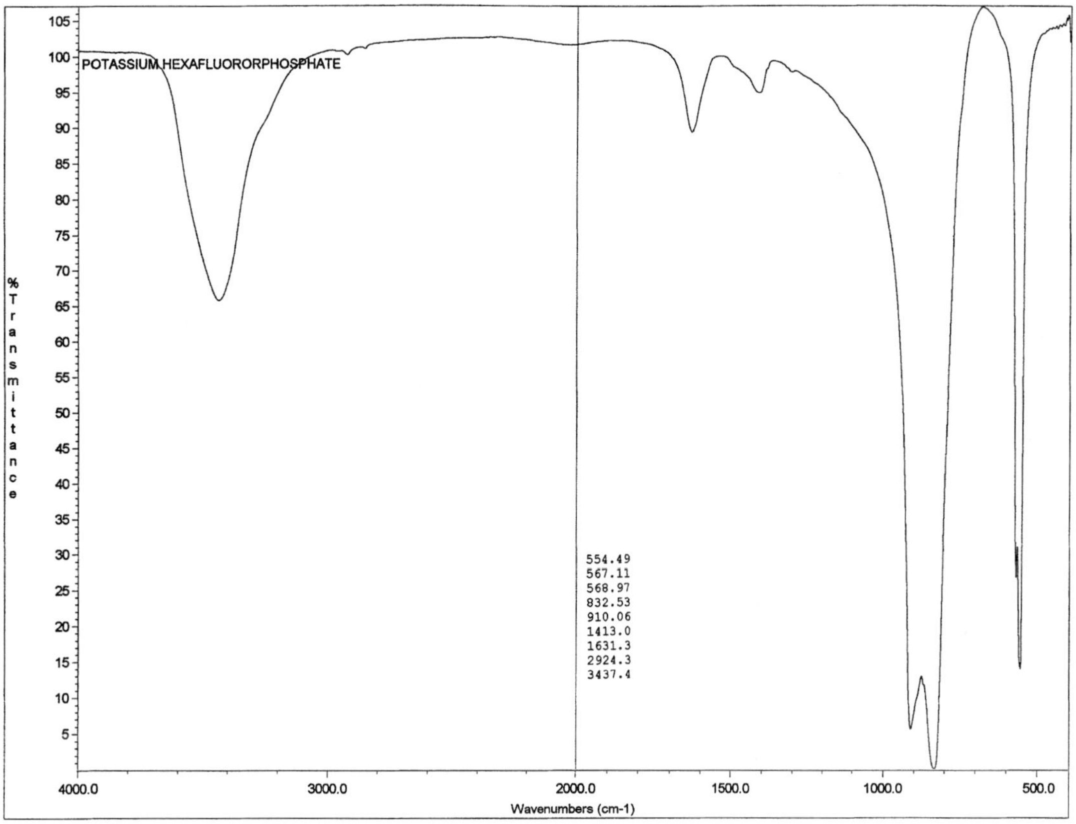

289 Potassium hexafluorophosphate $KPF_6 \cdot xH_2O$ or wet

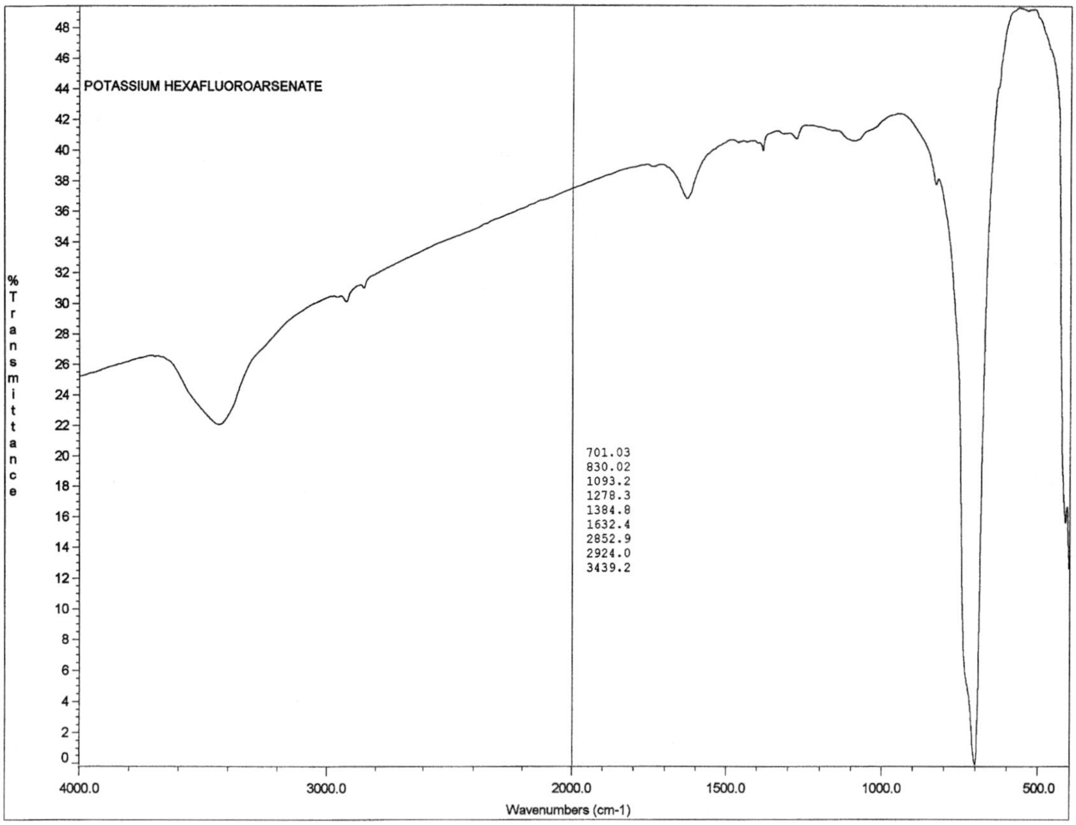

290 Potassium hexafluoroarsenate $KAsF_6$

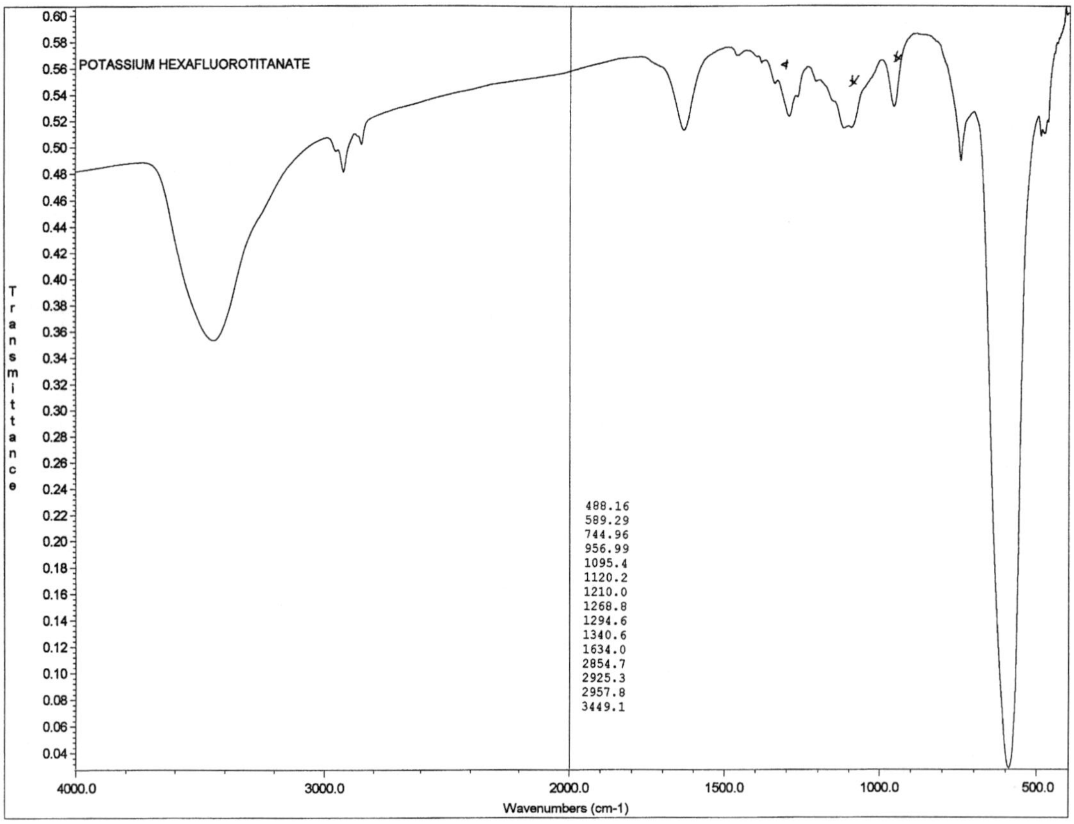

291 Potassium hexafluorotitanate (IV) K_2TiF_6

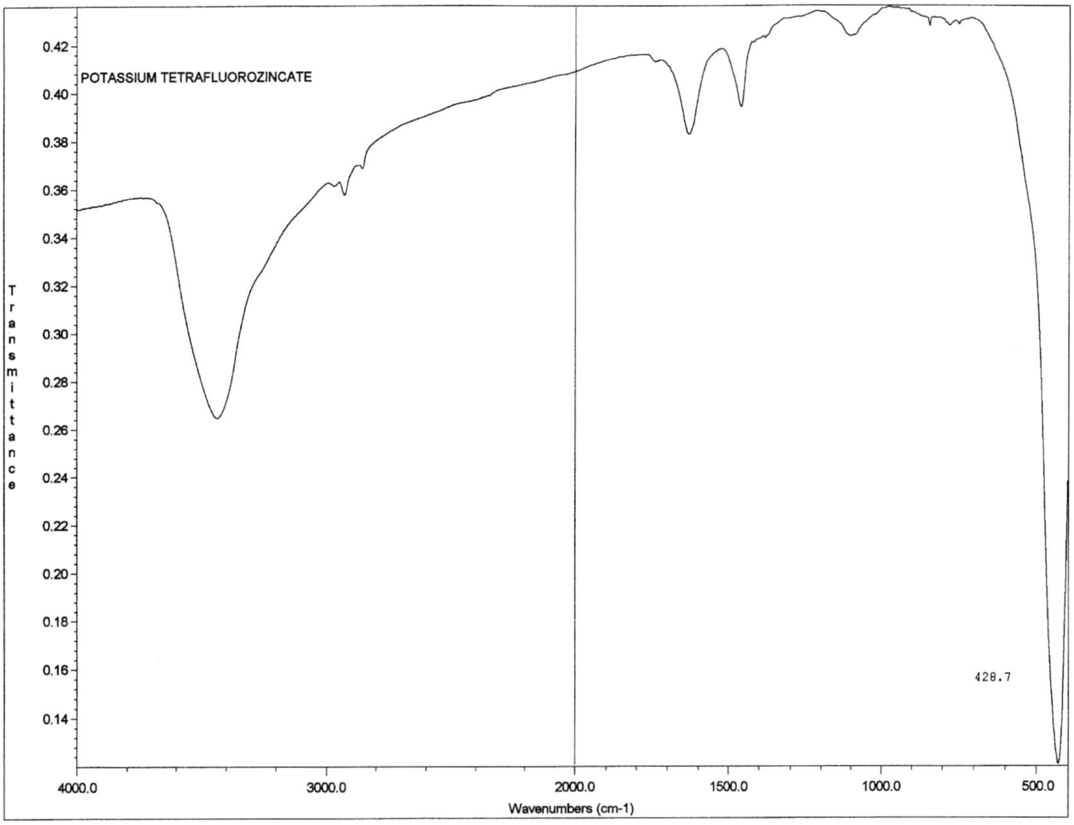

292 Potassium tetrafluorozincate $K_2ZnF_4 \cdot xH_2O$

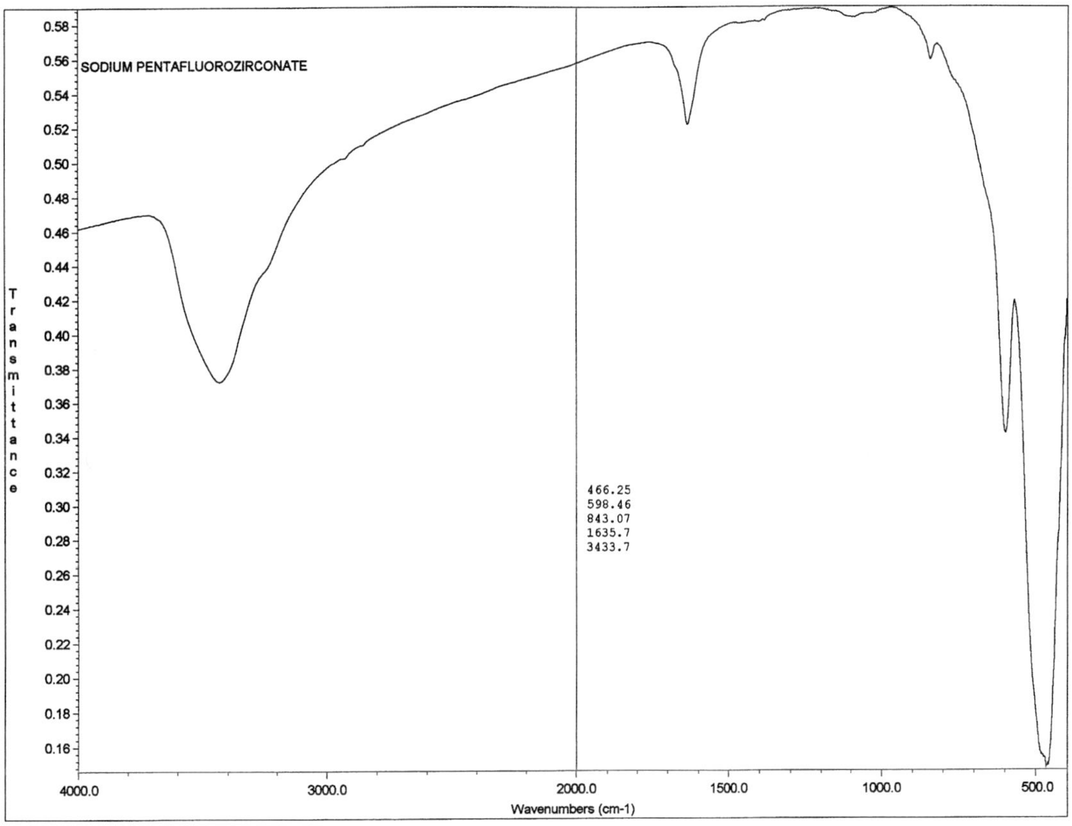

293 Sodium pentafluorozirconate $NaZrF_5 \cdot xH_2O$

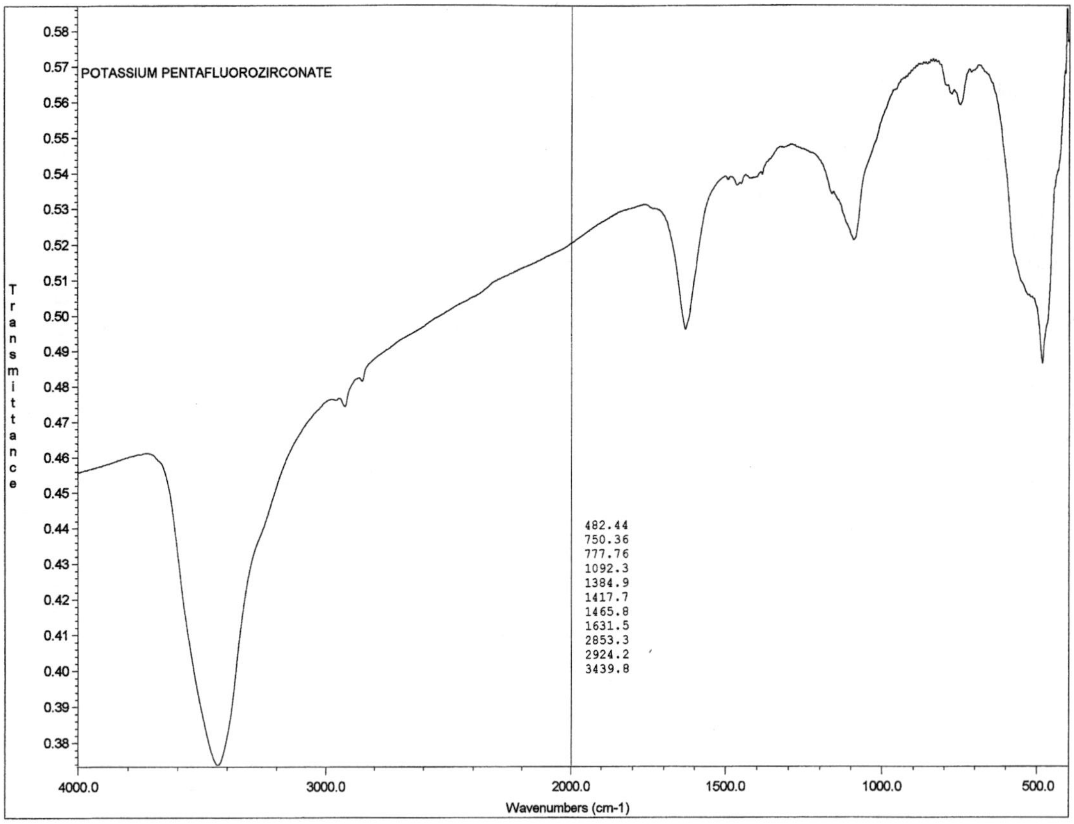

294 Potassium pentafluorozirconate $KZrF_5 \cdot xH_2O$

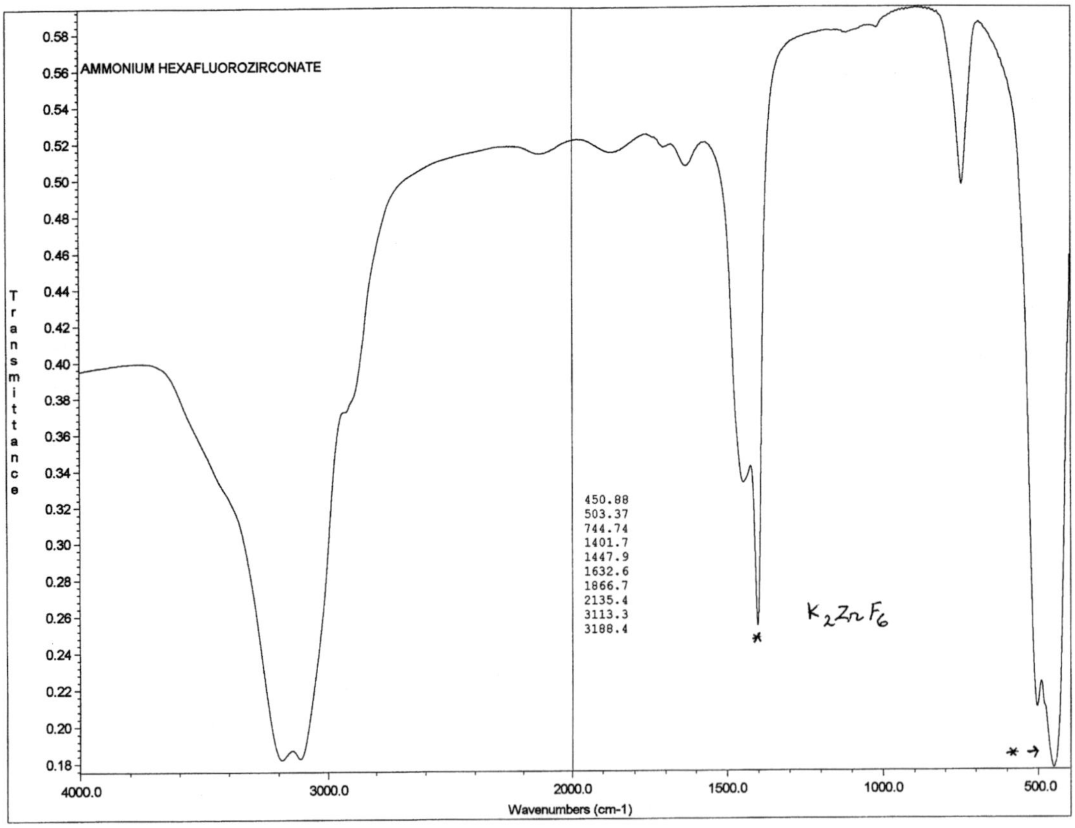

295 Ammonium hexafluorozirconate $(NH_4)_2ZrF_6$

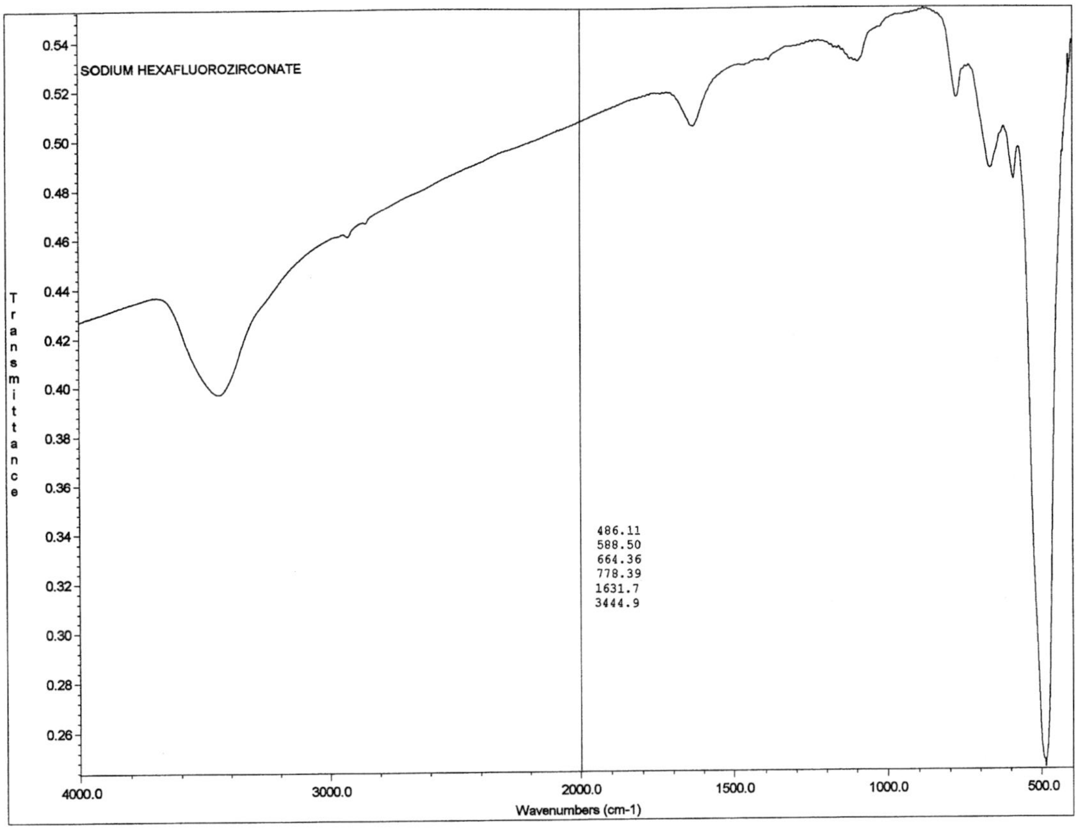

296 Sodium hexafluorozirconate Na_2ZrF_6

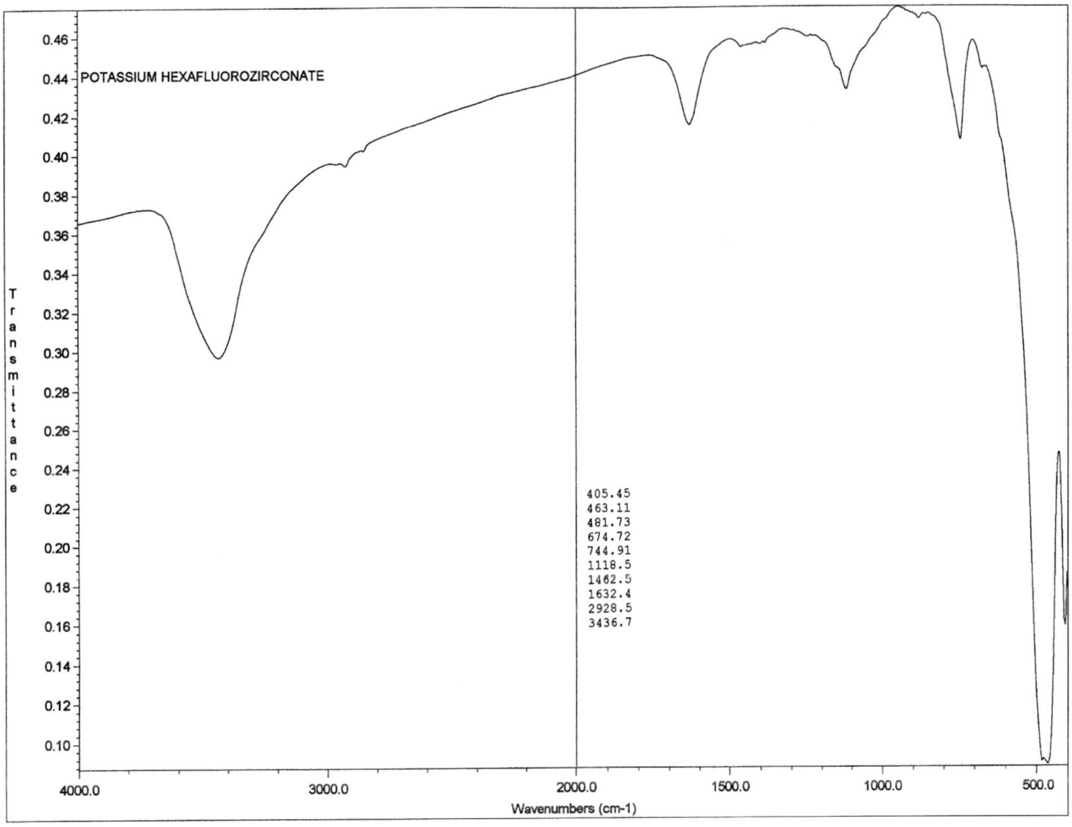

297 Potassium hexafluorozirconate $K_2ZrF_6 \cdot xH_2O$

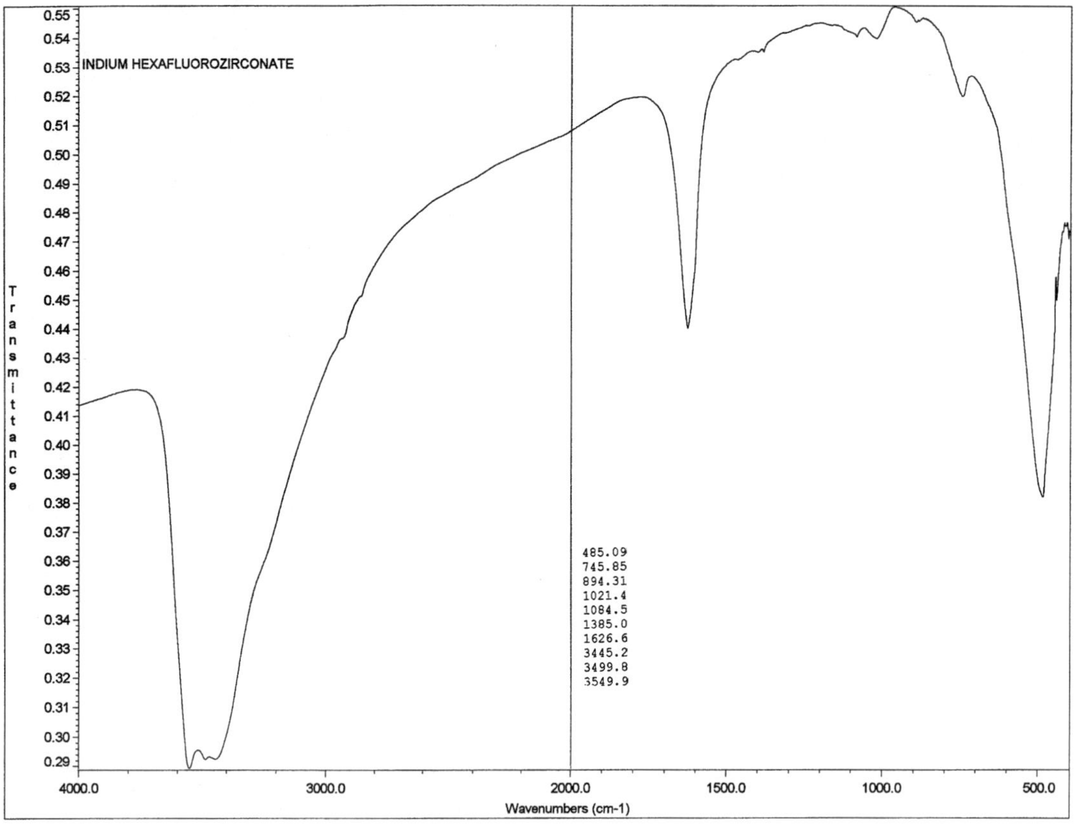

298 Indium hexafluorozirconate $In(ZrF_6)_3 \cdot xH_2O$

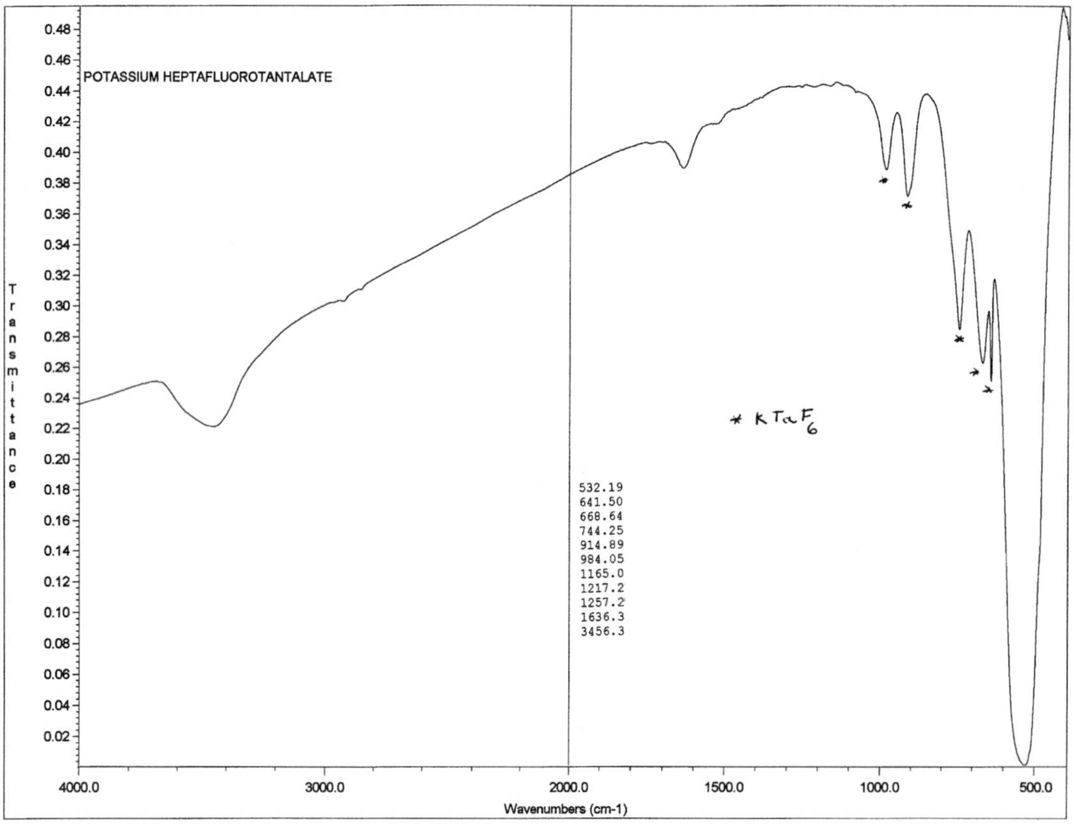

300 Potassium heptafluorotantalate K_3TaF_7

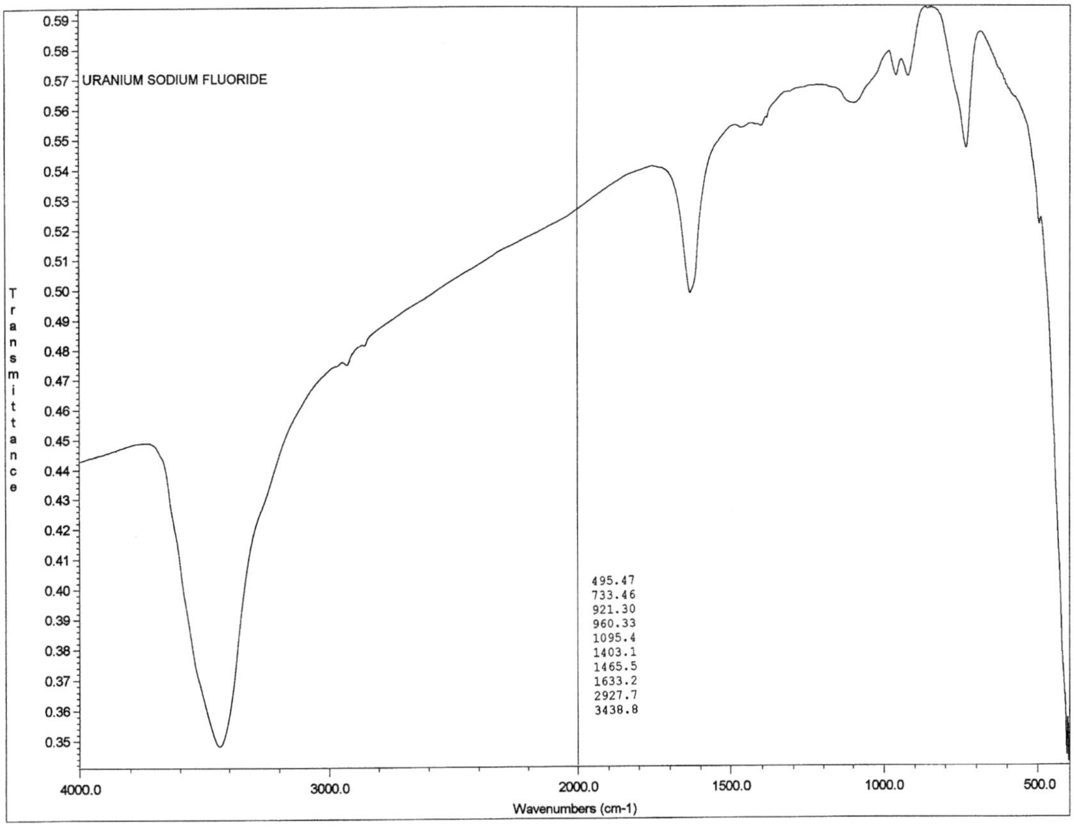

301 Sodium pentafluorouranate $NaUF_5 \cdot H_2O$

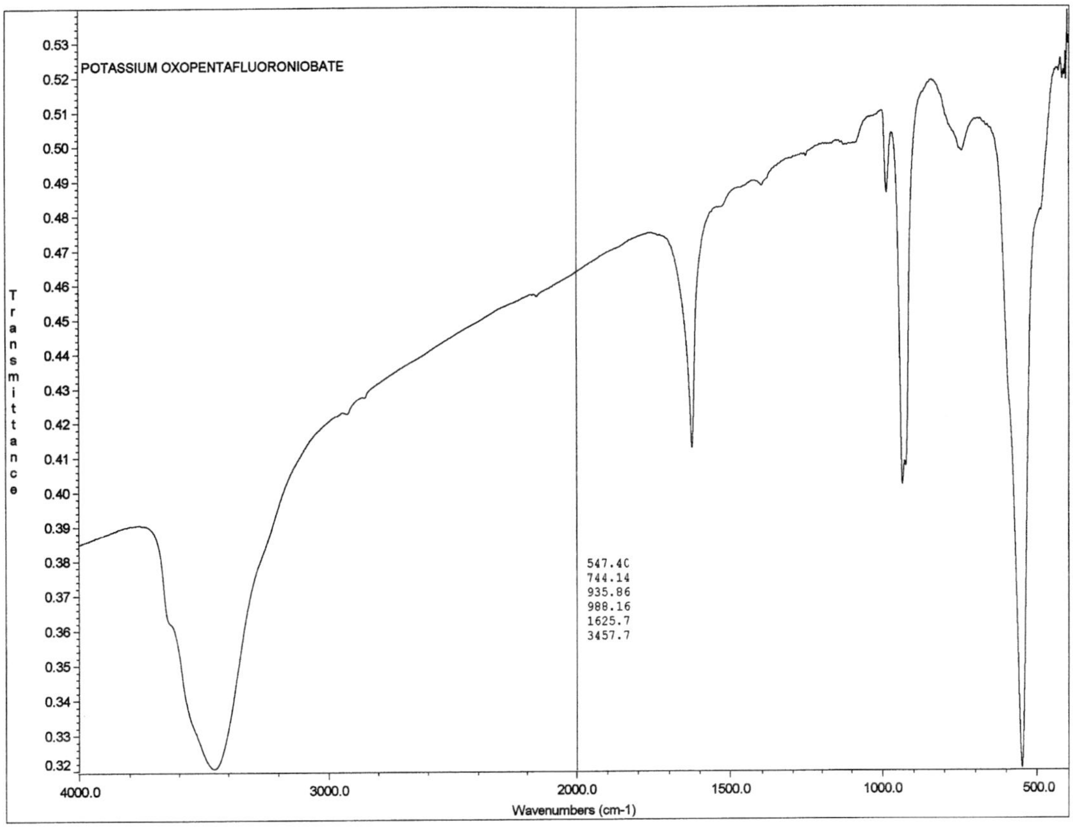

302 Potassium oxopentafluoroniobate $K_2NbOF_5 \cdot xH_2O$

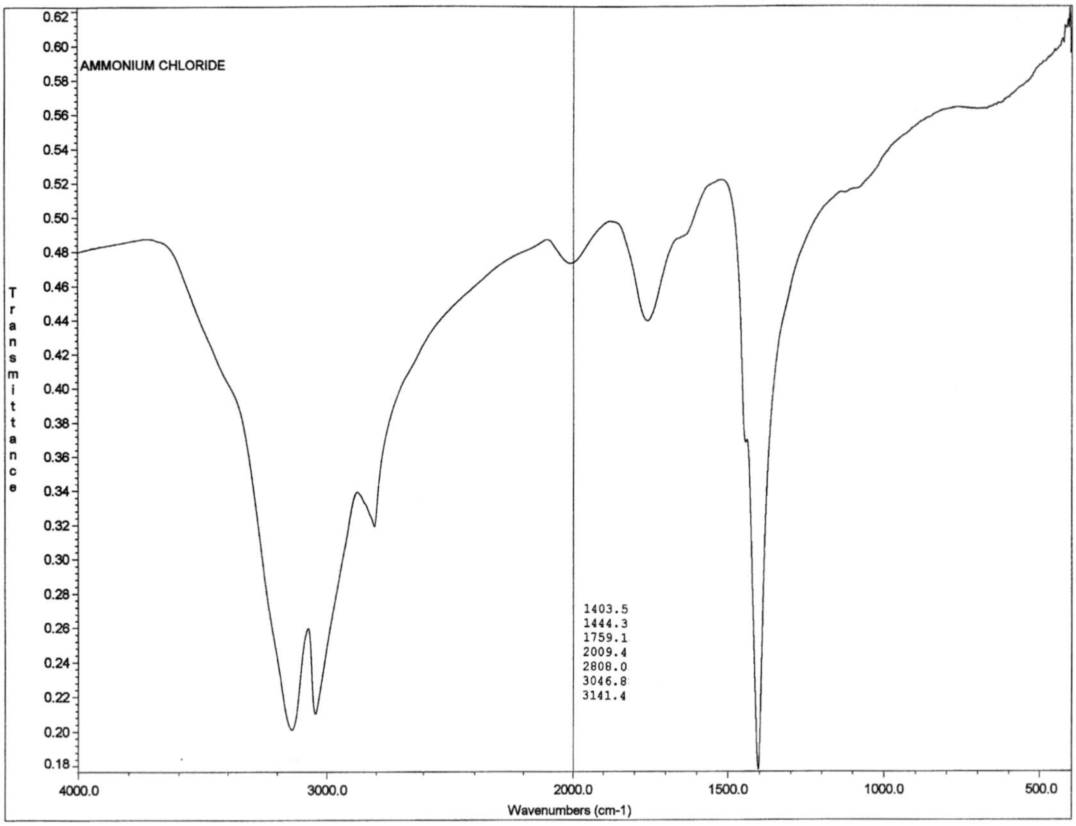

304 Ammonium chloride NH_4Cl

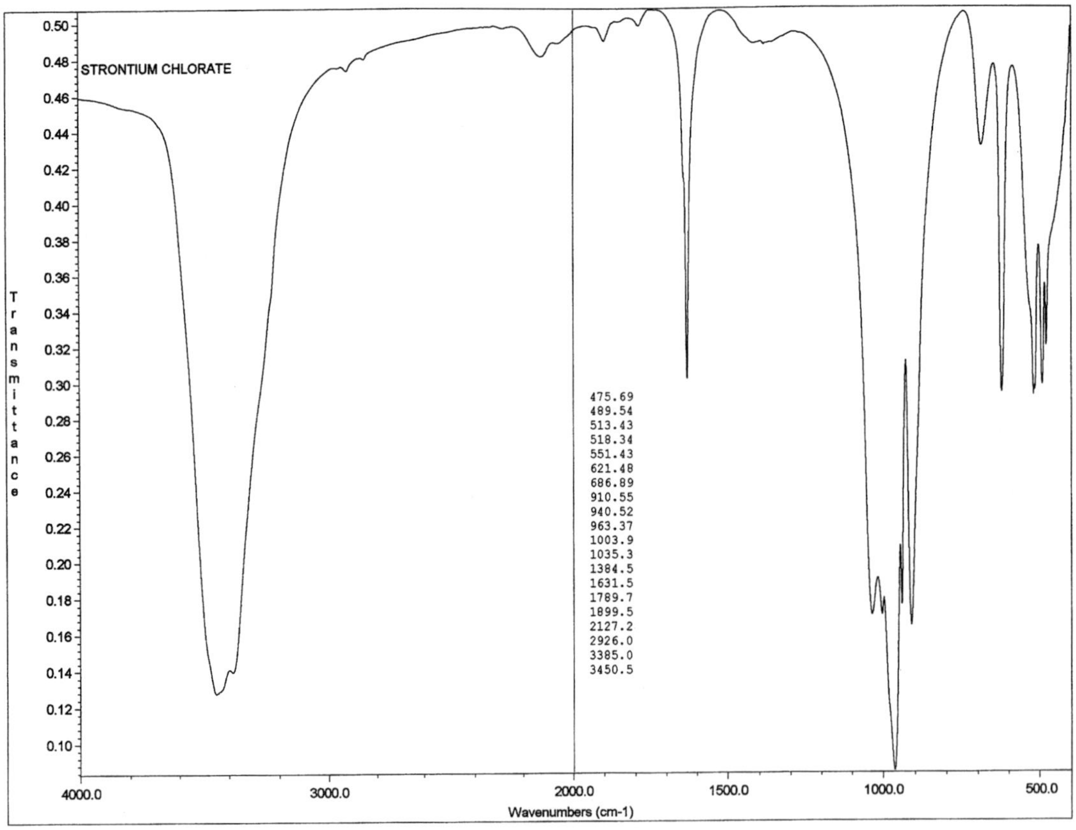

306 Strontium chlorate $Sr(ClO_3)_2 \cdot xH_2O$

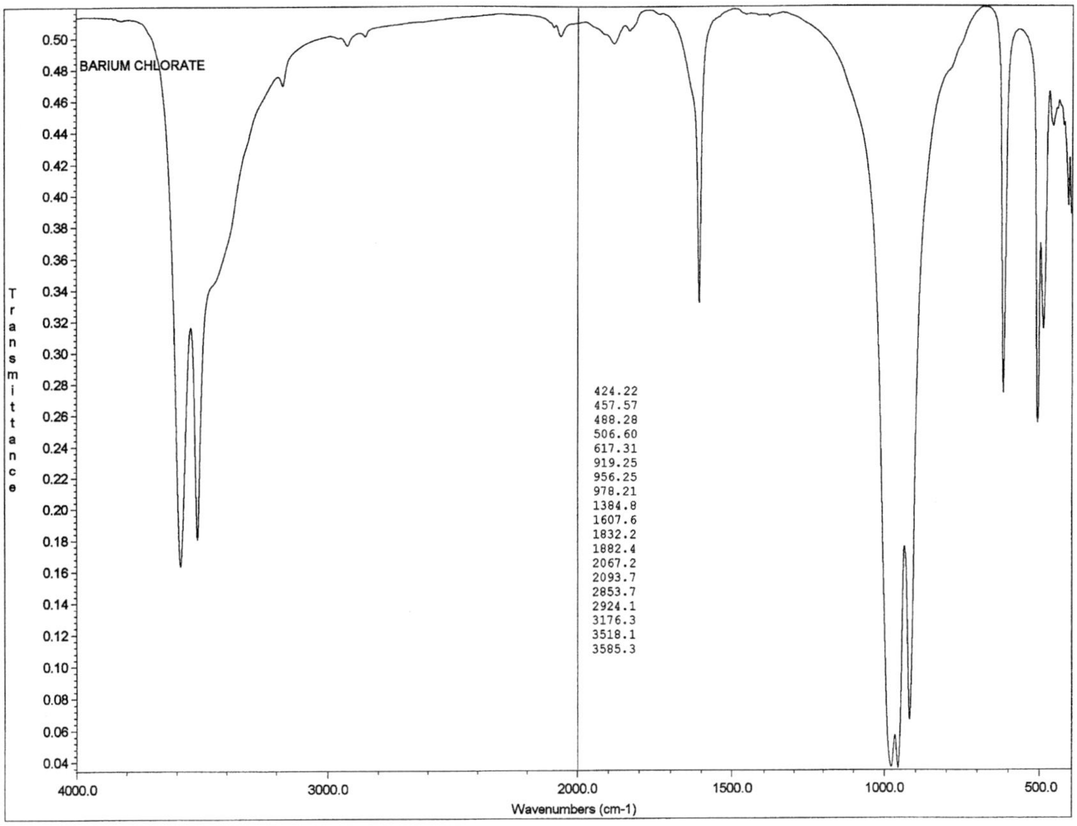

307 Barium chlorate $Ba(ClO_3)_2 \cdot H_2O$

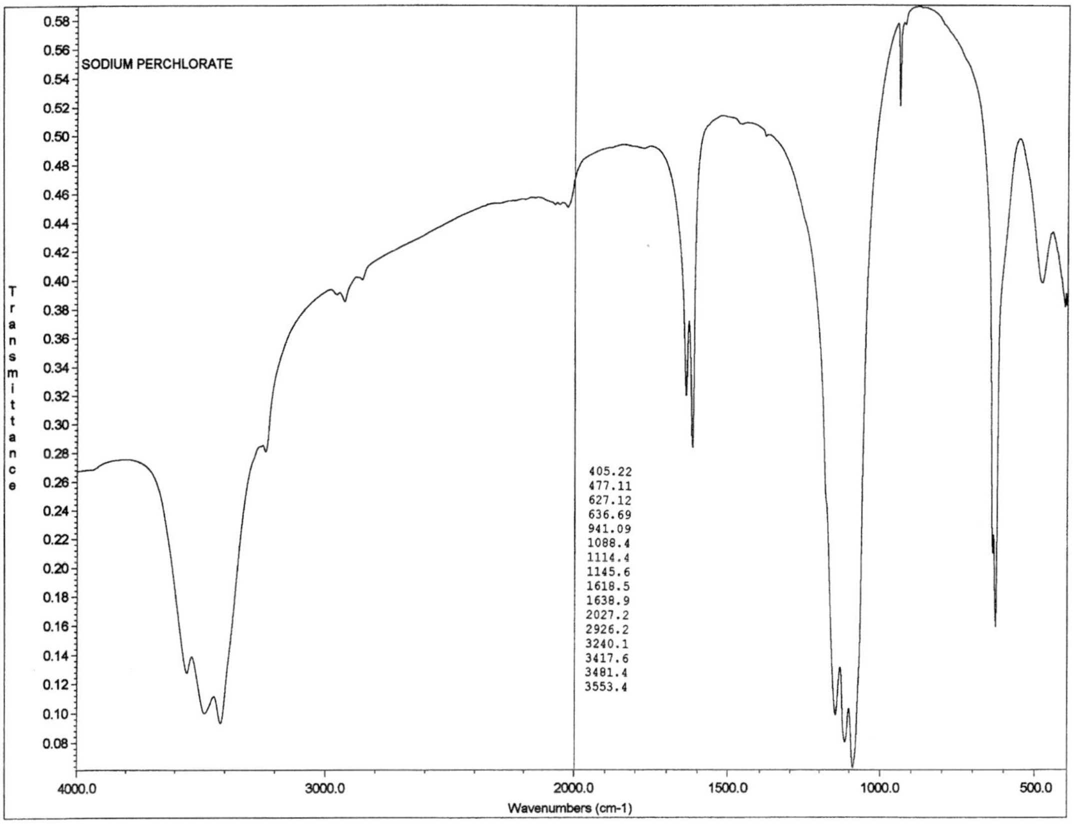

309 Sodium perchlorate $NaClO_4 \cdot H_2O$

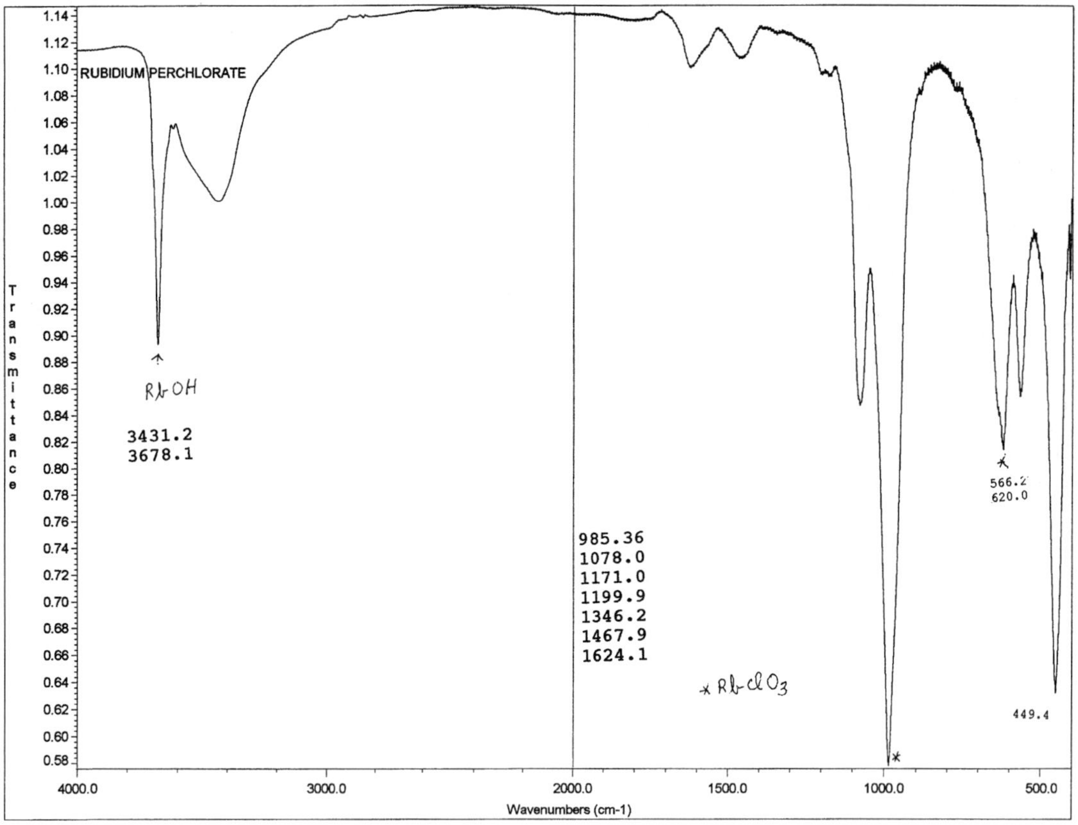

310 Rubidium perchlorate $RbClO_4$

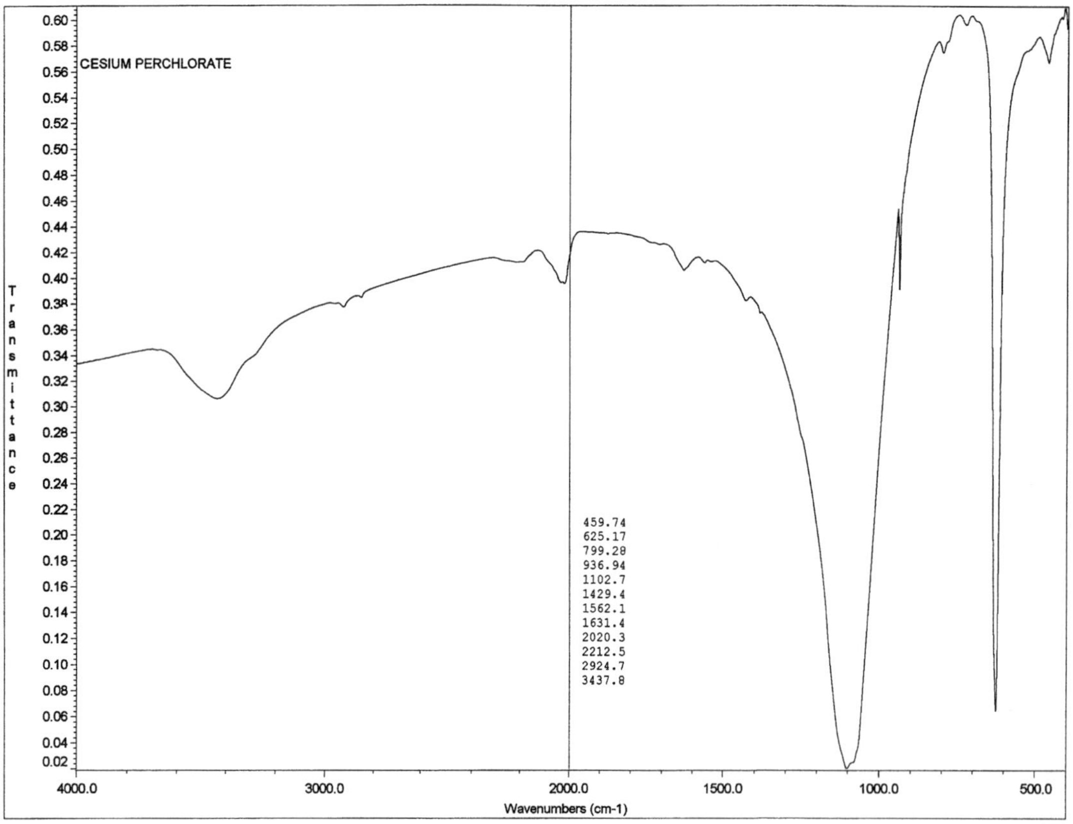

311 Cesium perchlorate $CsClO_4$

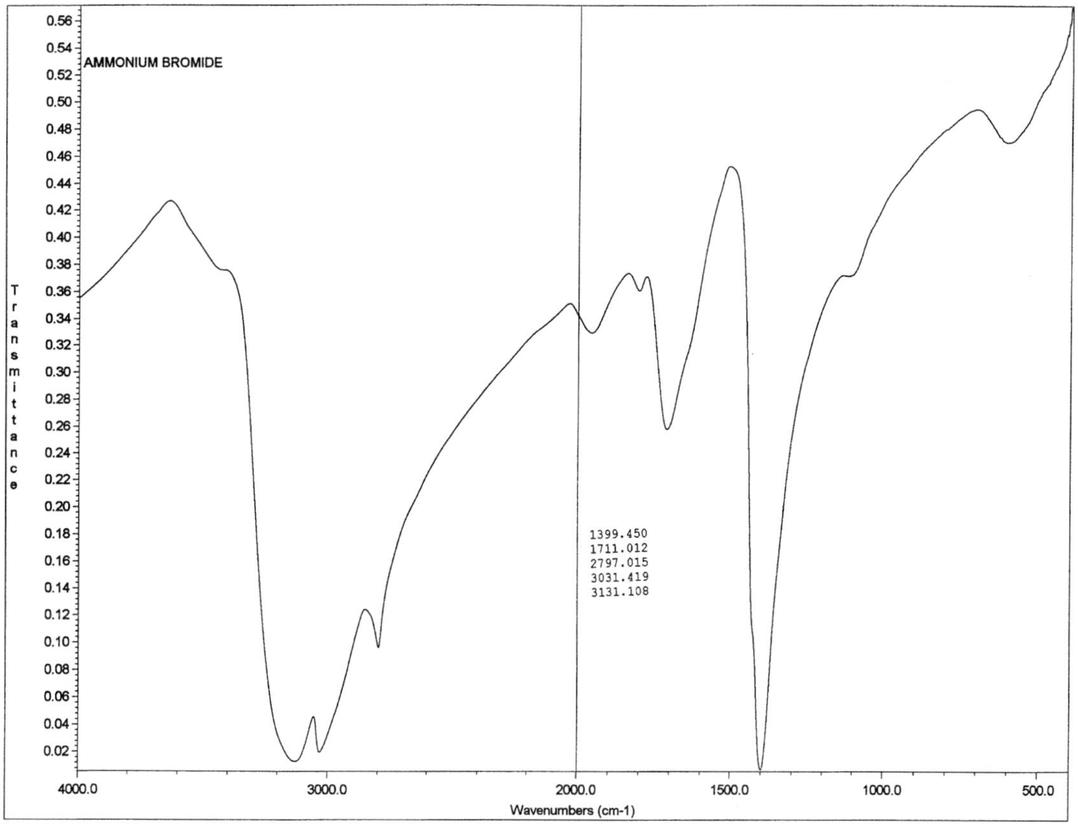

314 Ammonium bromide NH_4Br

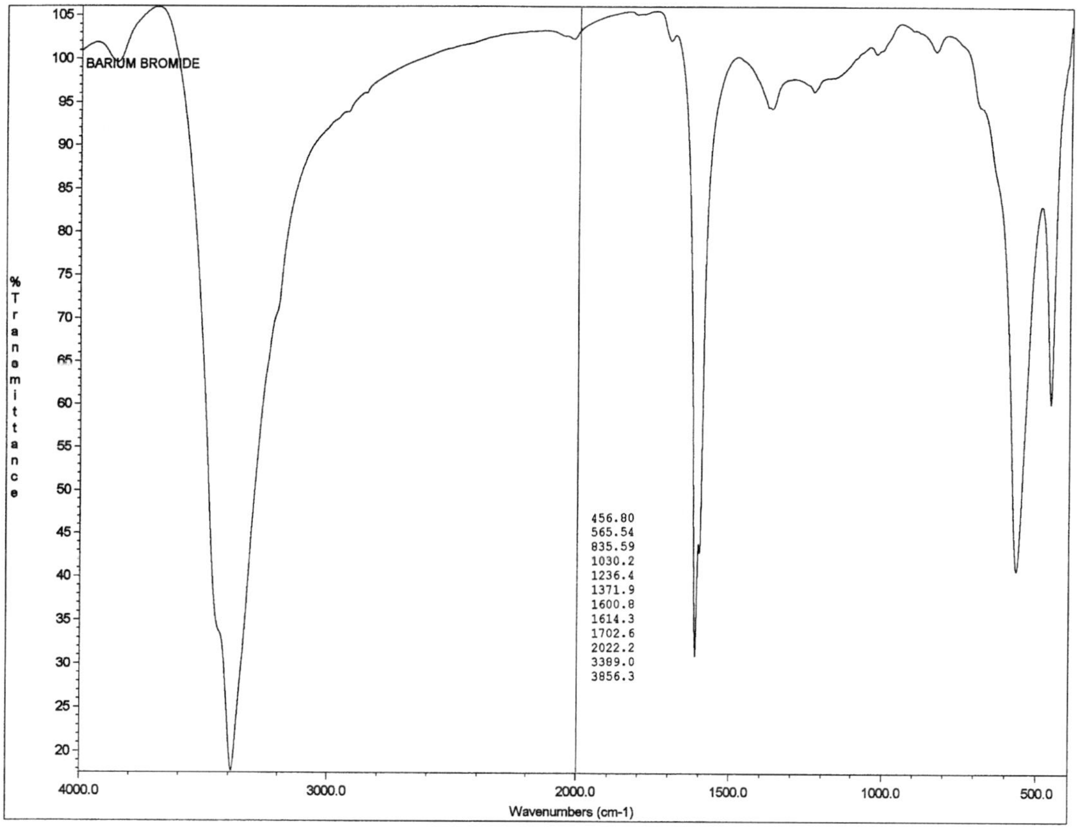

315 Barium bromide $BaBr_2 \cdot 2H_2O$

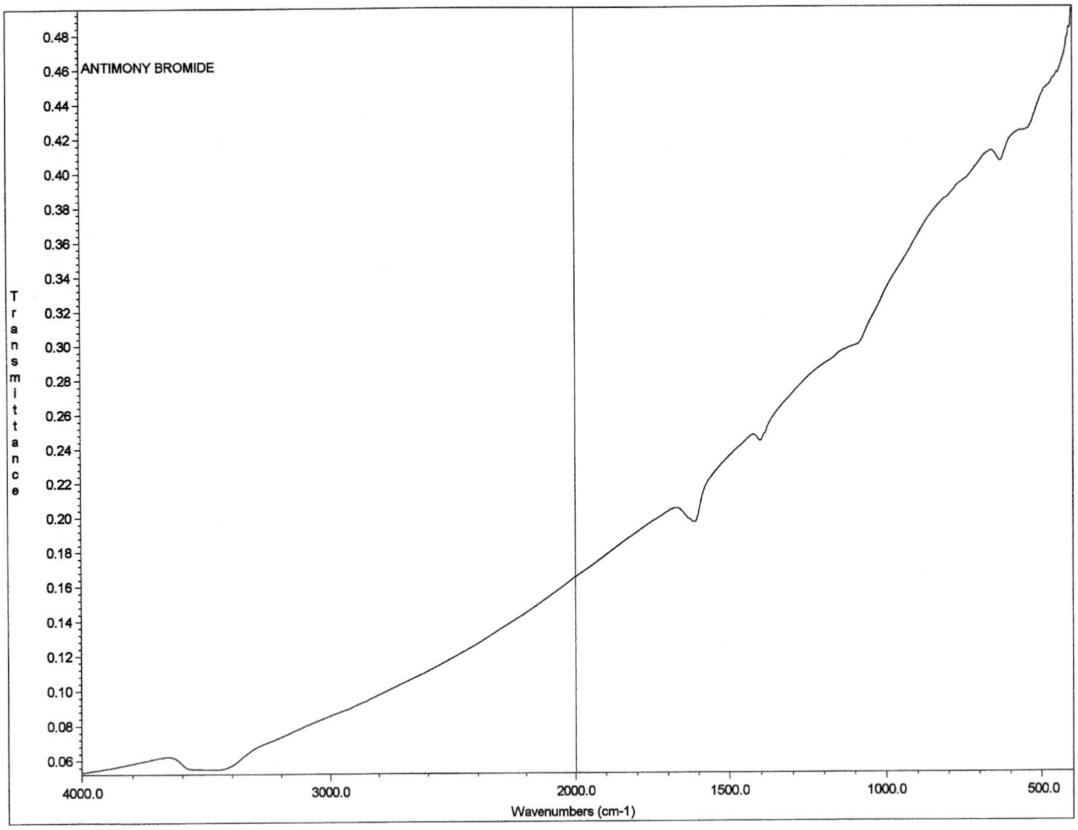

316 Antimony bromide $SbBr_3$

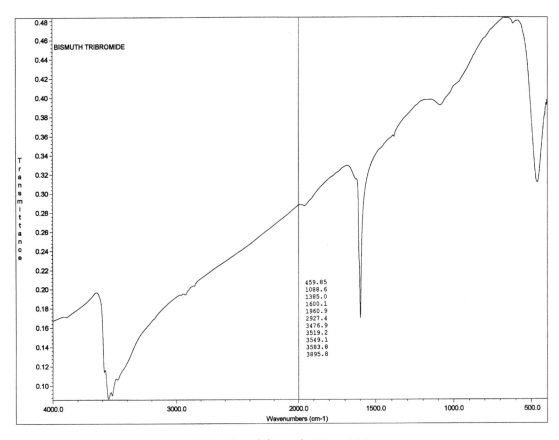

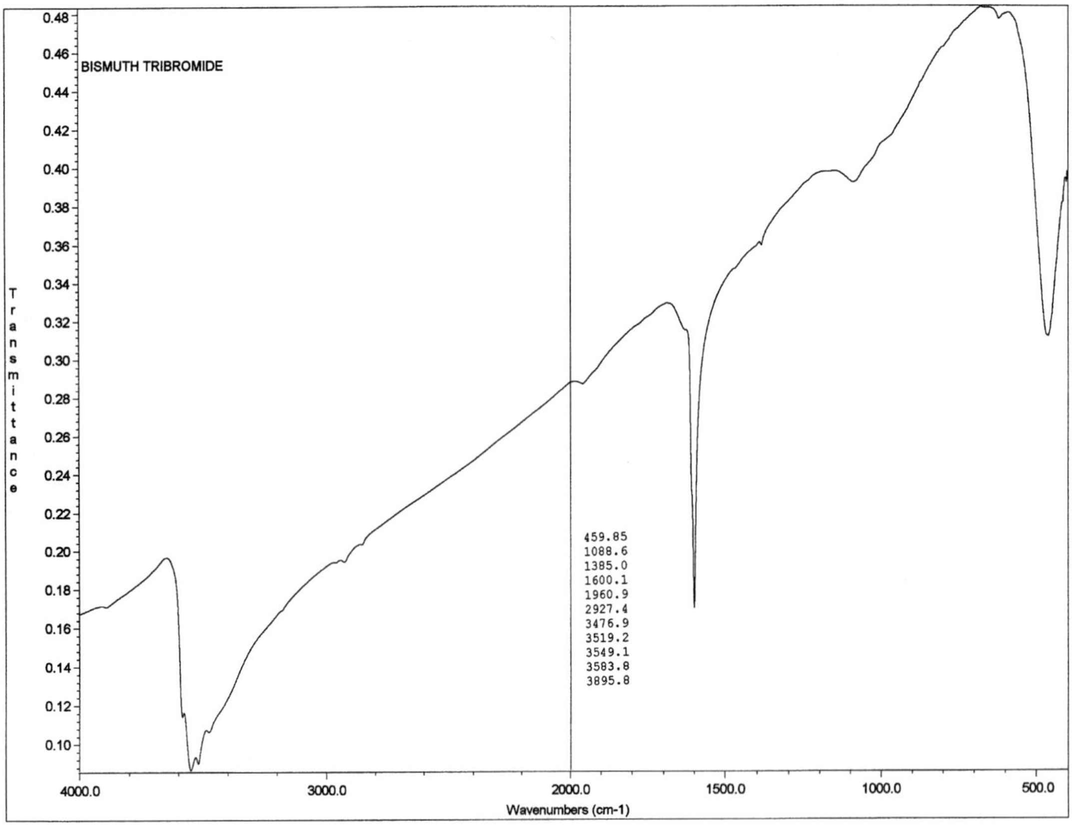

317 Bismuth bromide $BiBr_3 \cdot xH_2O$

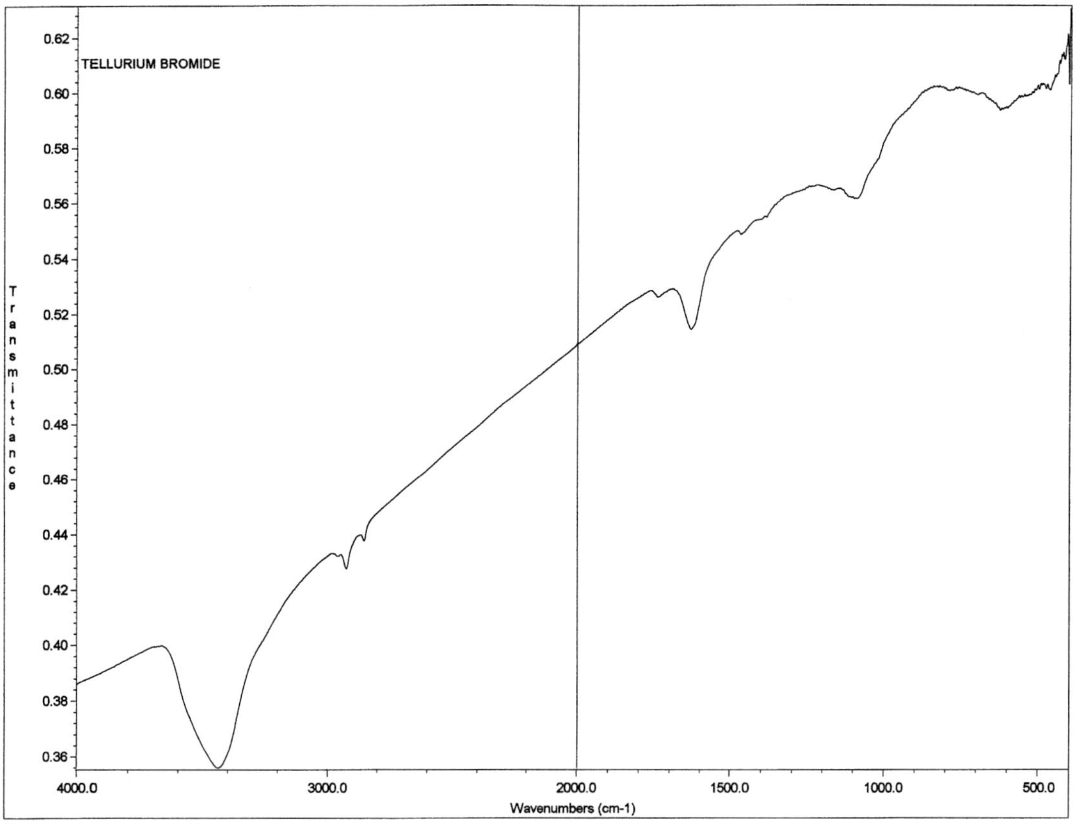

318 Tellurium bromide $TeBr_4 \cdot xH_2O$

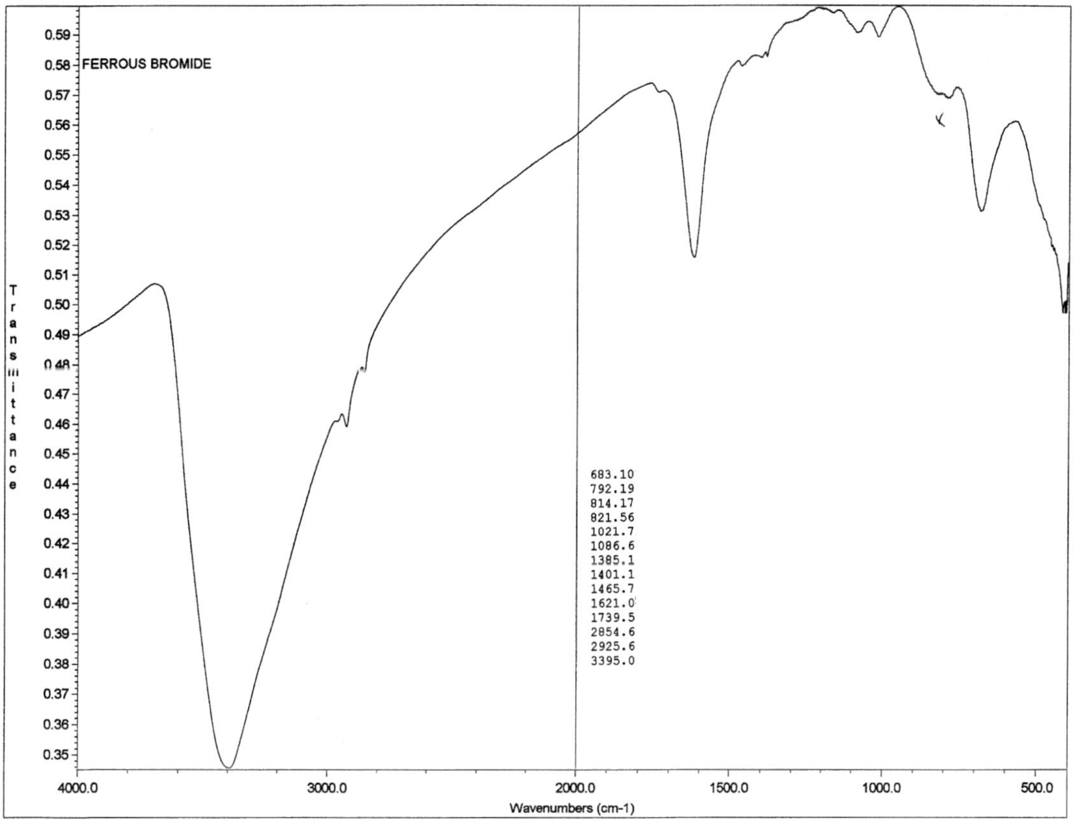

319 Iron (II) bromide $FeBr_2 \cdot xH_2O$

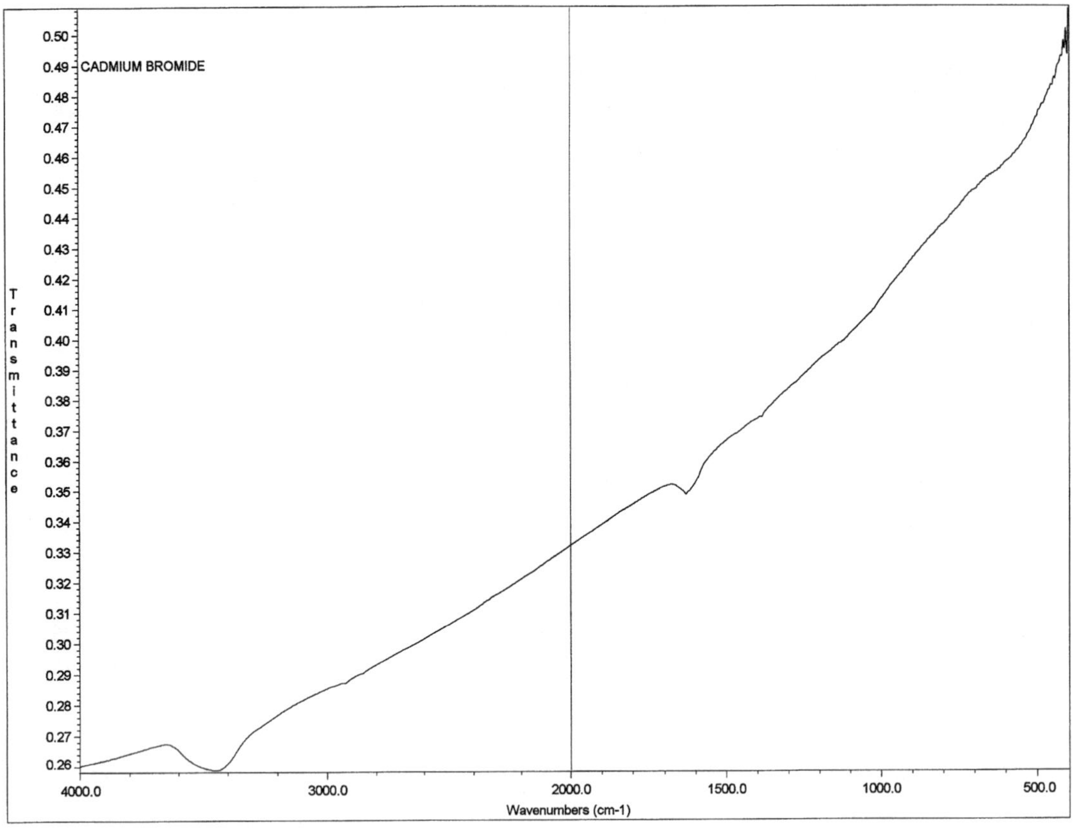

320 Cadmium bromide $CdBr_2$

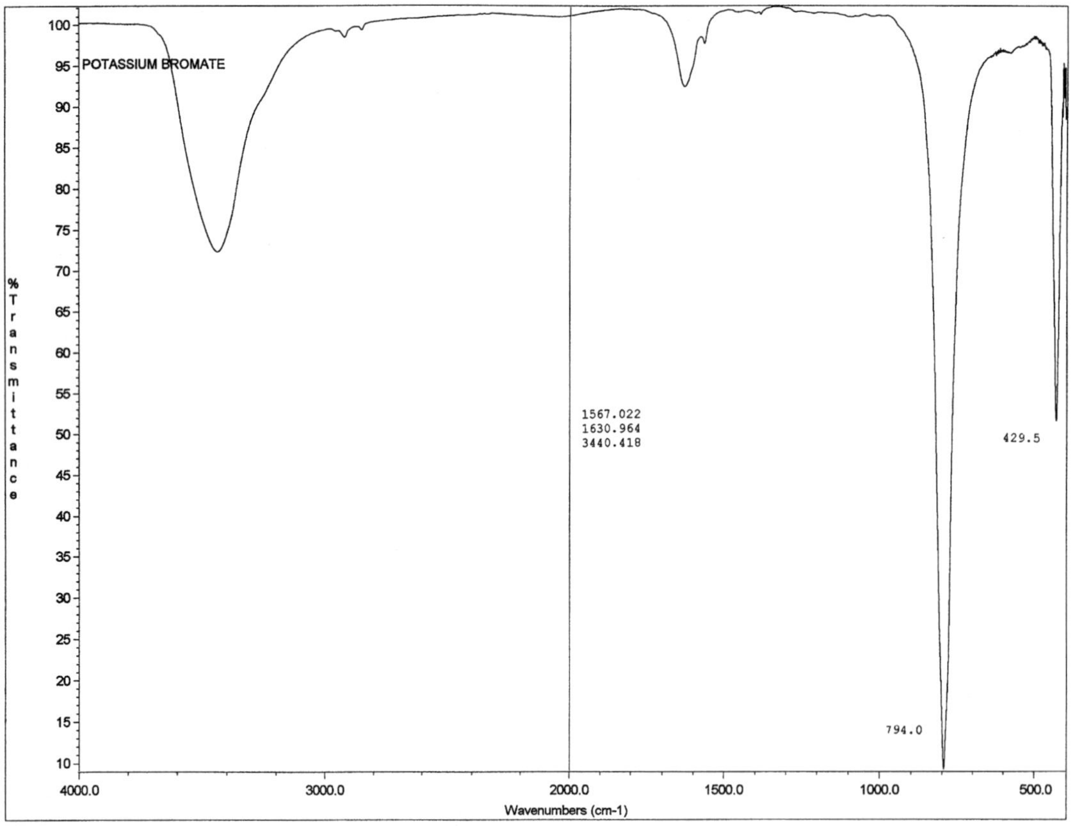

323 Potassium bromate $KBrO_3$

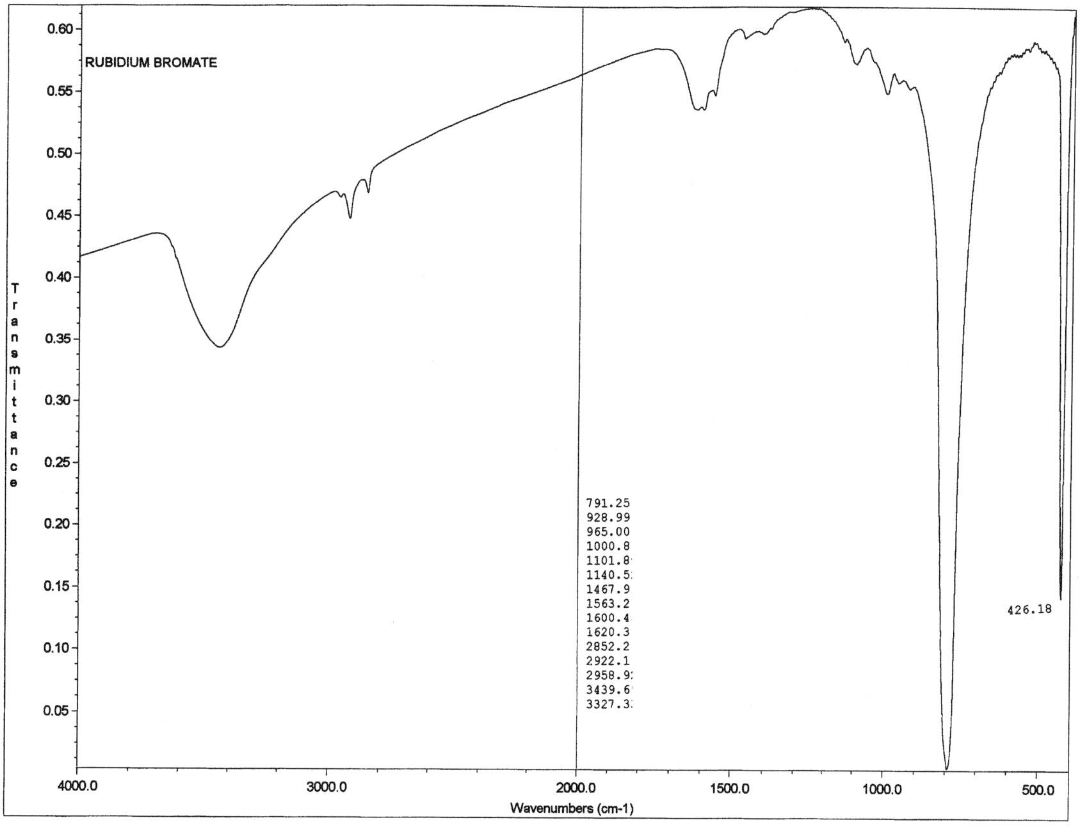

324 Rubidium bromate $RbBrO_3$

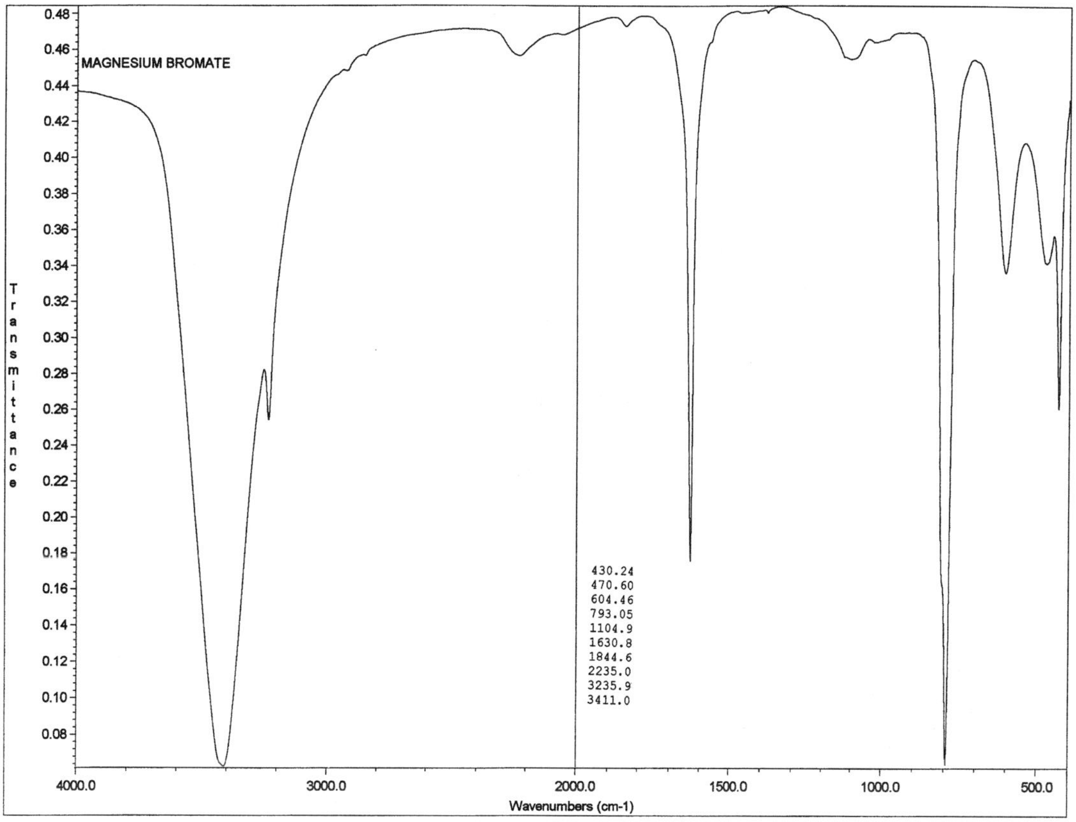

326 Magnesium bromate $Mg(BrO_3)_2 \cdot 6H_2O$

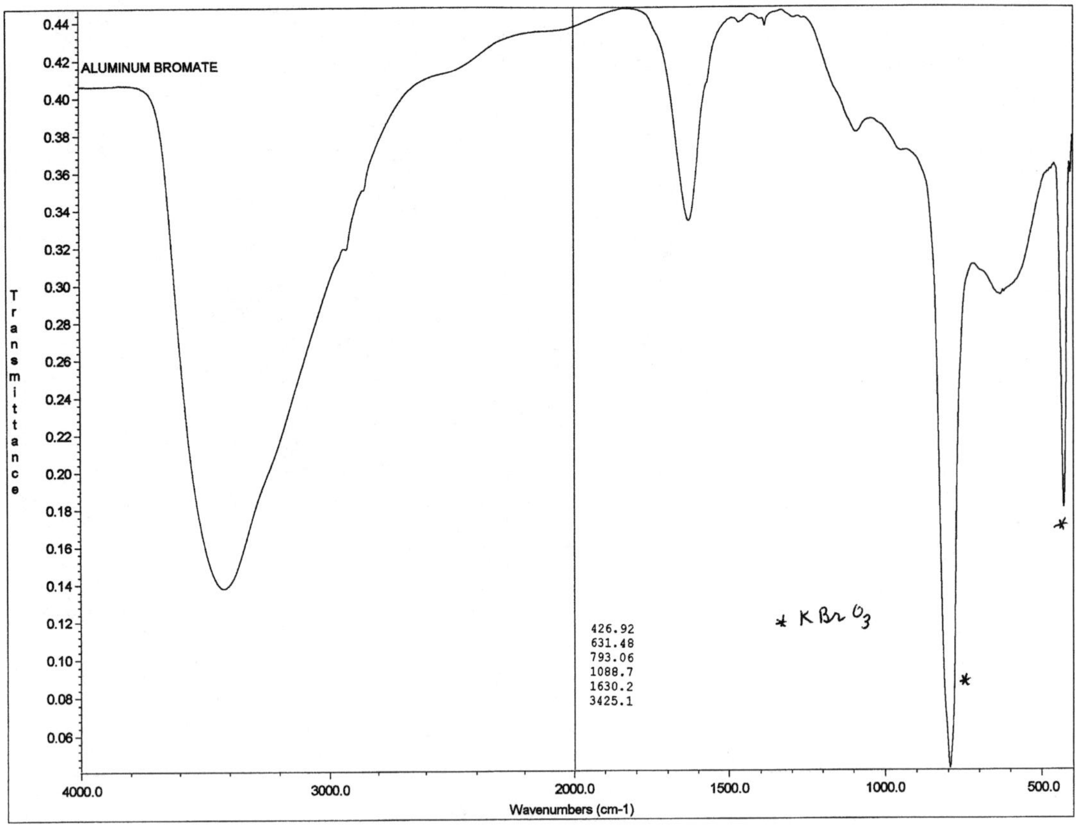

328 Aluminum bromate $Al(BrO_3)_3 \cdot 9H_2O$

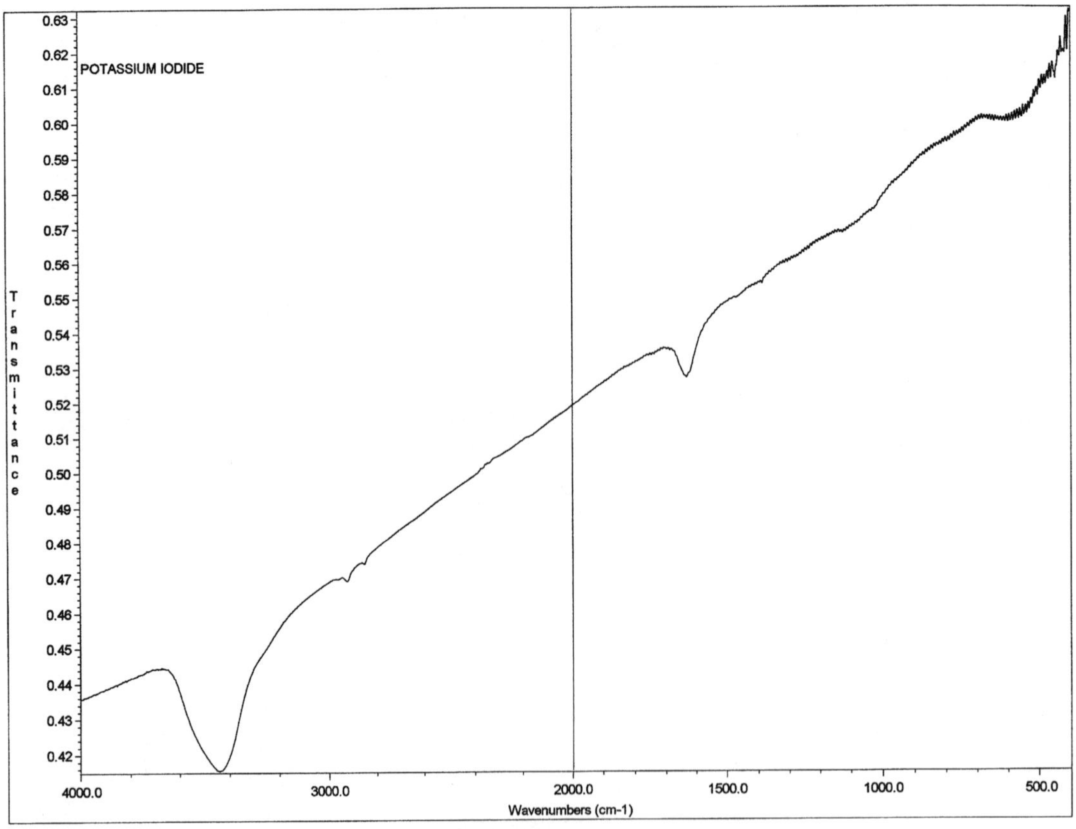

331 Potassium iodide KI

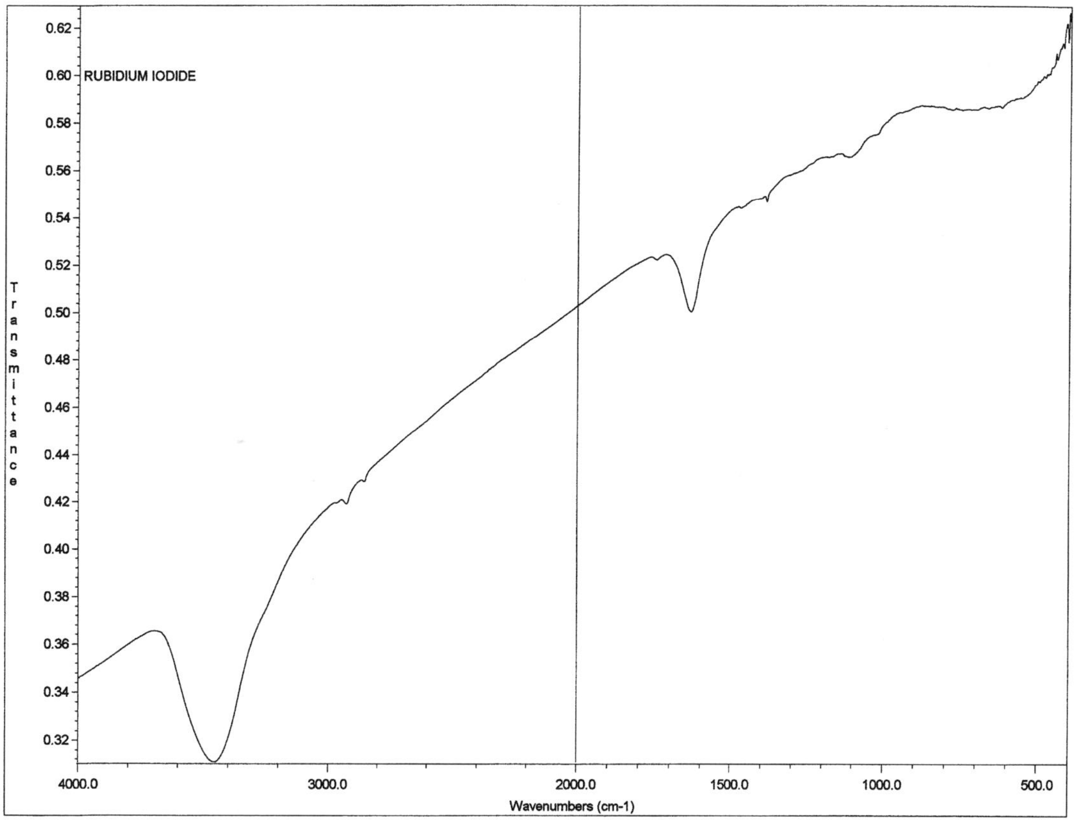

332 Rubidium iodide RbI

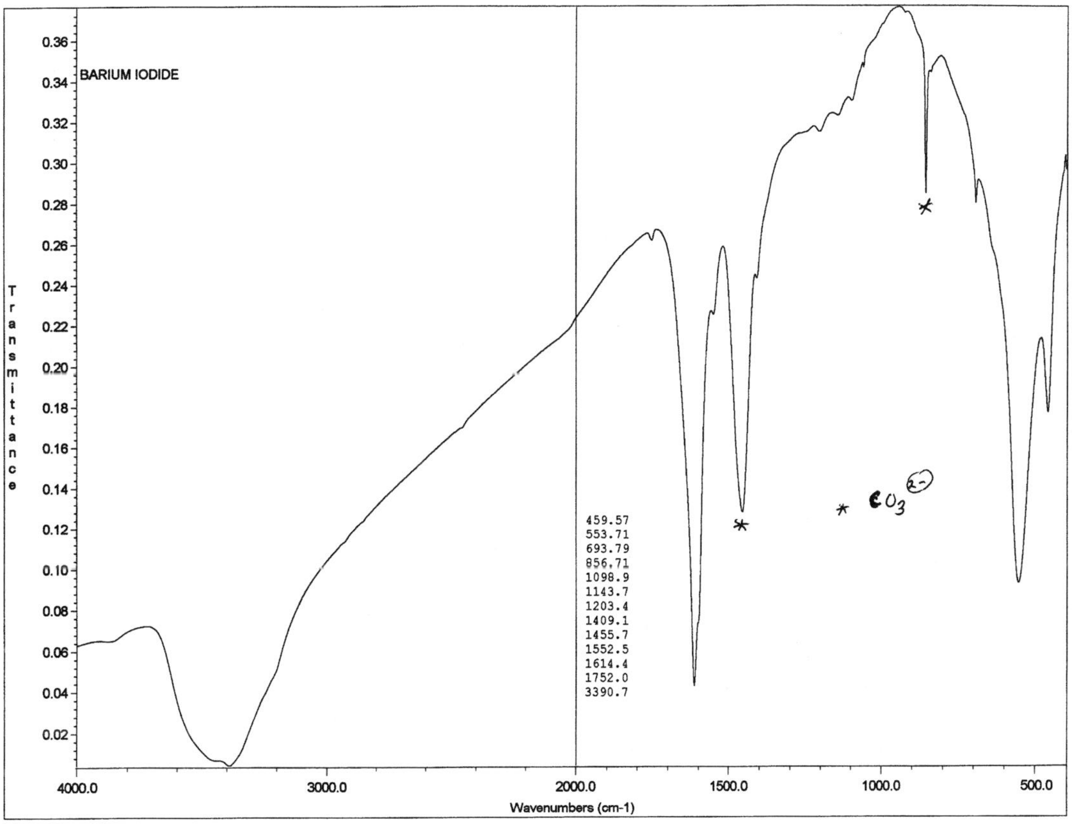

333 Barium iodide $BaI_2 \cdot 2H_2O$

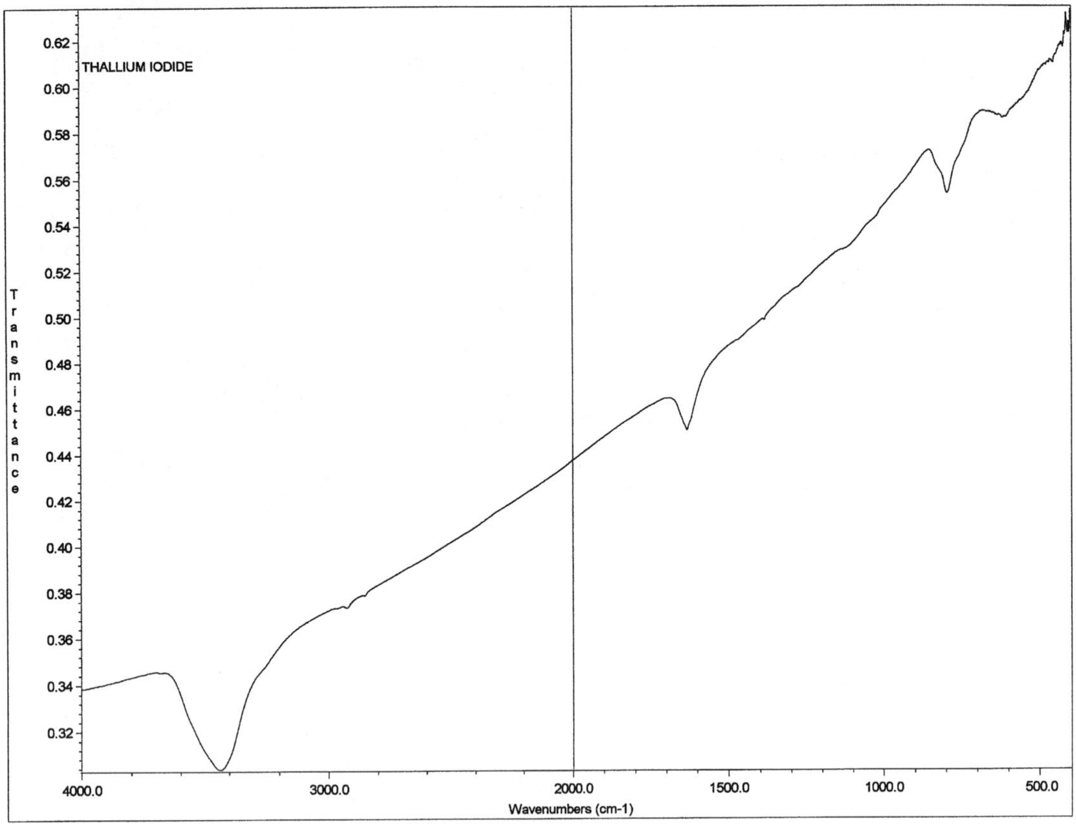

334 Thallium iodide TlI

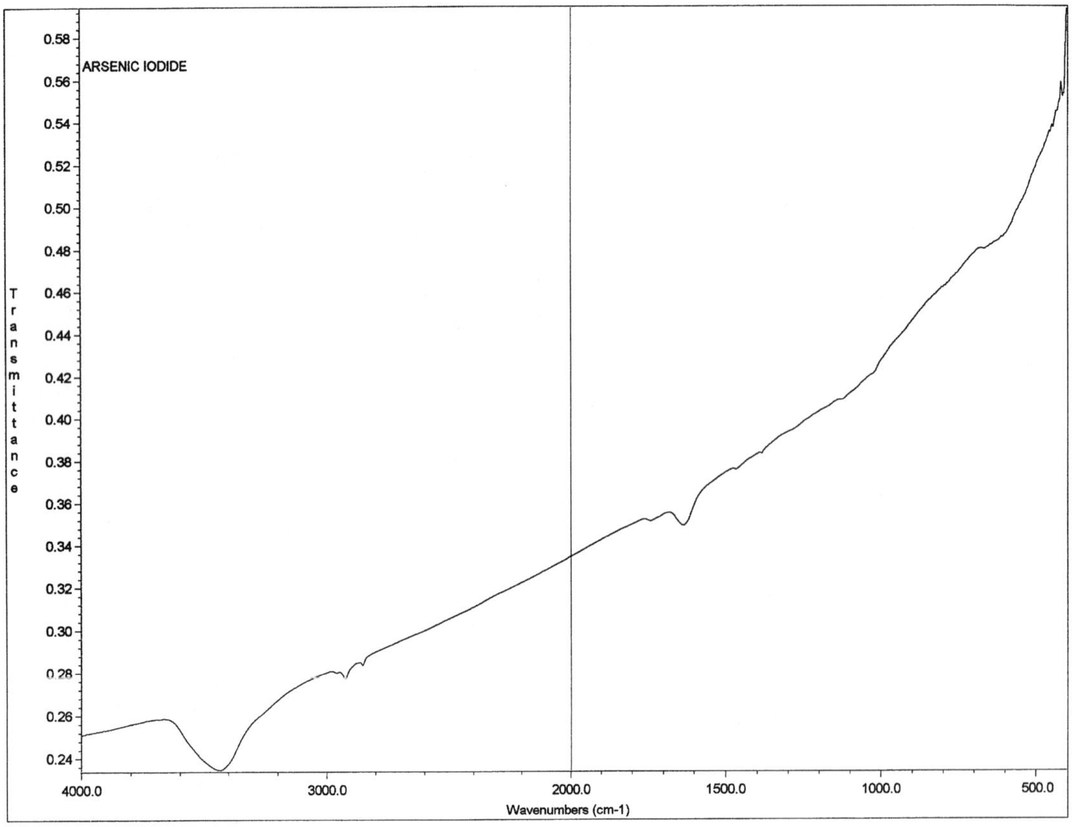

335 Arsenic iodide AsI_3

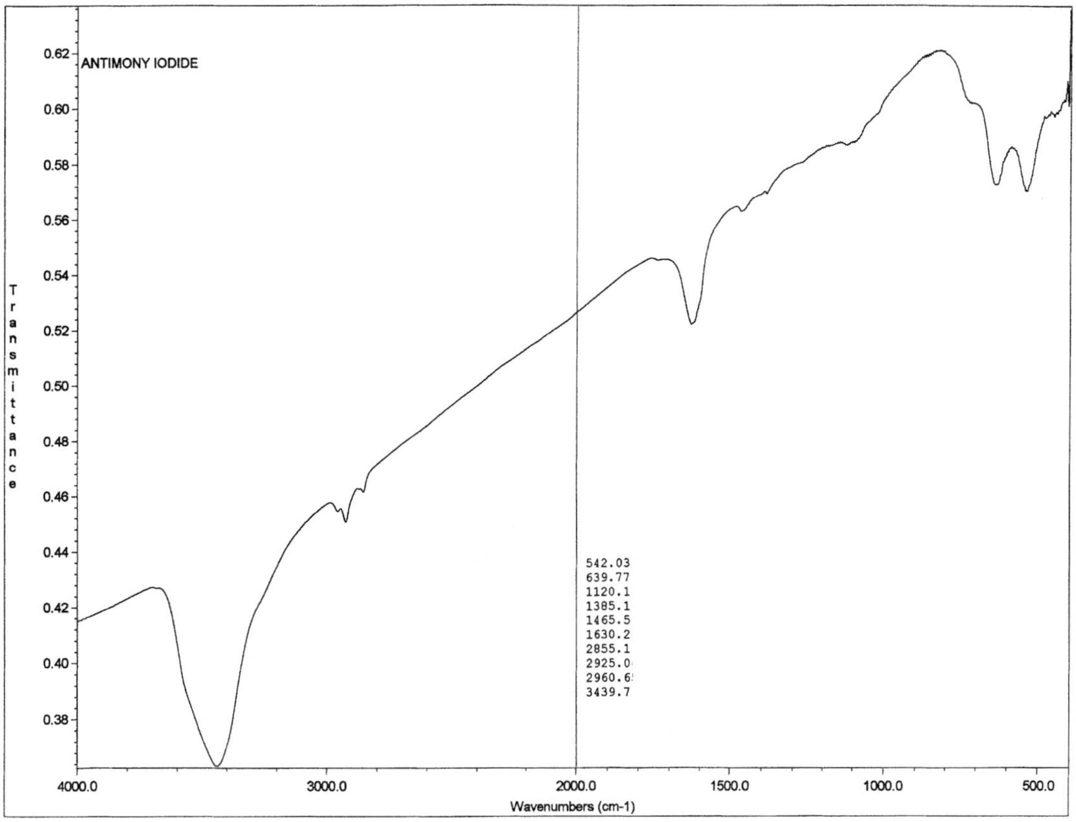

336 Antimony iodide SbI_3

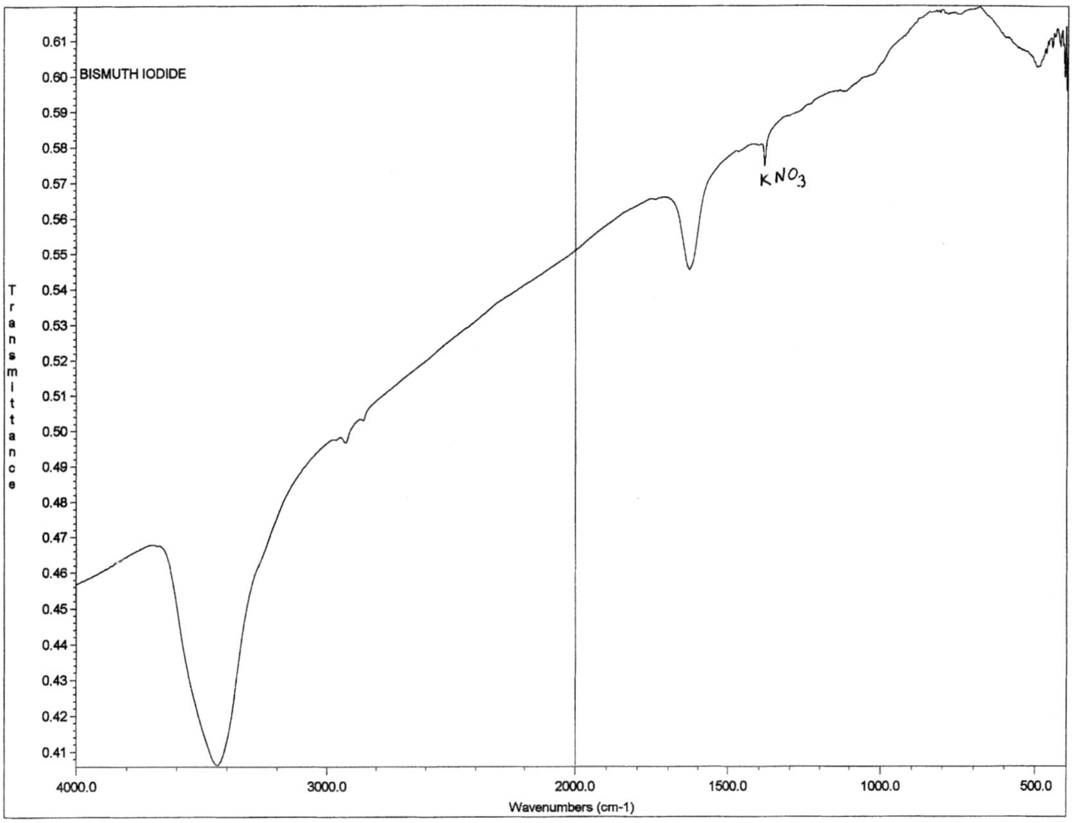

337 Bismuth iodide $BiI_3 \cdot xH_2O$ or wet

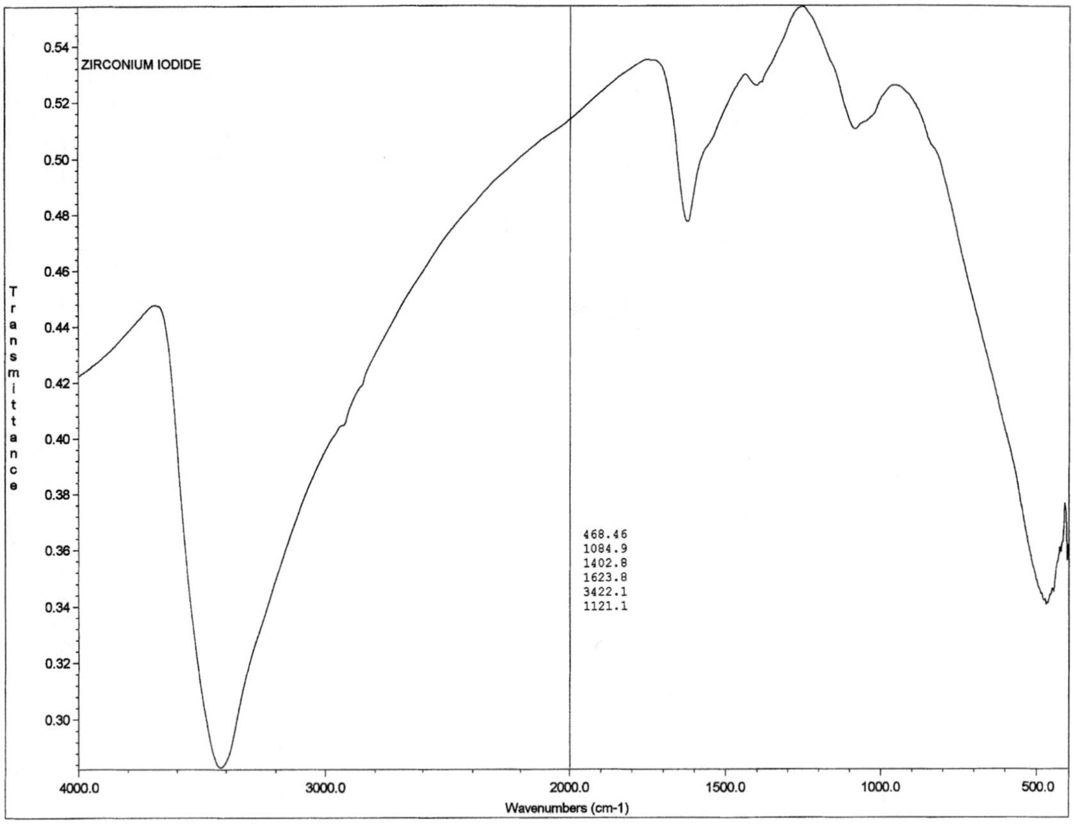

338 Zirconium iodide $ZrI_4 \cdot xH_2O$

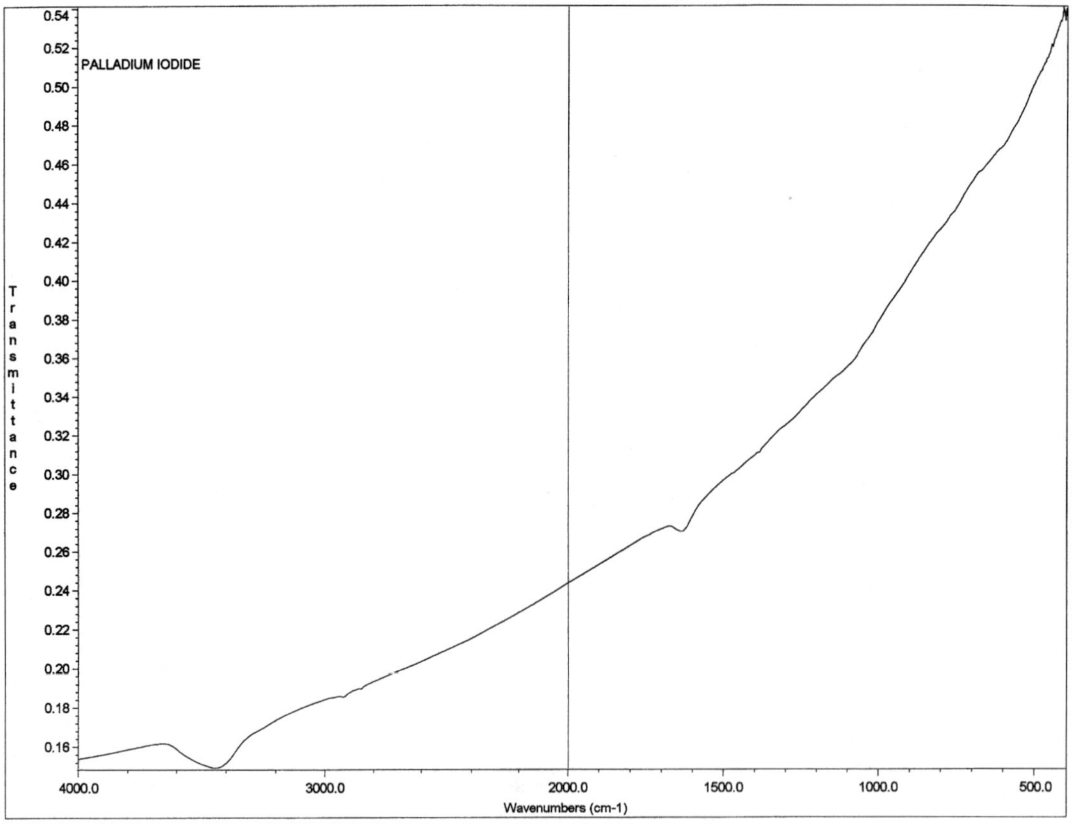

339 Palladium iodide PdI_2

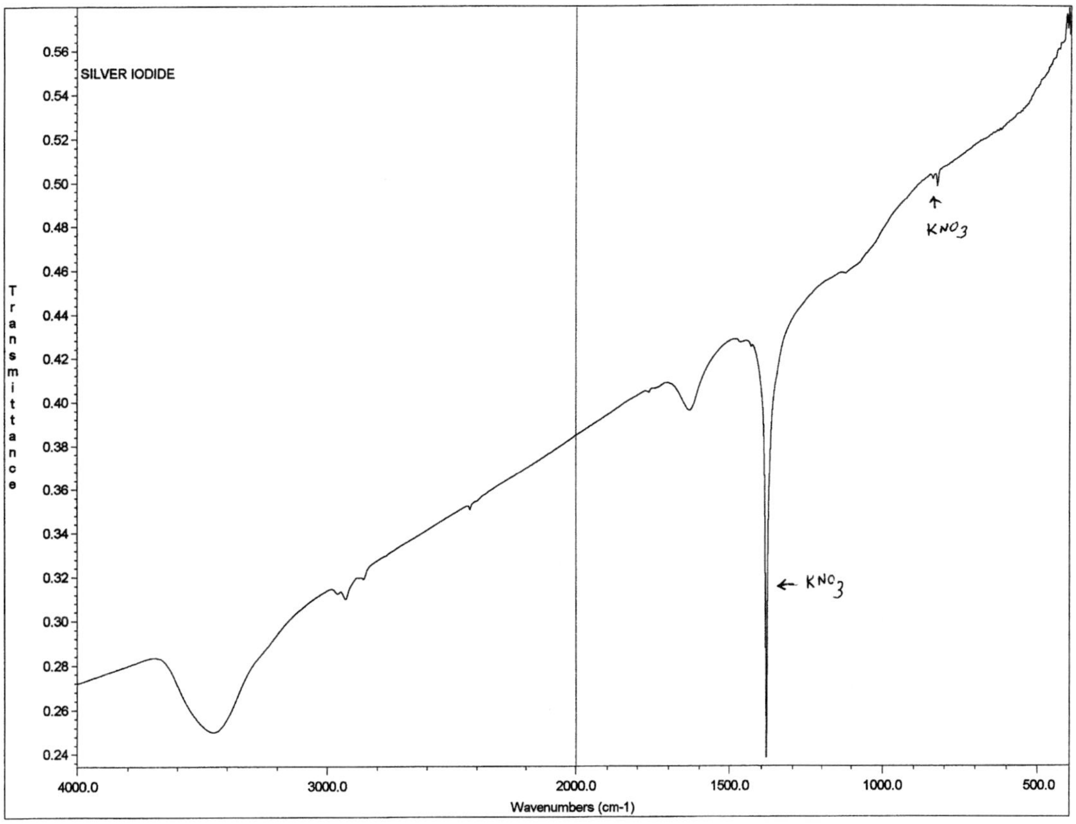

340 Silver iodide AgI_2

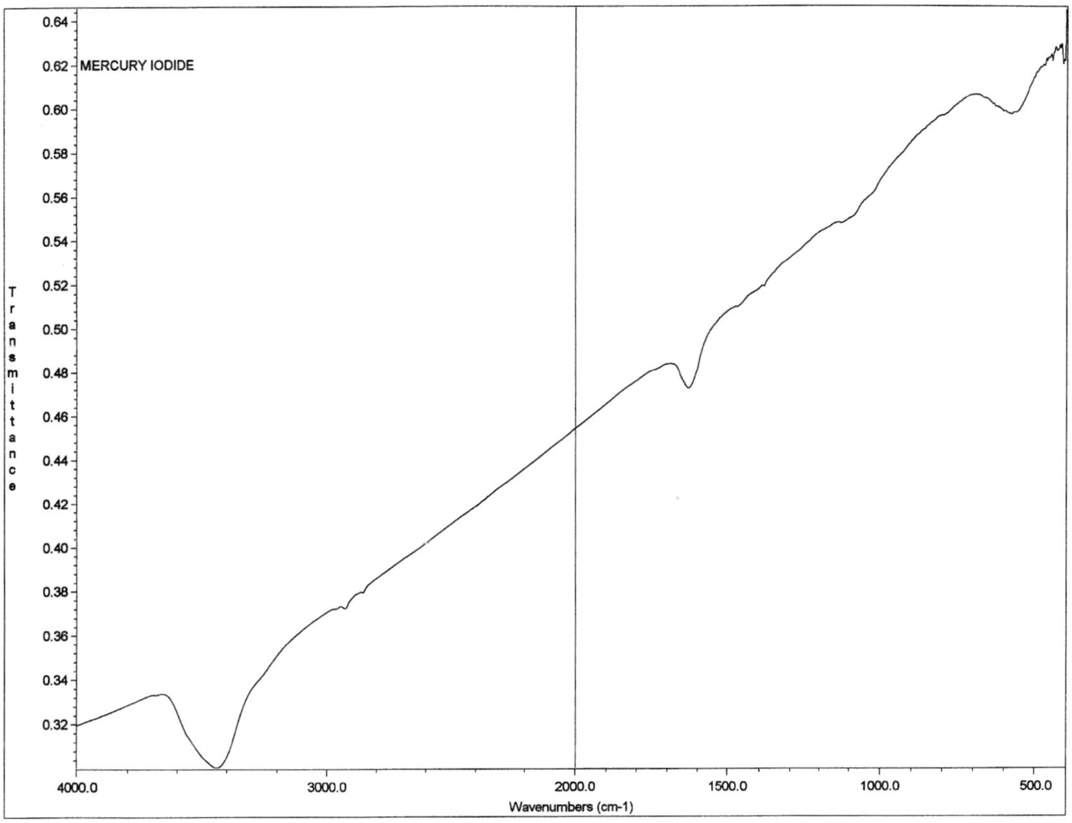

341 Mercury (II) iodide HgI

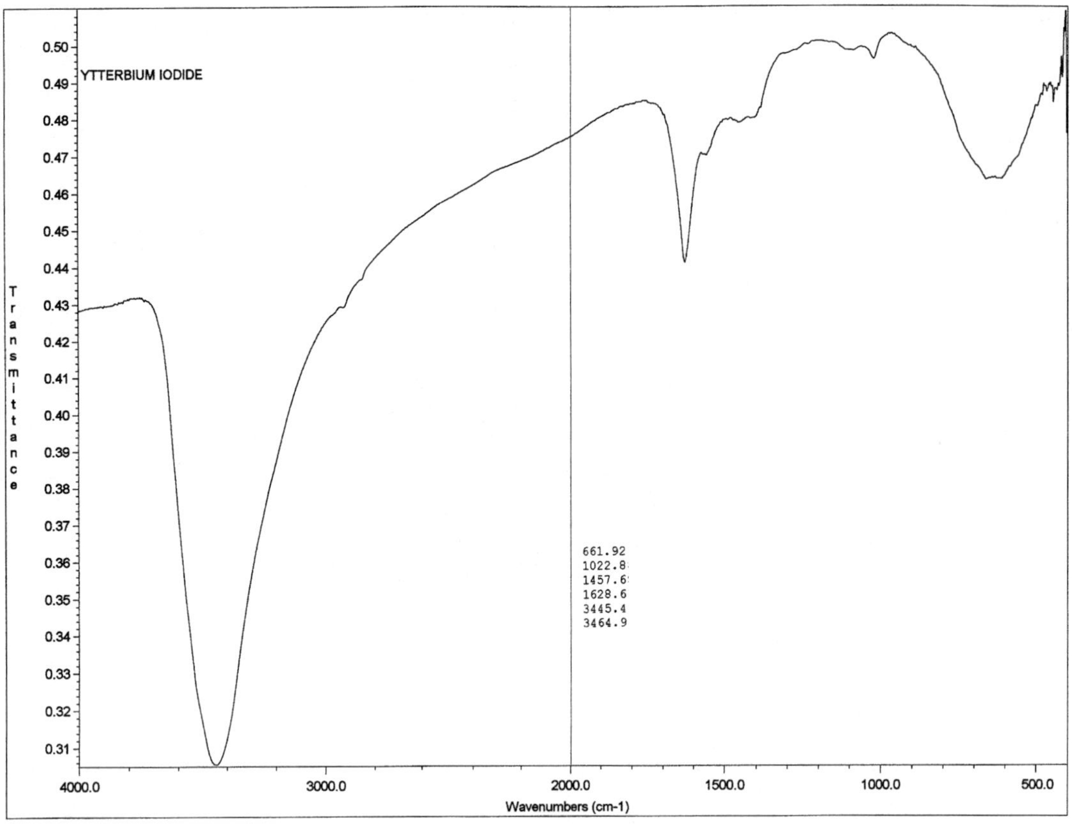

342 Ytterbium iodide $YbI_3 \cdot xH_2O$

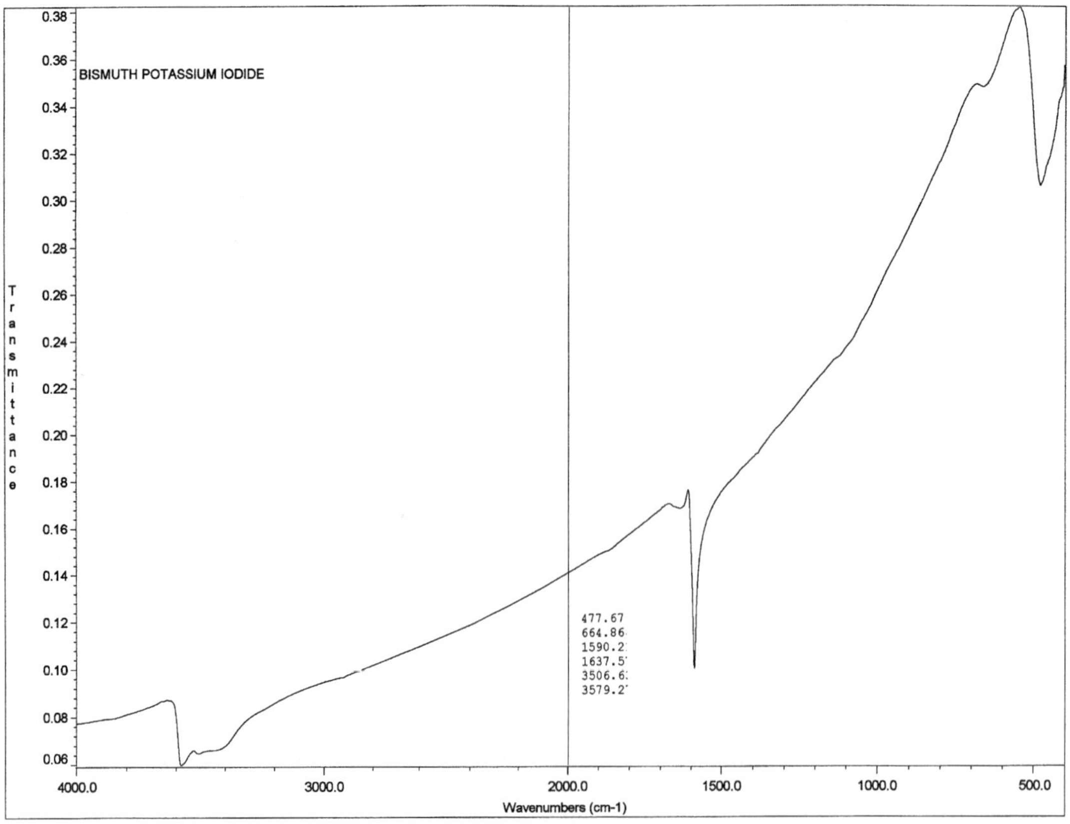

343 Potassium bismuth iodide $K_4BiI_7 \cdot xH_2O$

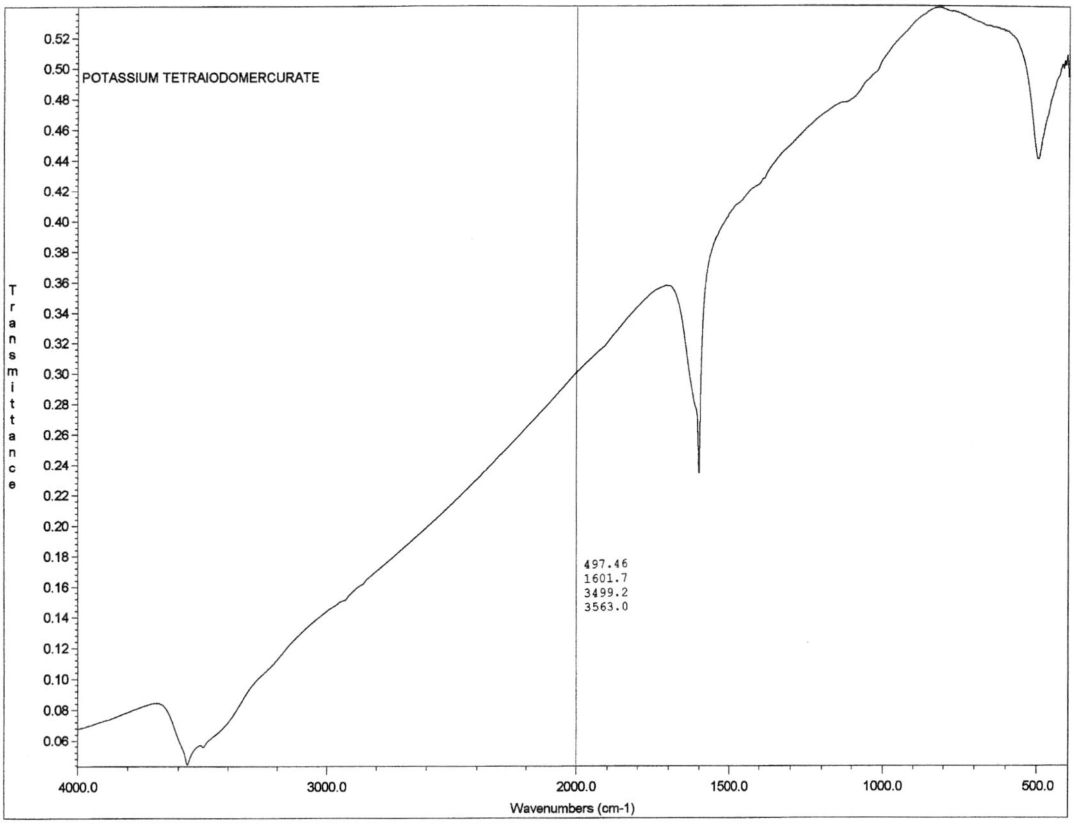

344 Potassium tetraiodomercurate (II) $K_2HgI_4 \cdot xH_2O$

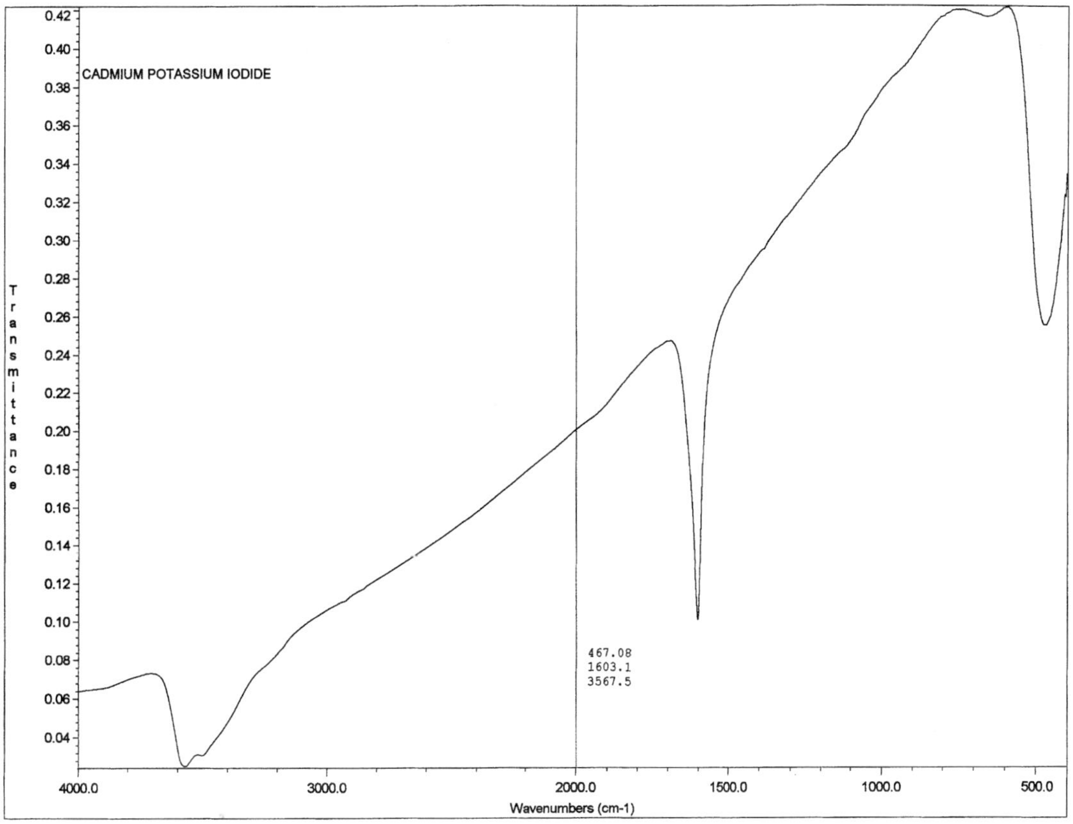

345 Potassium iodocadmate $K_2CdI_4 \cdot xH_2O$

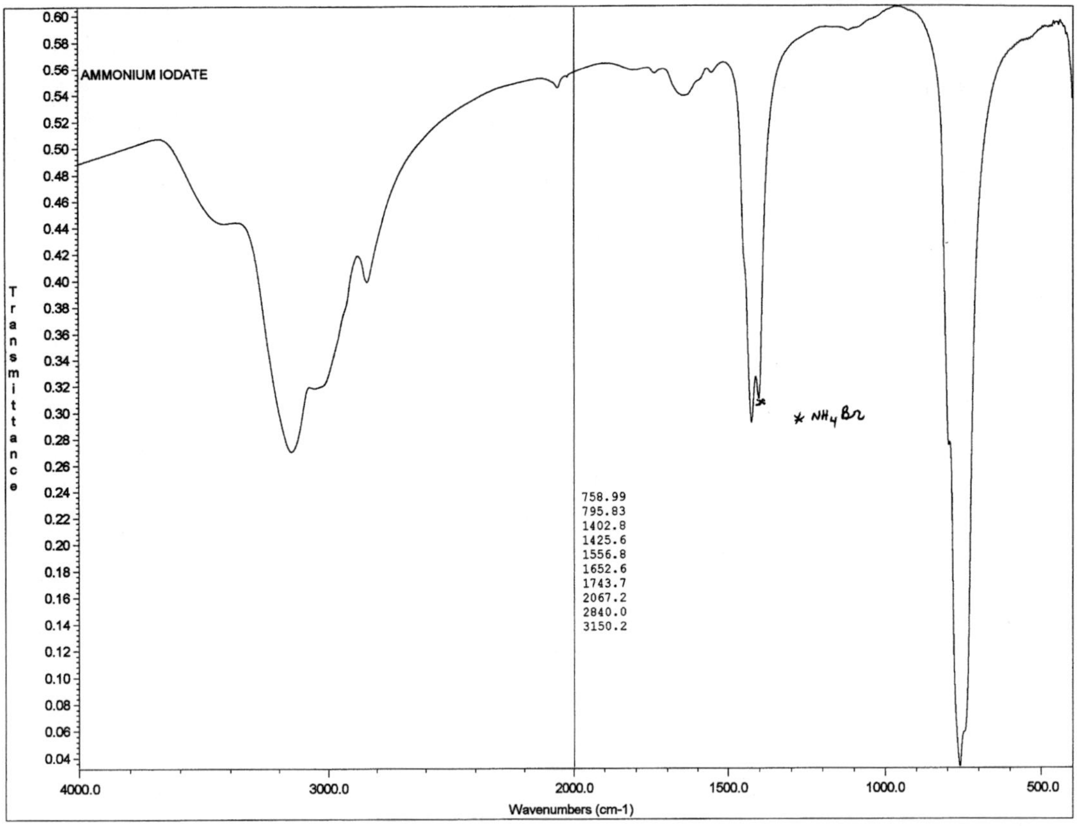

346 Ammonium iodate NH_4IO_3

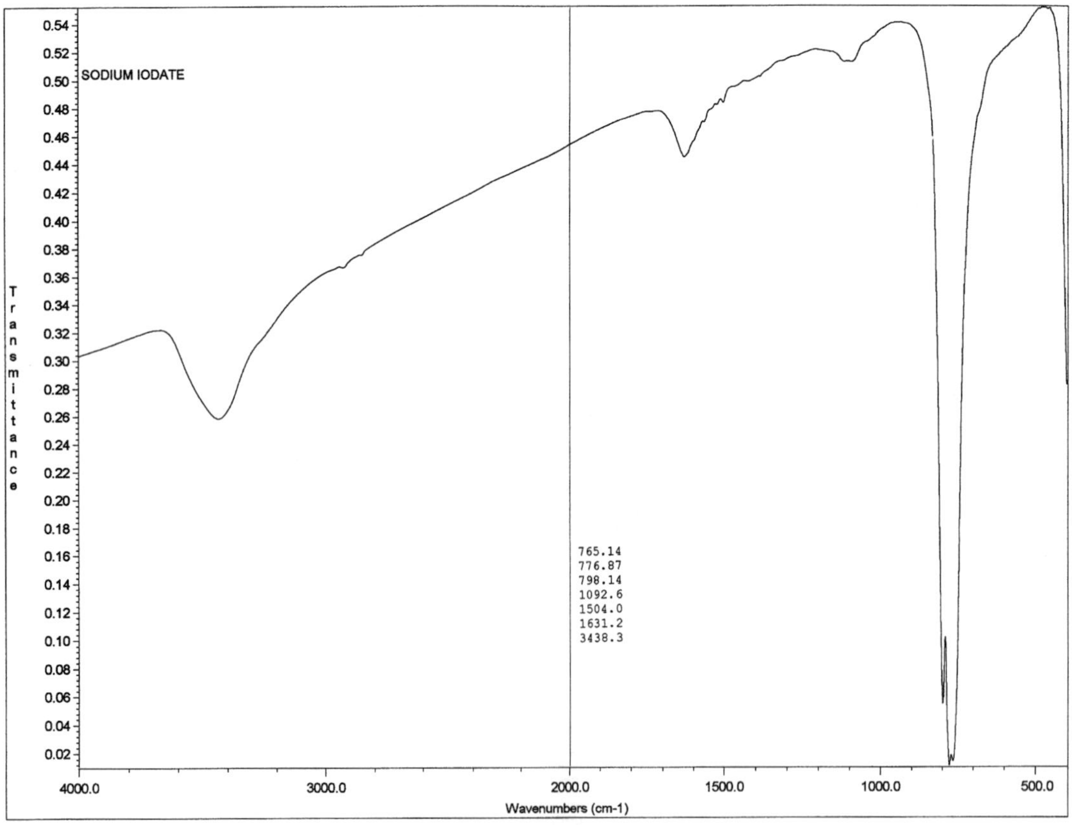

347 Sodium iodate $NaIO_3$

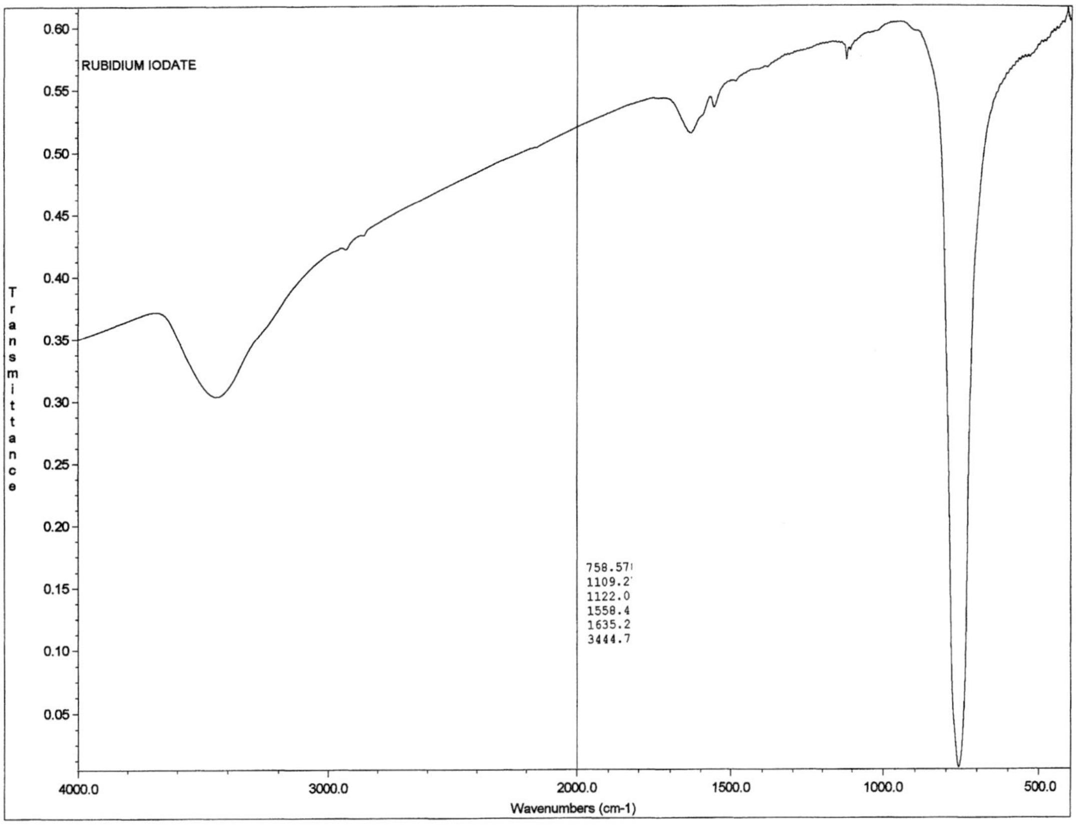

348 Rubidium iodate $RbIO_3$

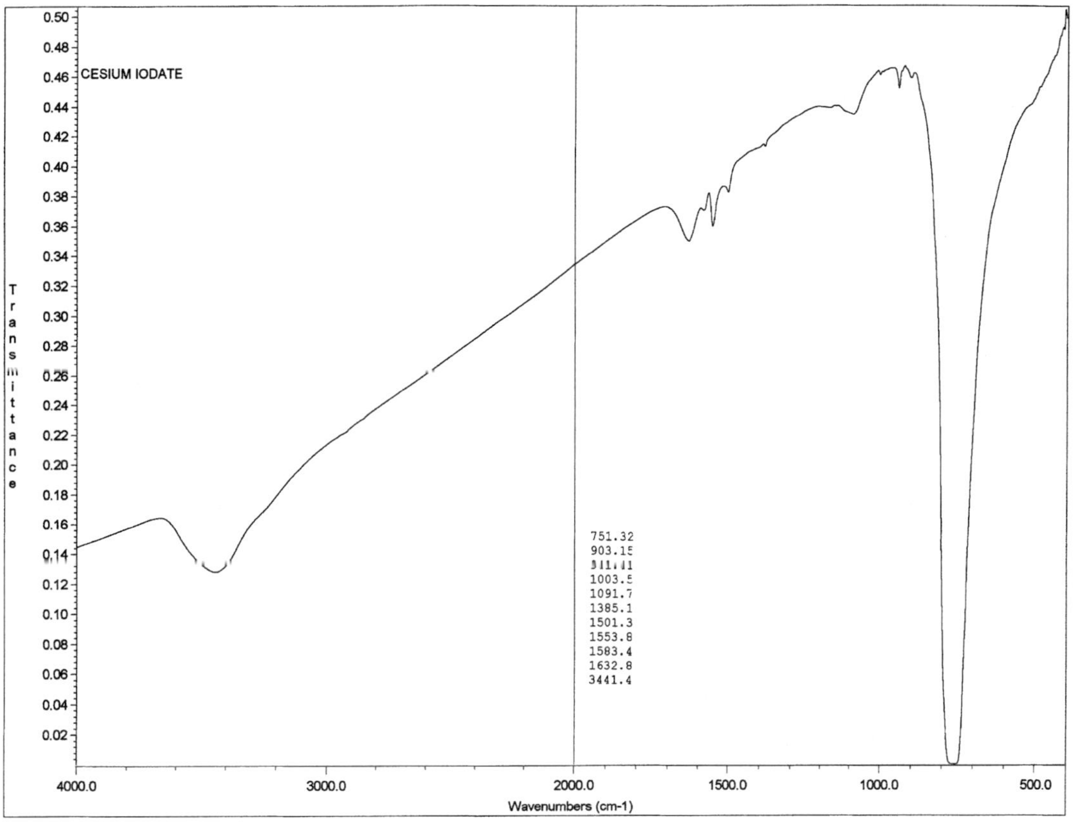

349 Cesium iodate $CsIO_3 \cdot xH_2O$

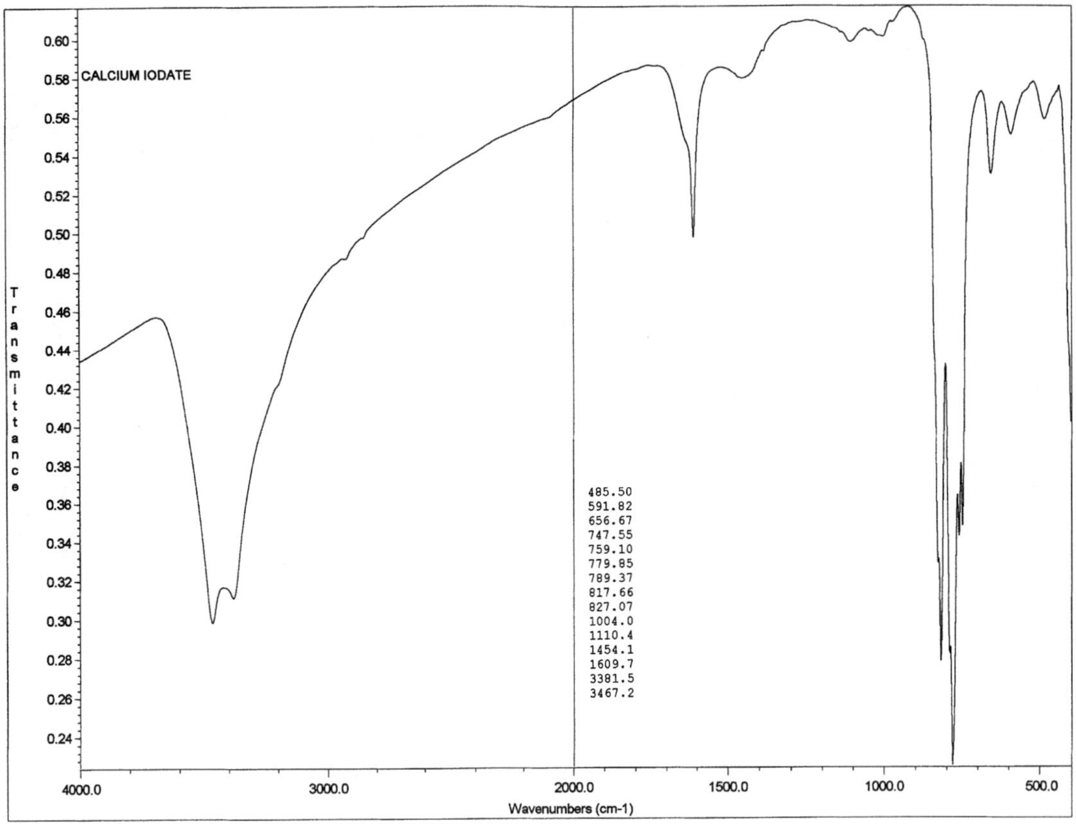

350 Calcium iodate $Ca(IO_3)_2 \cdot 6H_2O$

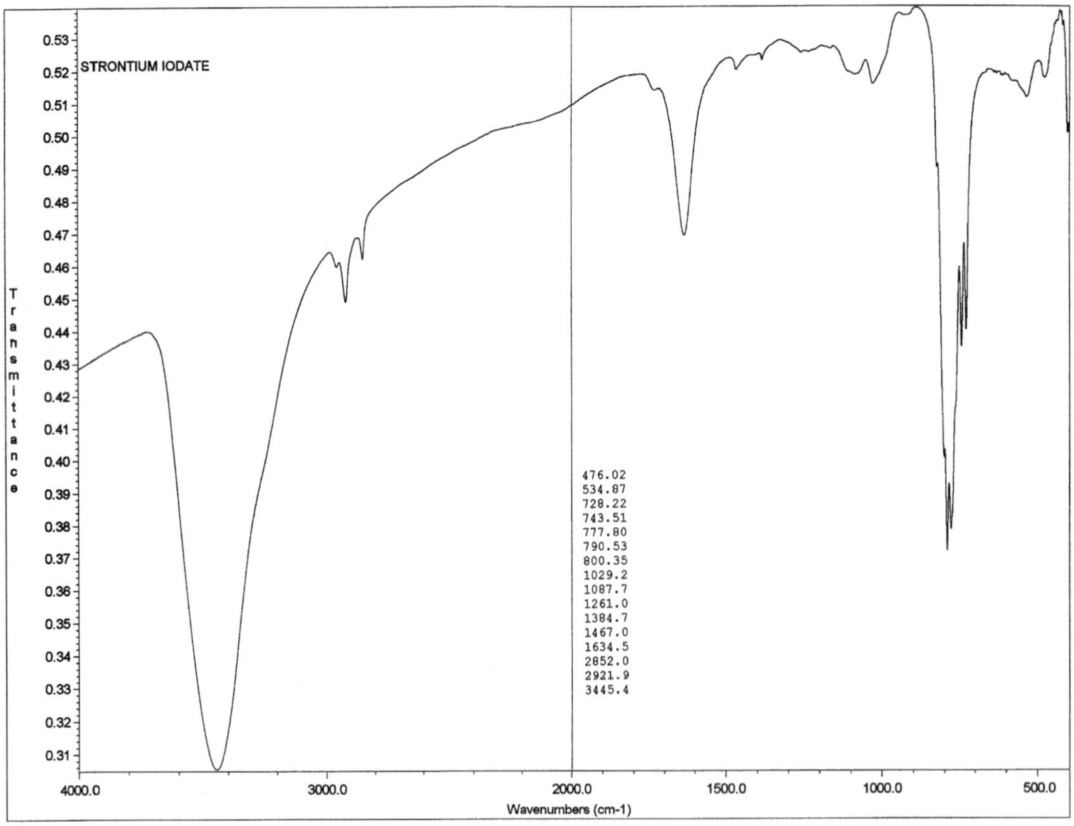

351 Strontium iodate $Sr(IO_3)_2 \cdot xH_2O$

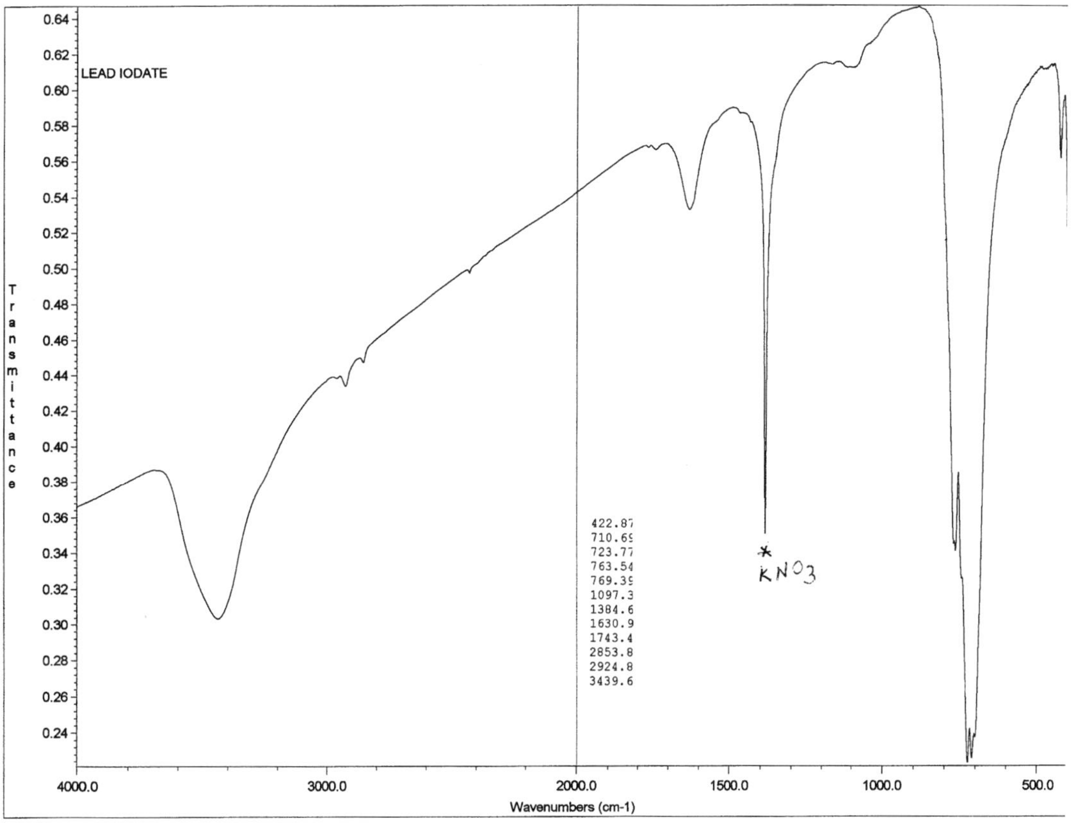

353 Lead iodate $Pb(IO_3)_2$

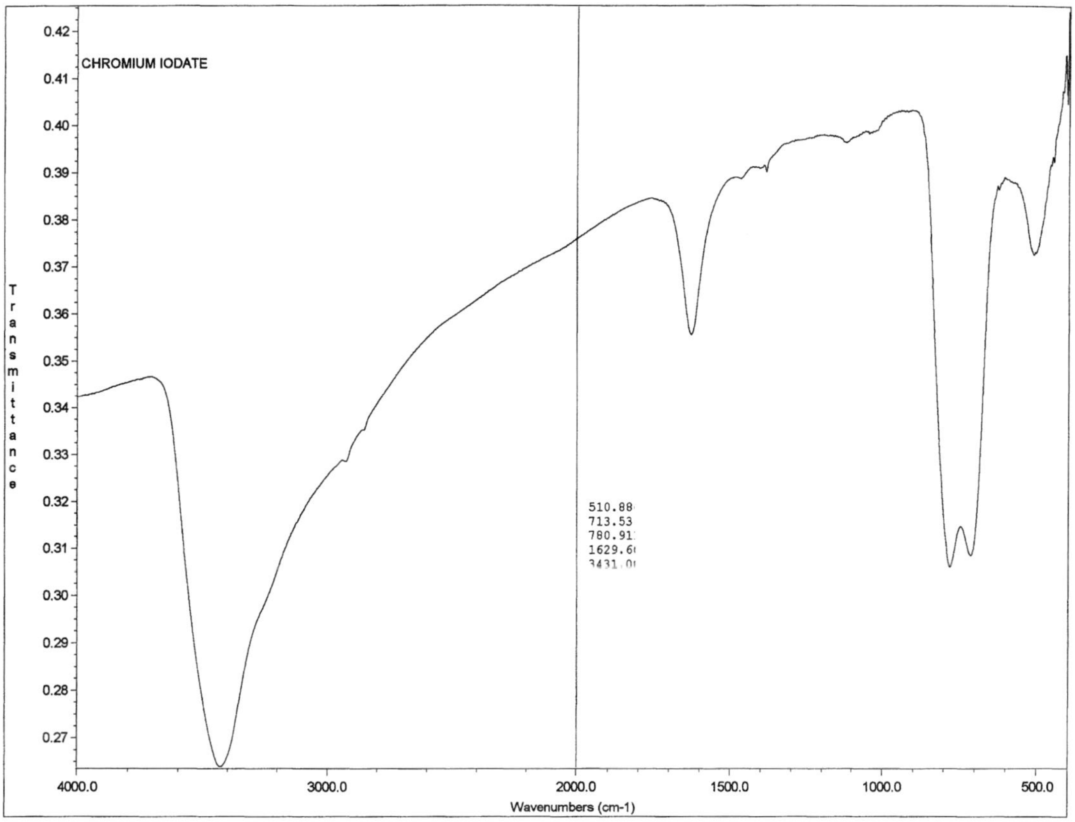

354 Chromium (III) iodate $Cr(IO_3)_3 \cdot xH_2O$

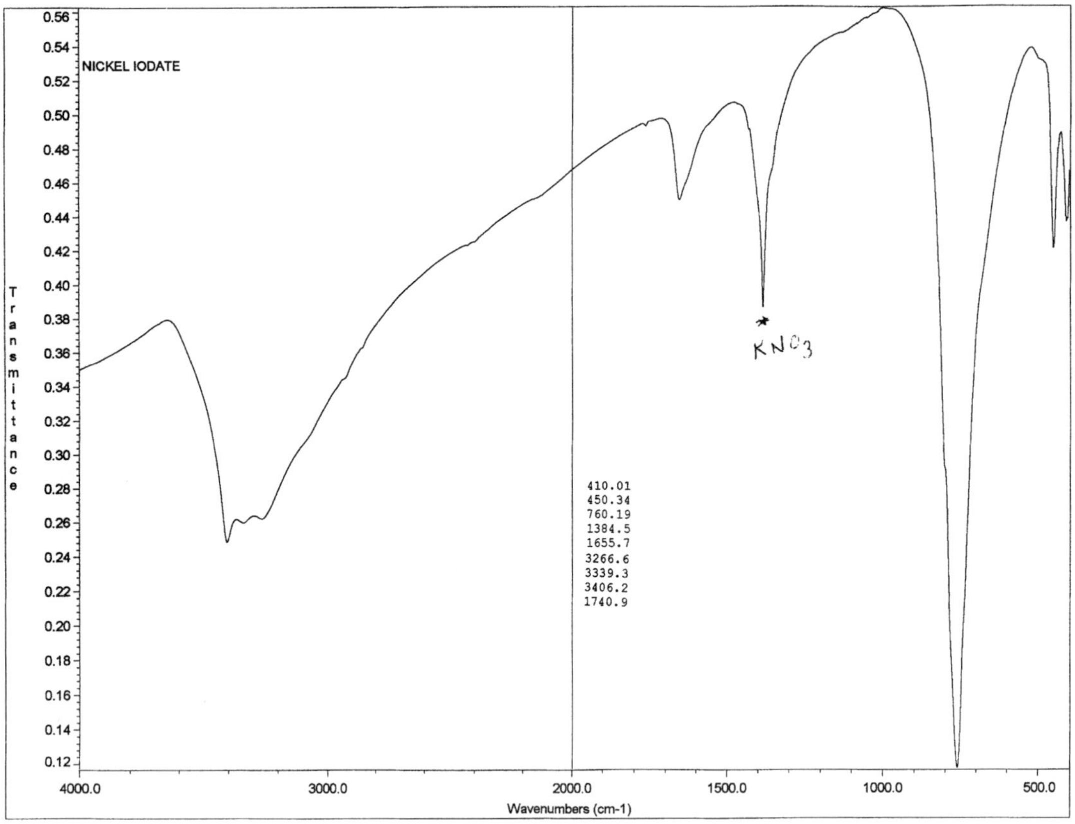

355 Nickel iodate $Ni(IO_3)_2 \cdot xH_2O$

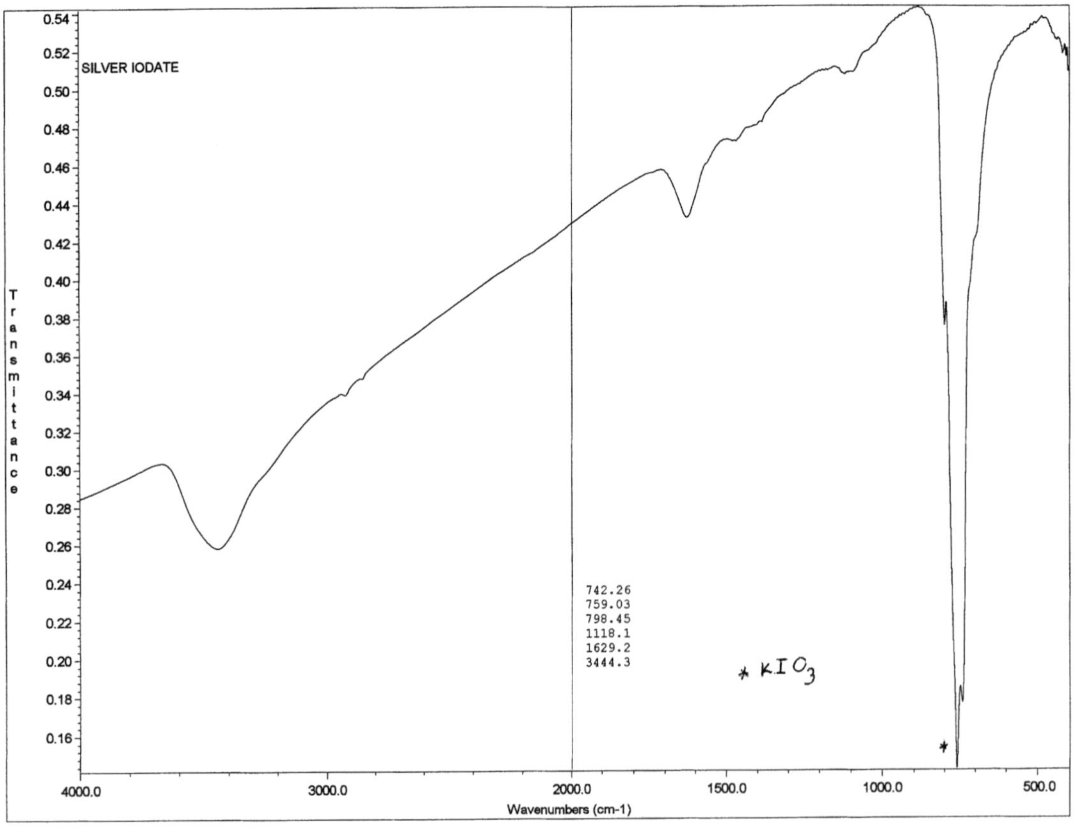

356 Silver iodate $AgIO_3$

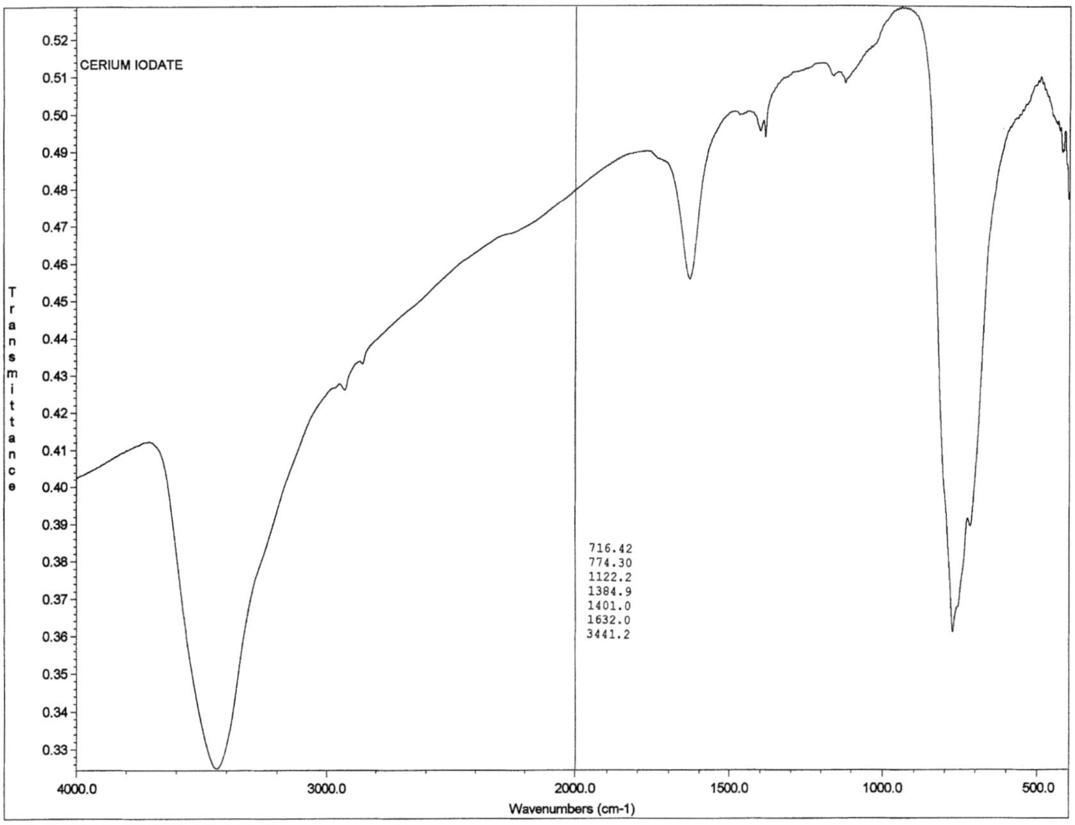

357 Cerium iodate $Ce(IO_3)_4 \cdot xH_2O$

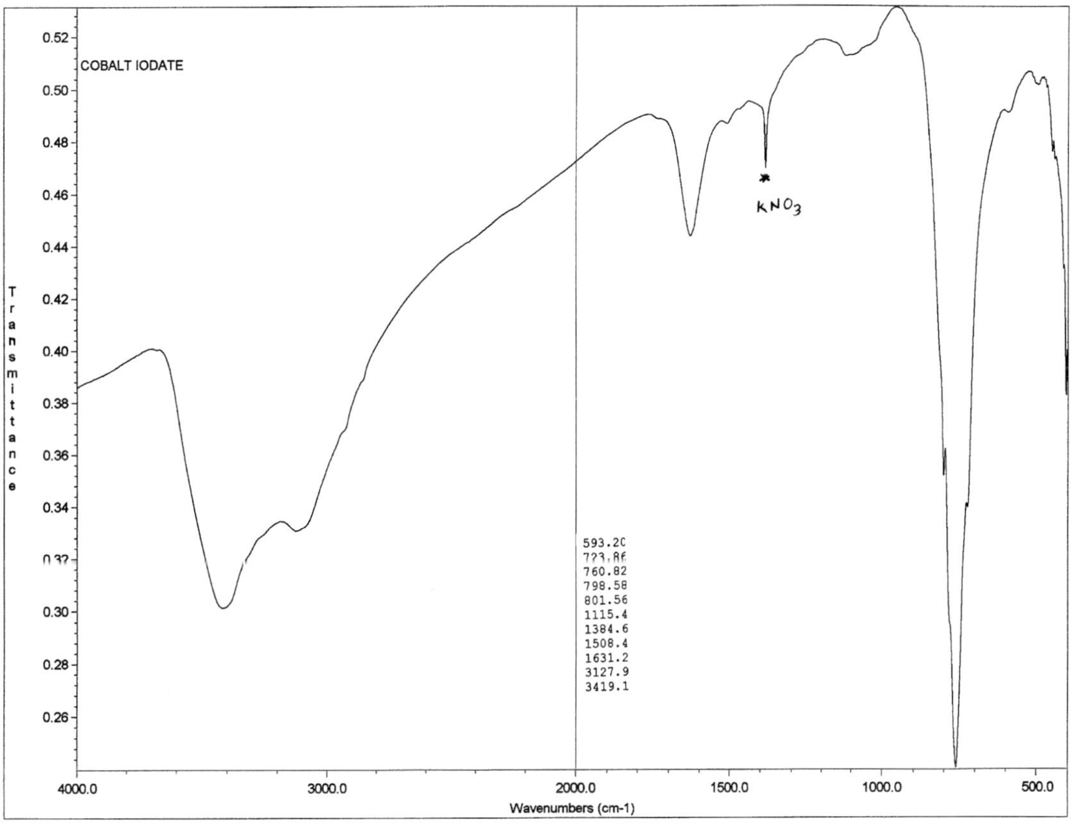

358 Cobalt iodate $Co(IO_3)_2 \cdot H_2O$

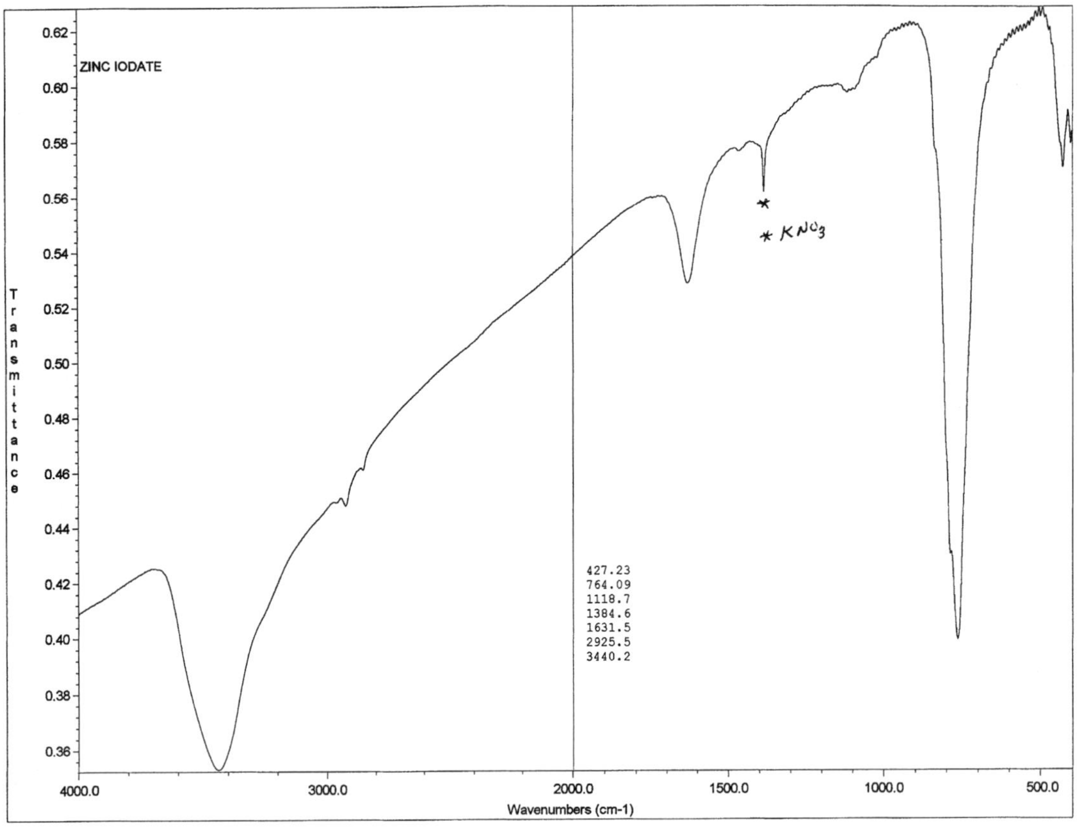

359 Zinc iodate $Zn(IO_3)_x \cdot xH_2O$

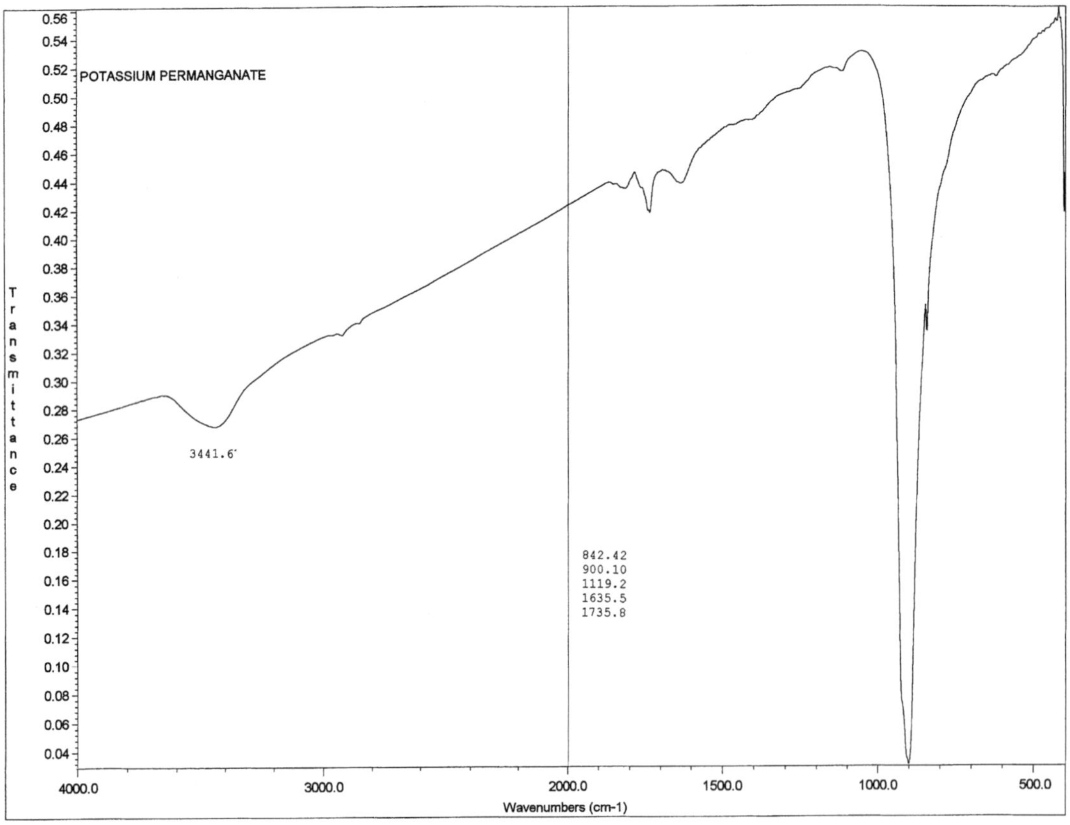

362 Potassium permanganate $KMnO_4$

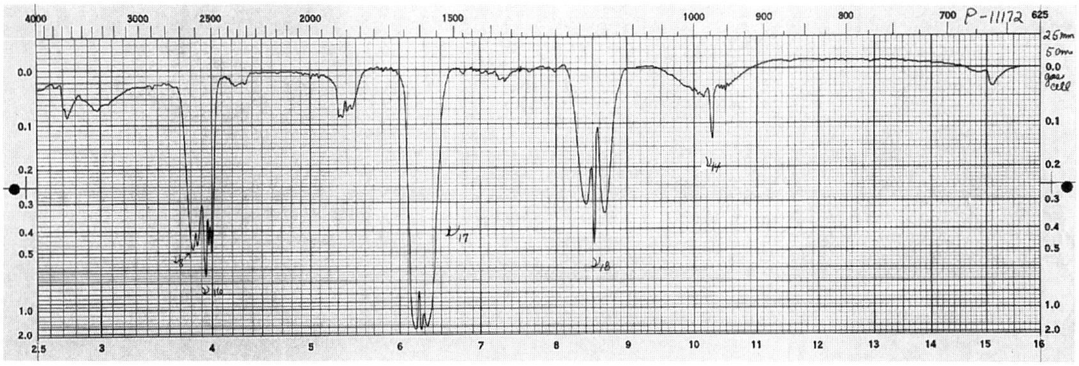

363 Diborane B_2H_6

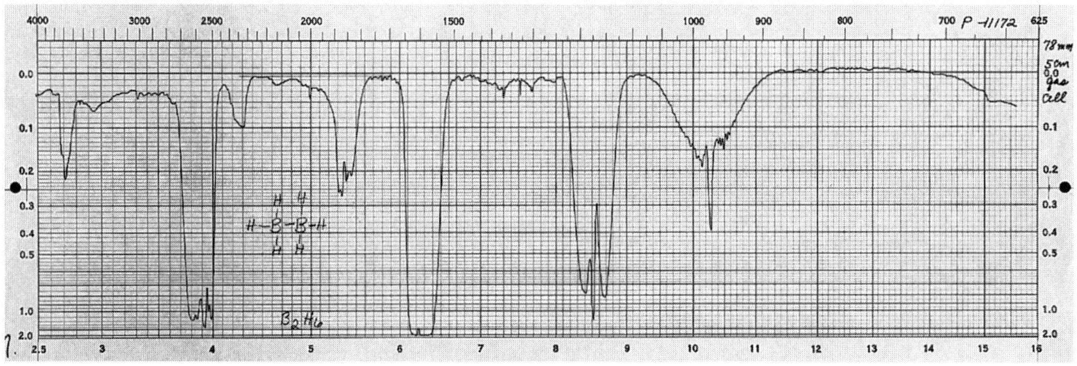

363a Diborane B_2H_6

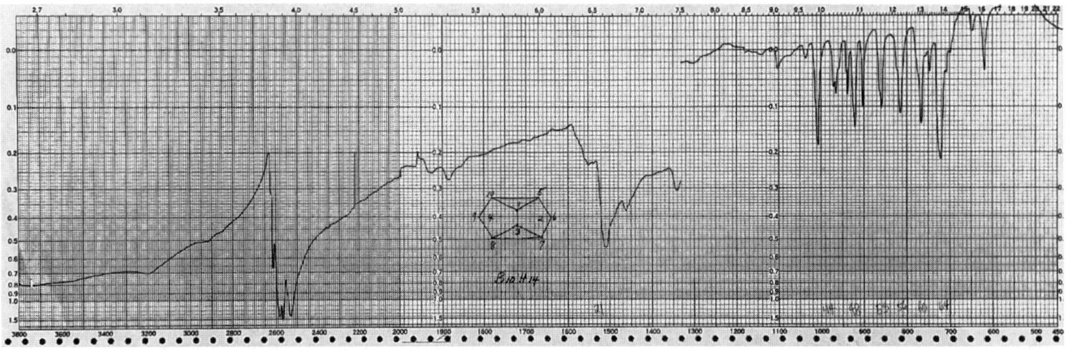

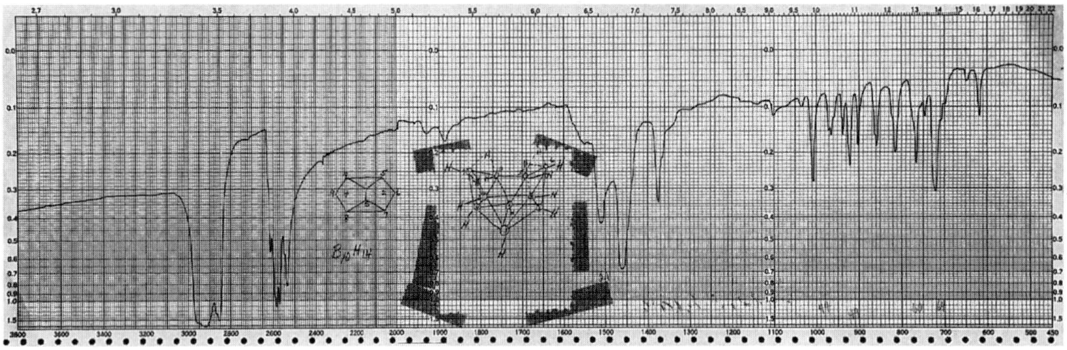

364 Decaborane $B_{10}H_{14}$

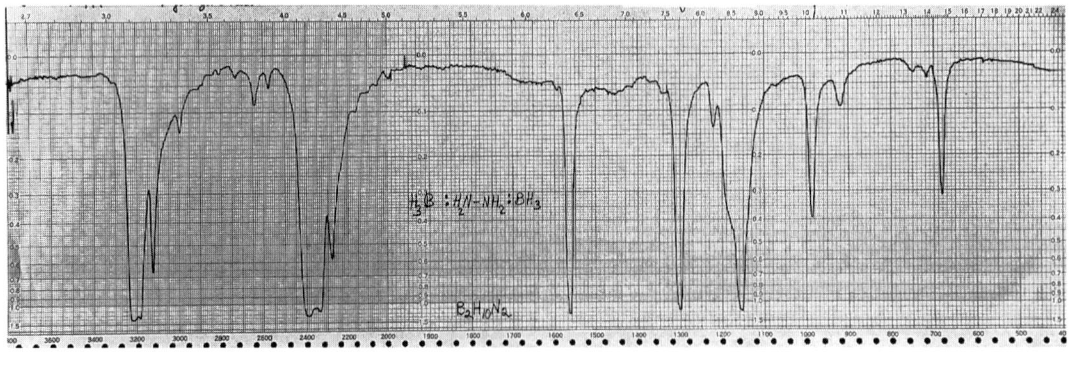

365 Hydrazine diborane $B_2H_{10}N_2$

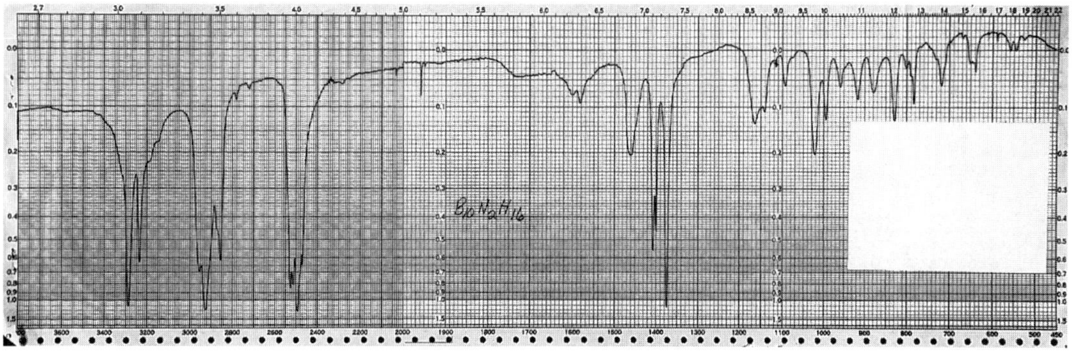

366 Decaborane monohydrazine $B_{10}H_{16}N_2$

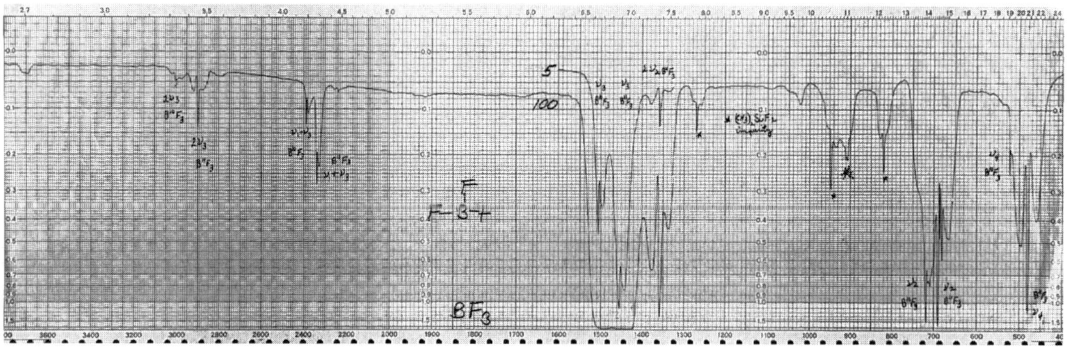

367 Boron trifluoride BF_3

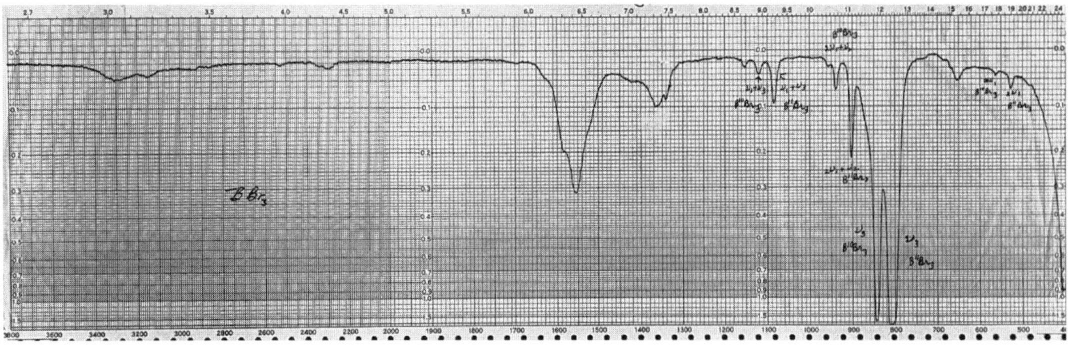

368 Boron tribromide BBr_3

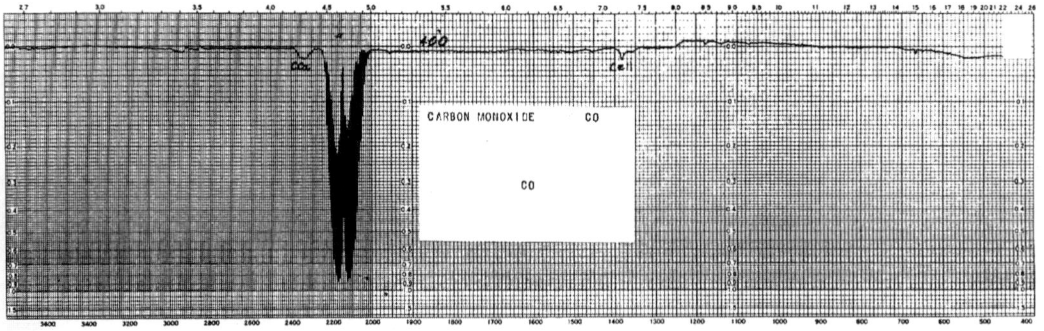

369 Carbon monoxide CO

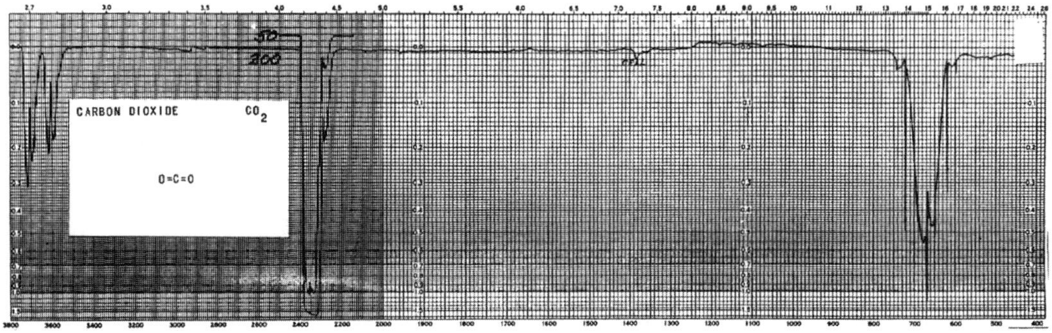

370 Carbon dioxide CO_2

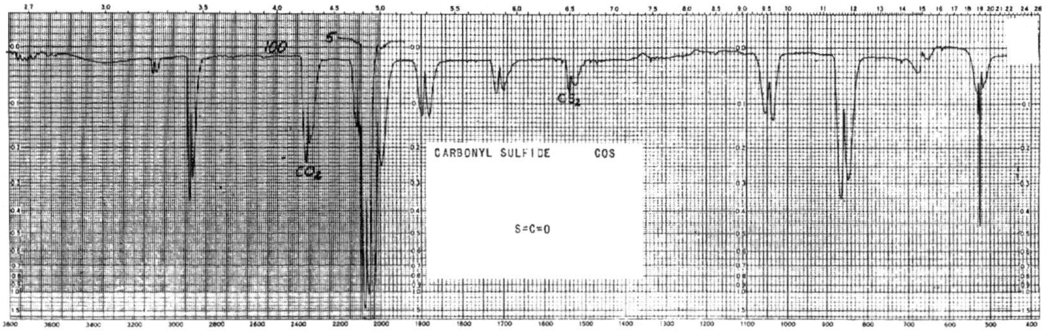

371 Carbonyl sulfide COS

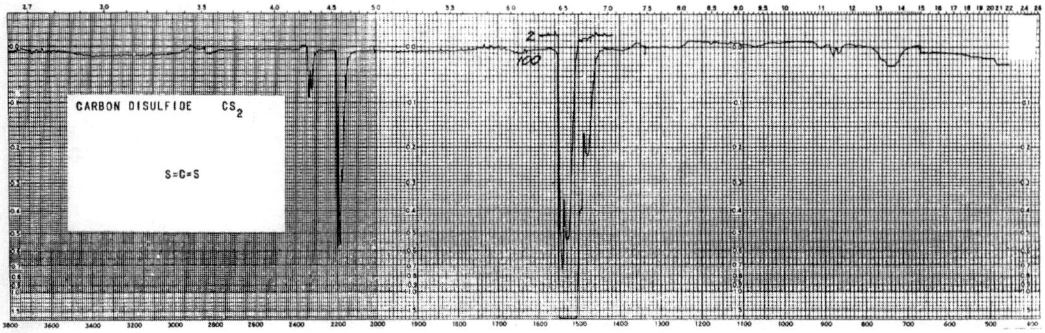

372 Carbon disulfide CS_2

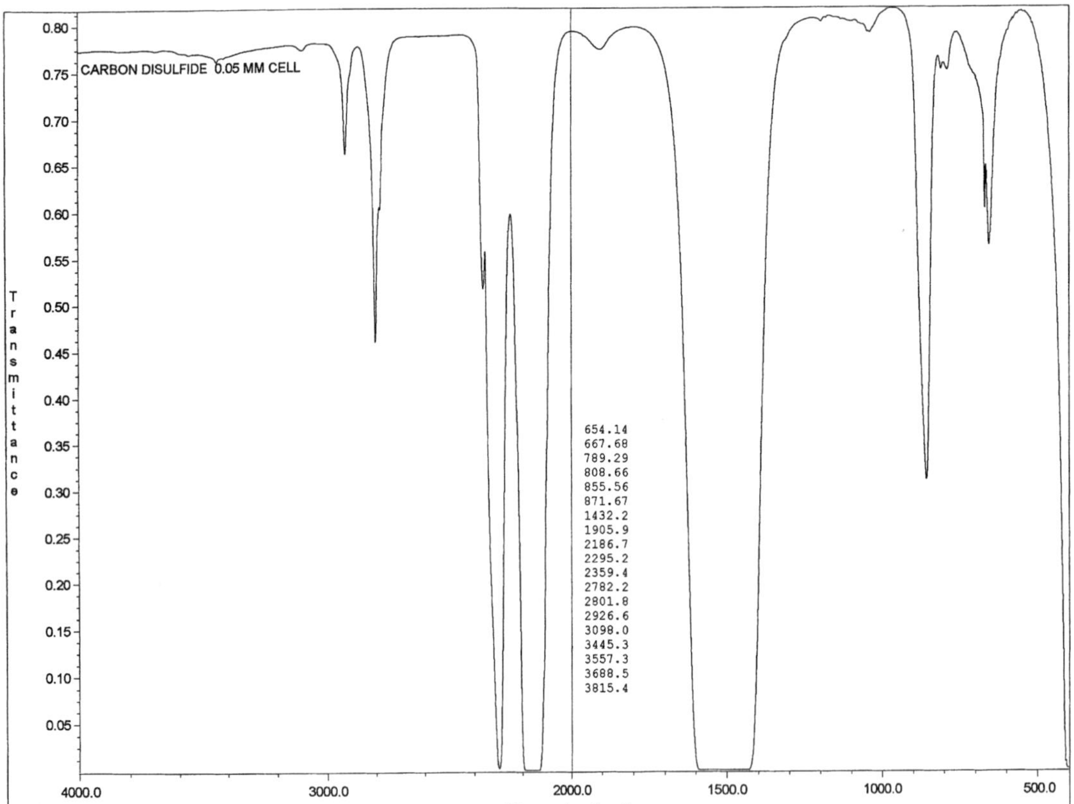

372a Carbon disulfide CS_2

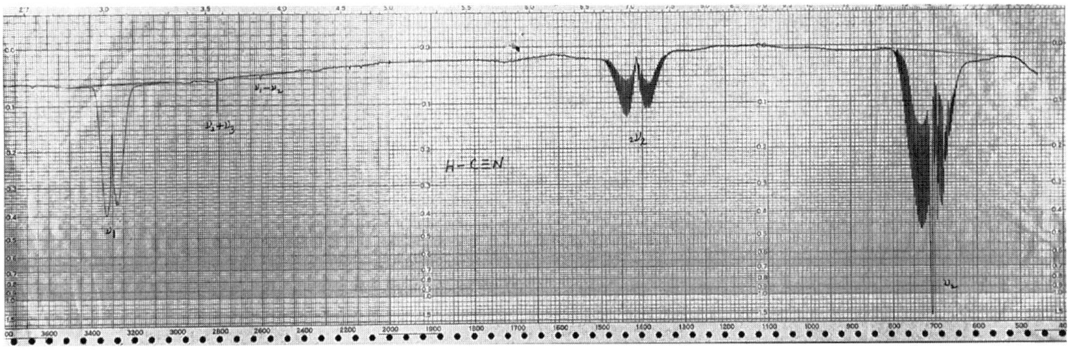

373 Hydrogen cyanide CHN

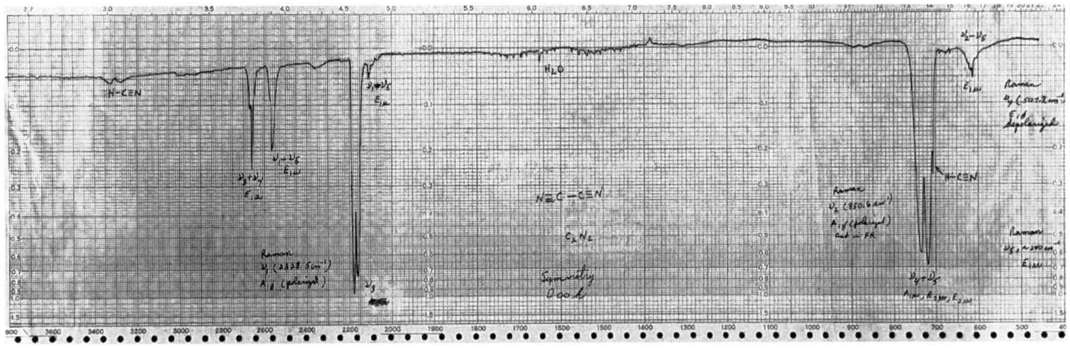

374 Cyanogen C_2N_2

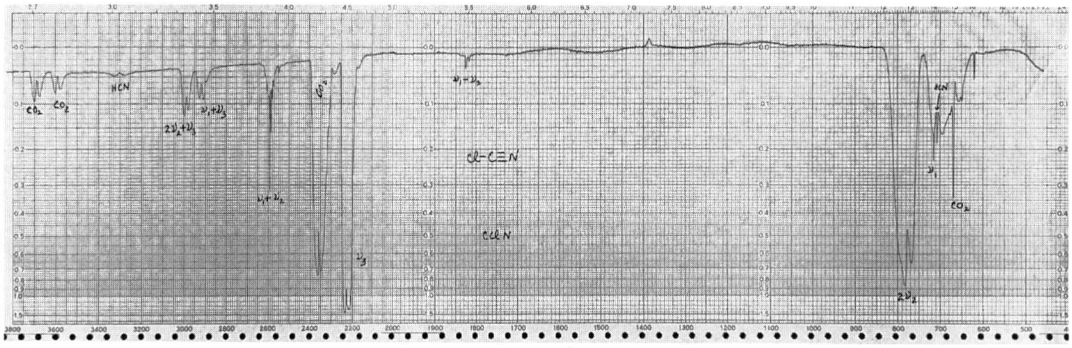

375 Cyanogen chloride CClN

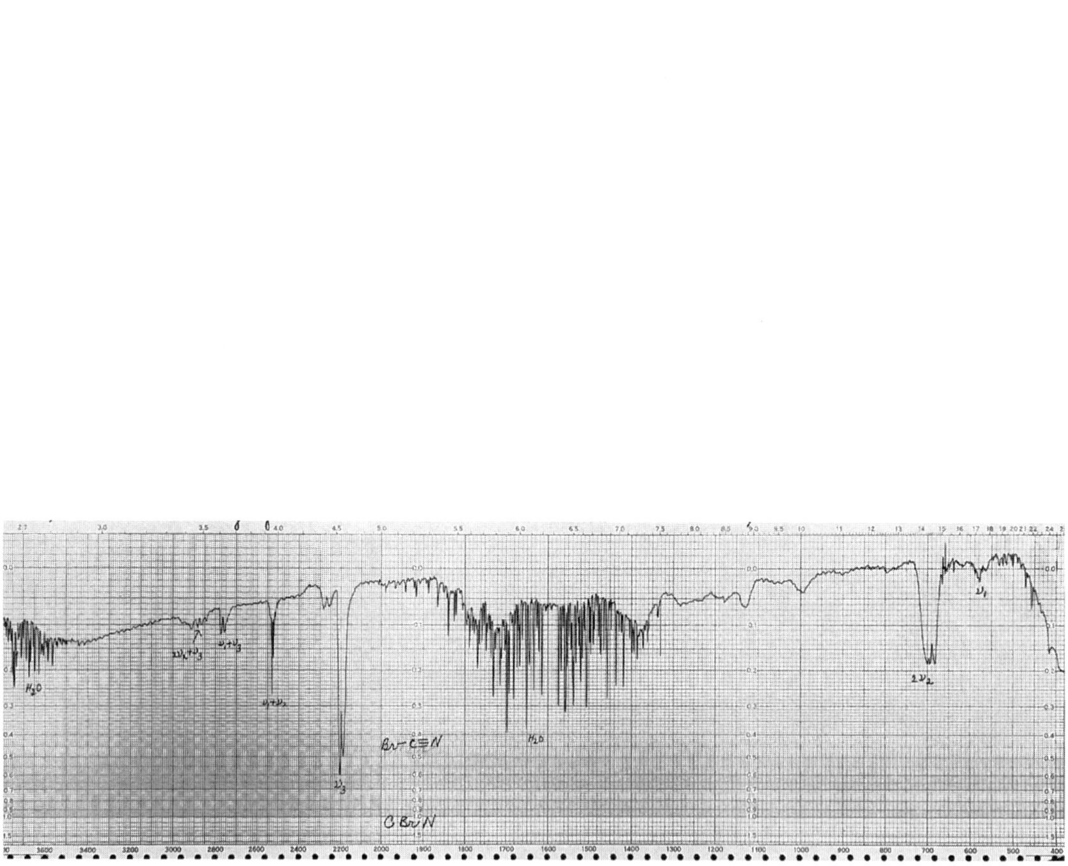

376 Cyanogen bromide CBrN

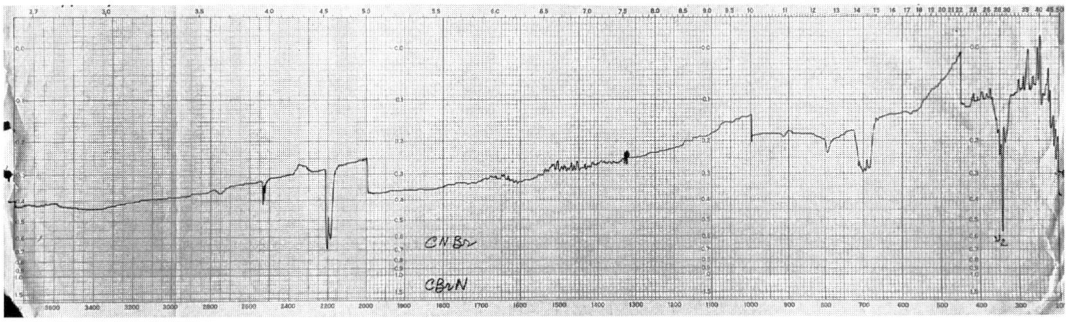

376a Cyanogen bromide CBrN

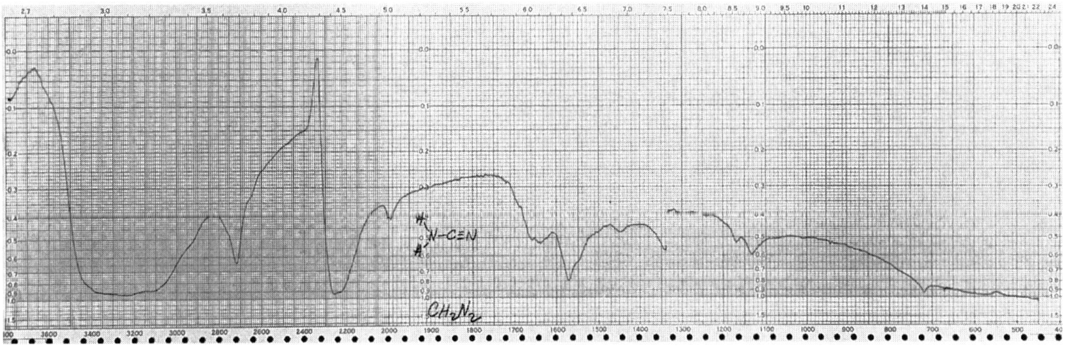

377 Cyanamide CH_2N_2

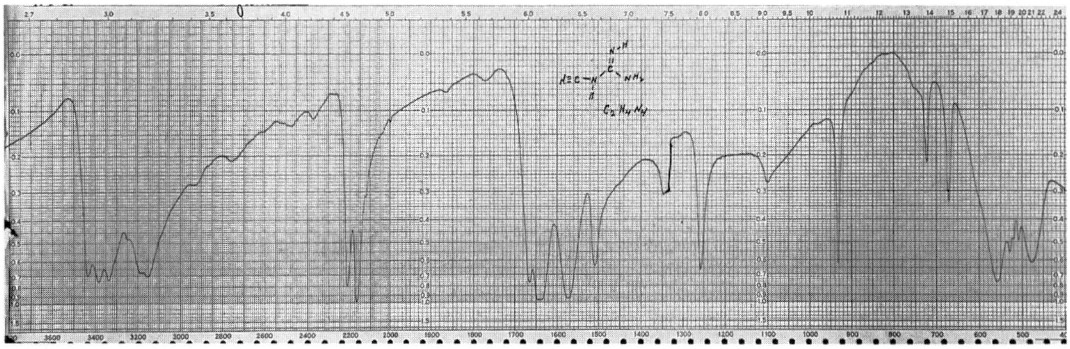

378 Cyanoquanidine $C_2H_4N_4$

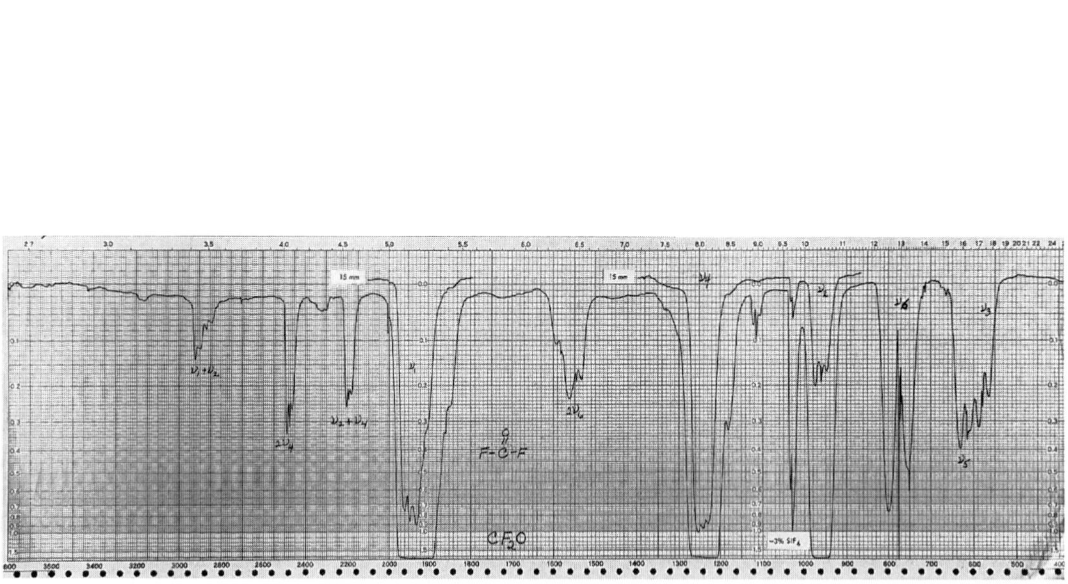

379 Carbonyl fluoride CF_2O

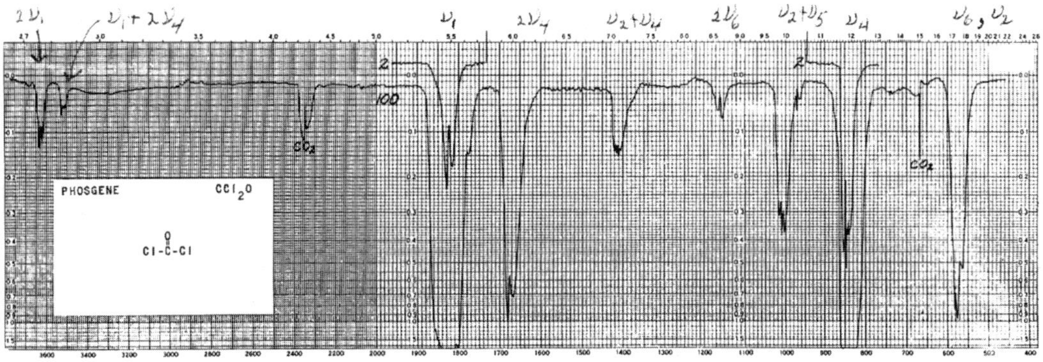

380 Carbonyl chloride CCl_2O

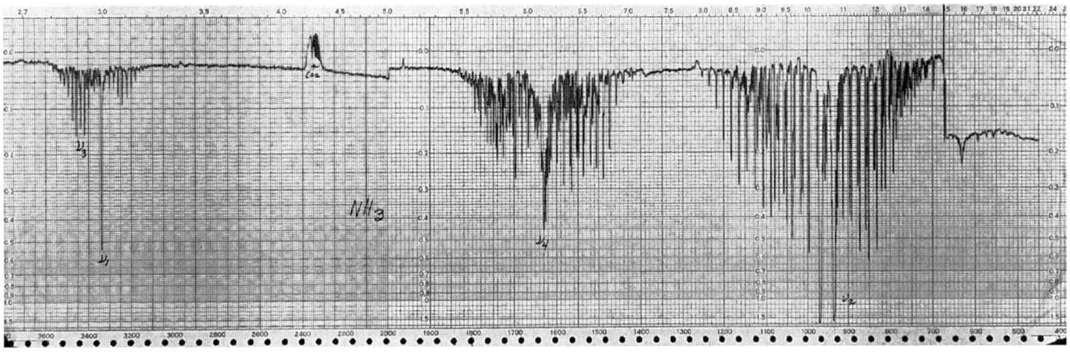

381 Ammonia NH_3

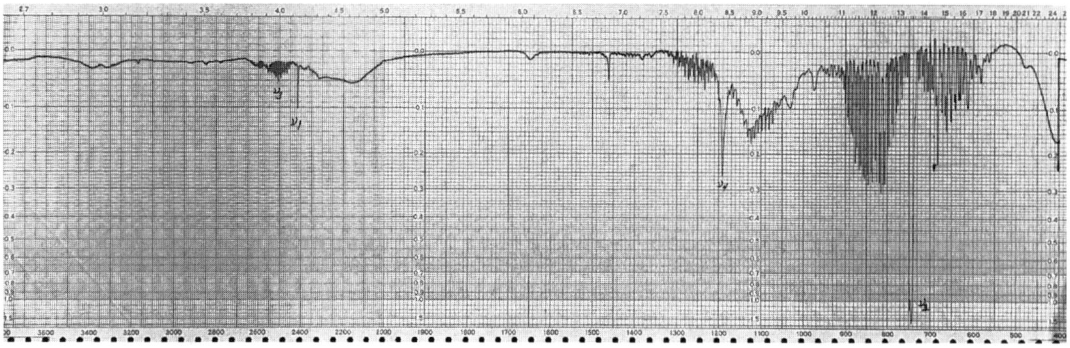

382 Ammonia-d_3 ND_3

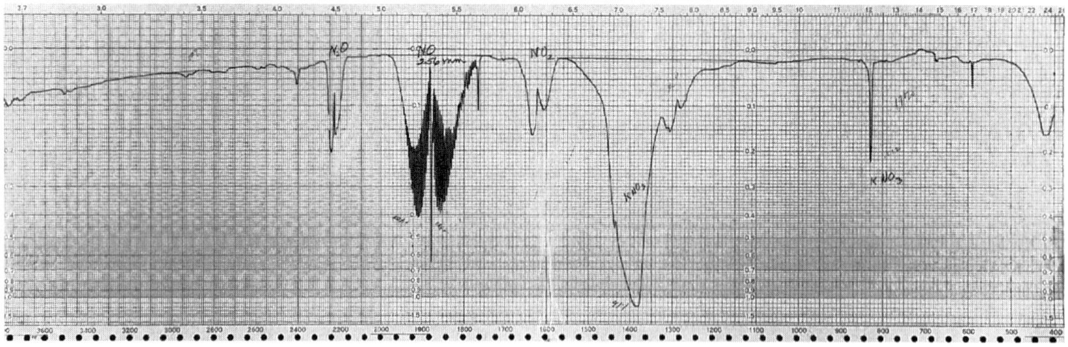

383 Nitrous oxide N_2O

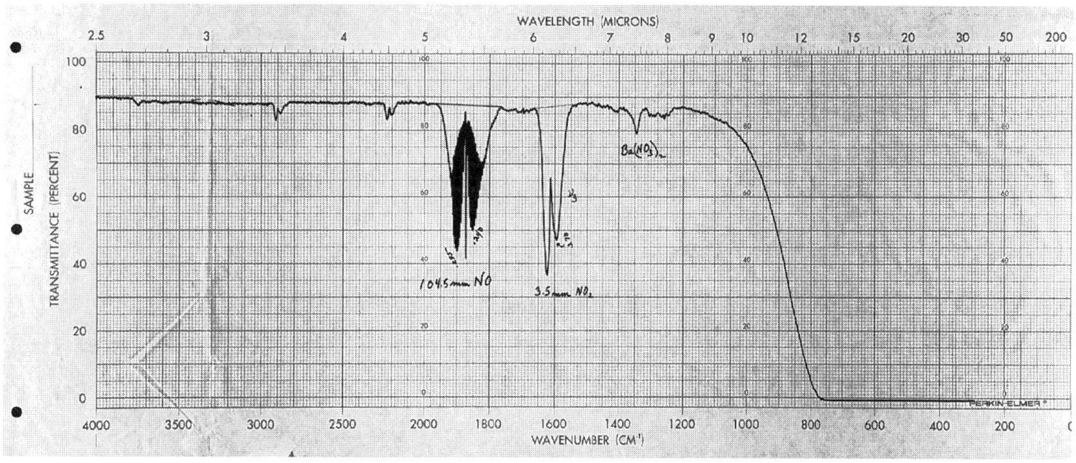

384 Nitric oxide NO plus NO_2

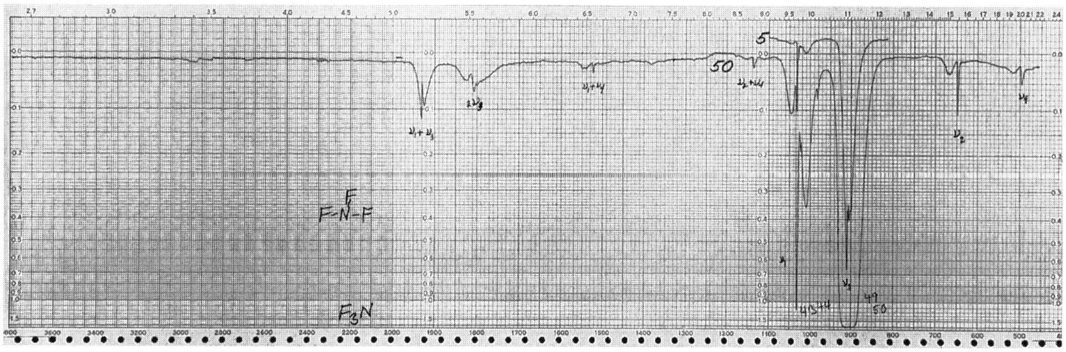

385 Nitrogen trifluoride NF_3

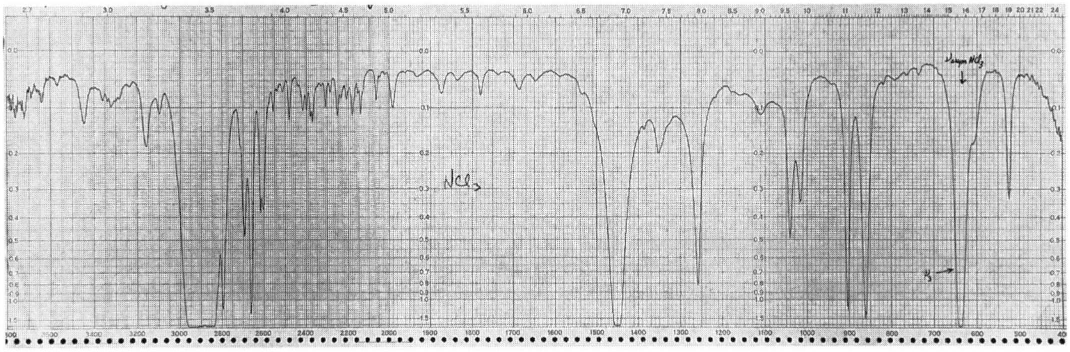

386 Nitrogen trichloride NCl_3

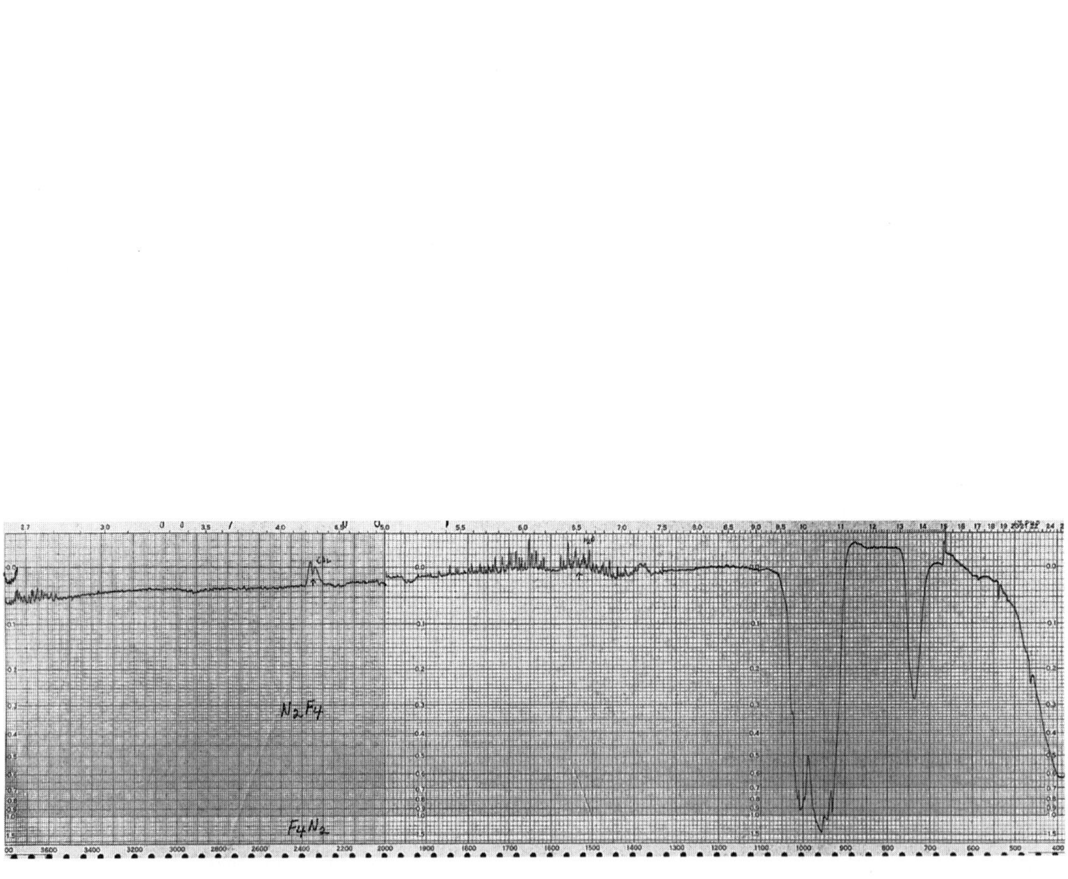

387 Hydrazine tetrafluoride N_2F_4

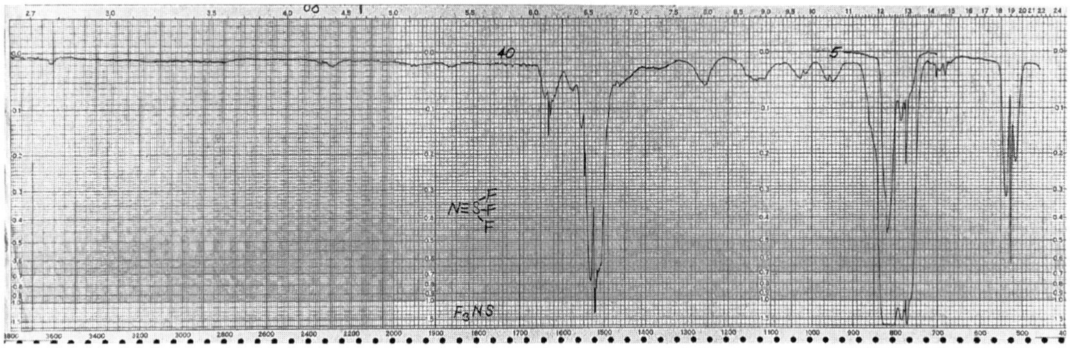

388 Thiazyl trifluoride NF_3S

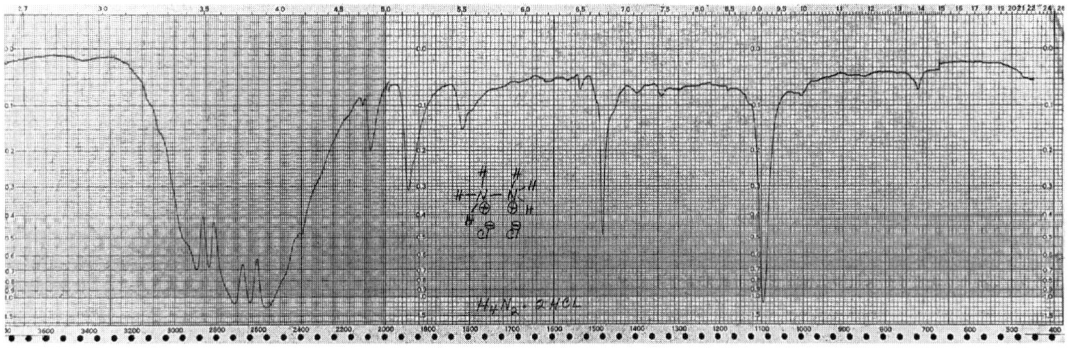

389 Hydrazine dichloride $N_2H_6Cl_2$

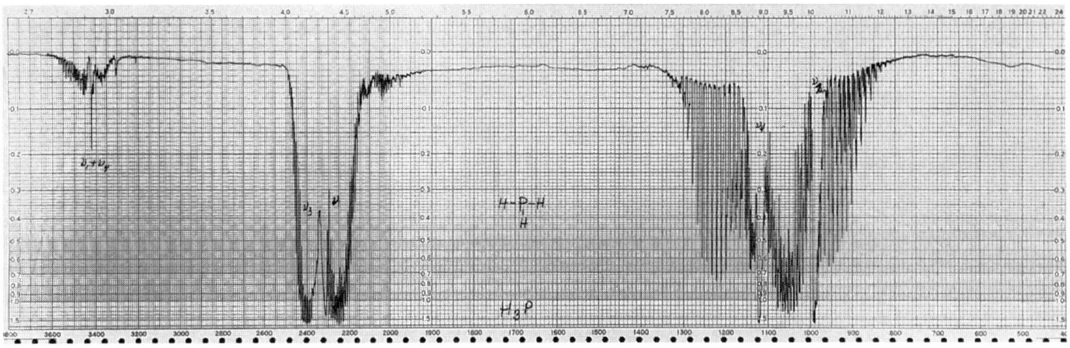

390 Phosphine PH_3

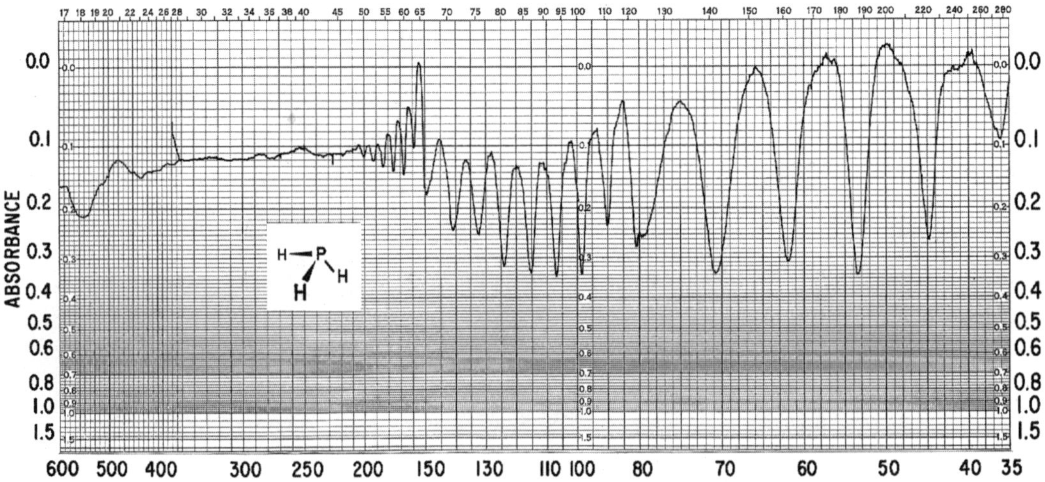

390a Phosphine PH_3

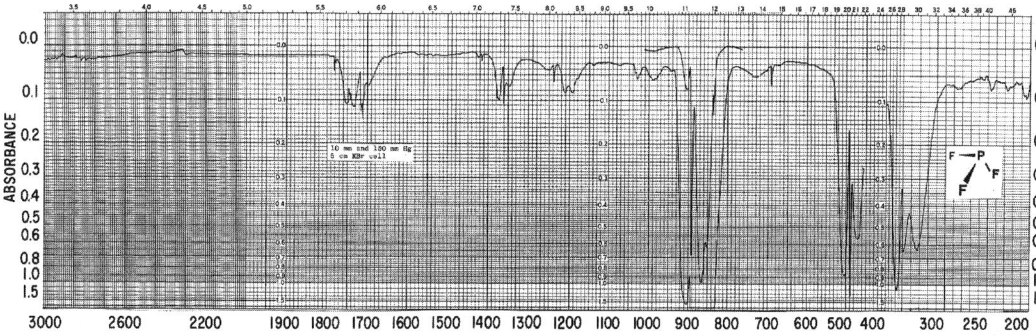

391 Phosphorus trifluoride PF_3

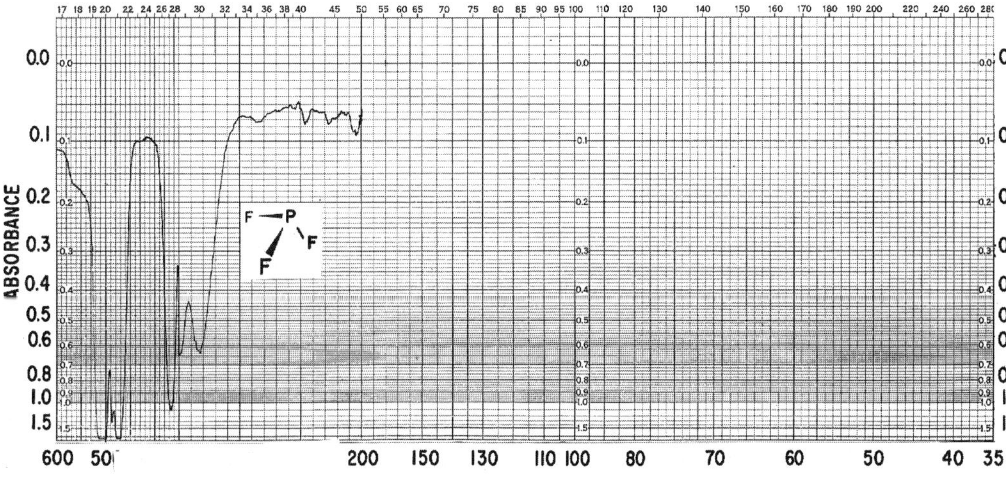

391 Phosphorus trifluoride PF_3

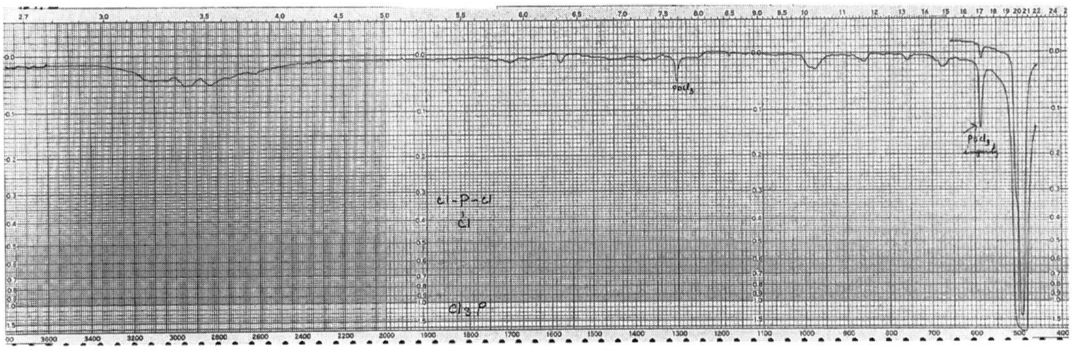

392 Phosphorus trichloride PCl_3

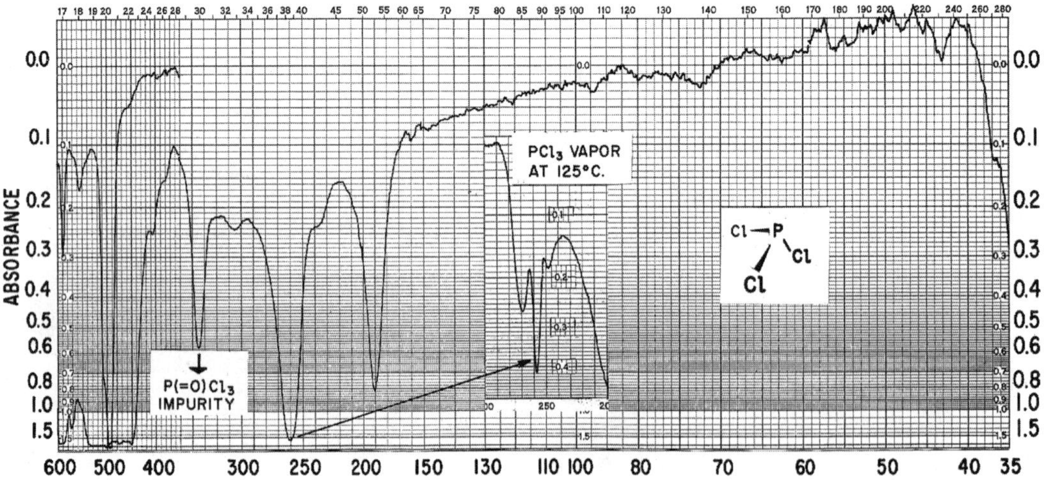

392a Phosphorus trichloride PCl_3

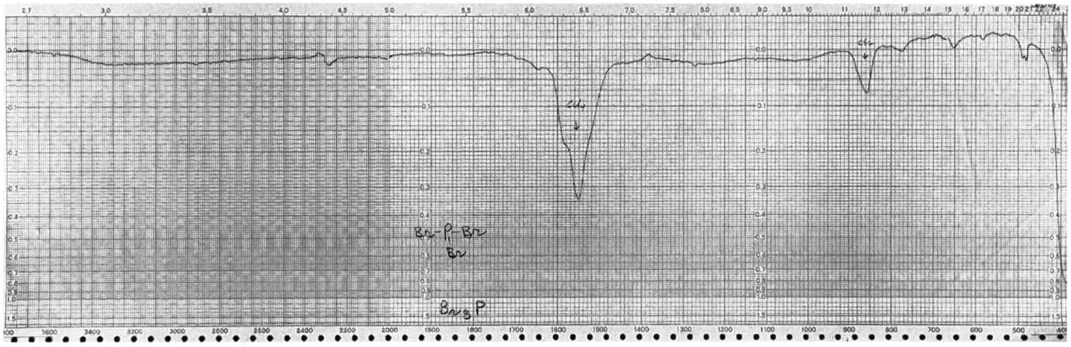

393 Phosphorus tribromide PBr_3

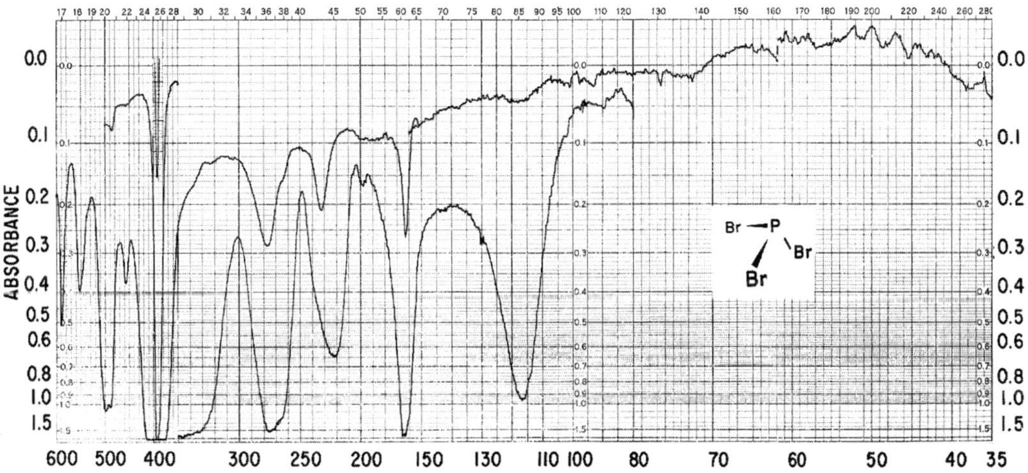

393a Phosphorus tribromide PBr_3

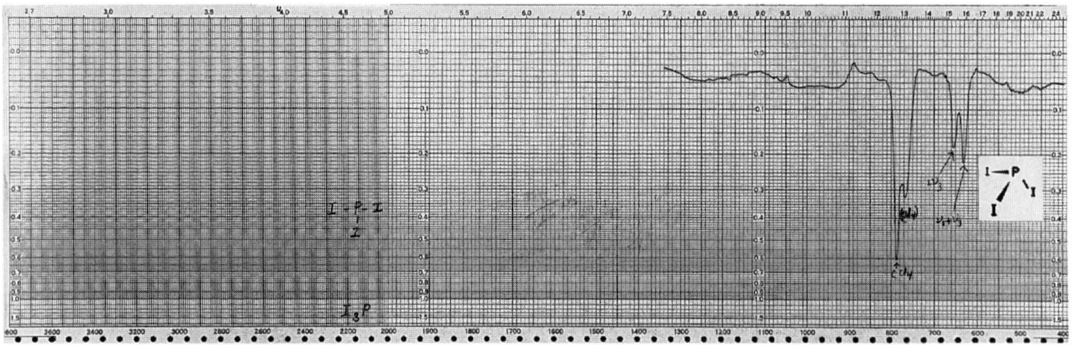

394 Phosphorus triiodide PI_3

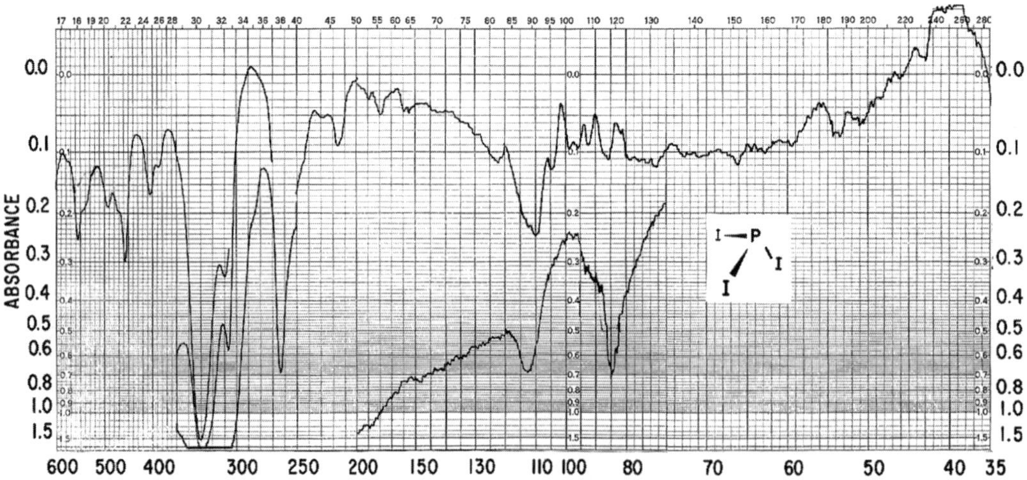

394a Phosphorus triiodide PI_3

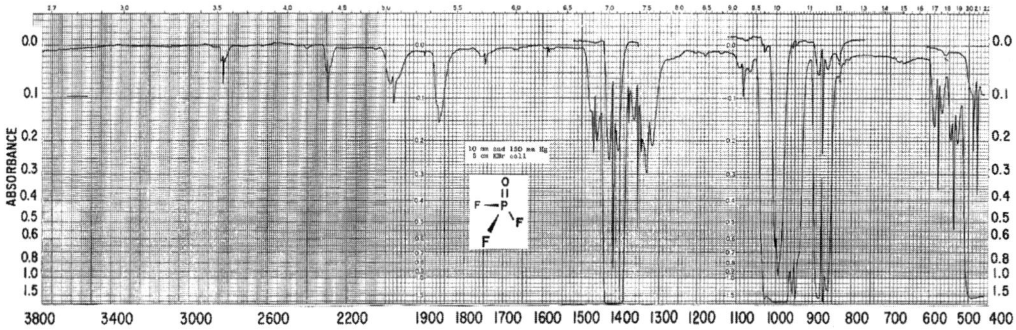

395 Phosphorus oxyfluoride PF_3O

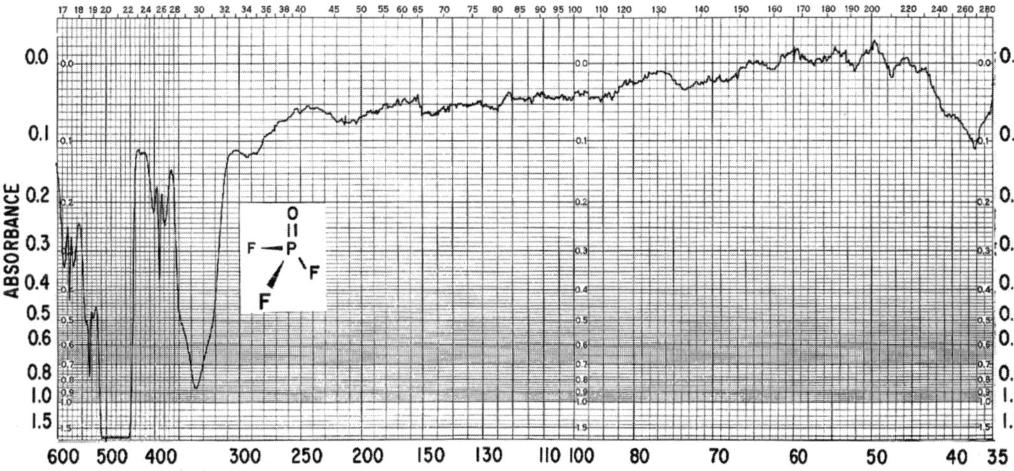

395a Phosphorus oxyfluoride PF_3O

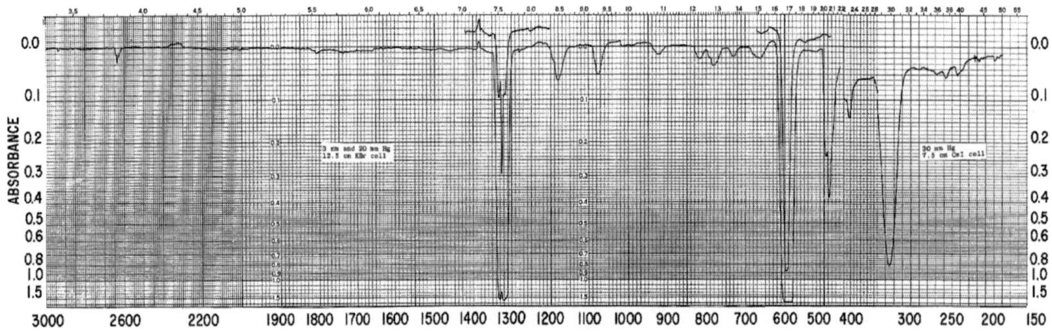

396 Phosphorus oxychloride PCl_3O

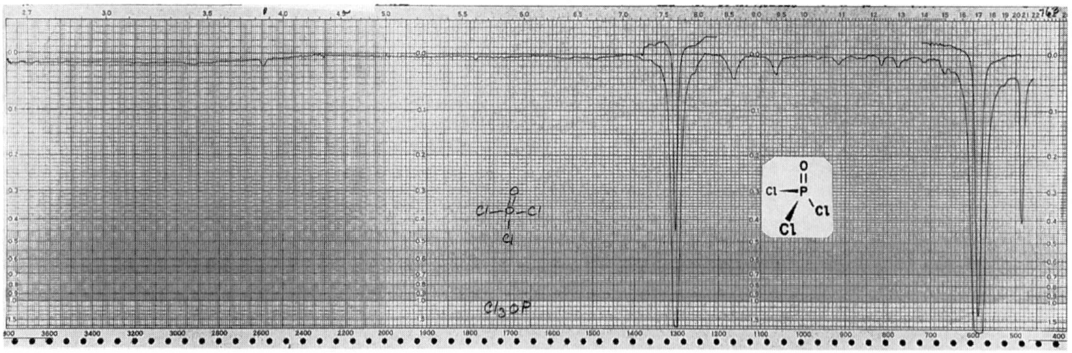

396 Phosphorus oxychloride PCl_3O

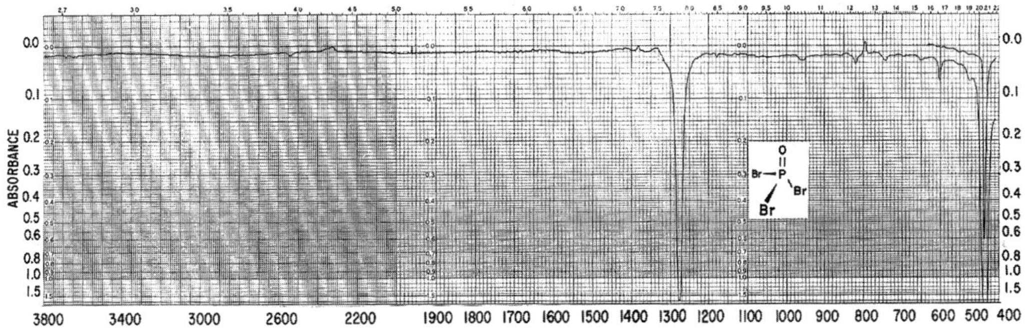

397 Phosphorus oxybromide PBr_3O

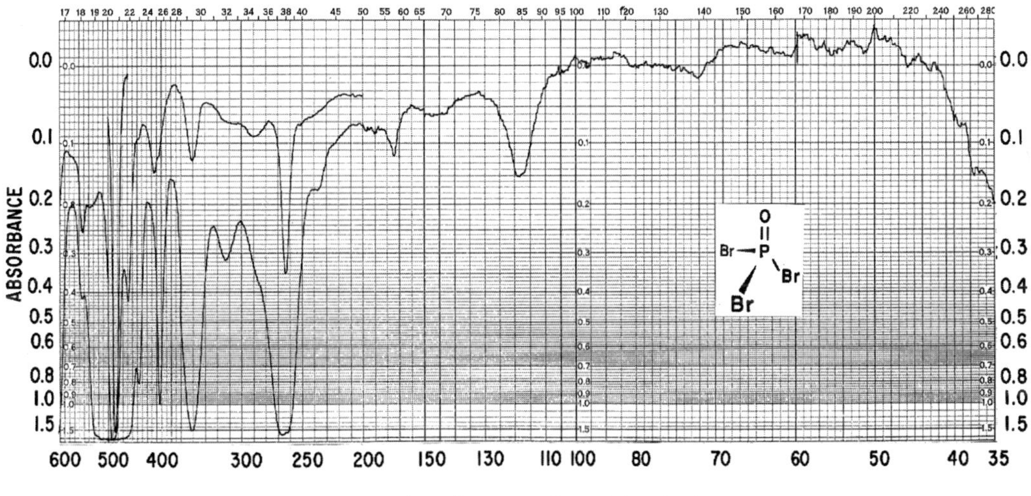

397 Phosphorus oxybromide PBr_3O

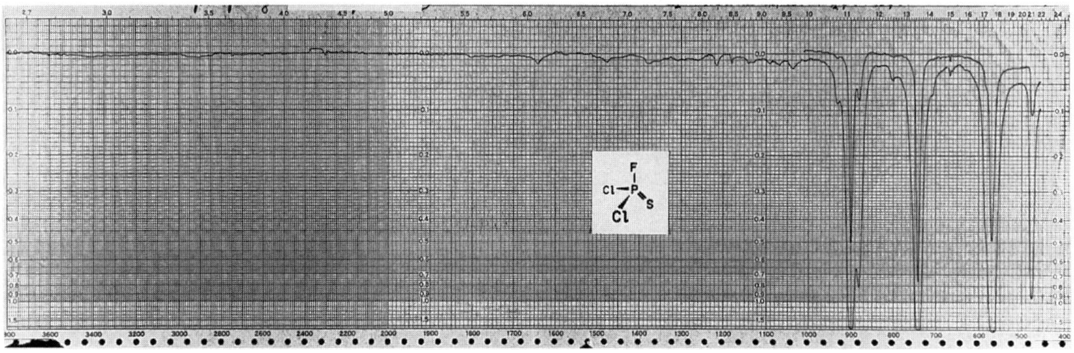

398 Thiophosphoryl dichloride fluoride PCl_2FS

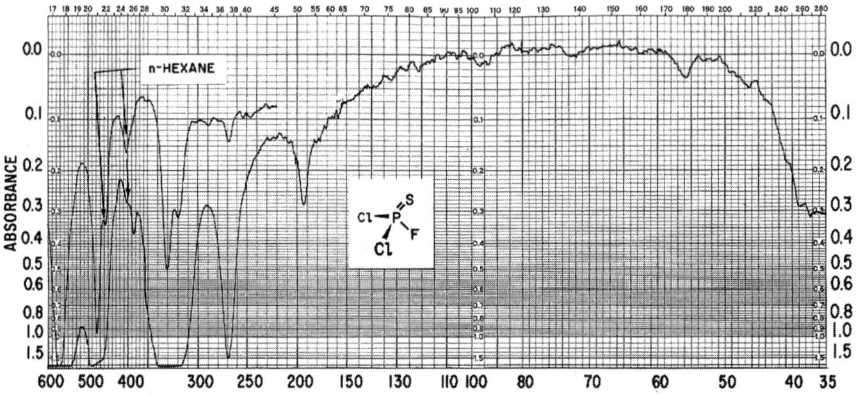

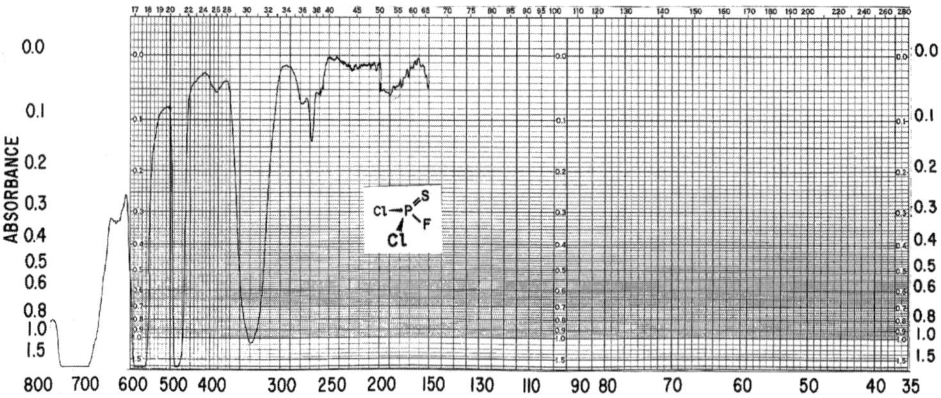

398a Thiophosphoryl dichloride fluoride PCl_2FS

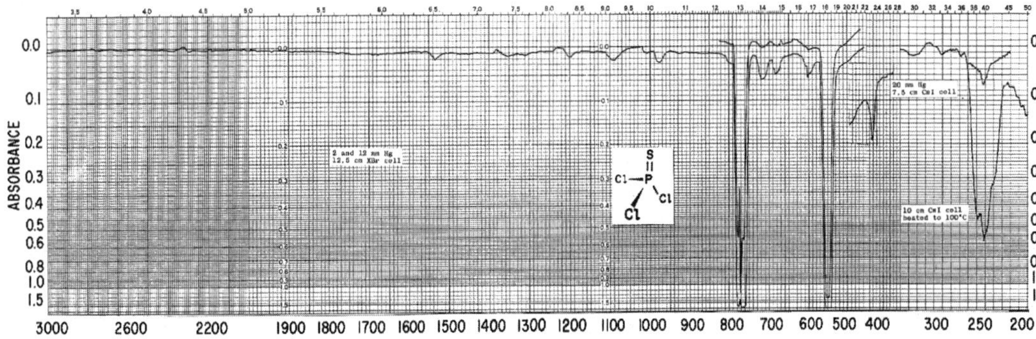

399 Thiophosphoryl chloride PCl_3S

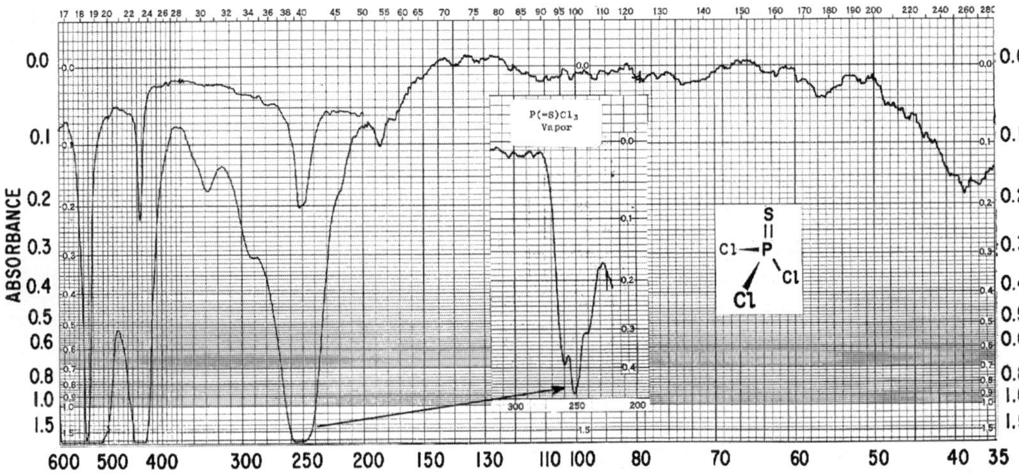

399a Thiophosphoryl chloride PCl_3S

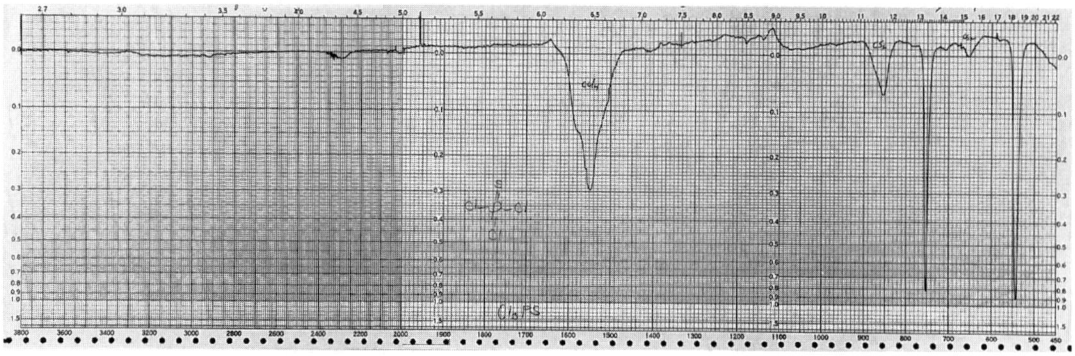

399b Thiophosphoryl chloride PCl_3S

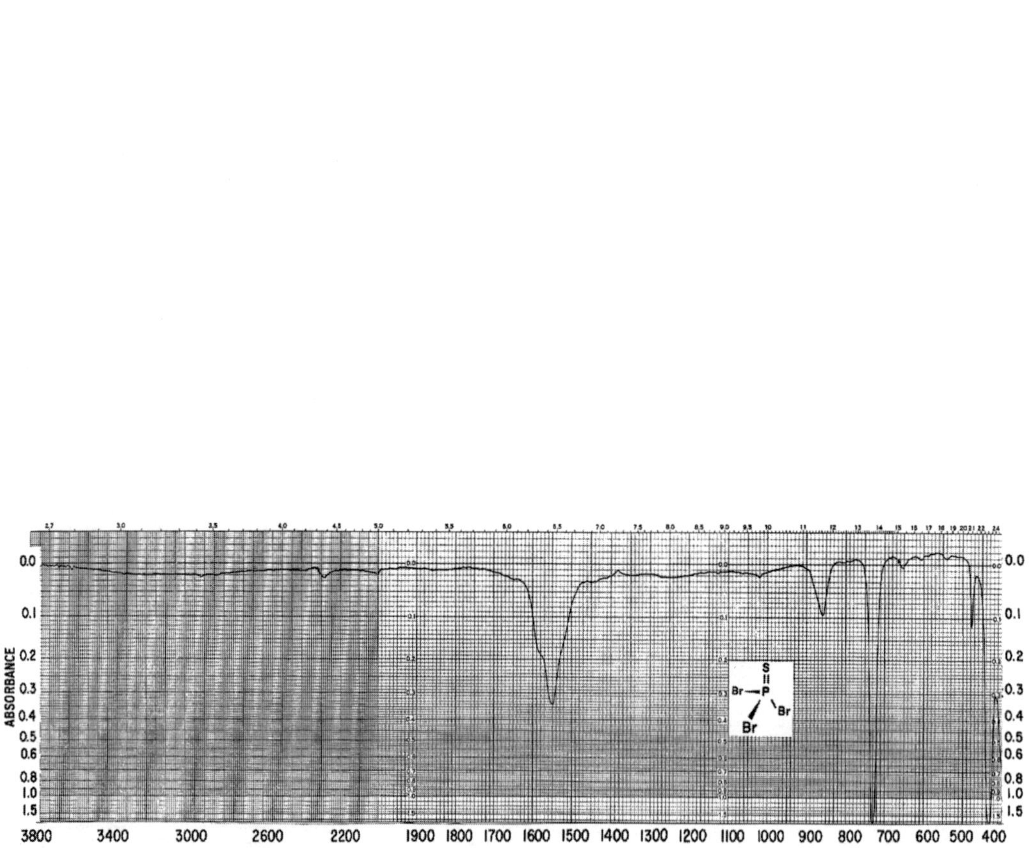

400 Thiophosphoryl bromide PBr_3S

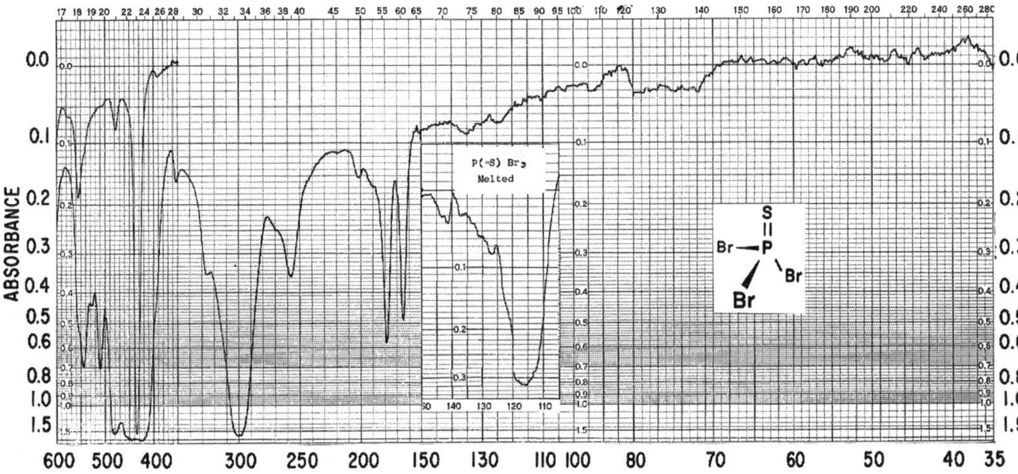

400a Thiophosphoryl bromide PBr_3S

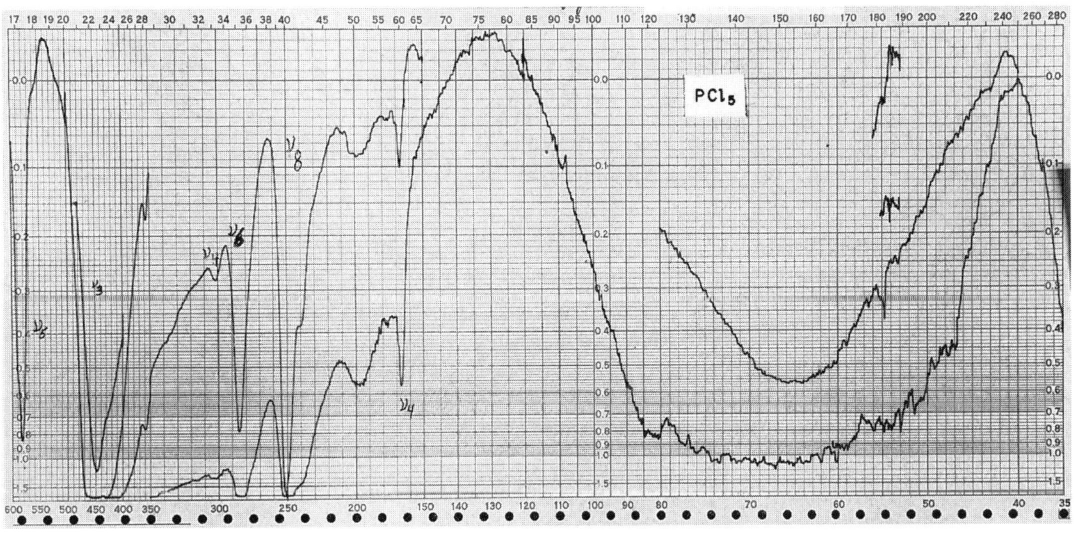

401 Phosphorus pentachloride PCl_5

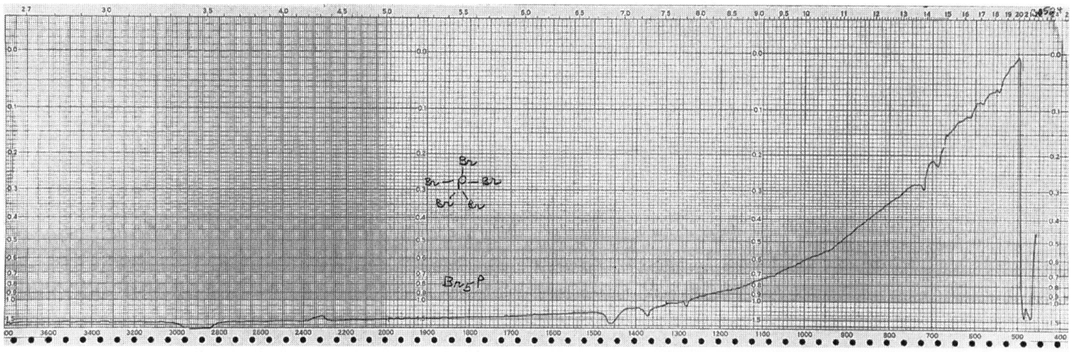

402 Phosphorus pentabromide PBr_5

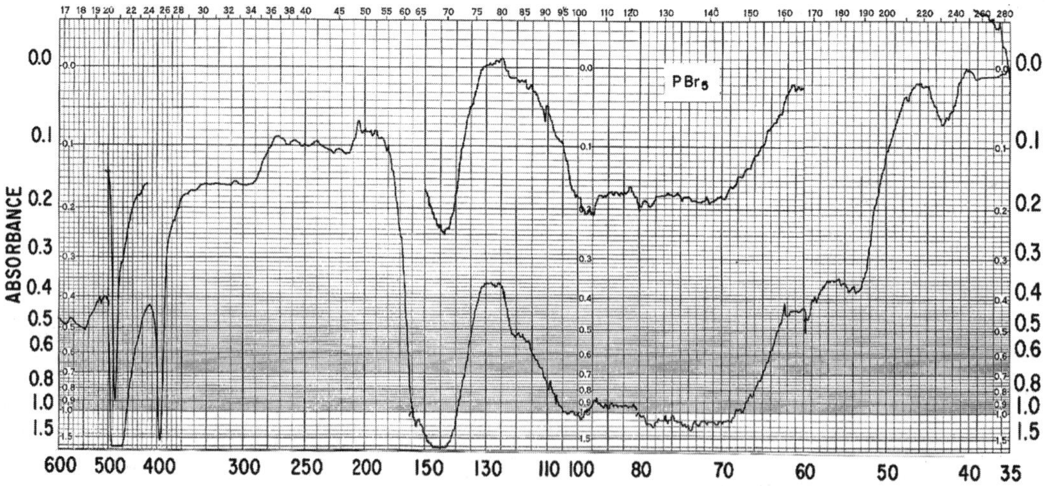

402a Phosphorus pentabromide PBr_5

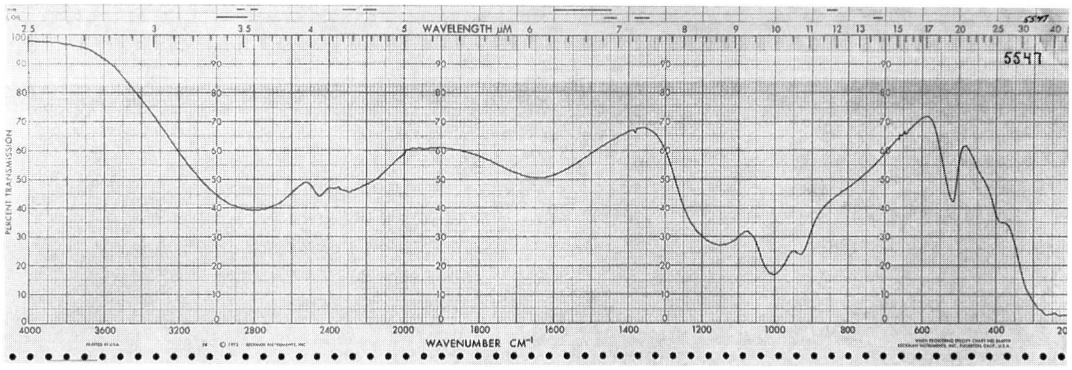

404 Phosphoric acid PH_3O_4

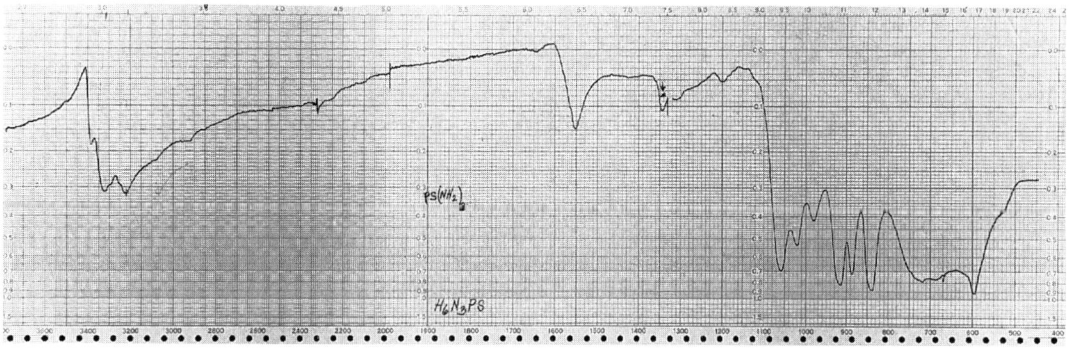

405 Phosphorus thioamide PH_6N_3S

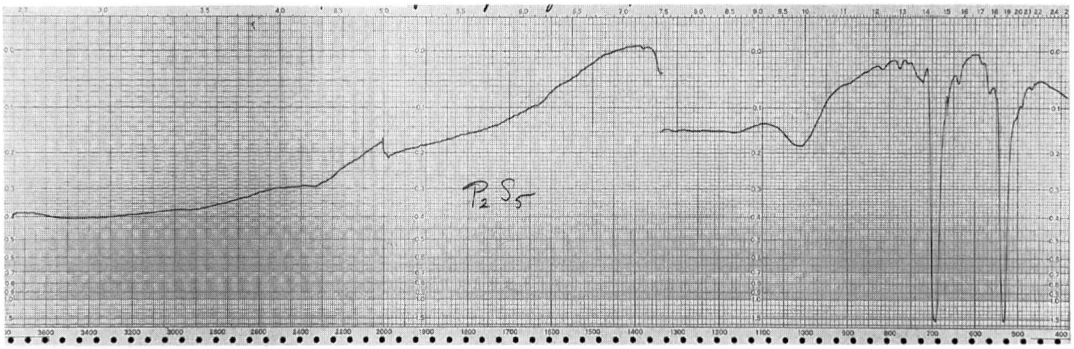

406 Phosphorus pentasulfide P_2S_5

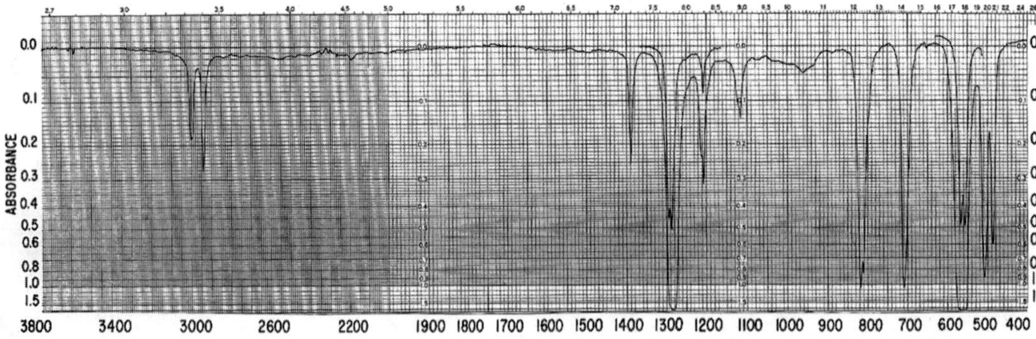

407 Chloromethylphosphonic dichloride PCH_2Cl_3O

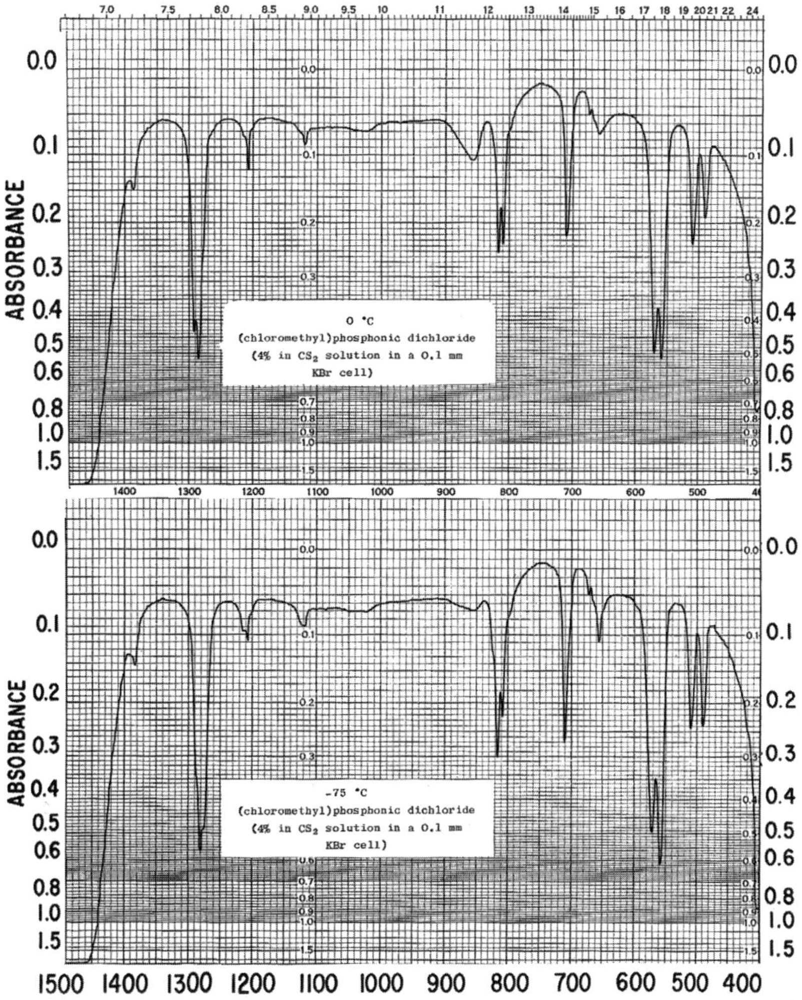

407a Chloromethylphosphonic dichloride PCH_2Cl_3O

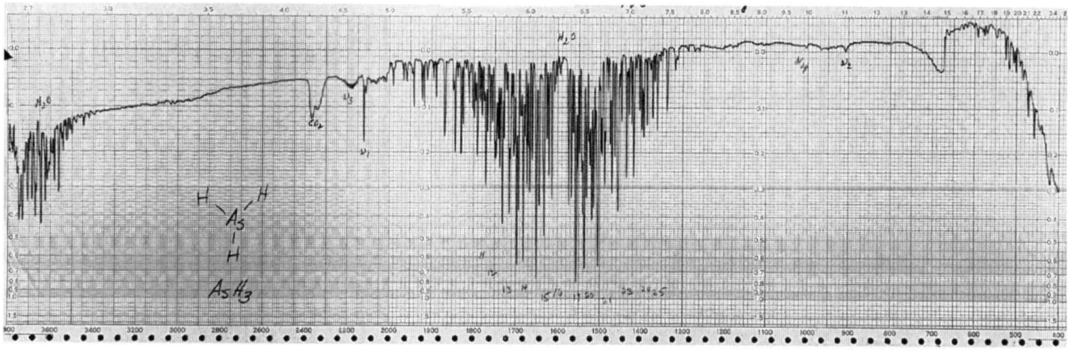

408 Arsine AsH_3

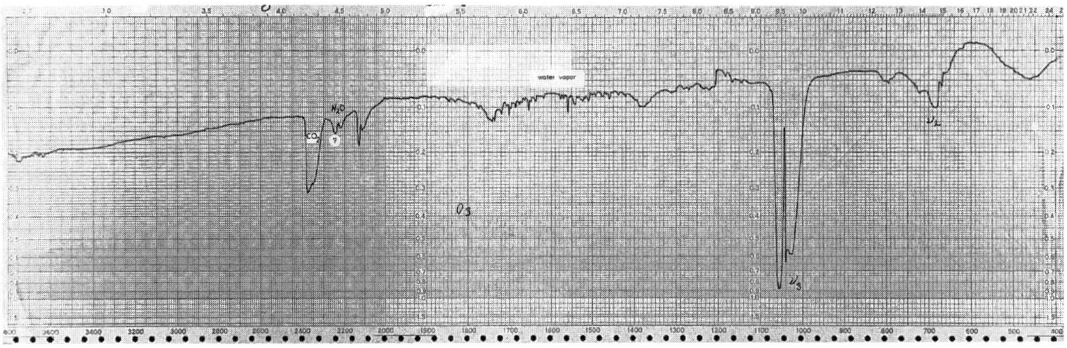

409 Ozone O_3

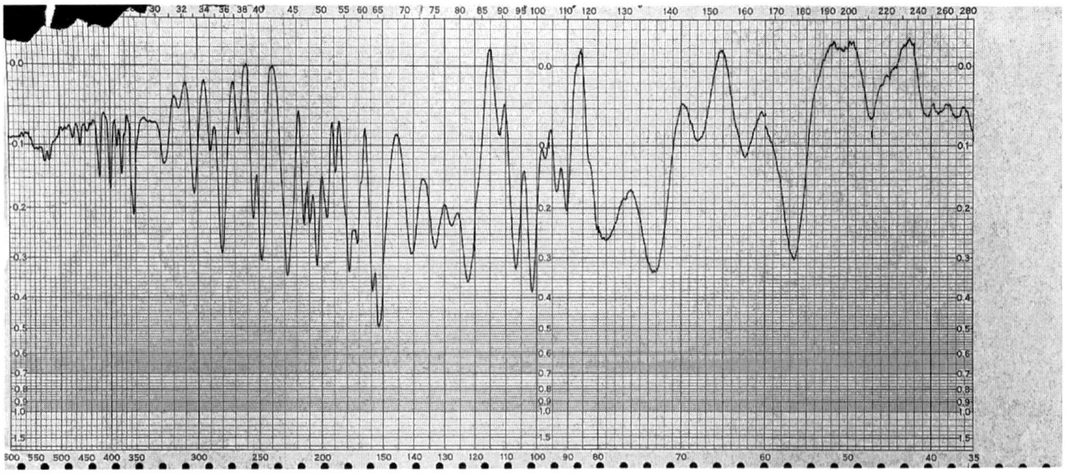

410 Water H_2O

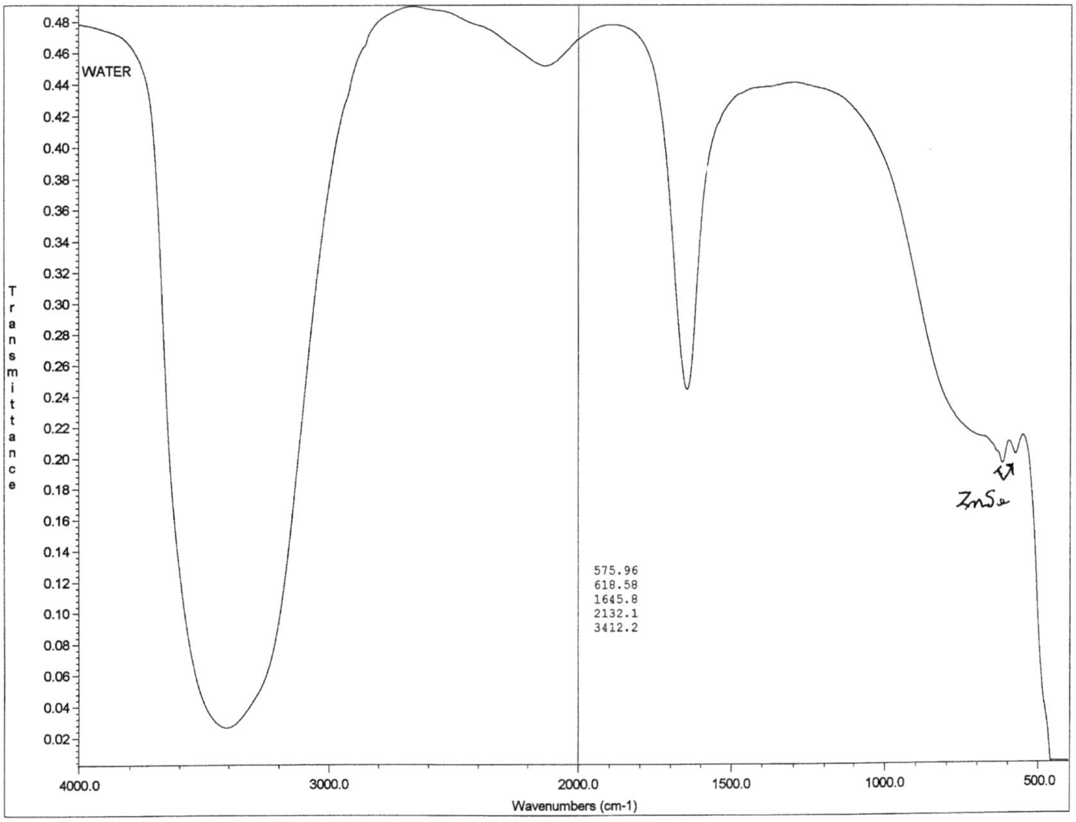

410 Water H_2O

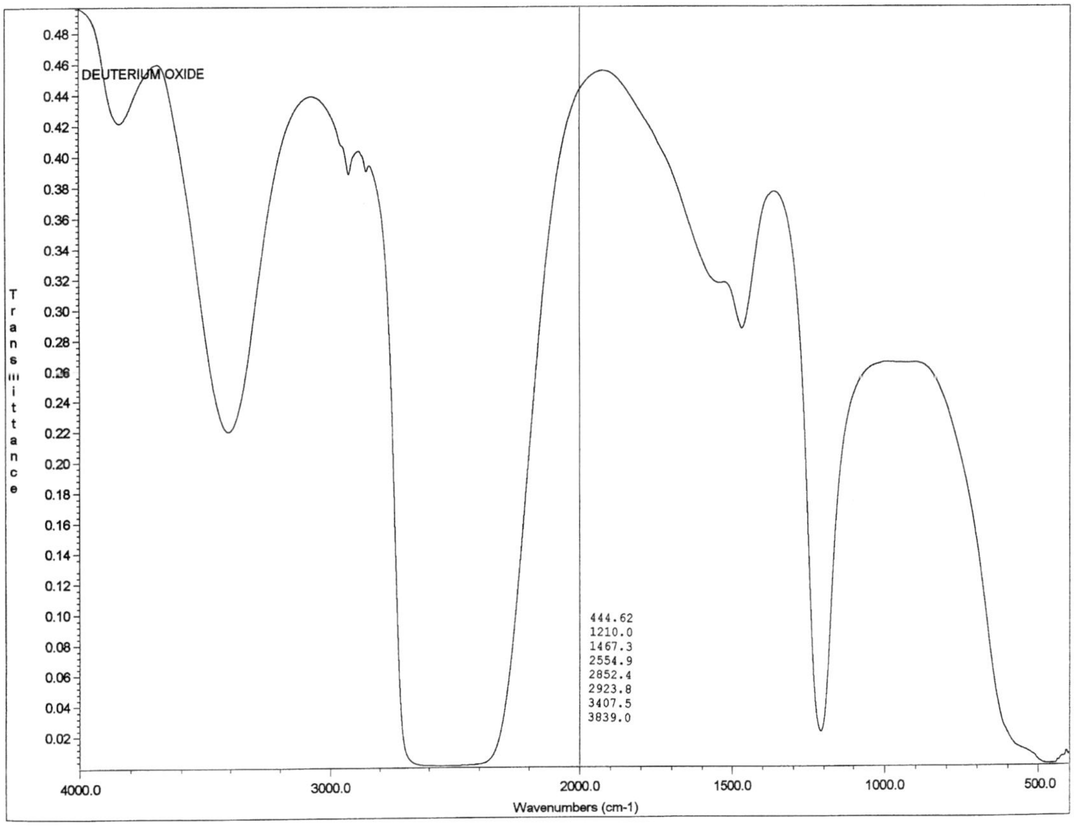

411 Deuteruim oxide OD_2

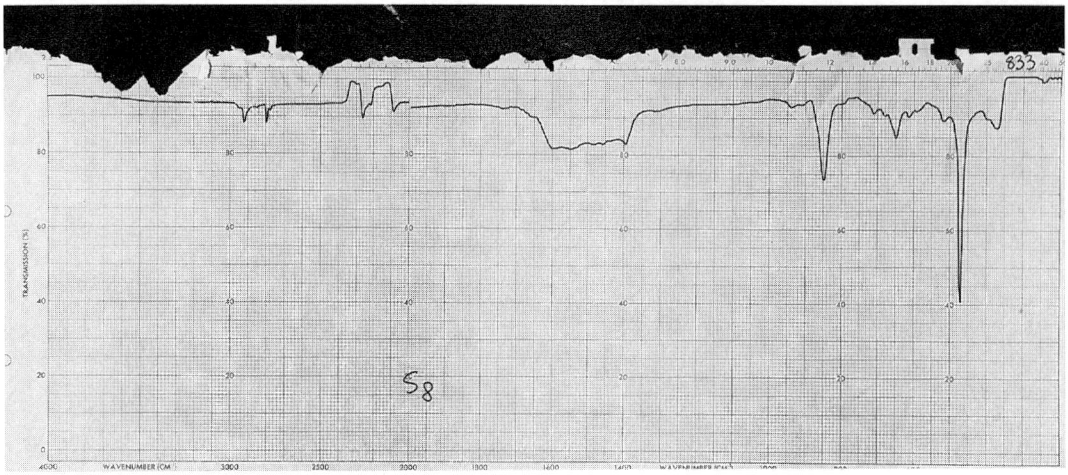

412 Sulfur S_8

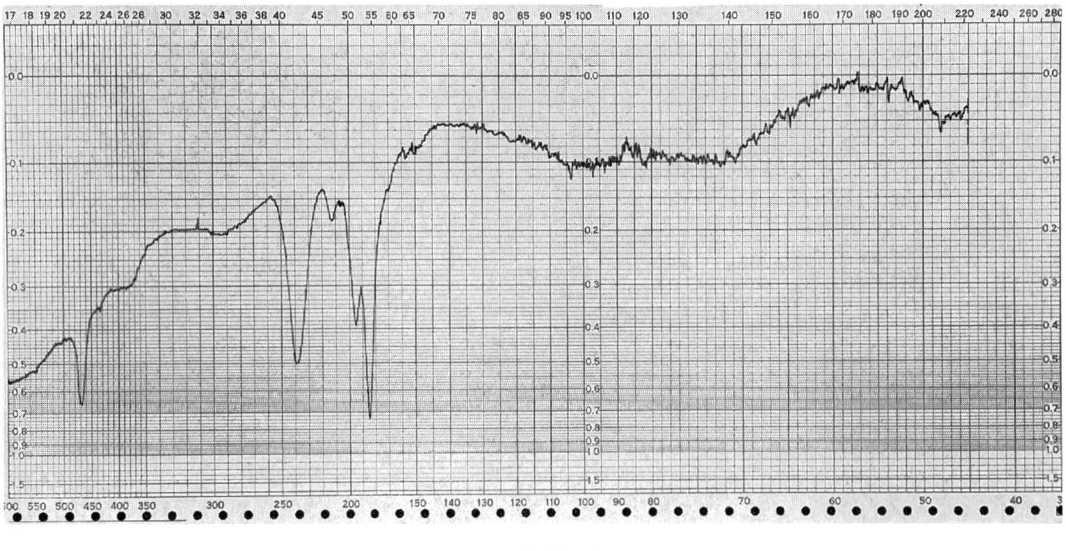

412a Sulfur S_8

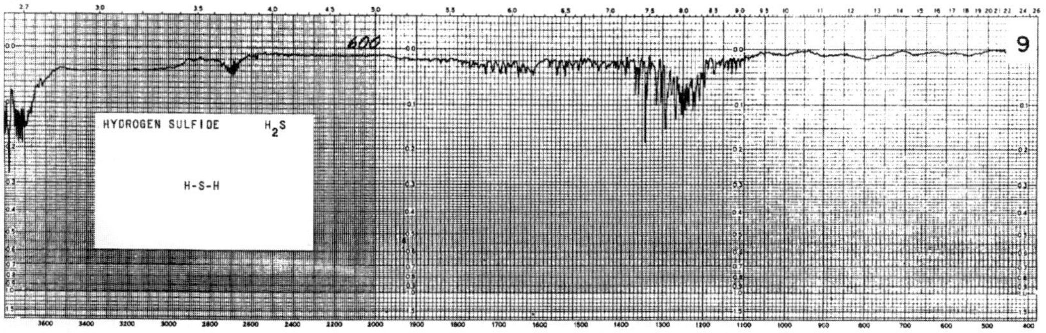

413 Hydrogen sulfide SH_2

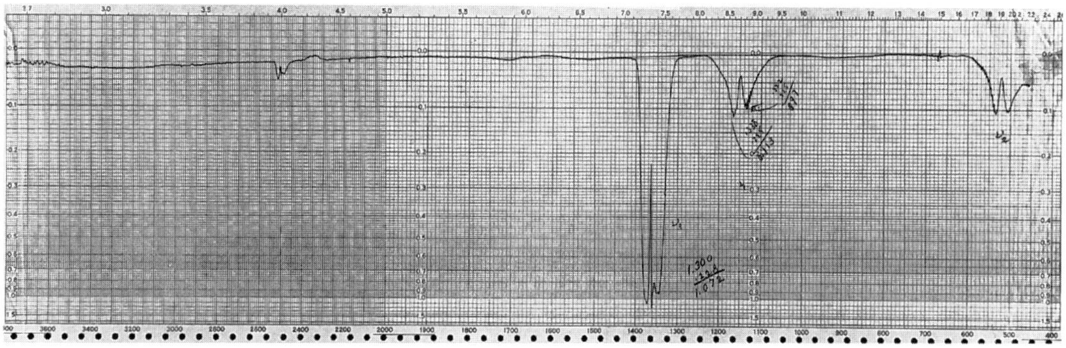

414 Sulfur dioxide SO_2

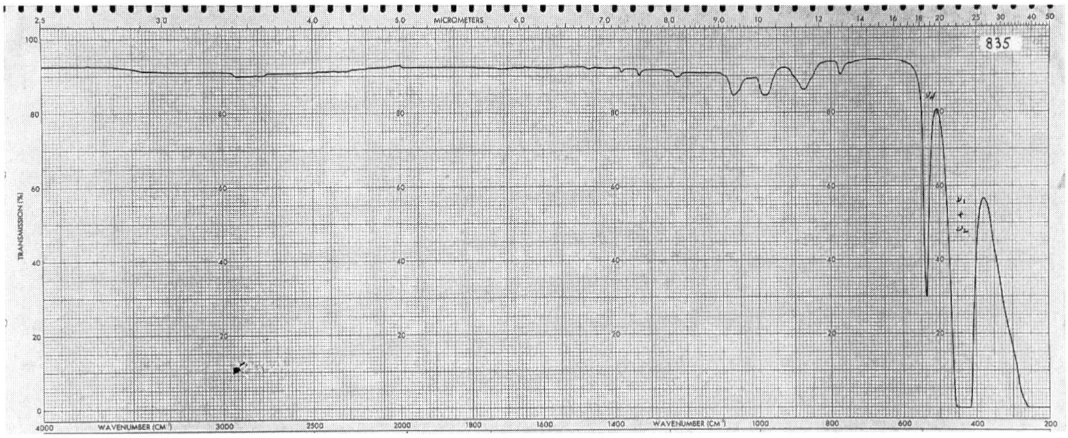

415 Sulfur monochloride S_2Cl_2

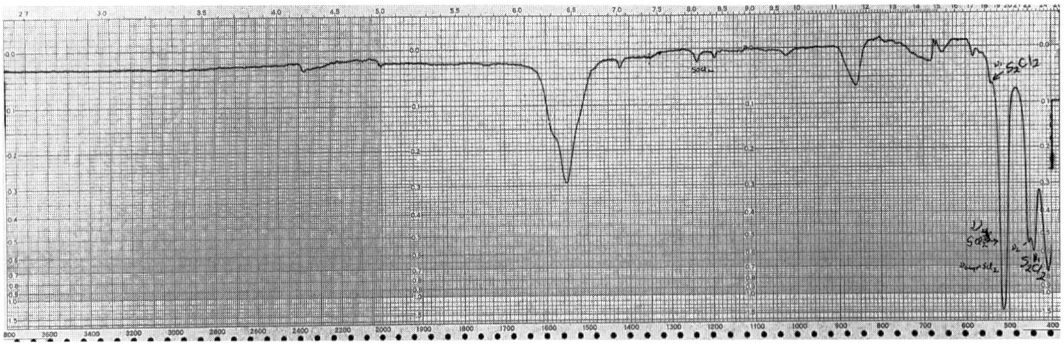

416 Sulfur dichloride SCl_2

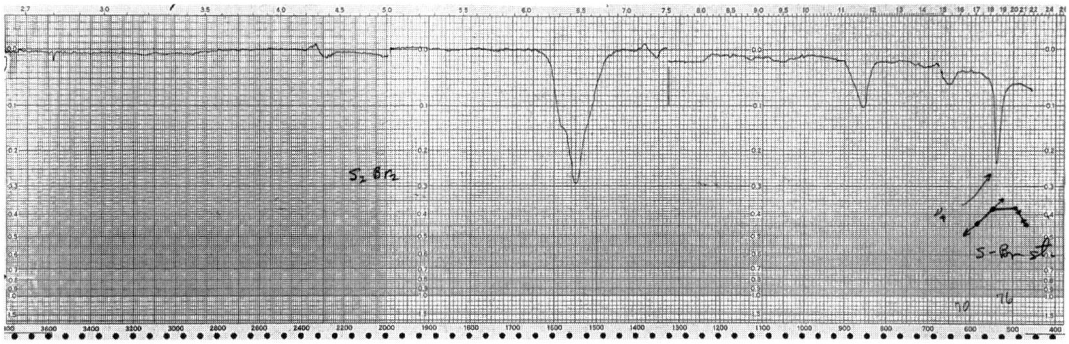

417 Sulfur monobromide S_2Br_2

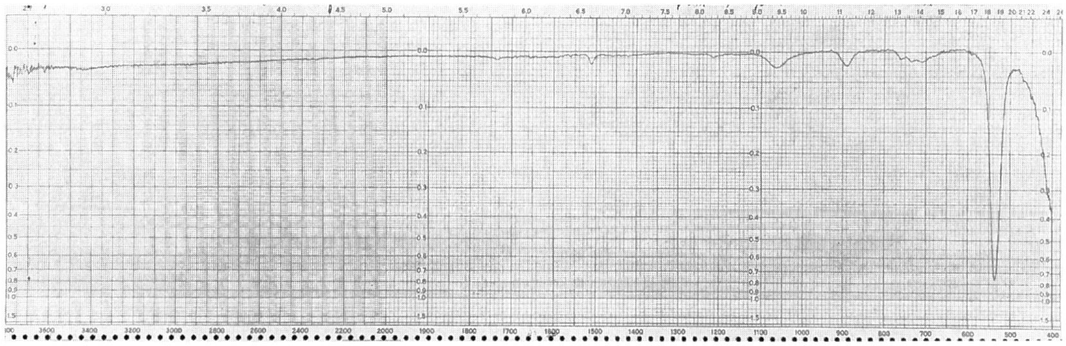

417a Sulfur monobromide S_2Br_2

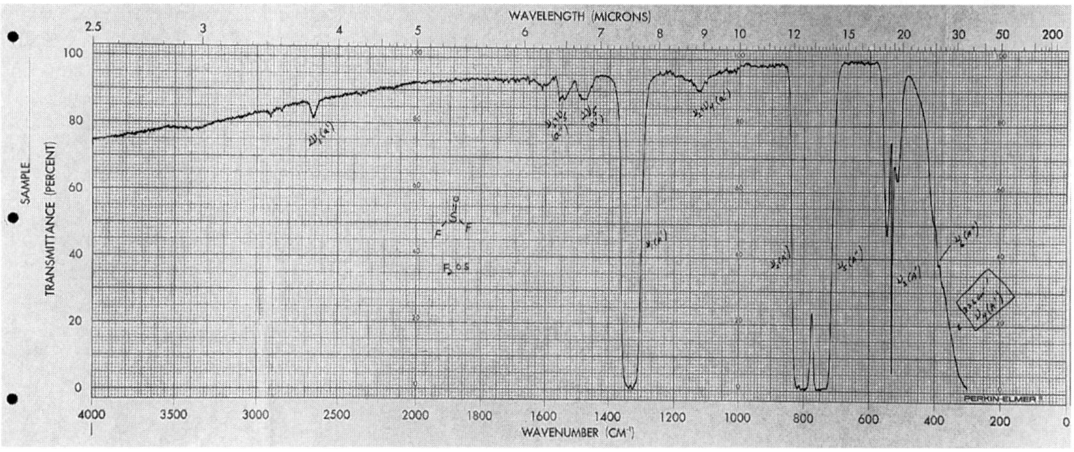

418 Thionyl fluoride SF_2O

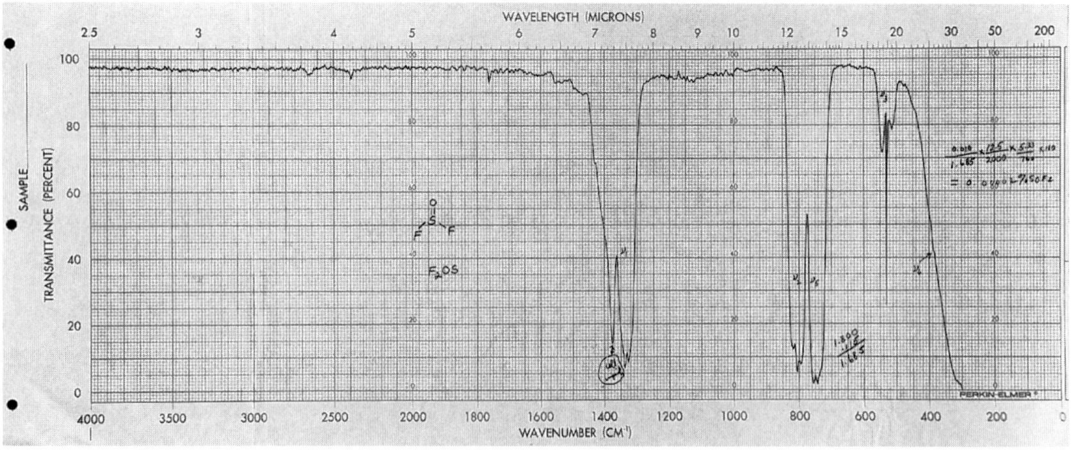

418a Thionyl fluoride SF_2O

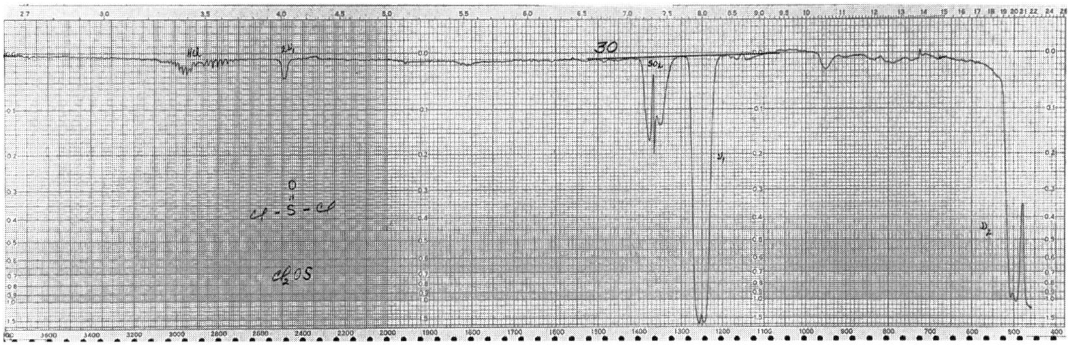

419 Thionyl chloride SCl_2O

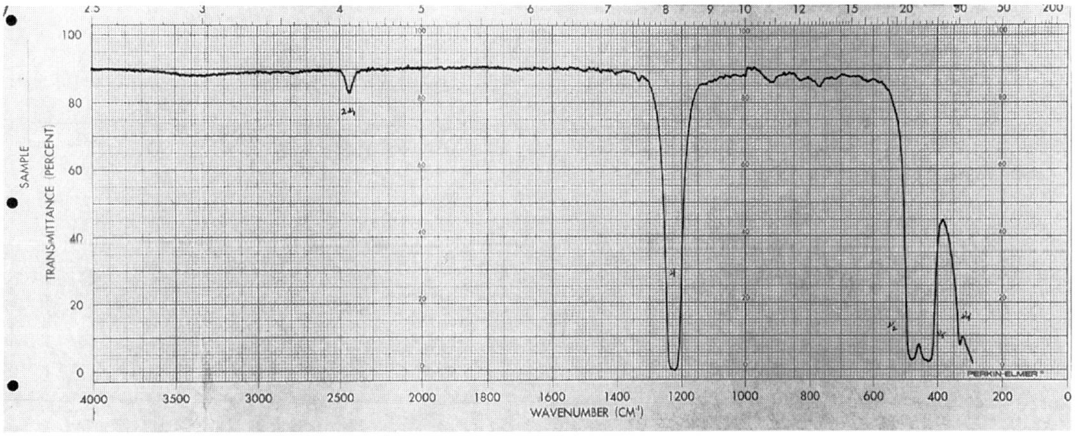

419a Thionyl chloride SCl_2O

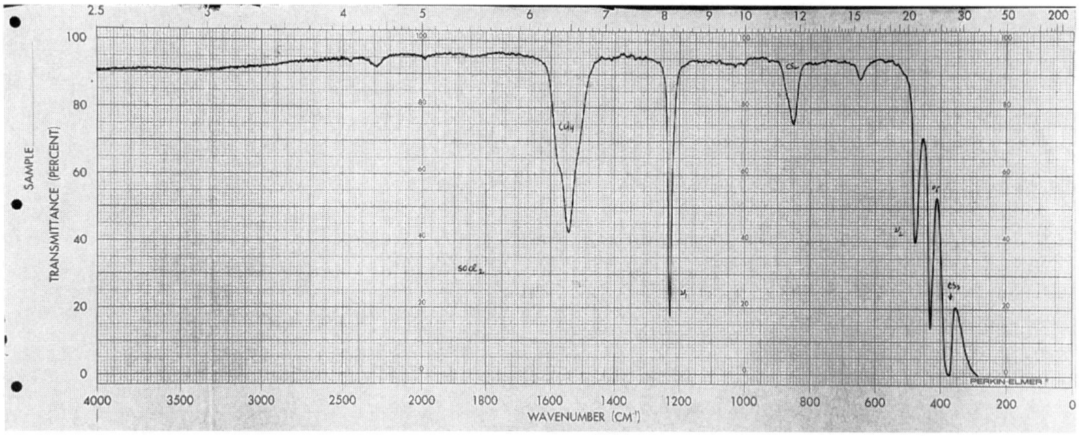

419b Thionyl chloride SCl_2O

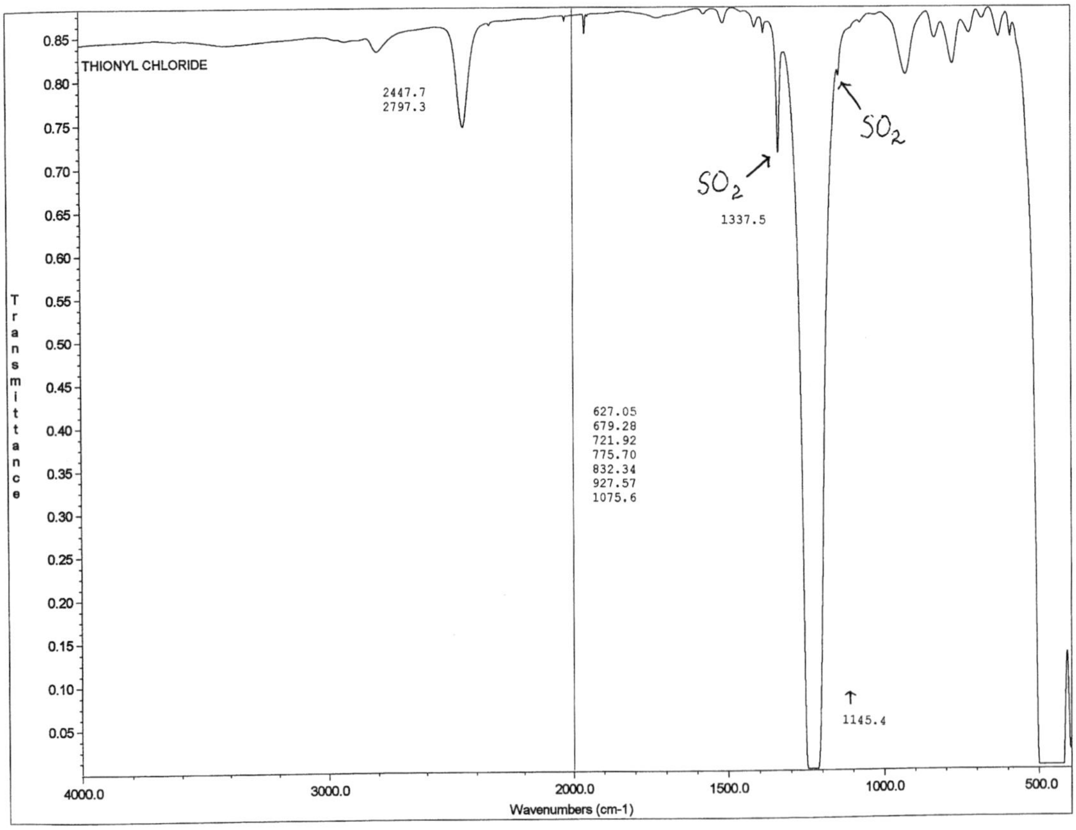

419c Thionyl chloride SCl_2O

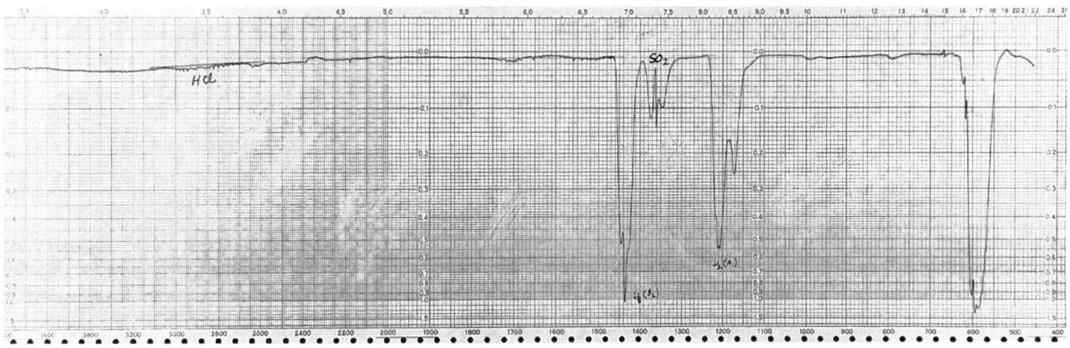

420 Sulfuryl chloride SCl_2O_2

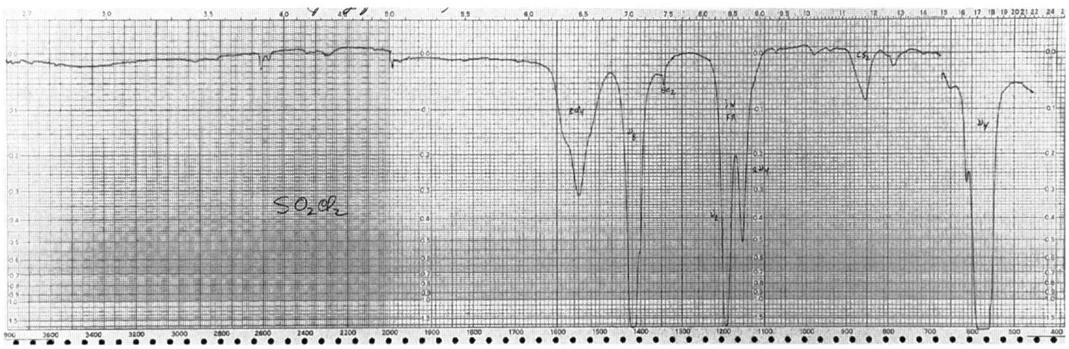

420a Sulfuryl chloride SCl_2O_2

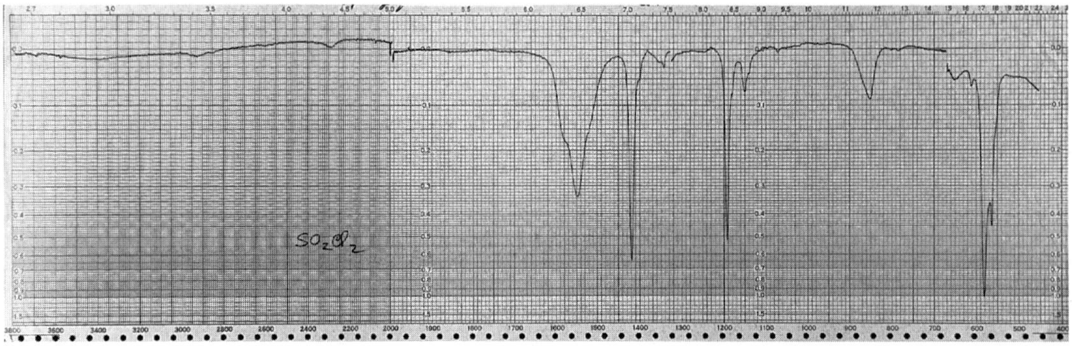

420b Sulfuryl chloride SCl_2O_2

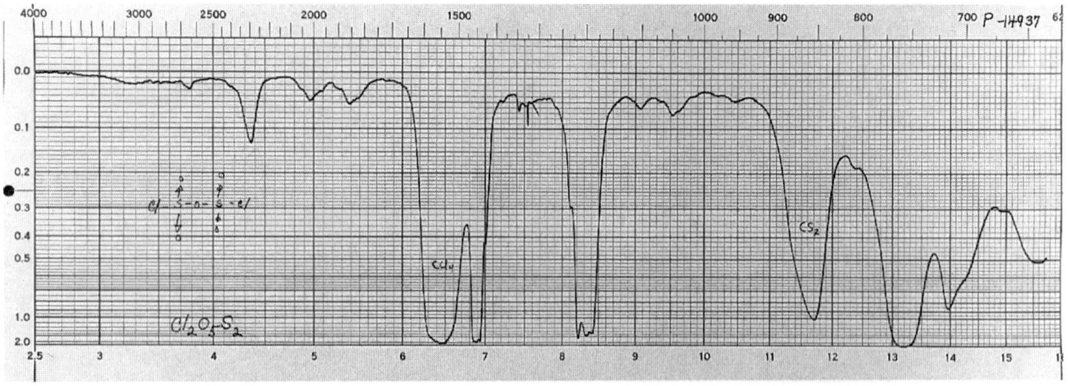

421 Pyrosulfuryl chloride $S_2Cl_2O_5$

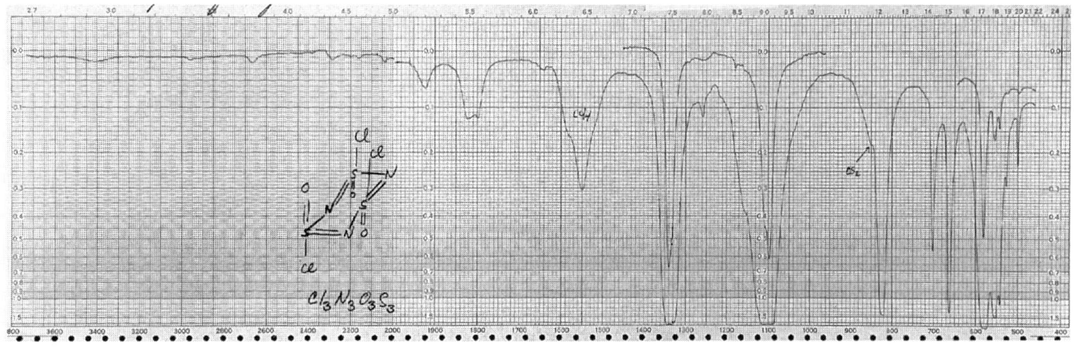

422 β-Sulfanuryl chloride $S_3Cl_3N_3O_3$

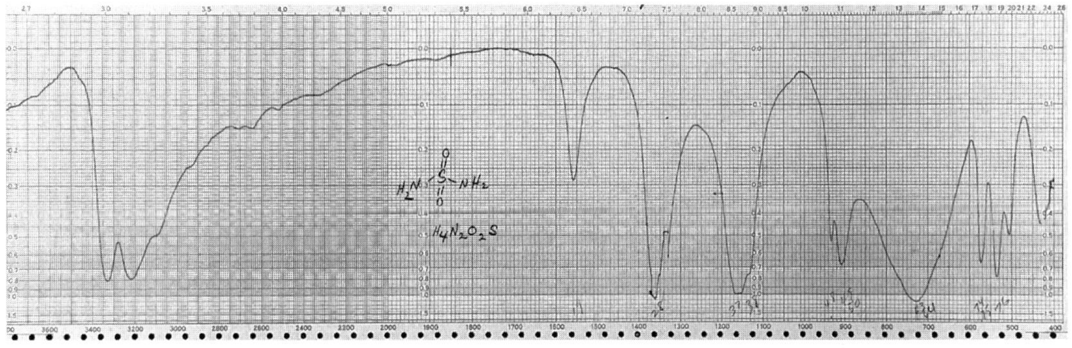

423 Sulfonamide $SH_4N_2O_2$

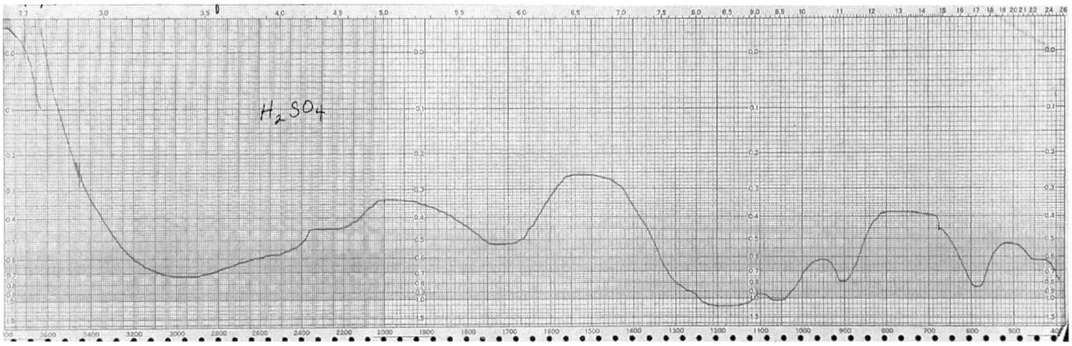

424 Sulfuric acid SH_2O_4

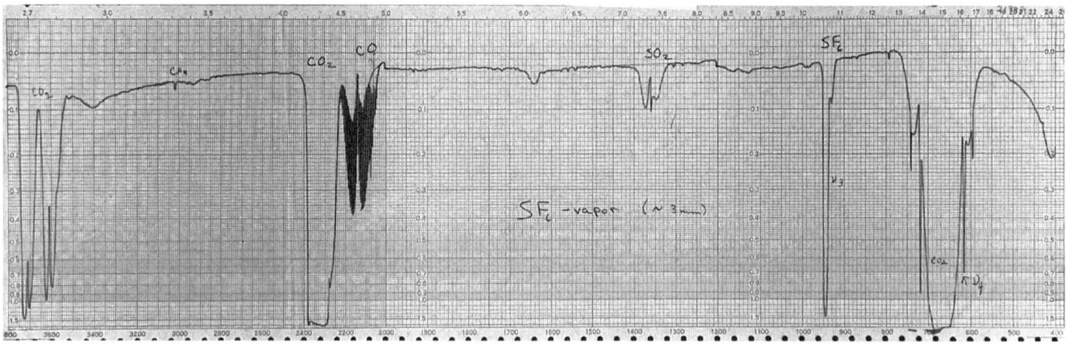

425 Sulfur hexafluoride SF_6

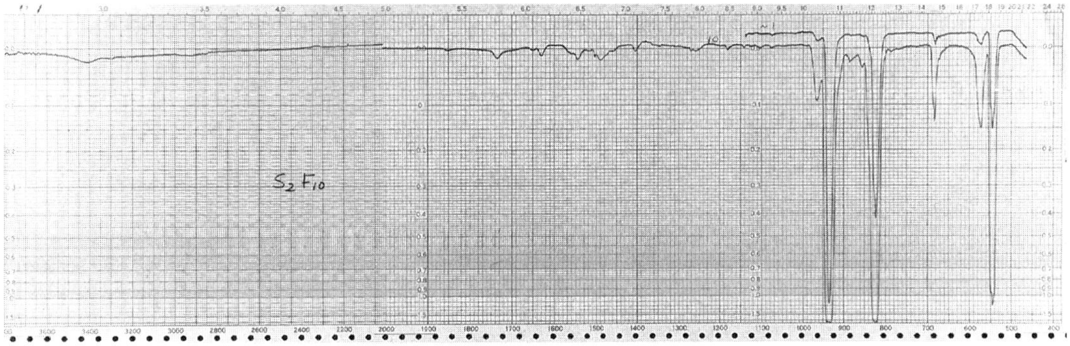

426 Decafluorodisulfide S_2F_{10}

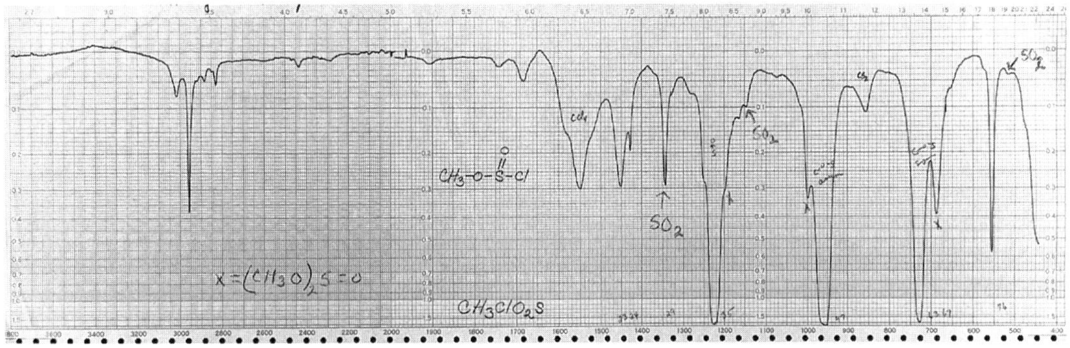

427 Methyl chlorosulfinate CH_3ClO_2S

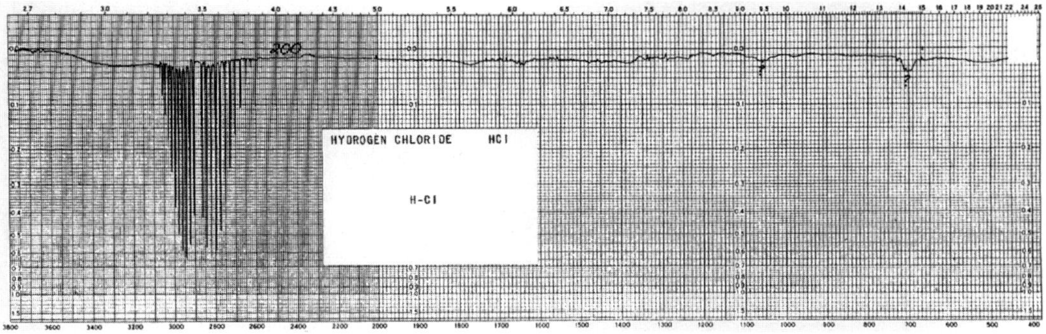

432 Hydrogen chloride ClH

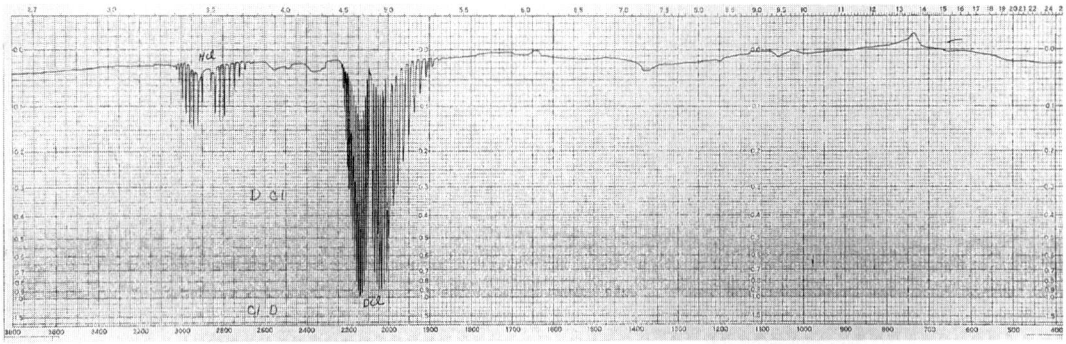

433 Deuterium chloride ClD

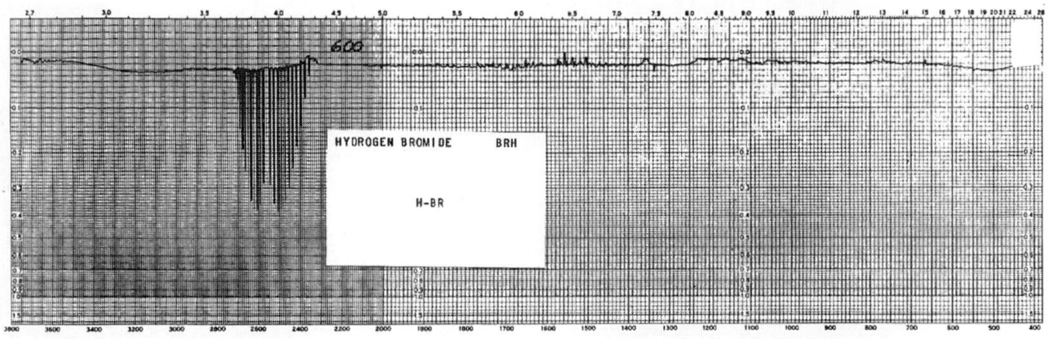

434 Hydrogen bromide BrH

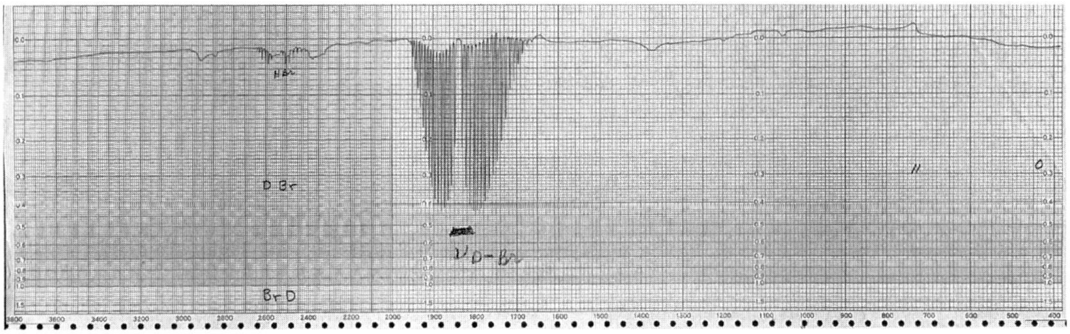

435 Deuterium bromide BrD

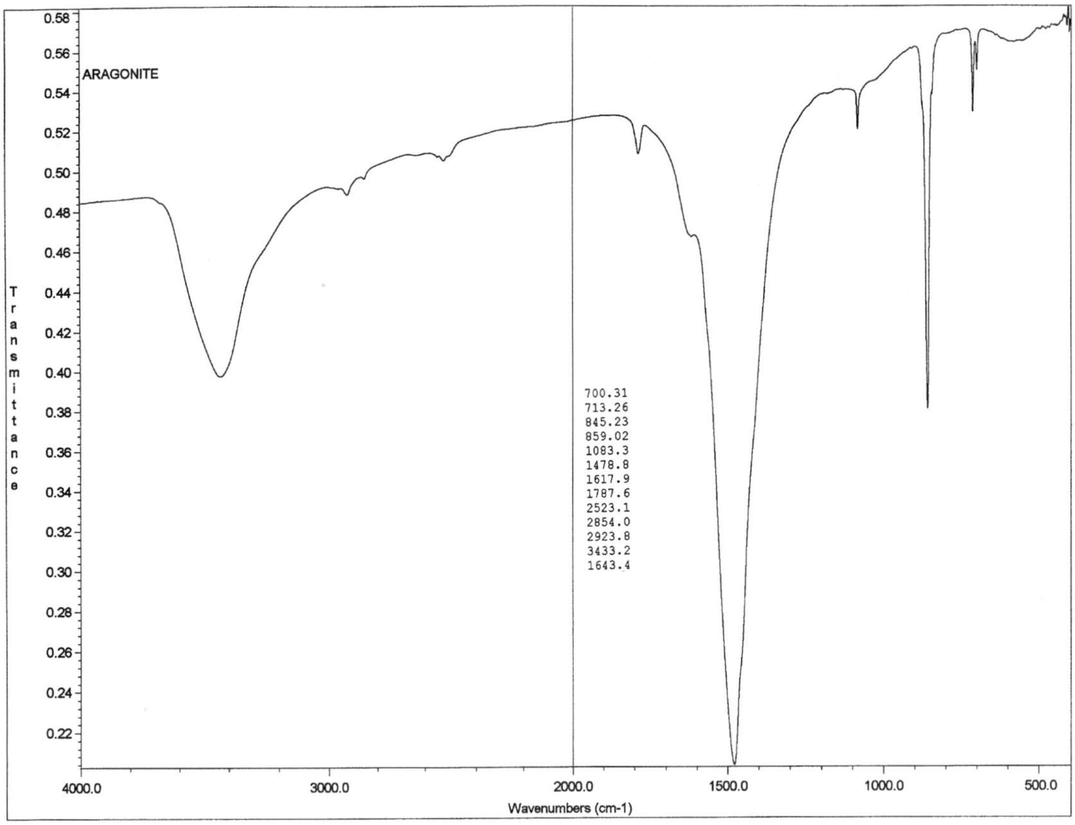

436 Aragonite CaCO3

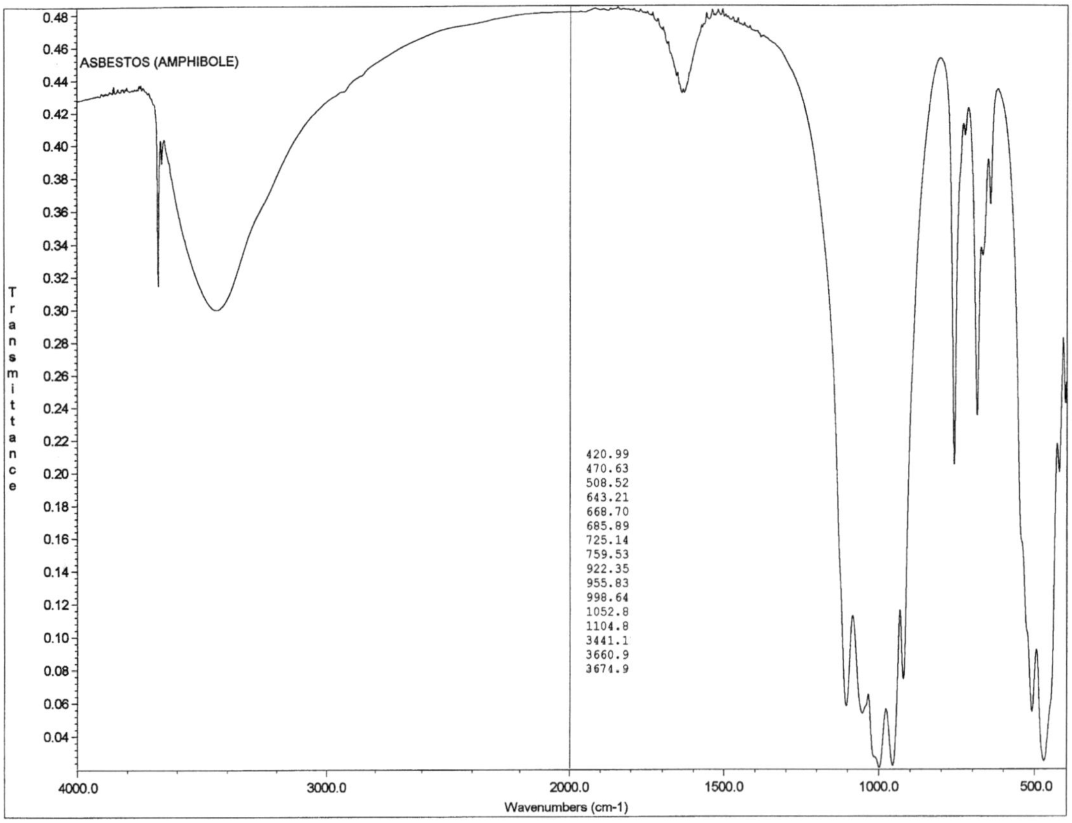

437 Asbestos (amphibole)

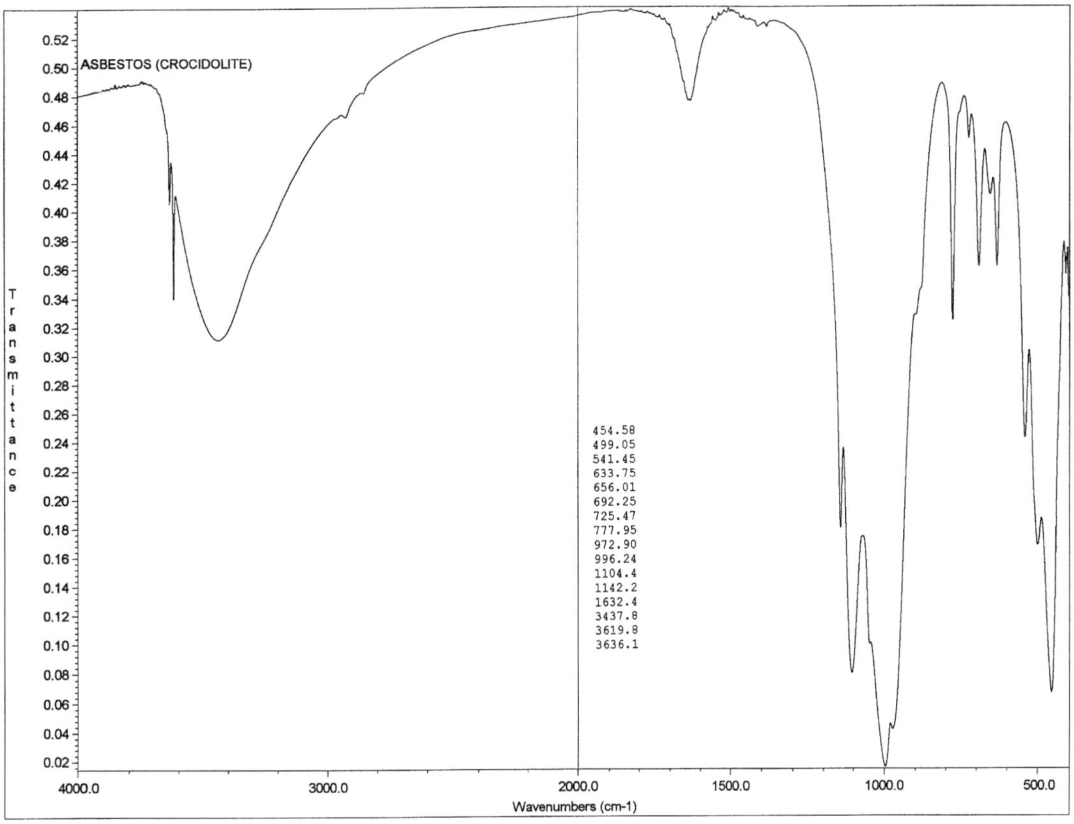

438 Asbestos (crocidolite)

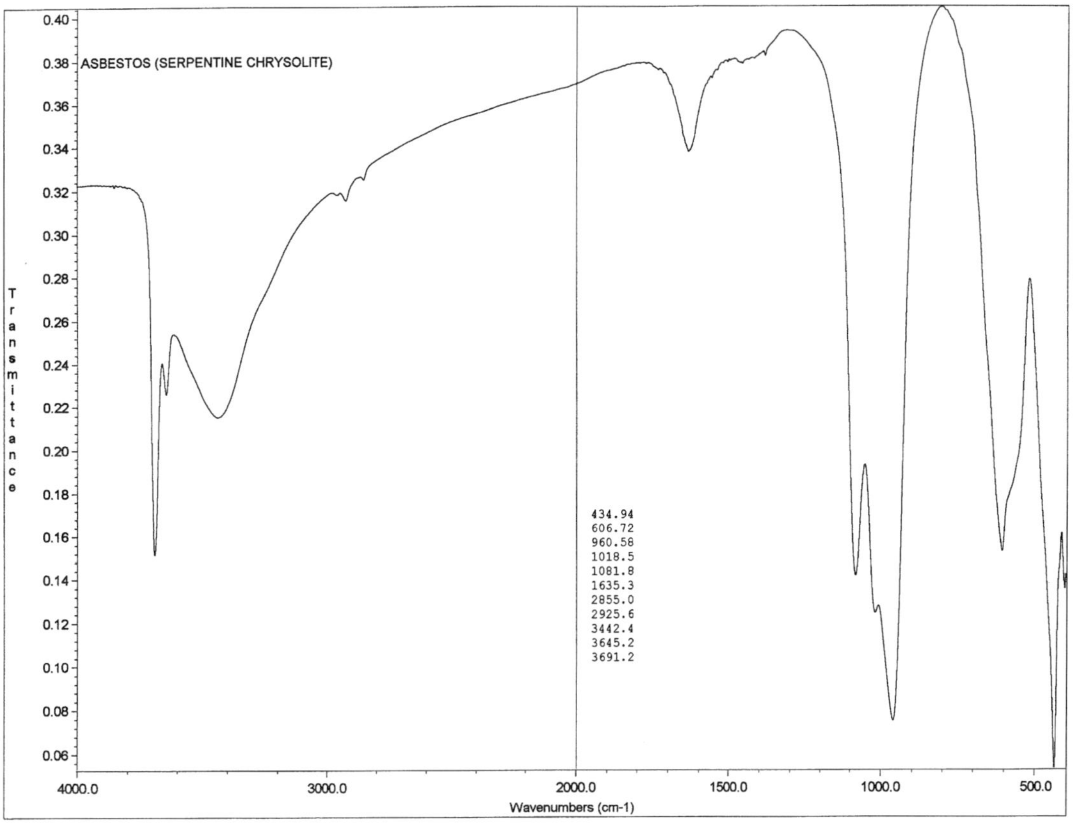

439 Asbestos (serpentine chrysolite)

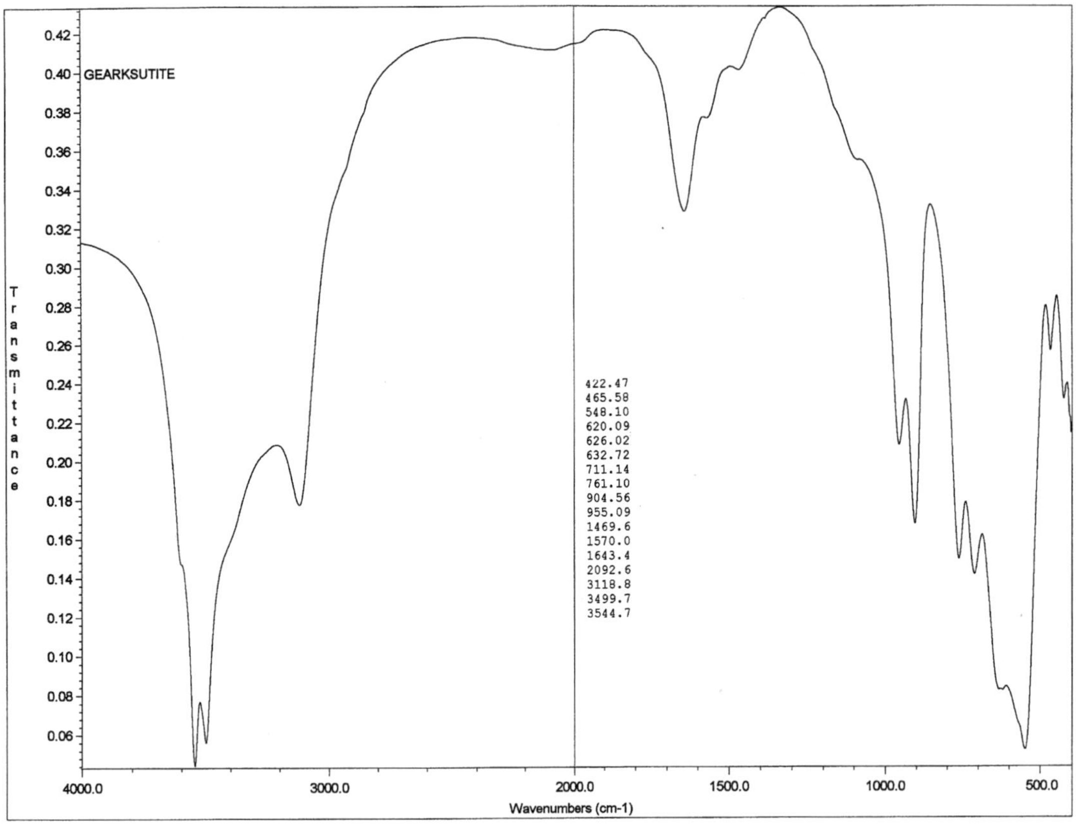

440 Gearksutite CaAlF(OH)

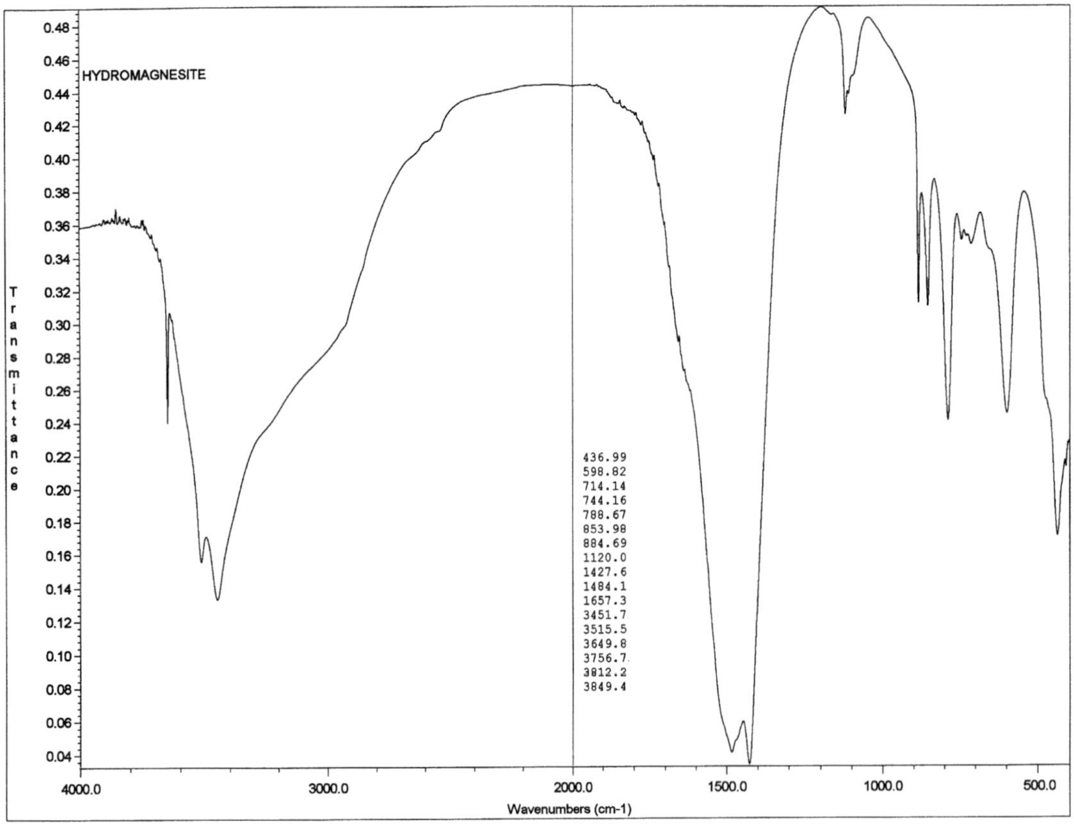

441 Hydromagnesite $3Mg \cdot Mg(OH)_2 \cdot 3H_2O$

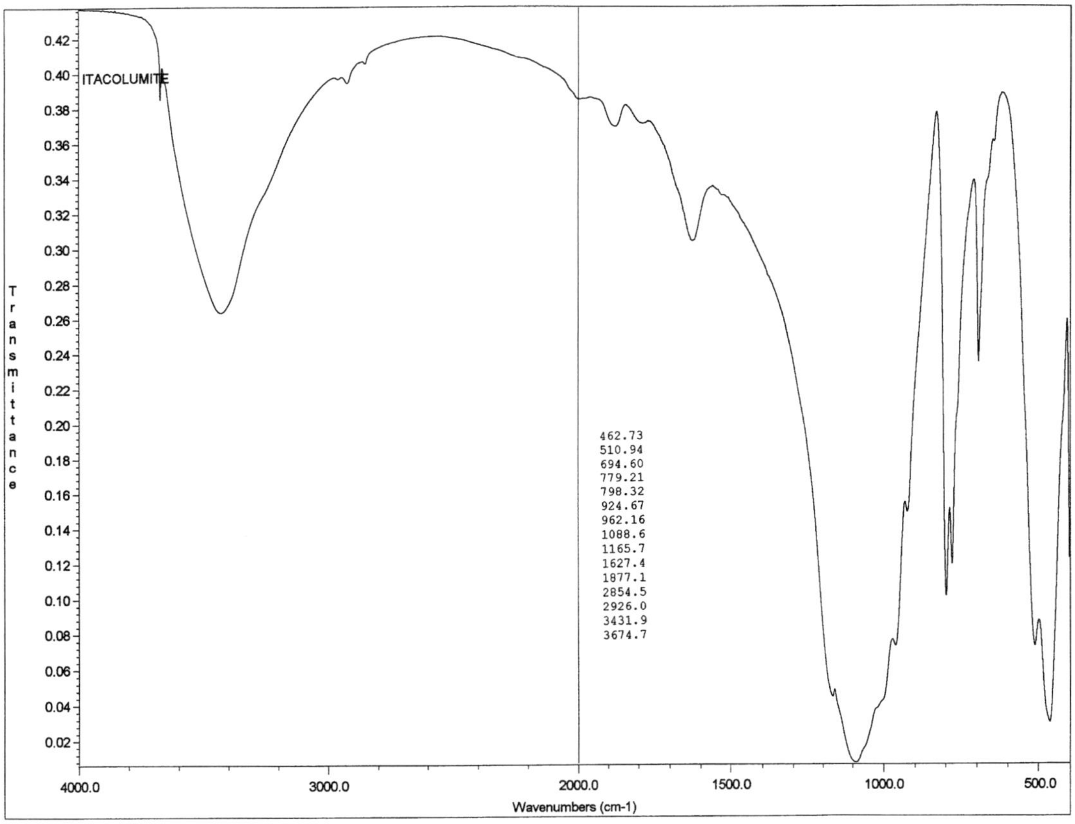

442 Itacolumite

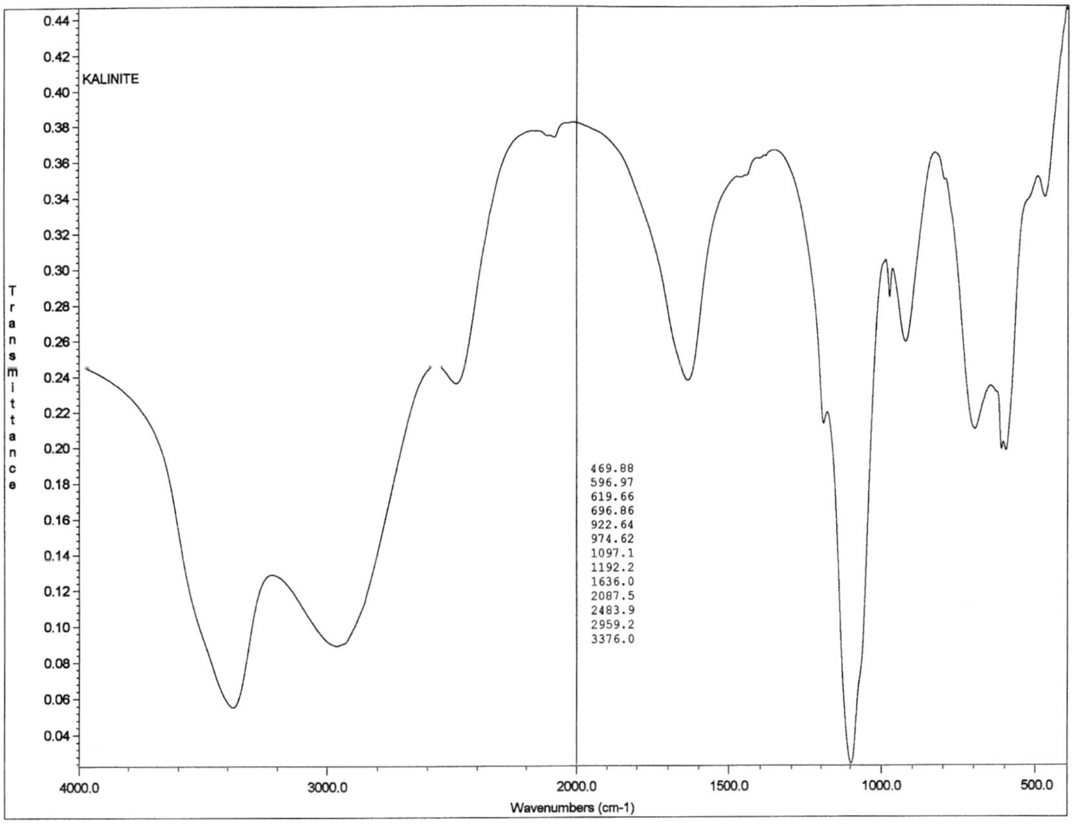

443 Kalinite $AlK(SO_4)_2 \cdot 12H_2O$

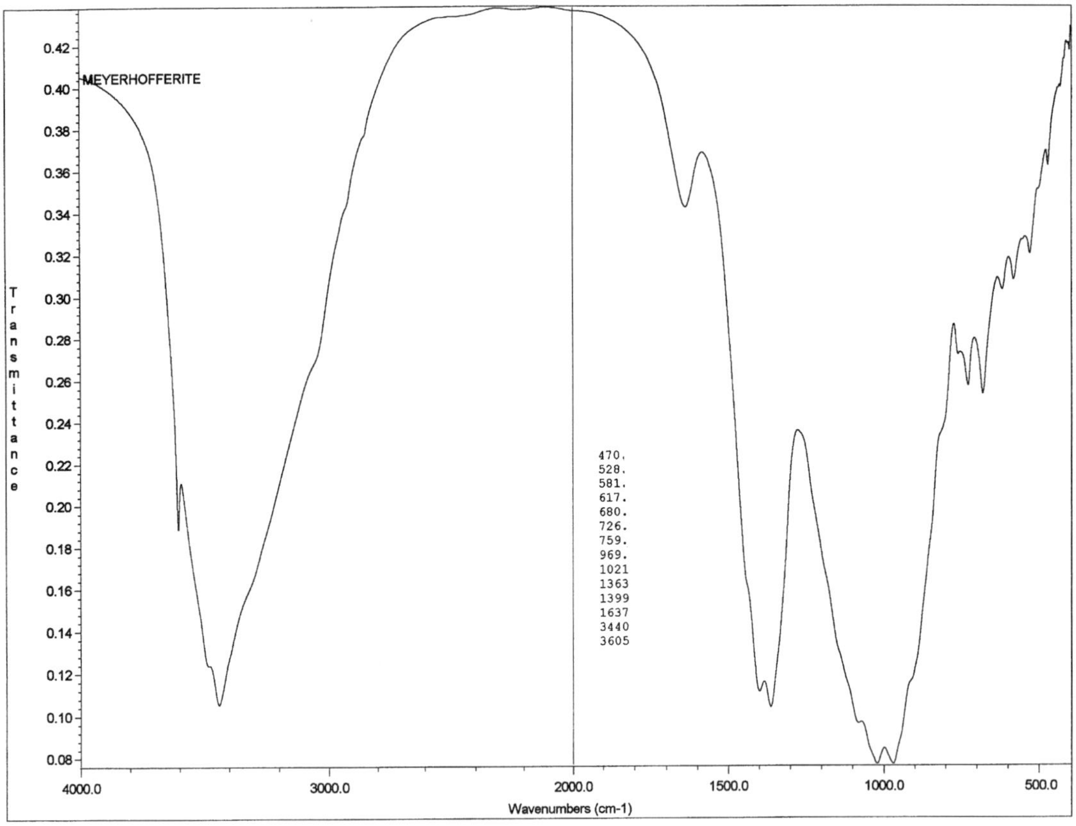

444 Meyerhofferite $2Ca \cdot 3B_2O_3 \cdot 7H_2O$

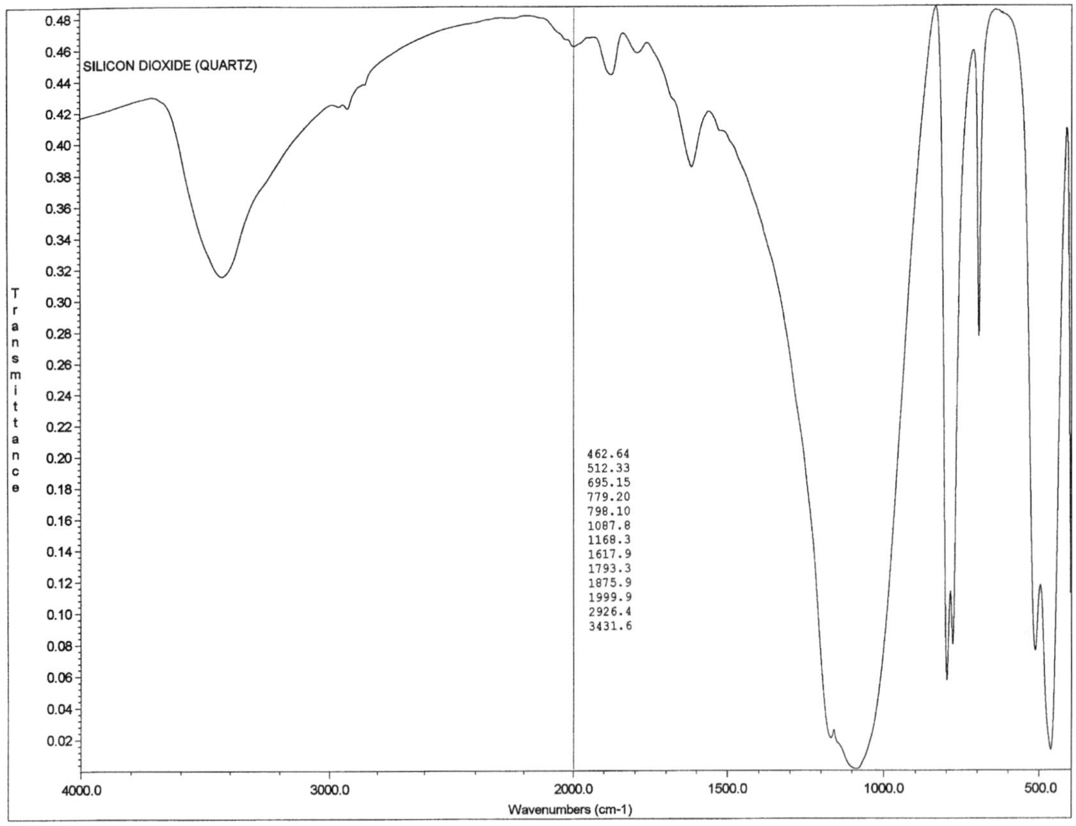

445 Quartz SiO_2

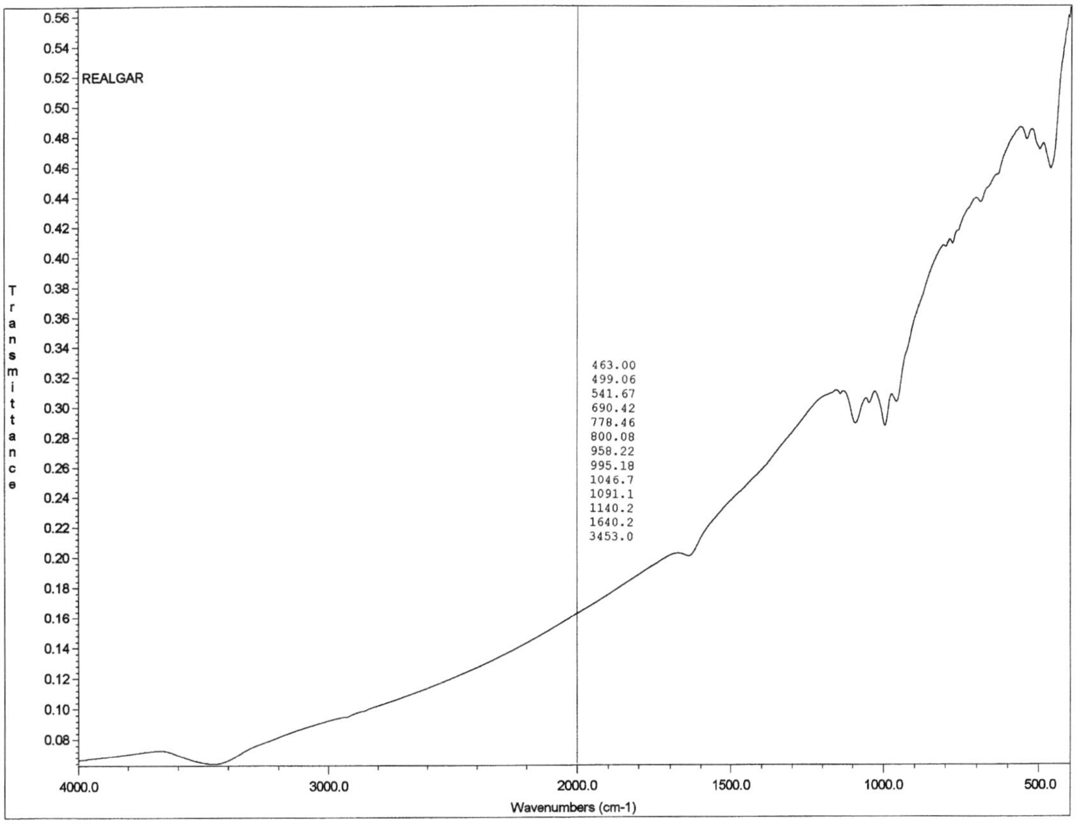

446 Realgar AsS

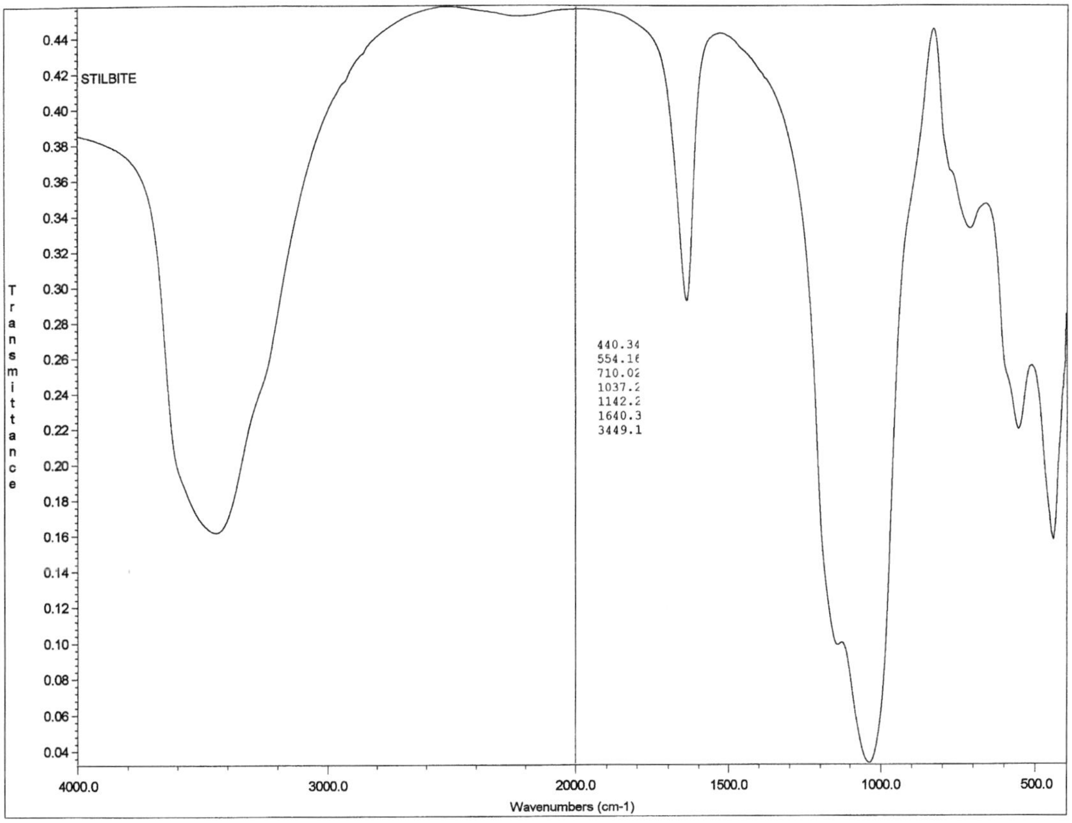

447 Stilbite $H_4(Na_2,Ca)Al_2Si_6O_{18} \cdot 4H_2O$

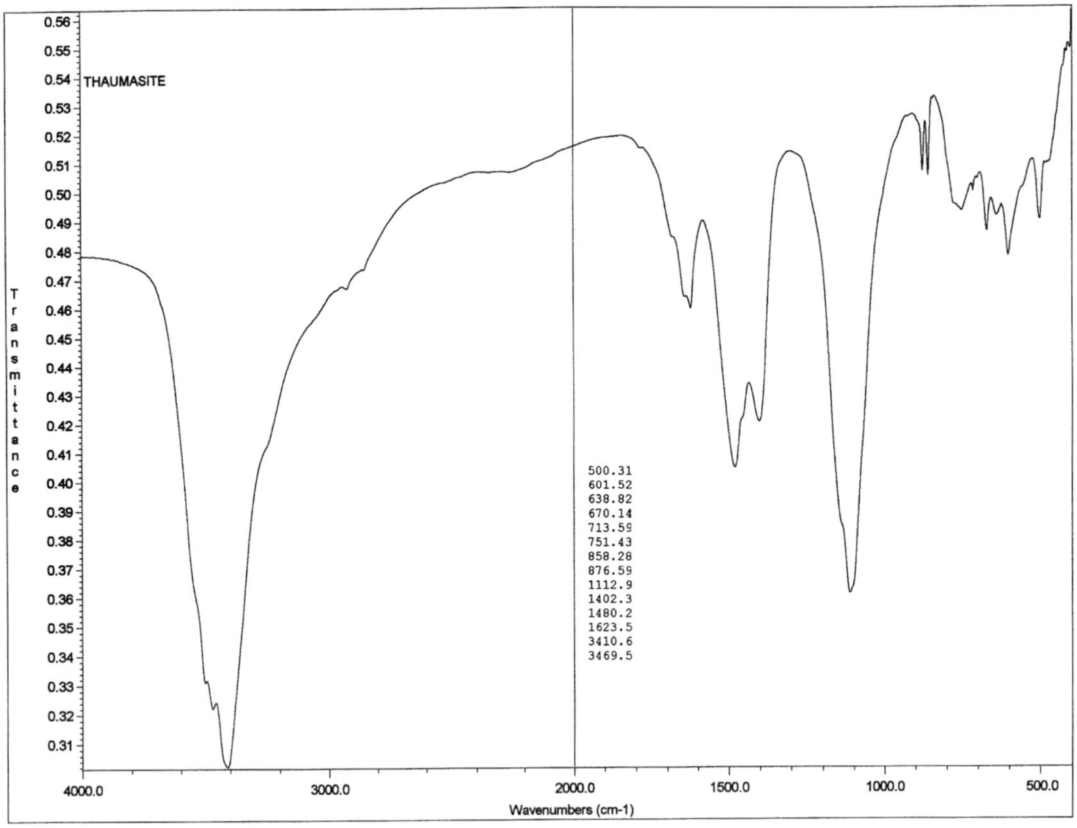

448 Thaumasite $CaSiO_3 \cdot CaCO_3 \cdot CaSO_4 \cdot 15H_2OX$

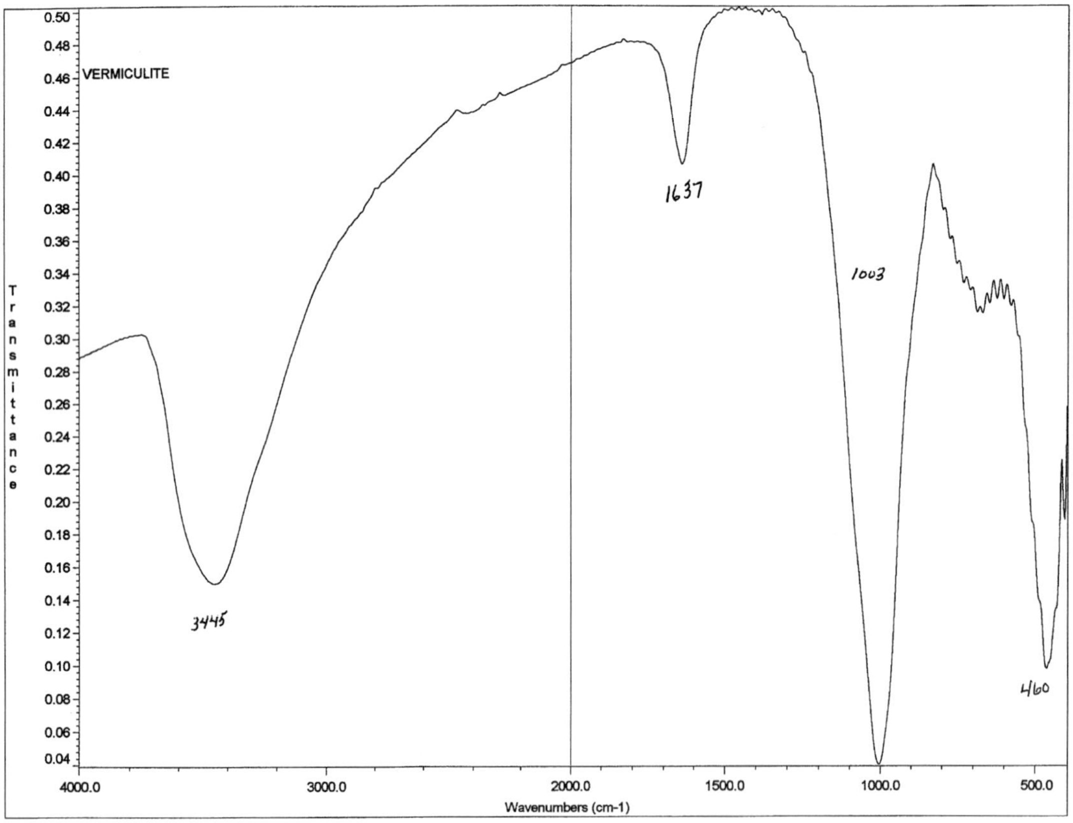

449 Vermiculite

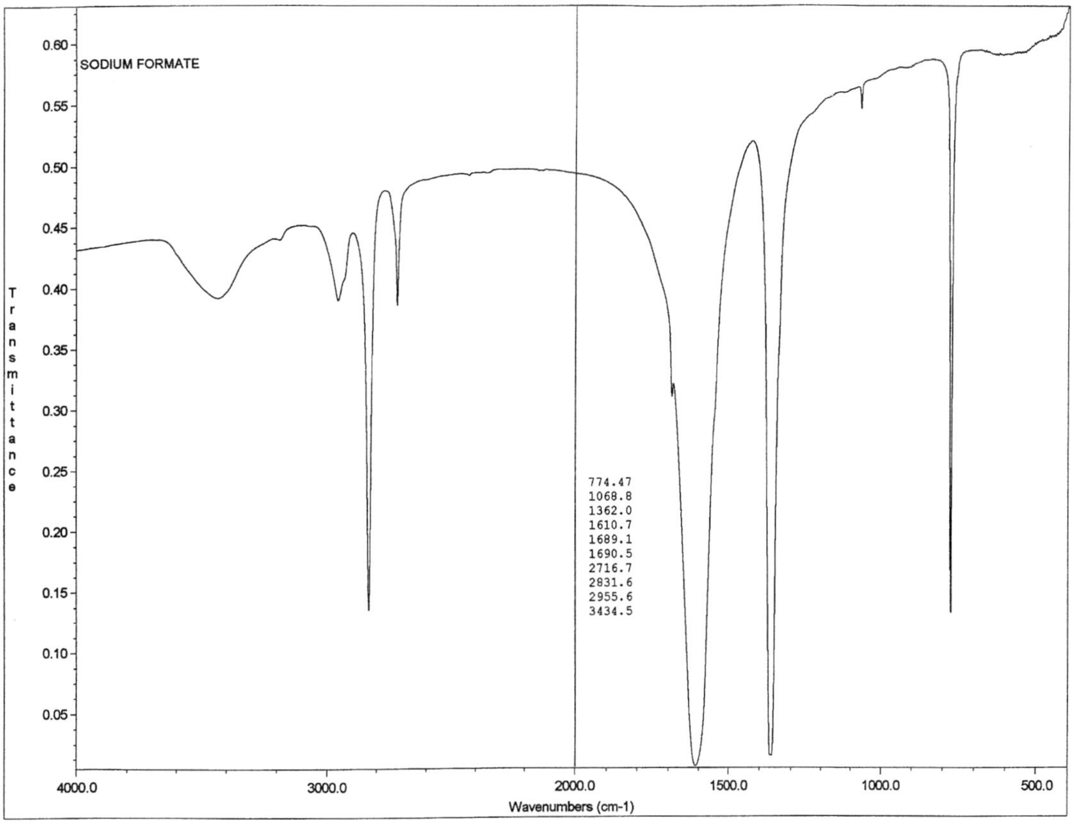

1 Sodium formate CHO_2Na

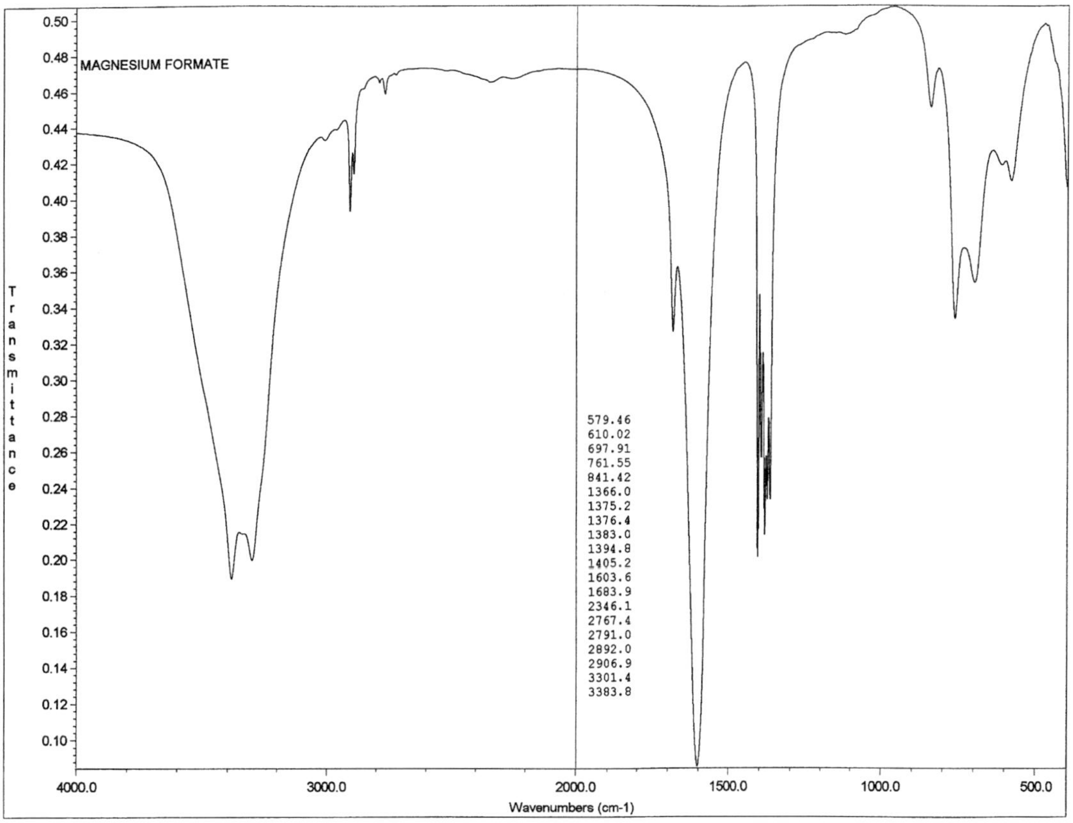

2 Magnesium formate $(CHO_2)_2Mg \cdot xH_2O$

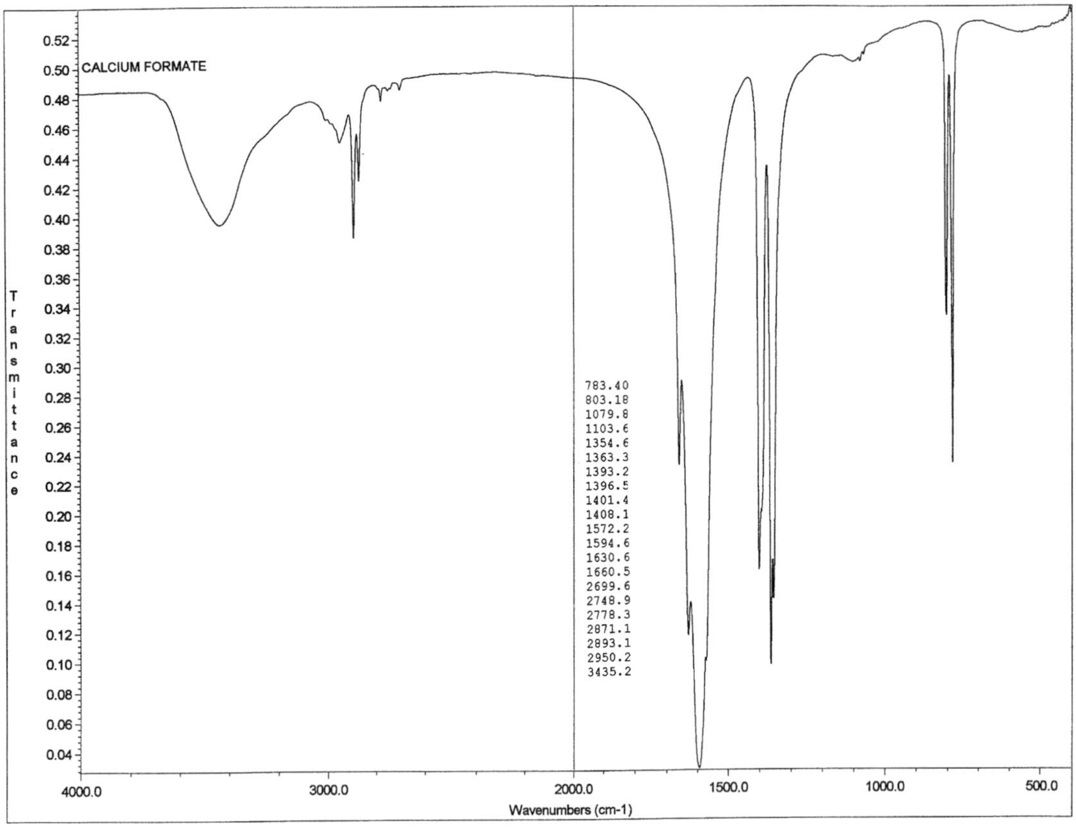

3 Calcium formate $(CHO_2)_2Ca$

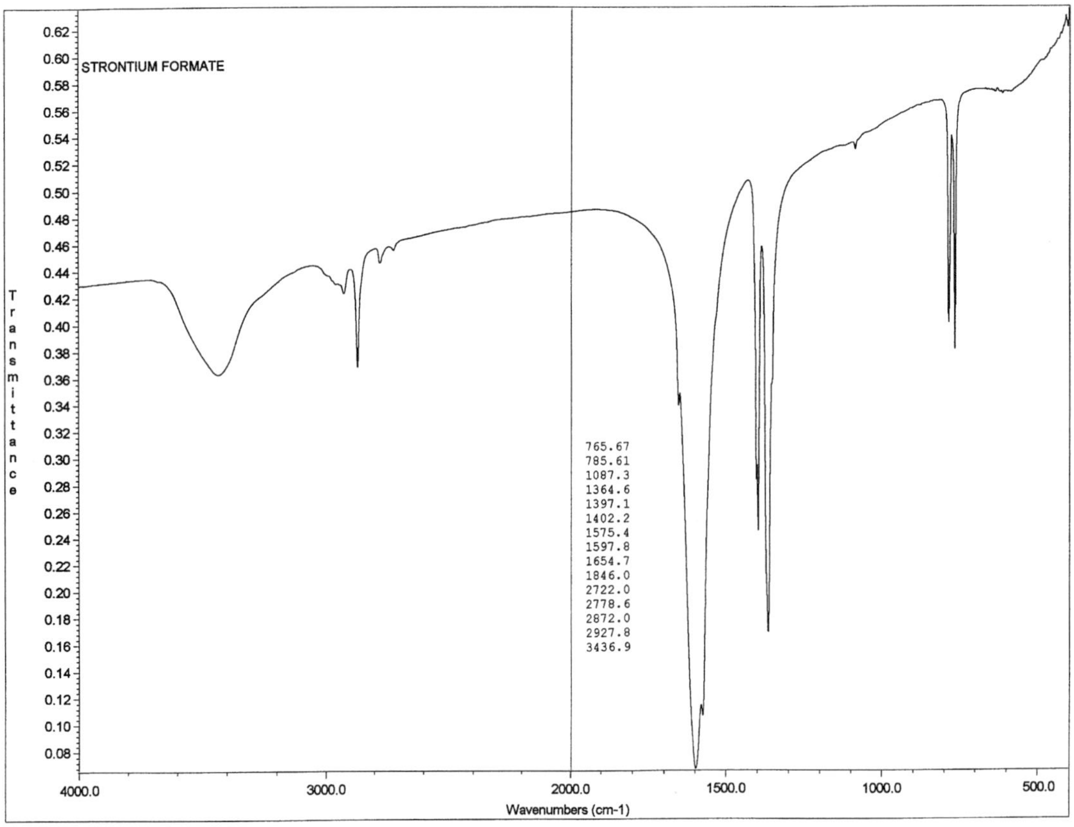

4 Strontium formate $(CHO_2)_2Sr$

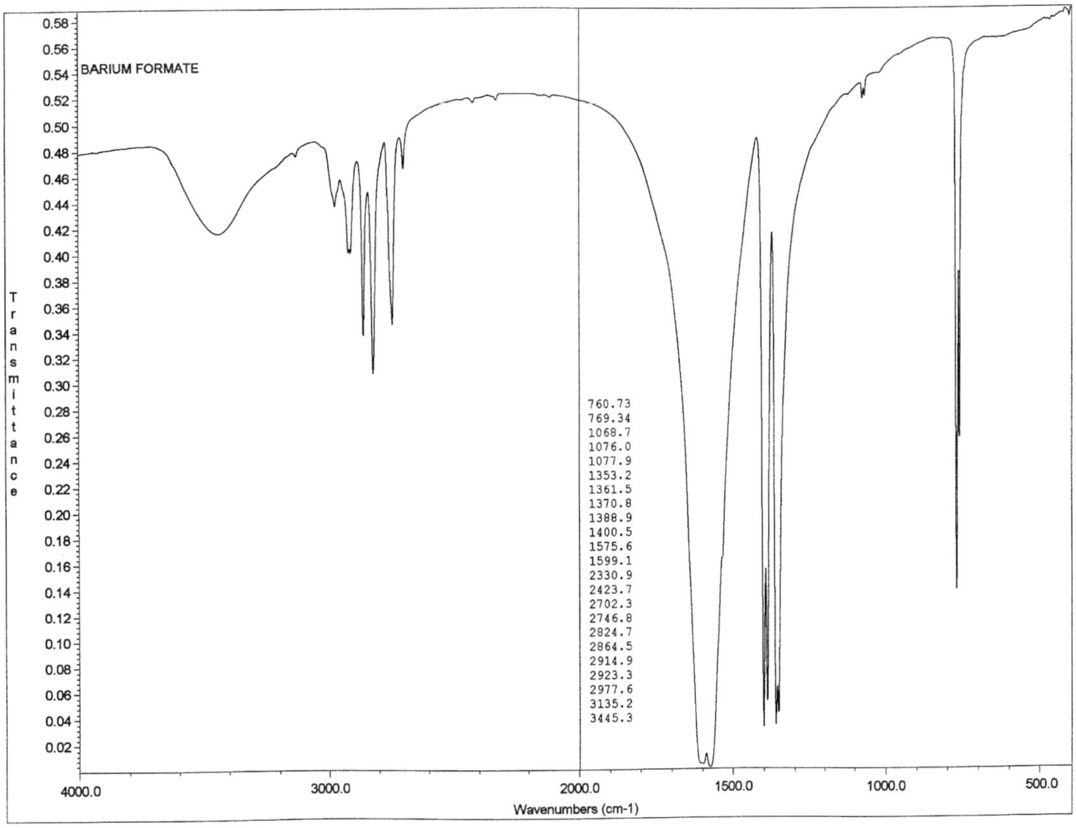

5 Barium formate $(CHO_2)_2Ba$

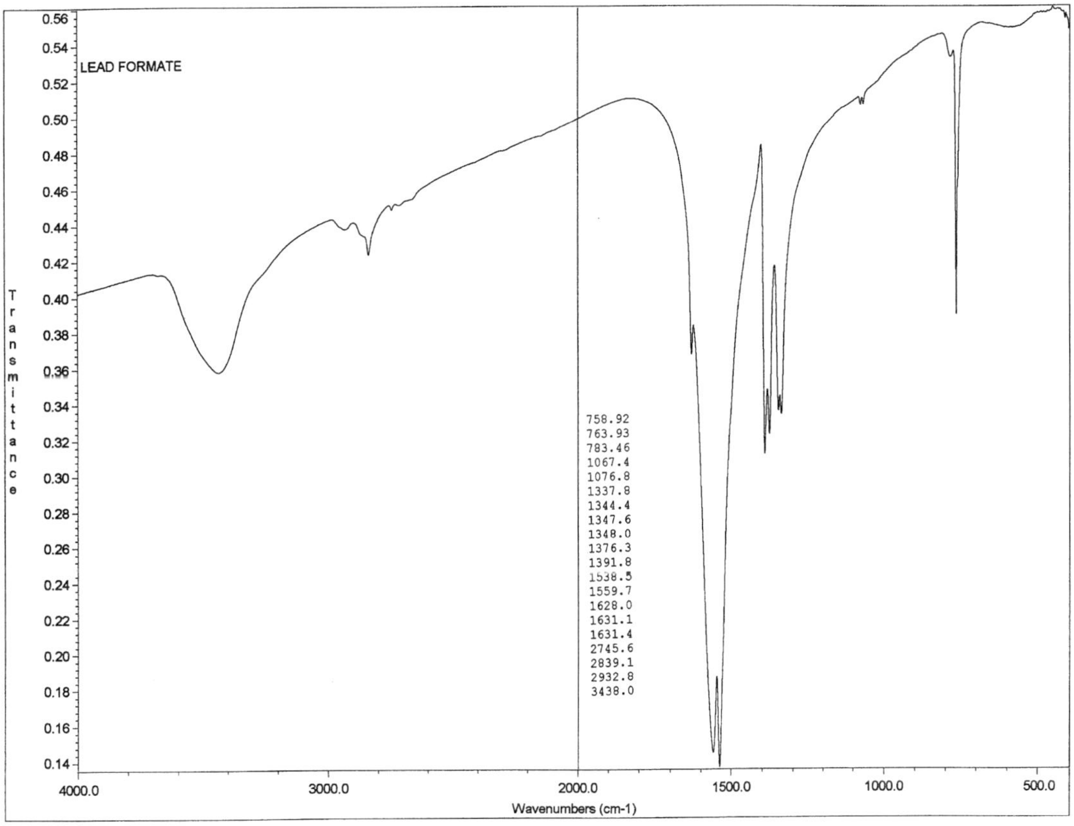

6 Lead formate $(CHO_2)_2Pb$

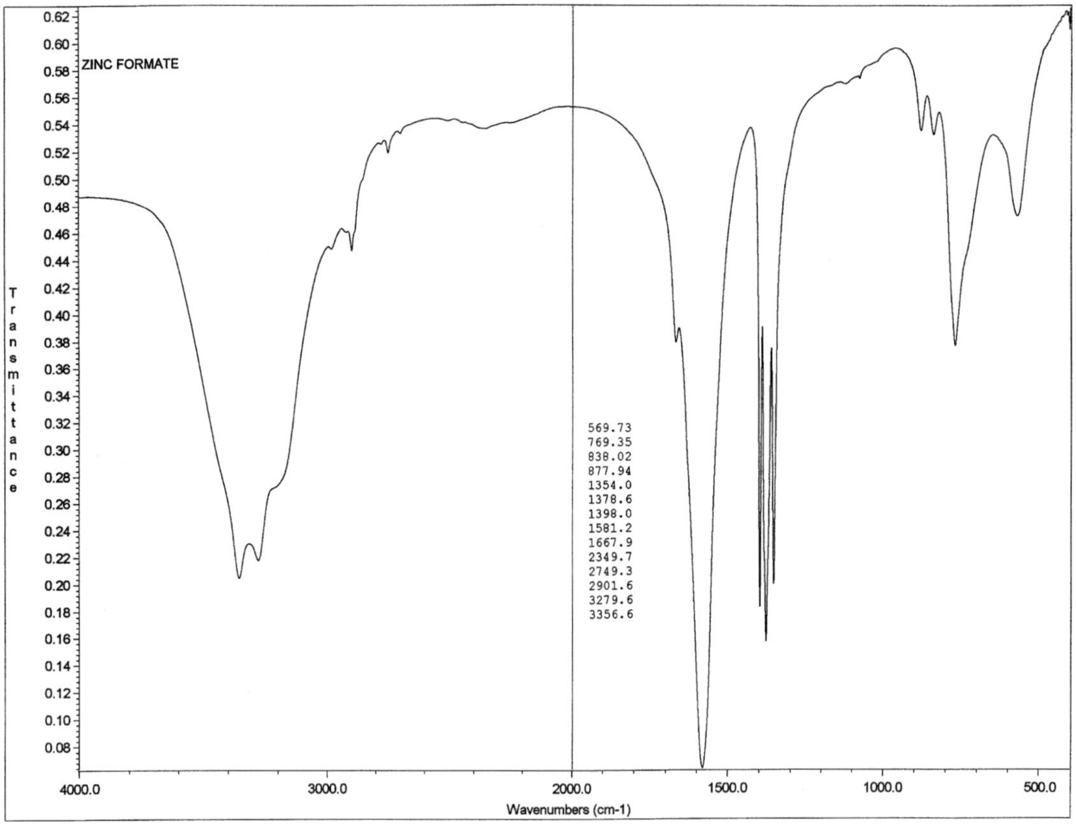

7 Zinc formate $(CHO_2)_2Zn \cdot xH_2O$

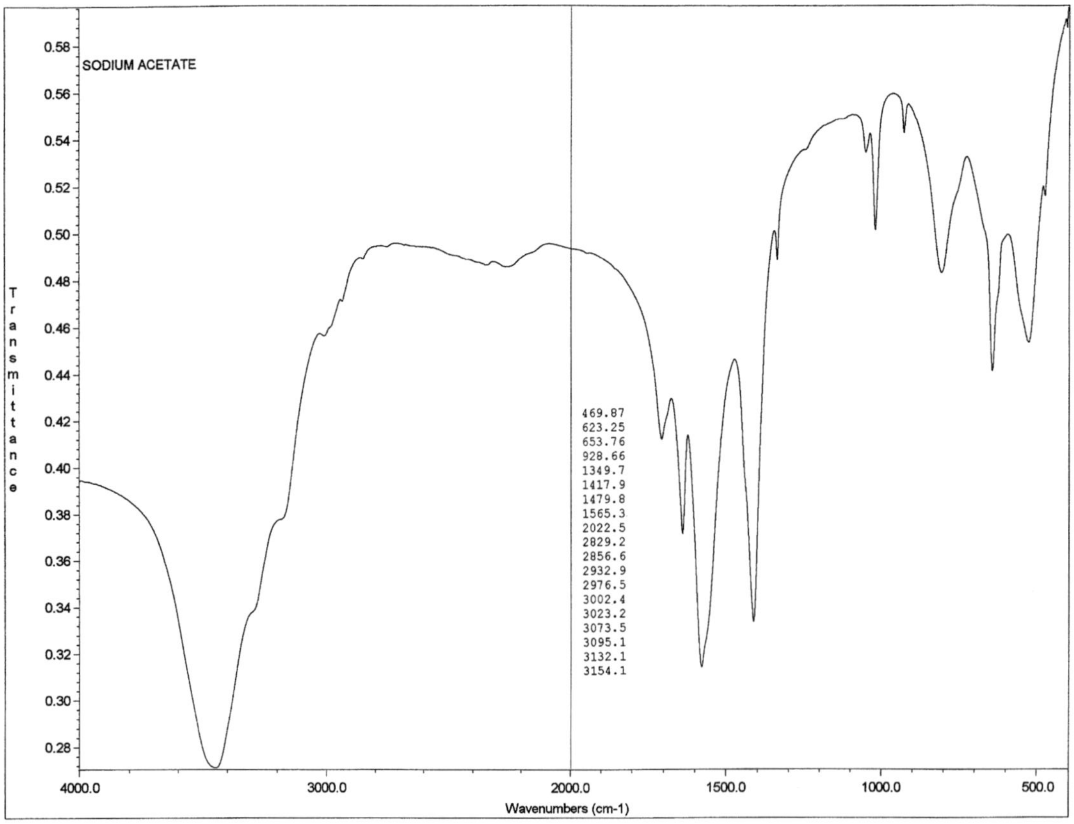

8 Sodium acetate $(CH_3CO_2)_2Na \cdot xH_2O$

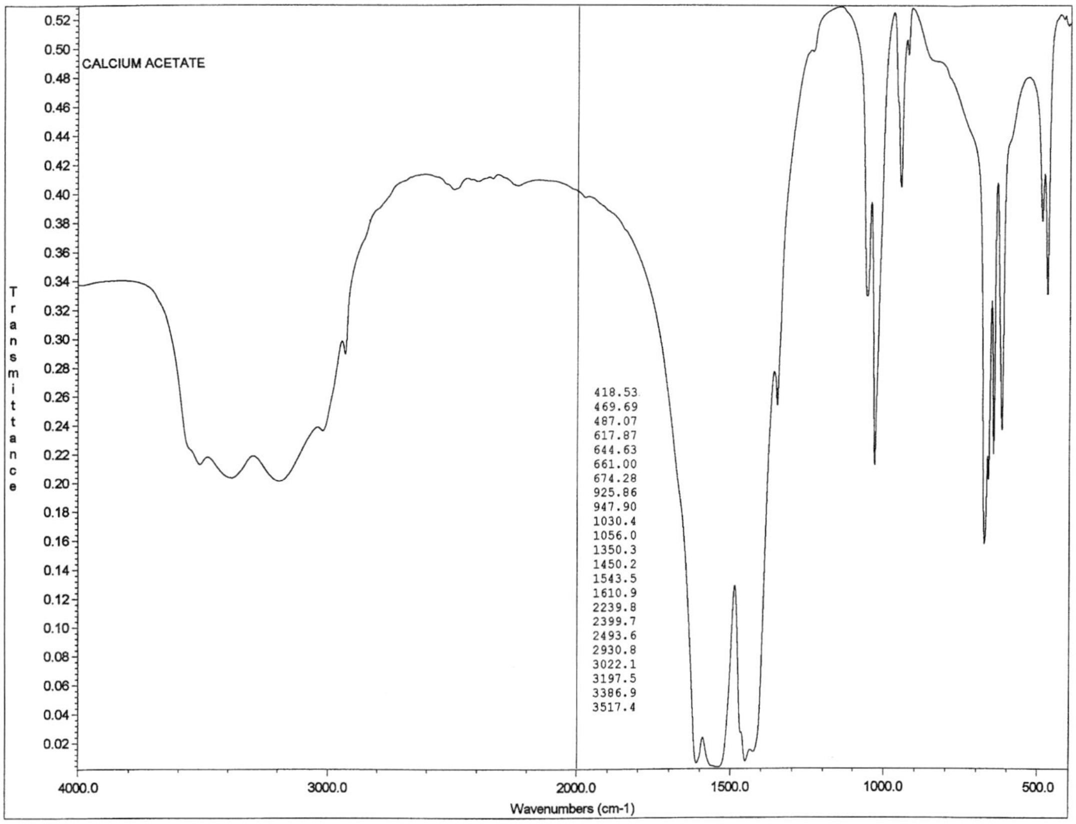

9 Calcium acetate $(CH_3CO_2)_2Ca \cdot xH_2O$

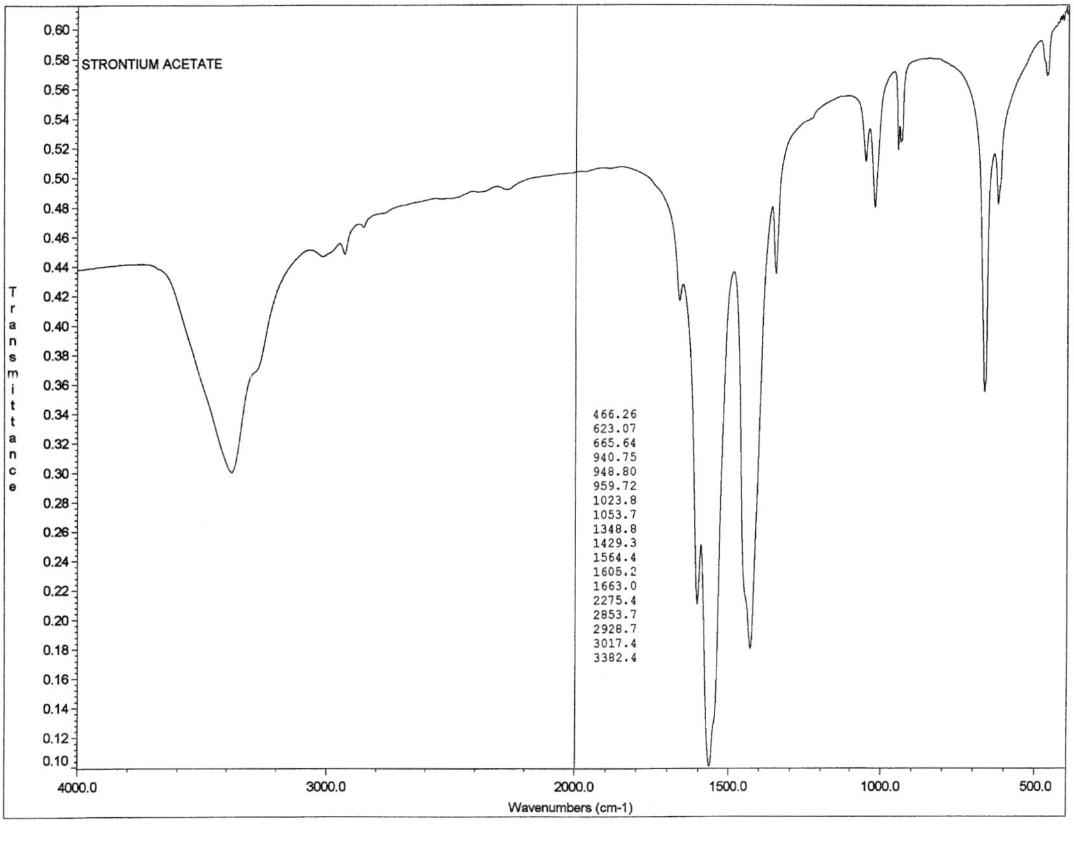

10 Strontium acetate $(CH_3CO_2)_2Sr \cdot xH_2O$

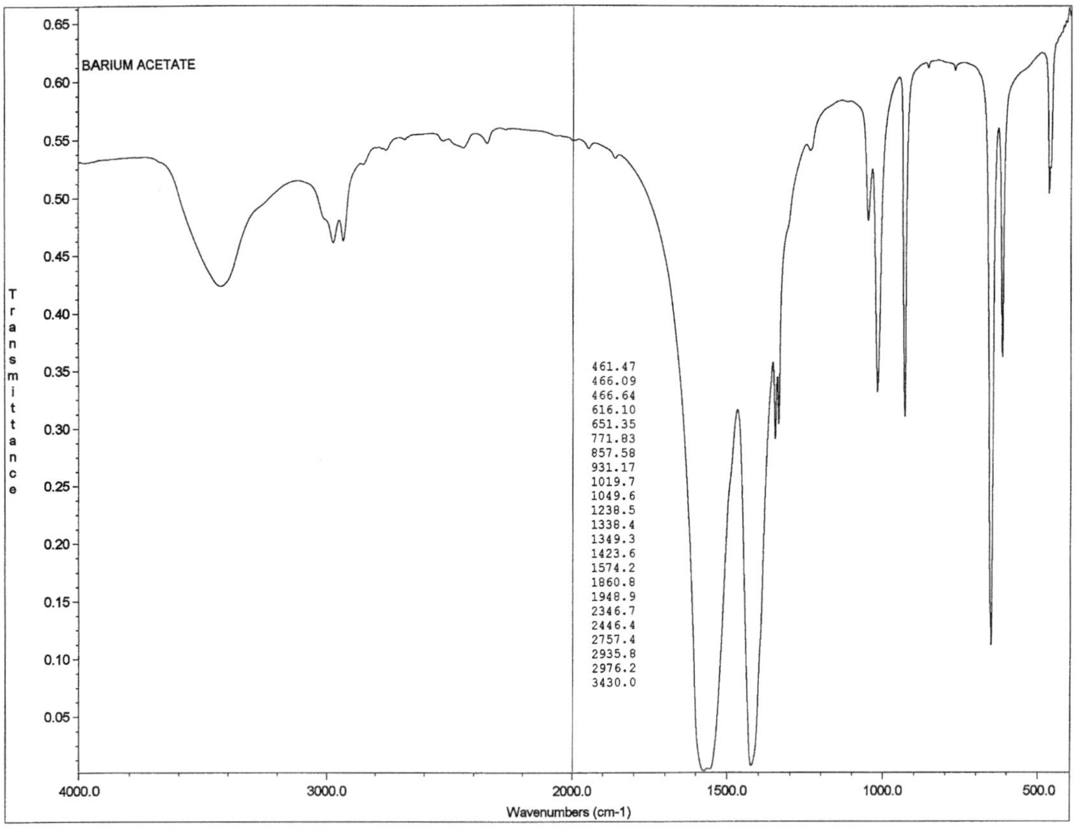

11 Barium acetate $(CH_3CO_2)_2Ba \cdot xH_2O$

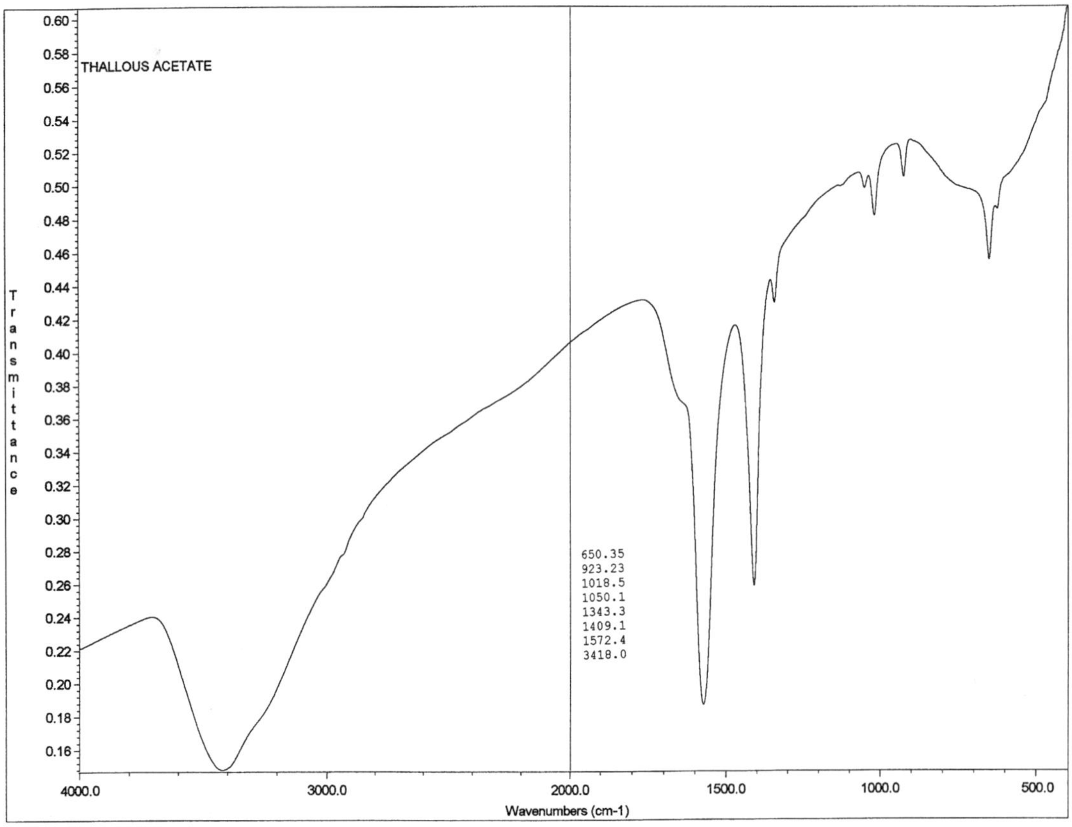

12 Thallous acetate $(CH_3CO_2)Tl \cdot xH_2O$

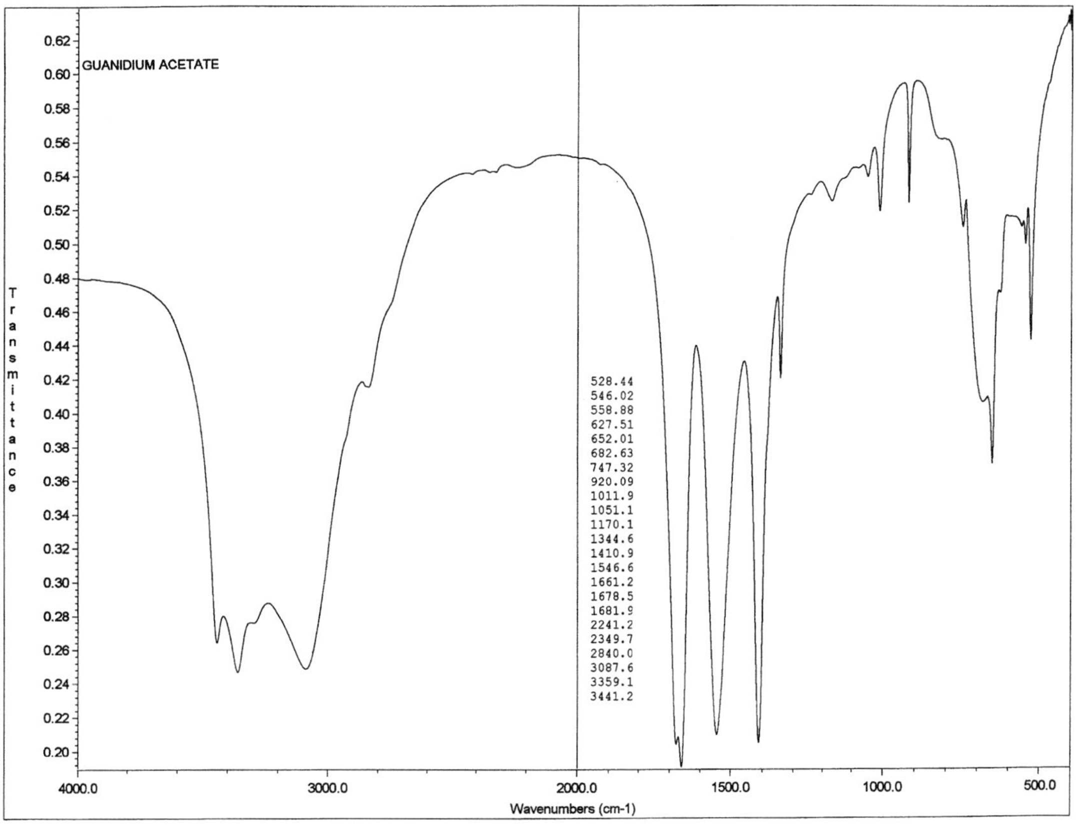

13 Guanidinium acetate $(CH_3CO_2)(H_2N)_2C{=}NH_2$

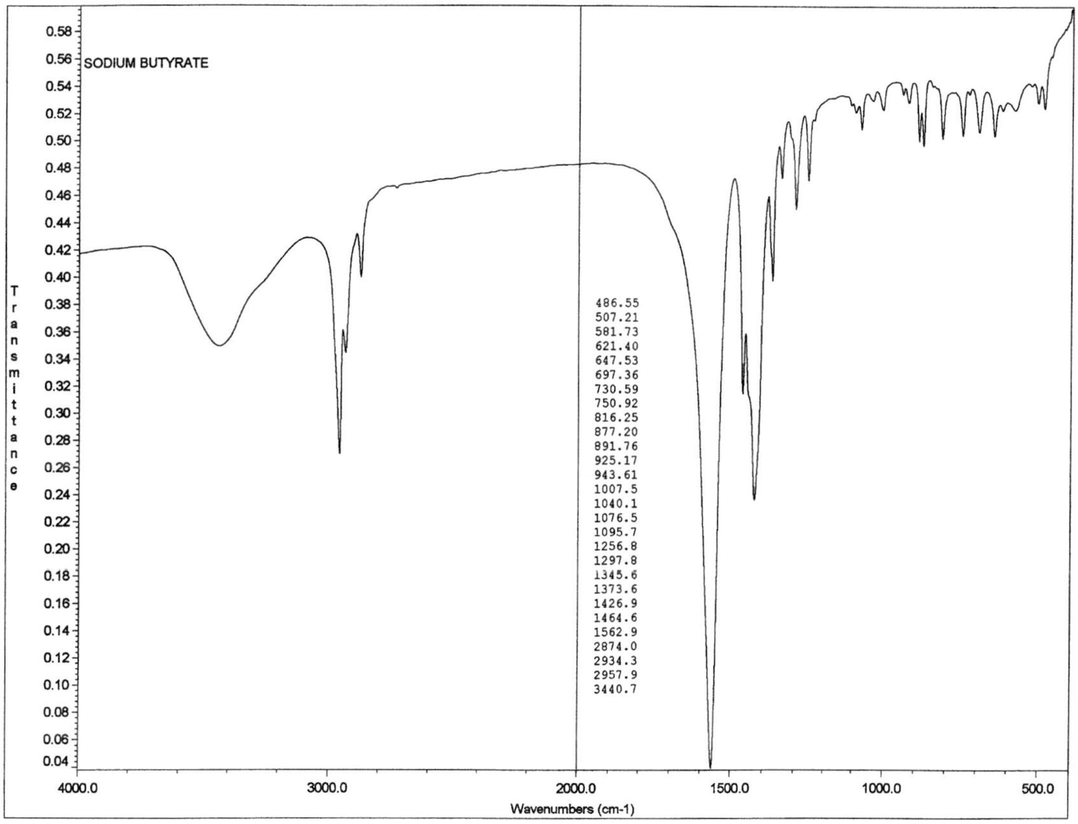

14 Sodium butyrate $(n\text{-}C_3H_7CO_2)Na$

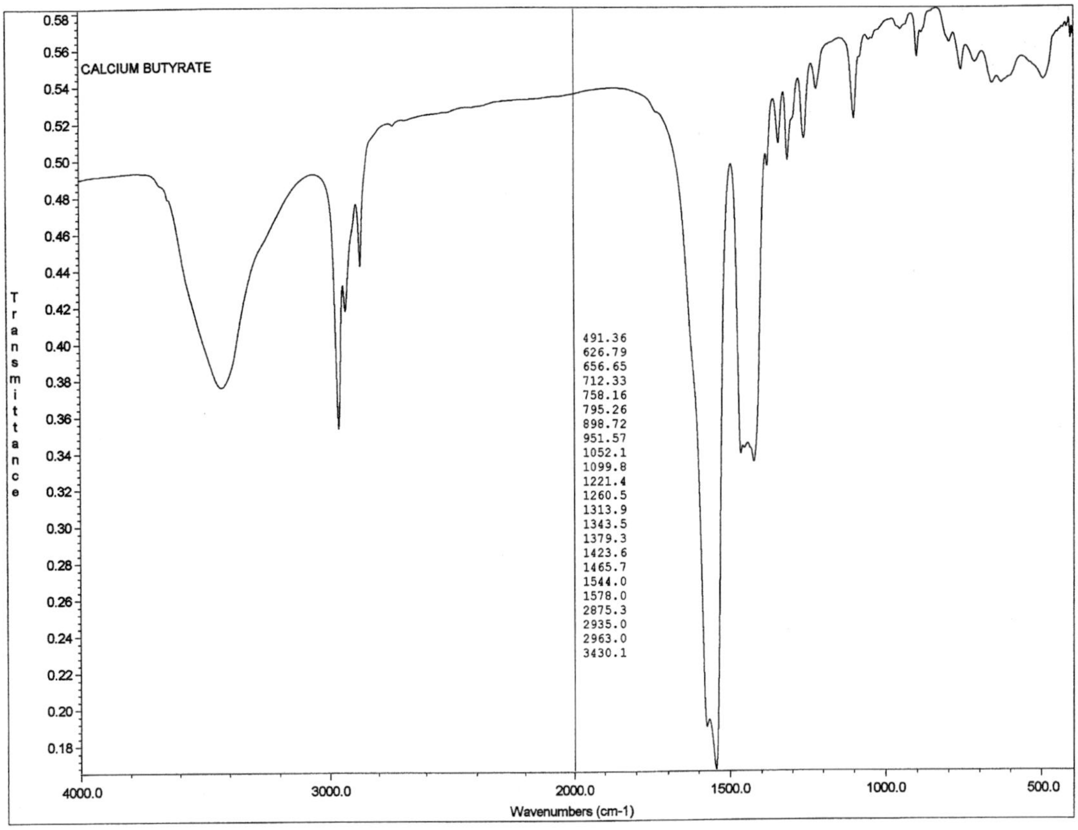

15 Calcium butyrate $(n\text{-}C_3H_7CO_2)_2Ca$

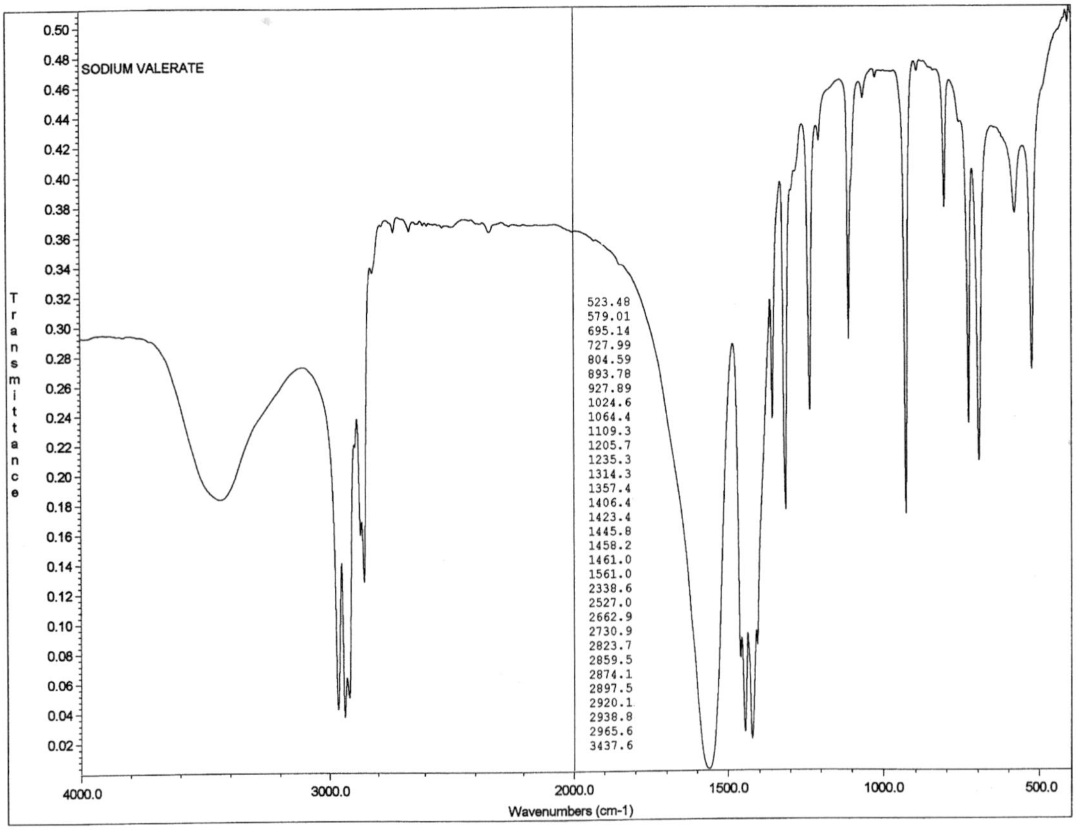

16 Sodium valerate $(n\text{-}C_4H_9CO_2)Na \cdot xH_2O$

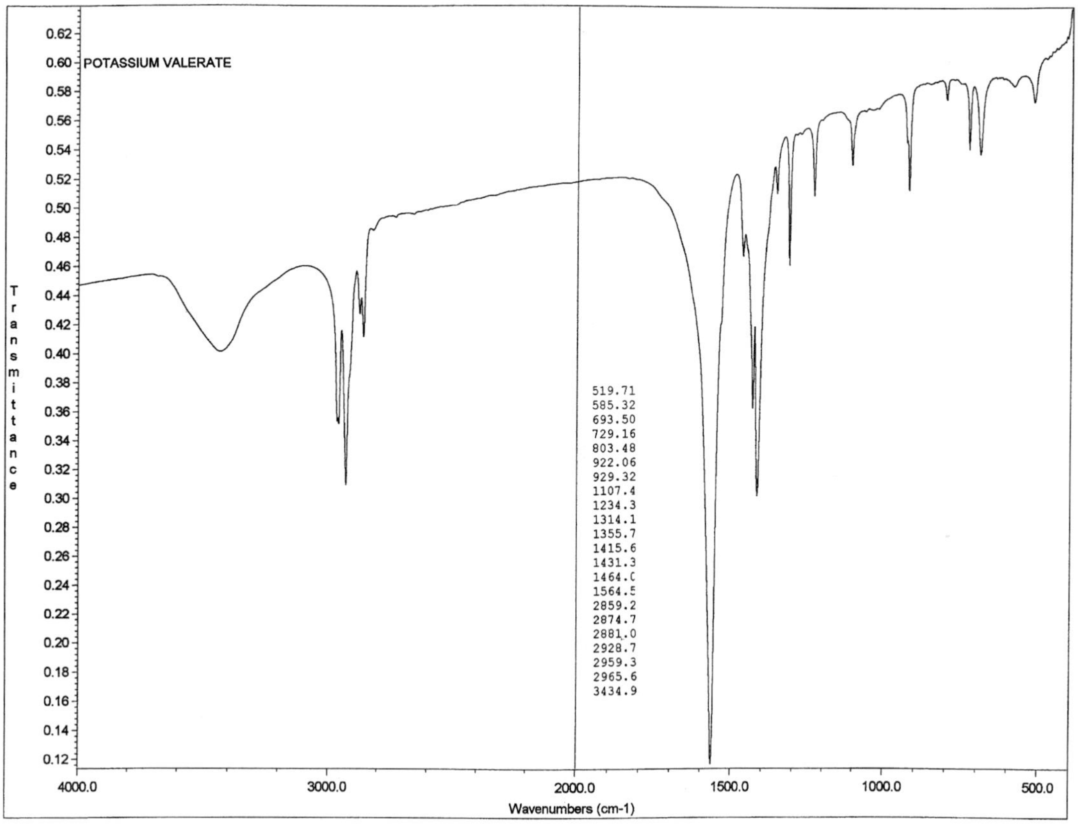

17 Potassium valerate ($n\text{-}C_4H_9CO_2$)K

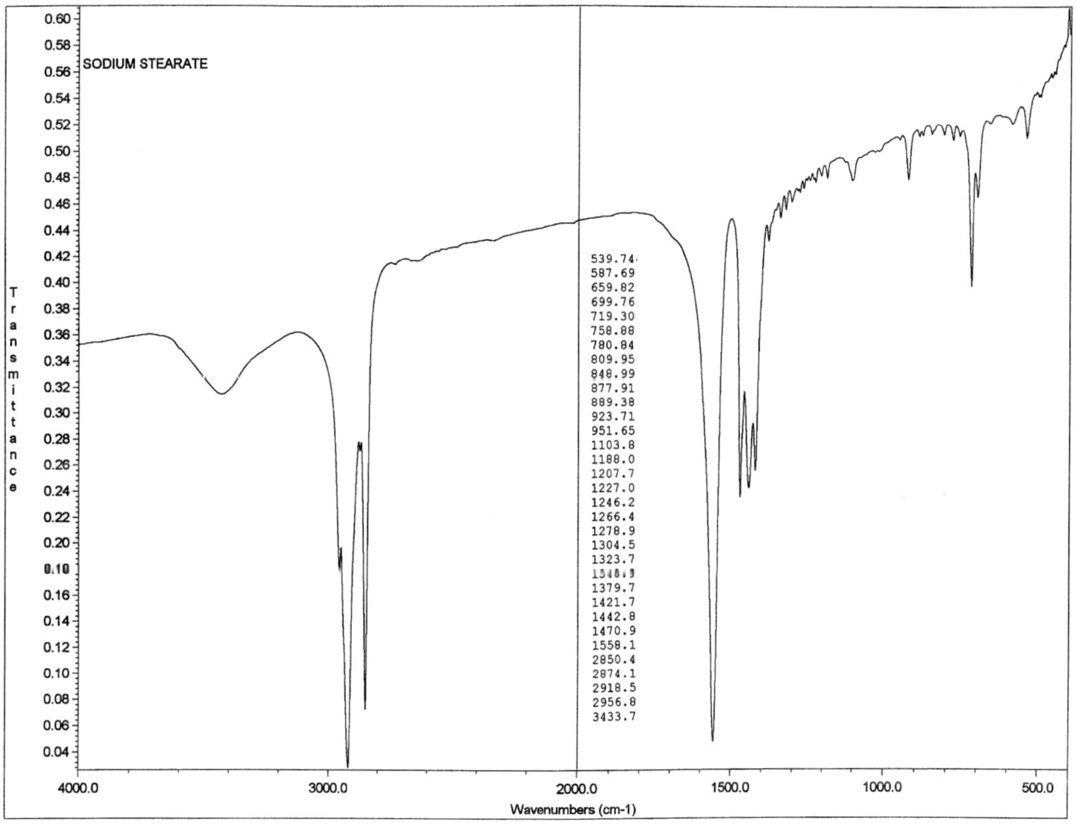

18 Sodium stearate ($n\text{-}C_{17}H_{35}CO_2$)Na

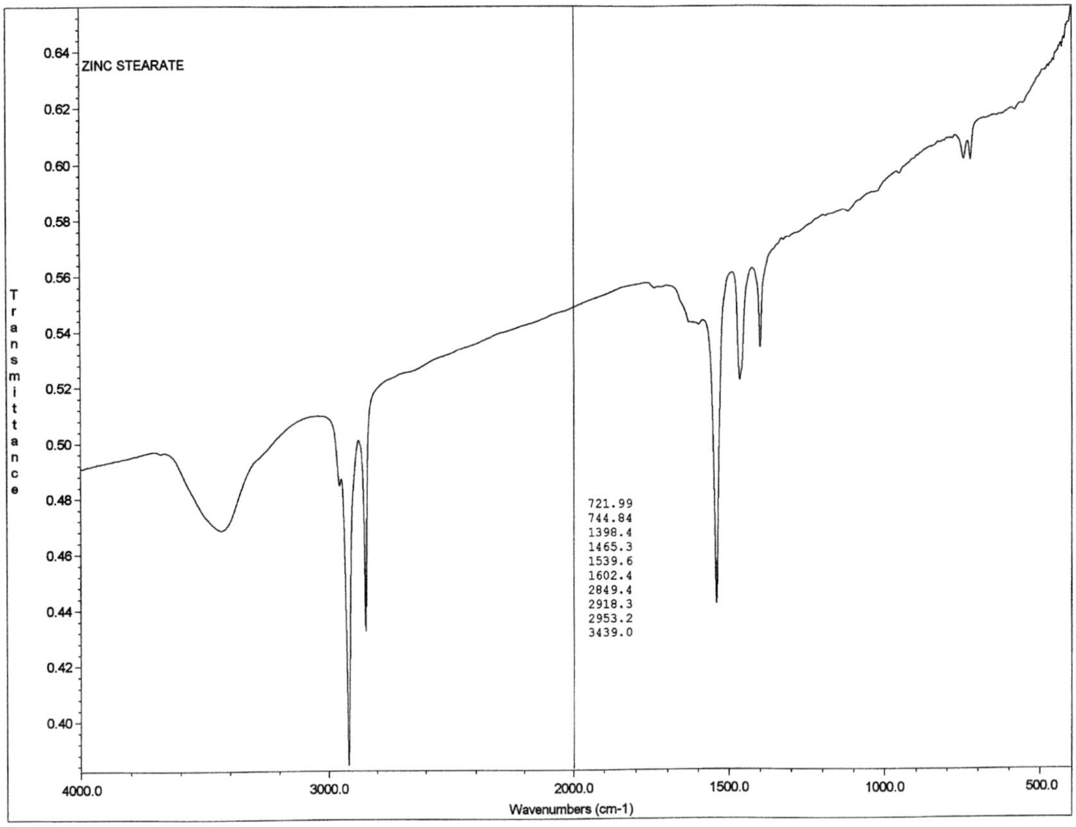

19 Zinc stearate $(n\text{-}C_{17}H_{35}CO_2)_2Zn$

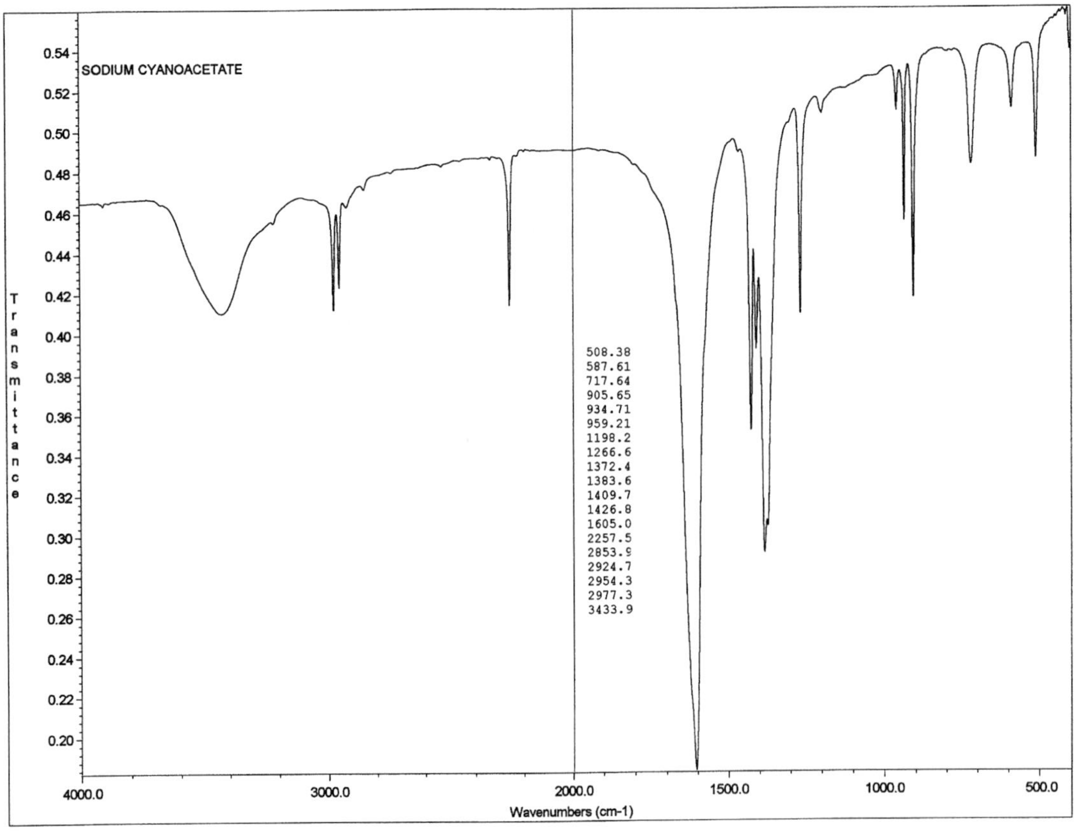

20 Sodium cyanoacetate $(NCCH_2CO_2)Na$

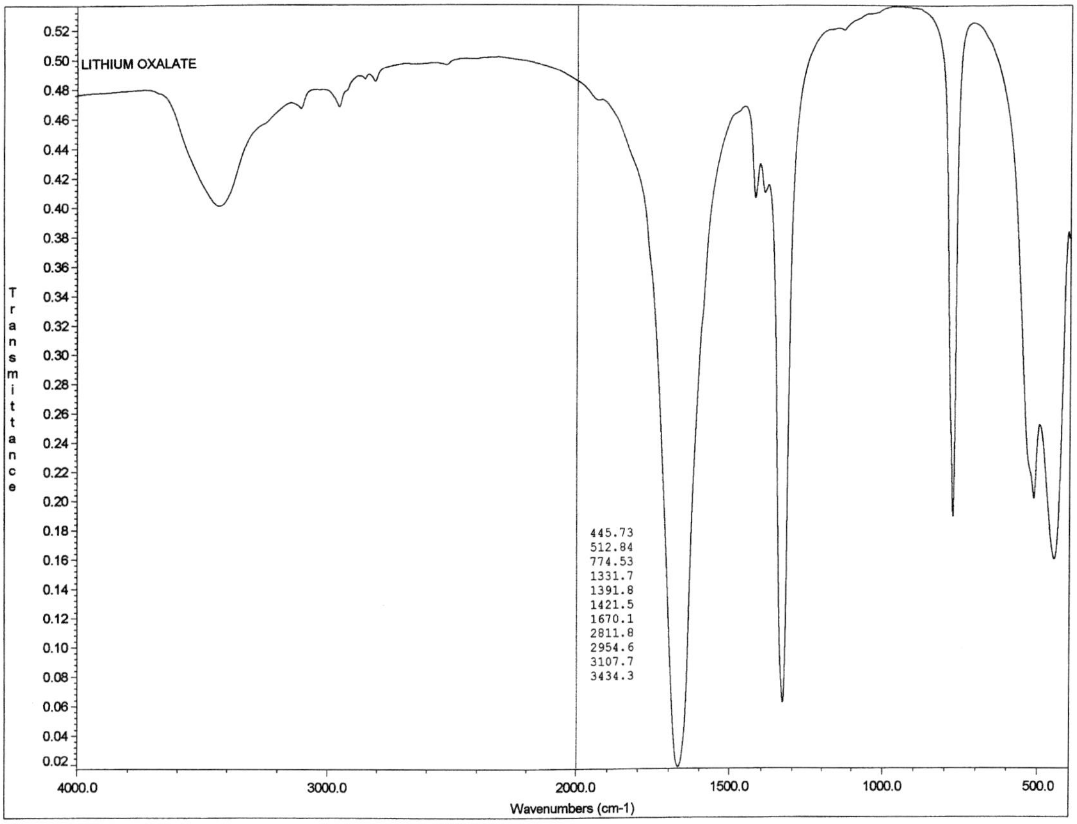

21 Lithium oxalate $(C_2O_4)Li_2$

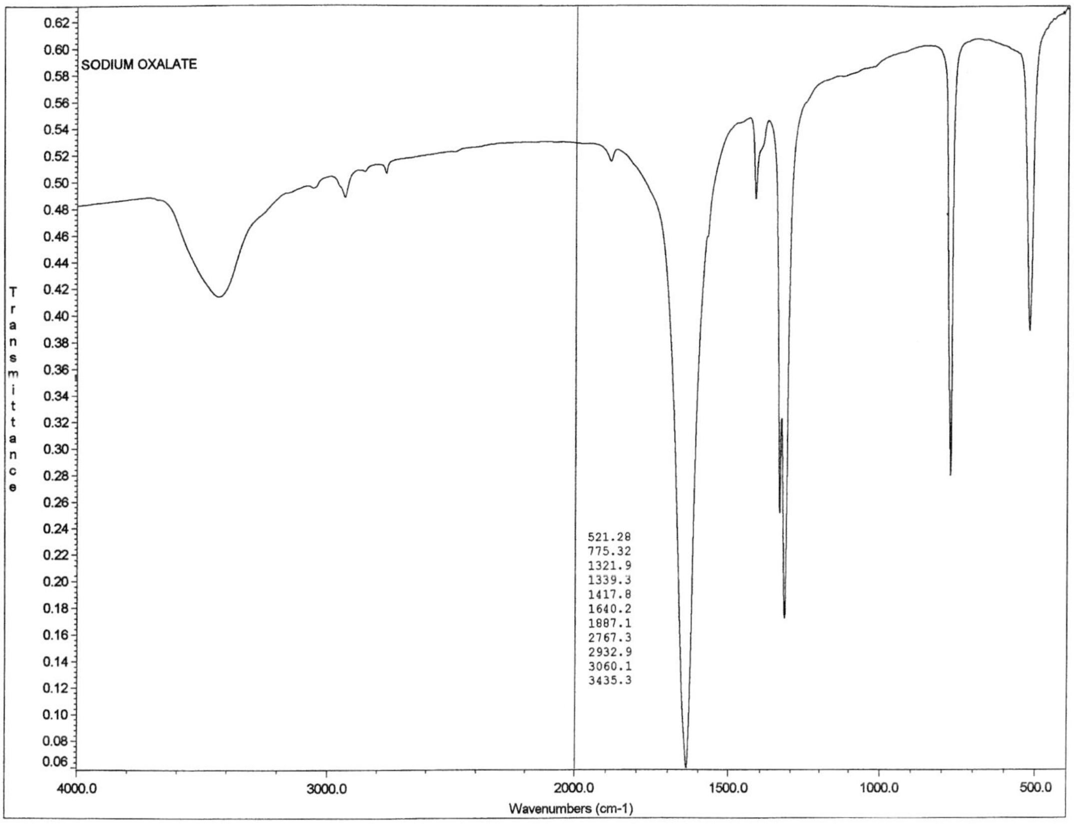

22 Sodium oxalate $(C_2O_4)Na_2$

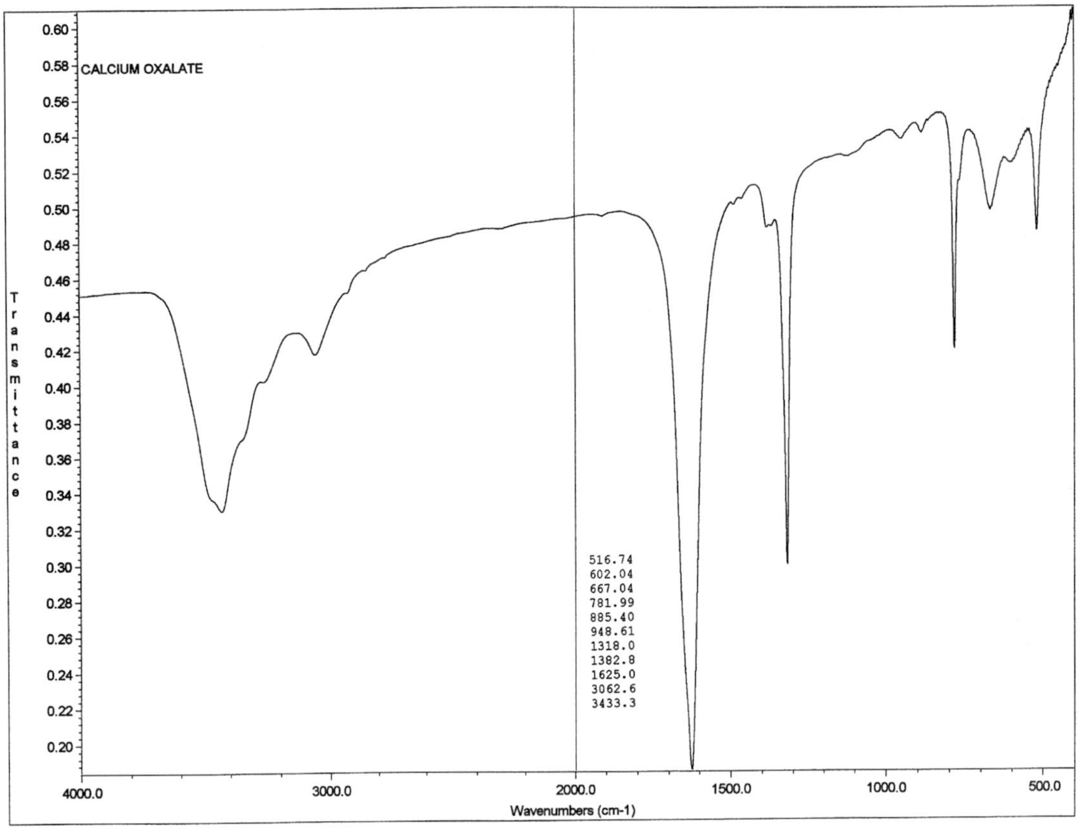

24 Calcium oxalate $(C_2O_4)Ca$

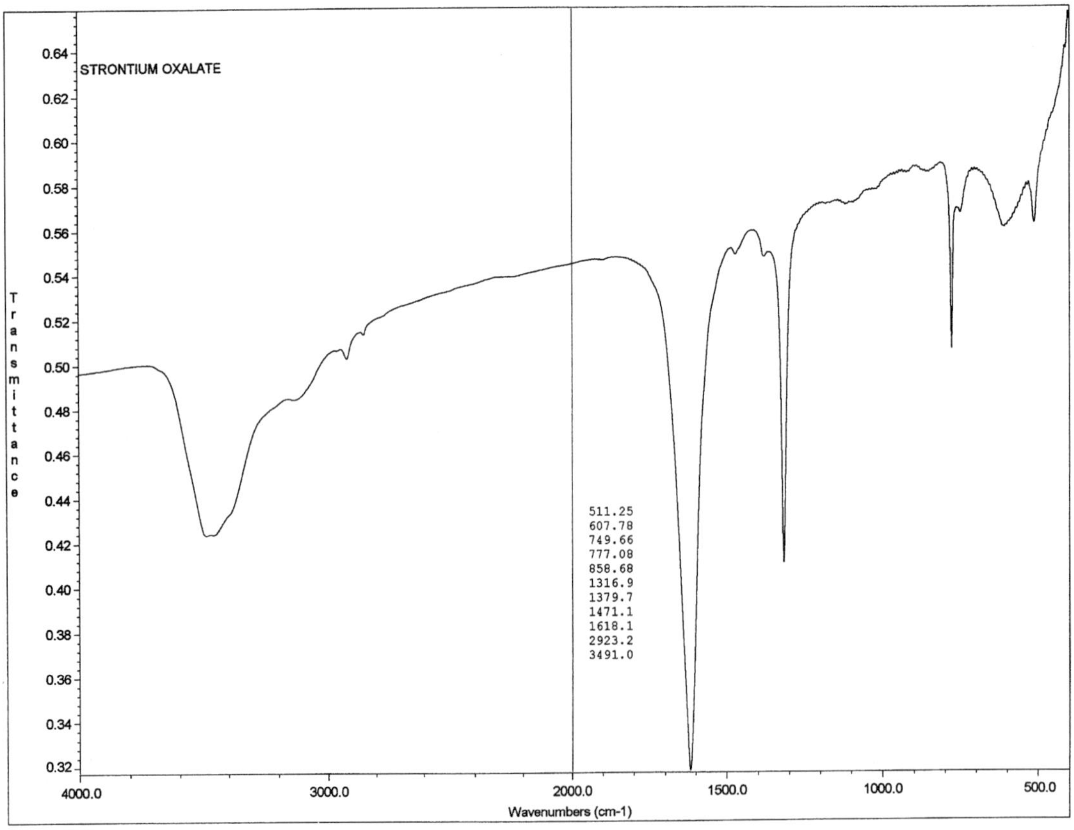

25 Strontium oxalate $(C_2O_4)Sr \cdot xH_2O$

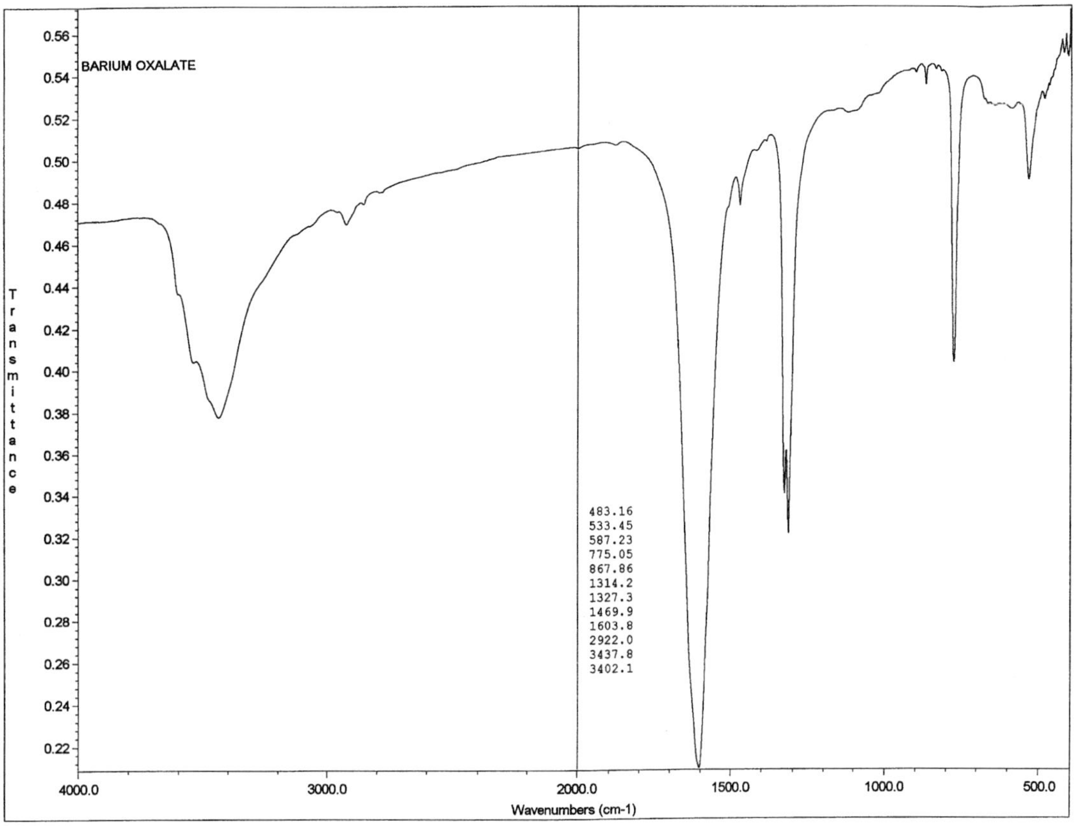

26 Barium oxalate $(C_2O_4)Ba \cdot xH_2O$

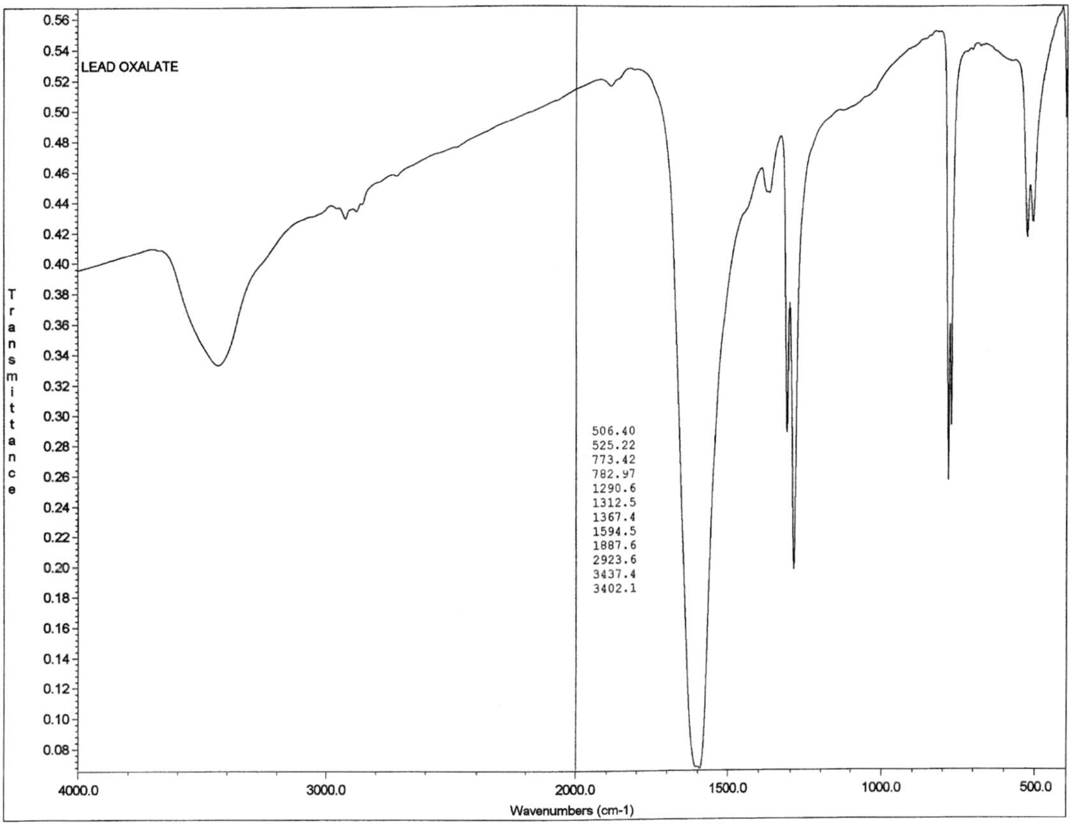

27 Lead oxalate $(C_2O_4)Pb$

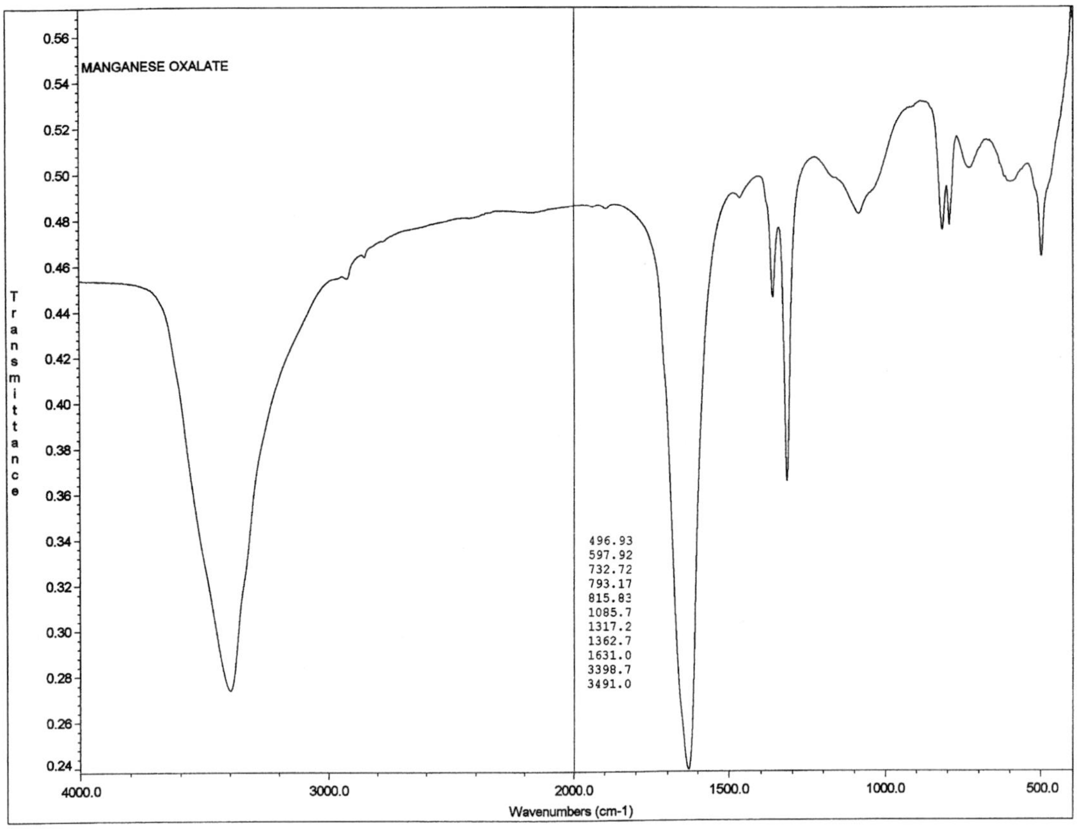

28 Manganese oxalate $(C_2O_4)Mn \cdot xH_2O$

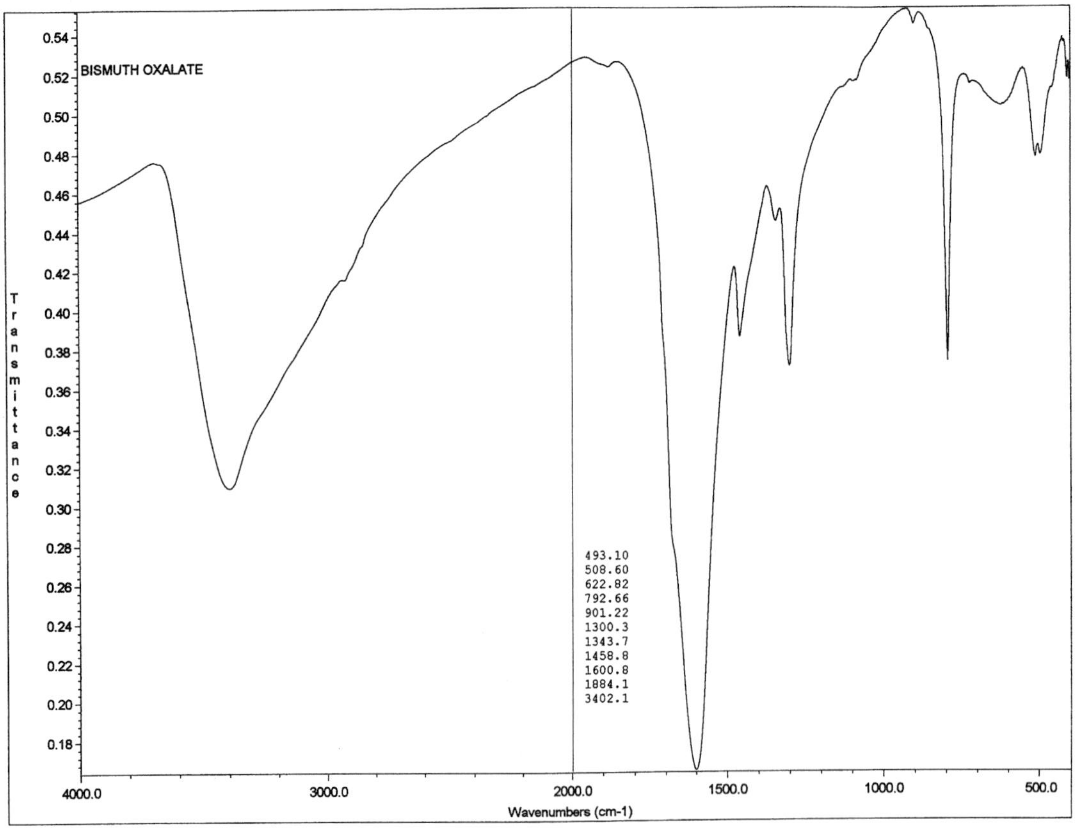

30 Bismuth oxalate $(C_2O_4)Bi \cdot xH_2O$

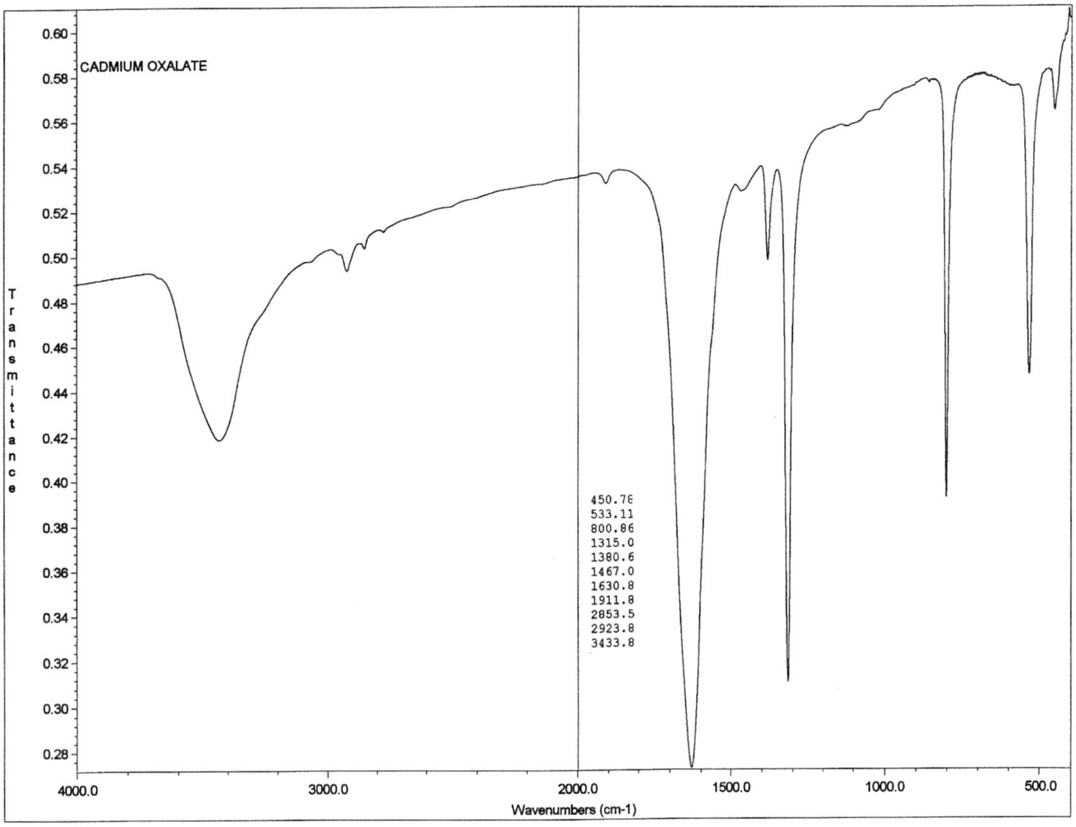

31 Cadmium oxalate $(C_2O_4)Cd$

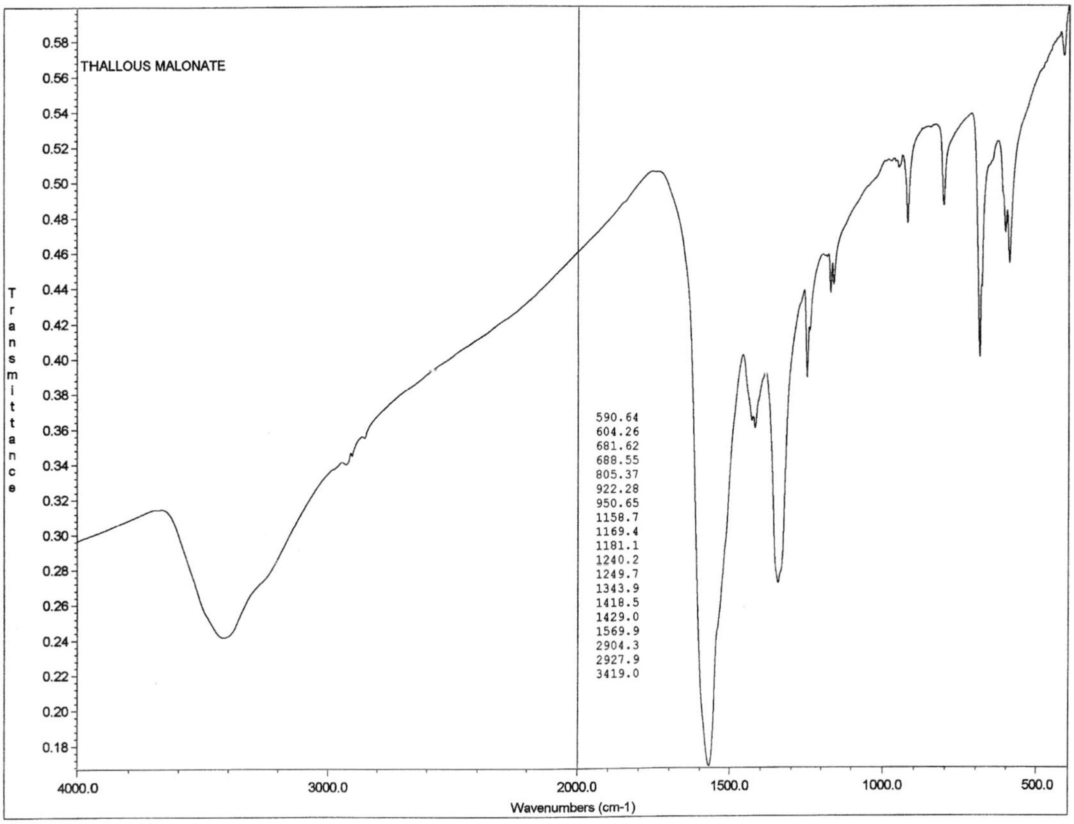

32 Thallous malonate $(CH_2(CO_2)_2)Tl_2 \cdot xH_2O$

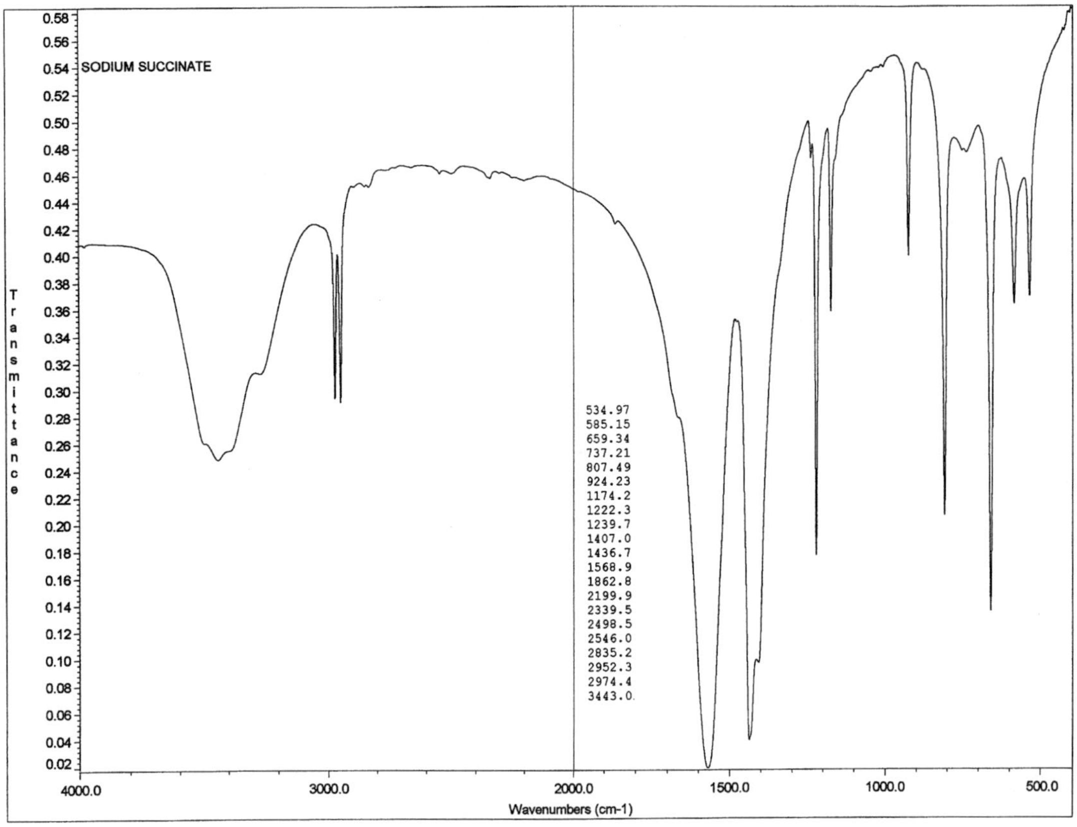

33 Sodium succinate $(CH_2CO_2)_2Na_2 \cdot xH_2O$

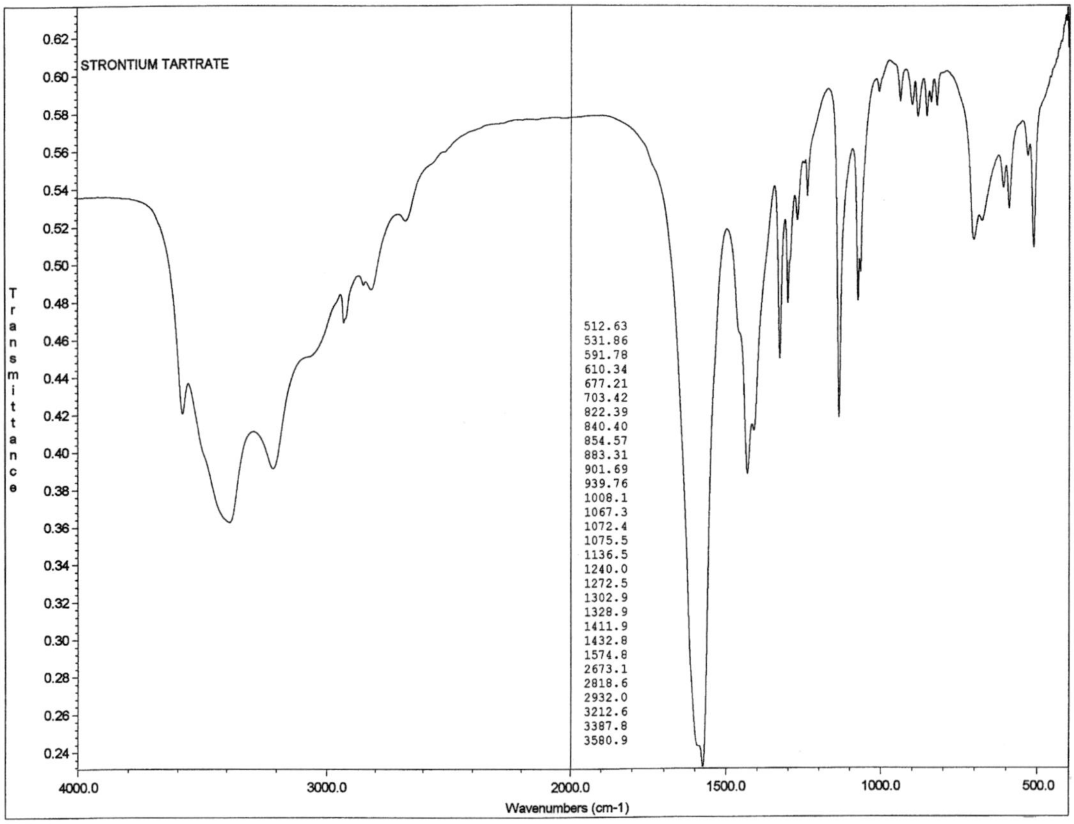

35 Strontium tartrate $(CHOHCO_2)_2Sr$

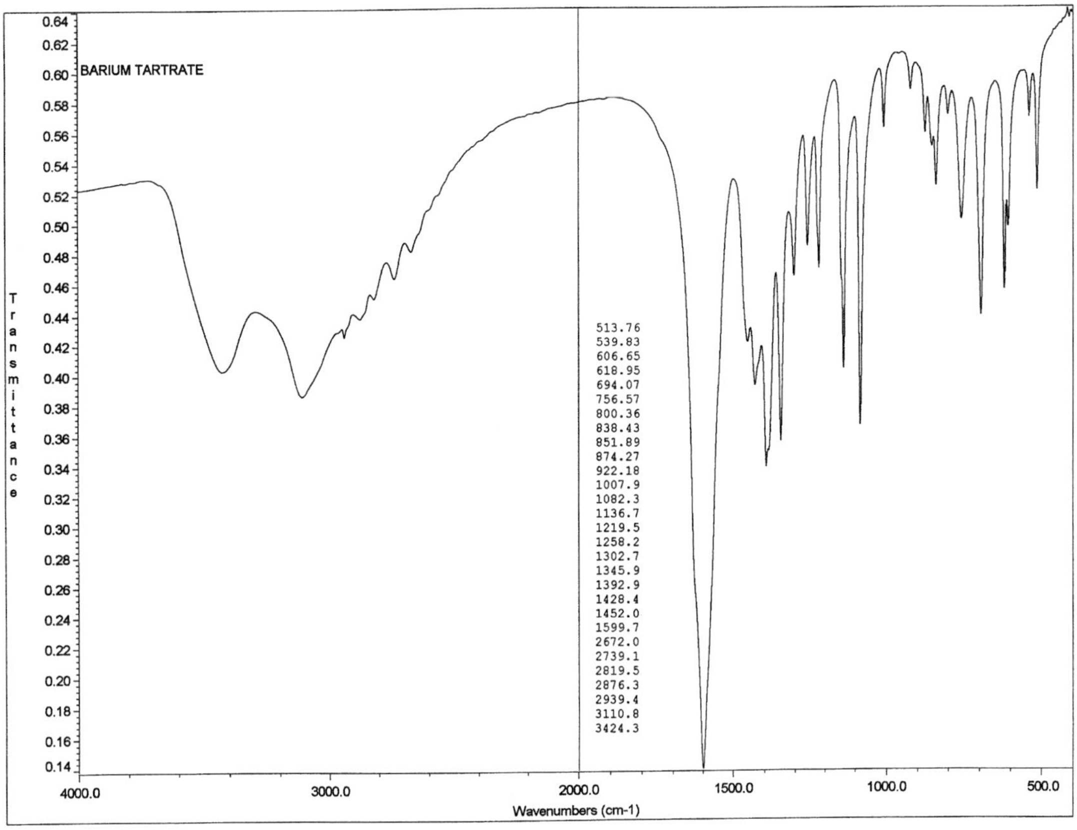

36 Barium tartrate $(CHOHCO_2)_2Ba$

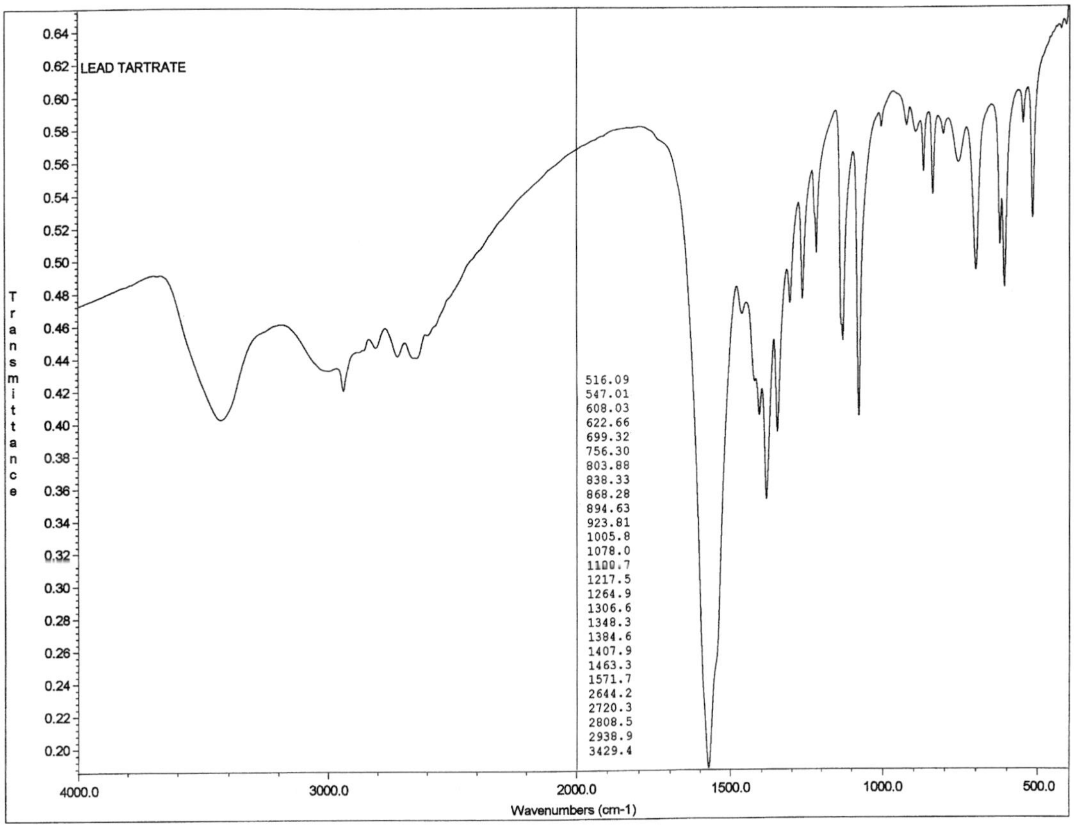

37 Lead tartrate $(CHOHCO_2)_2Pb \cdot xH_2O$

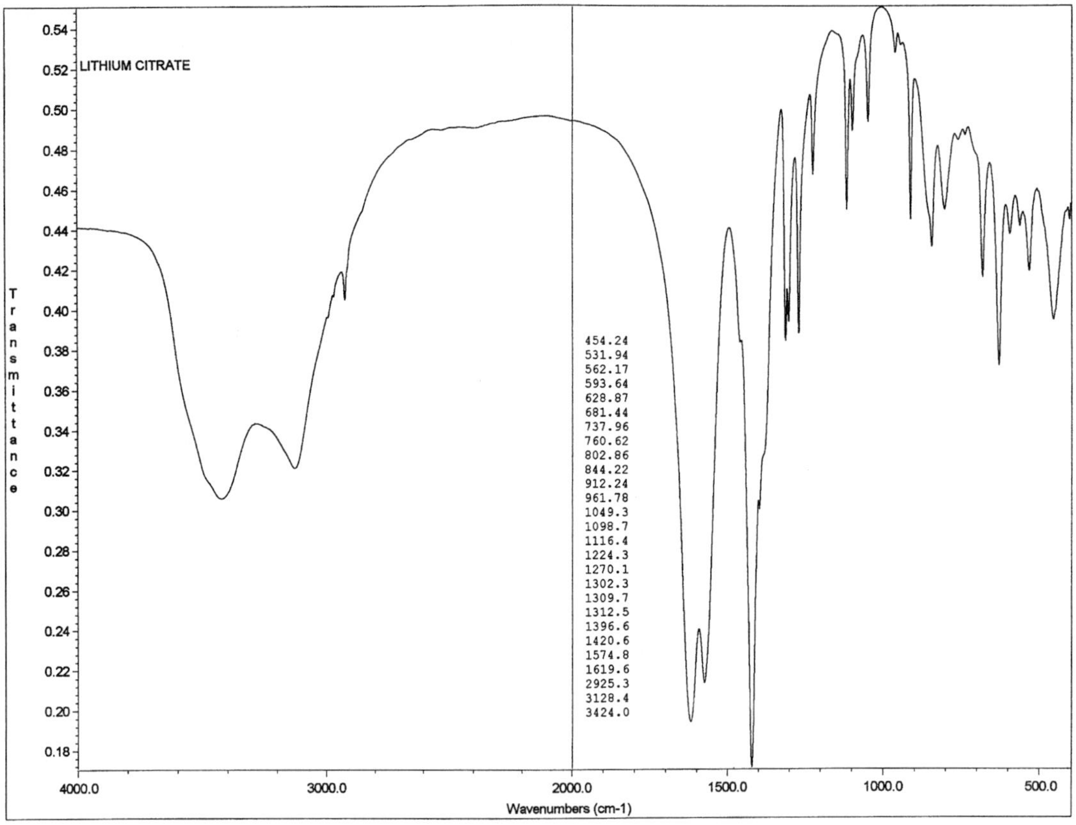

38 Lithium citrate $((O_2CCH_2)C(OH)(CO_2))Li_3$

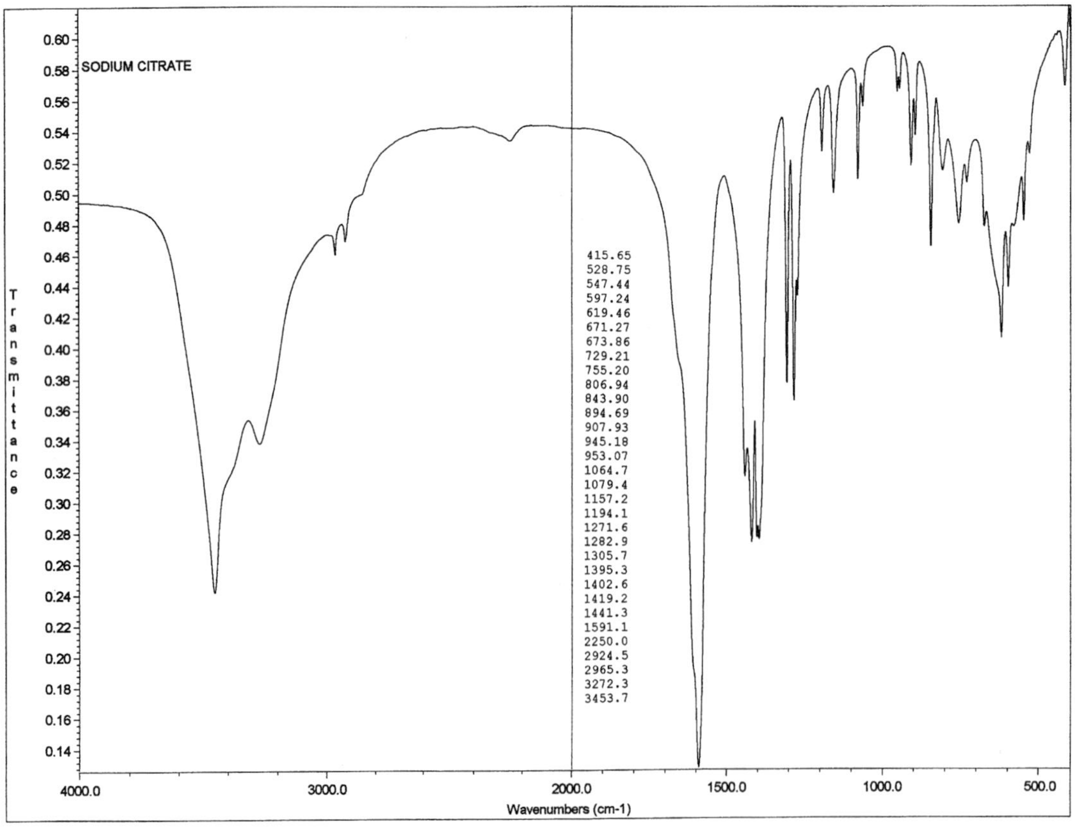

39 Sodium citrate $((O_2CCH_2)_2C(OH)(CO_2))Na_3$

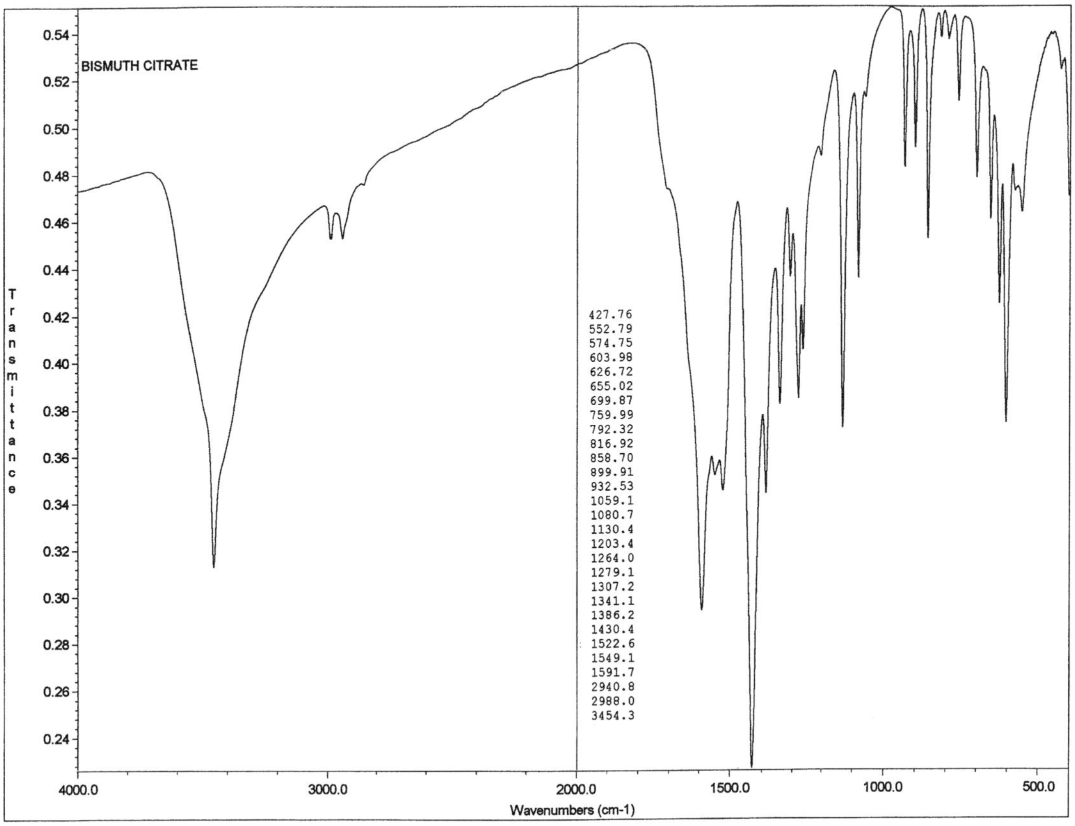

41 Bismuth citrate $((O_2CCH_2)_2C(OH)(CO_2))_2Bi_3$

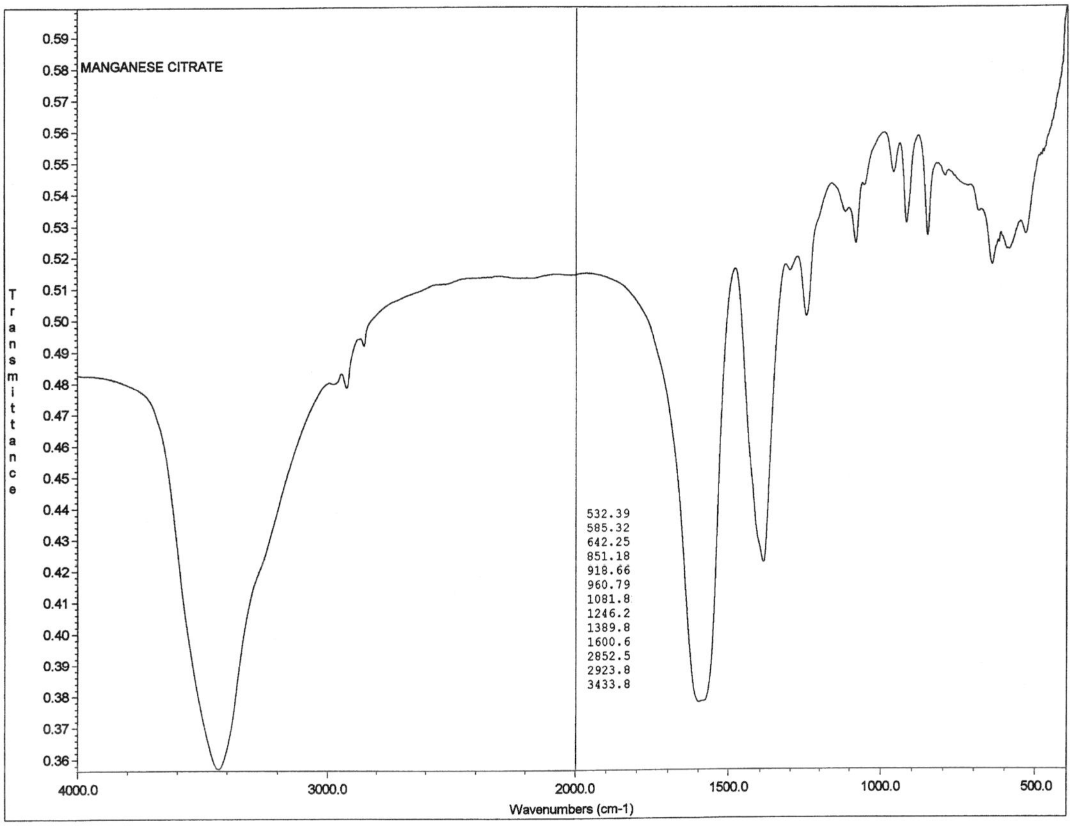

42 Manganese citrate $((O_2CCH_2)_2C(OH)(CO_2))_2Mn$

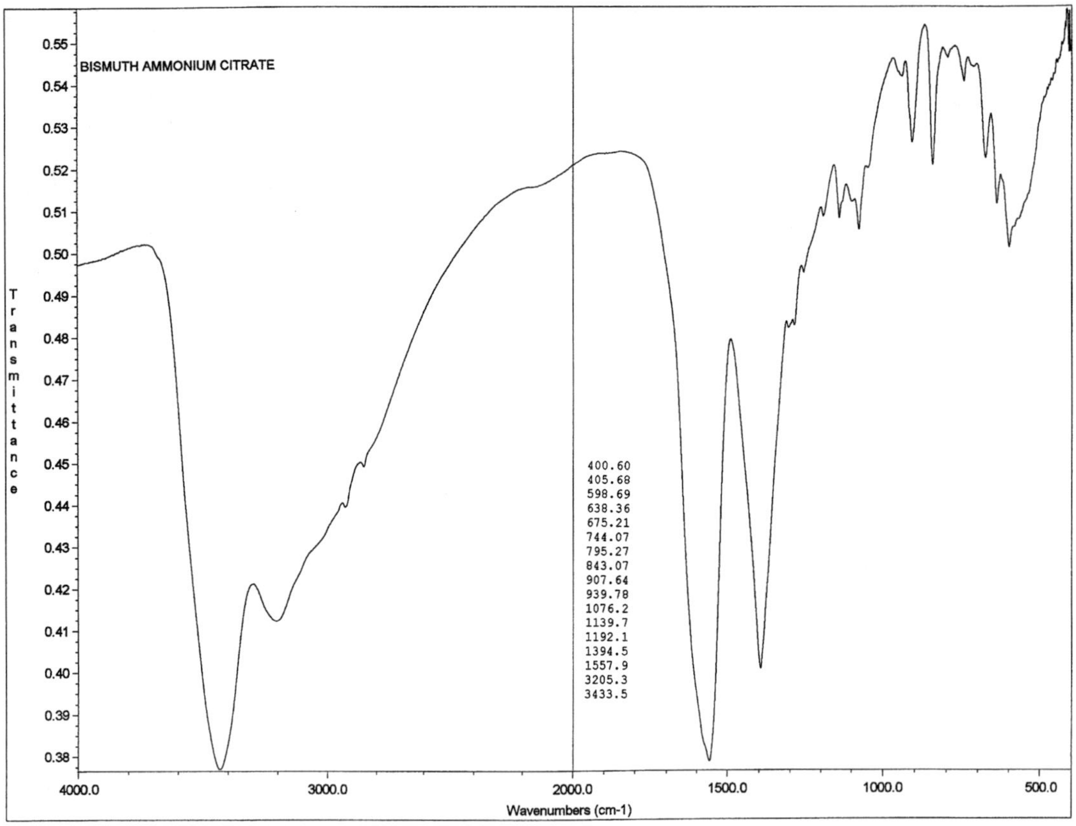

43 Bismuth ammonium citrate $((O_2CCH_2)C(OH)(CO_2))BiNH_4$

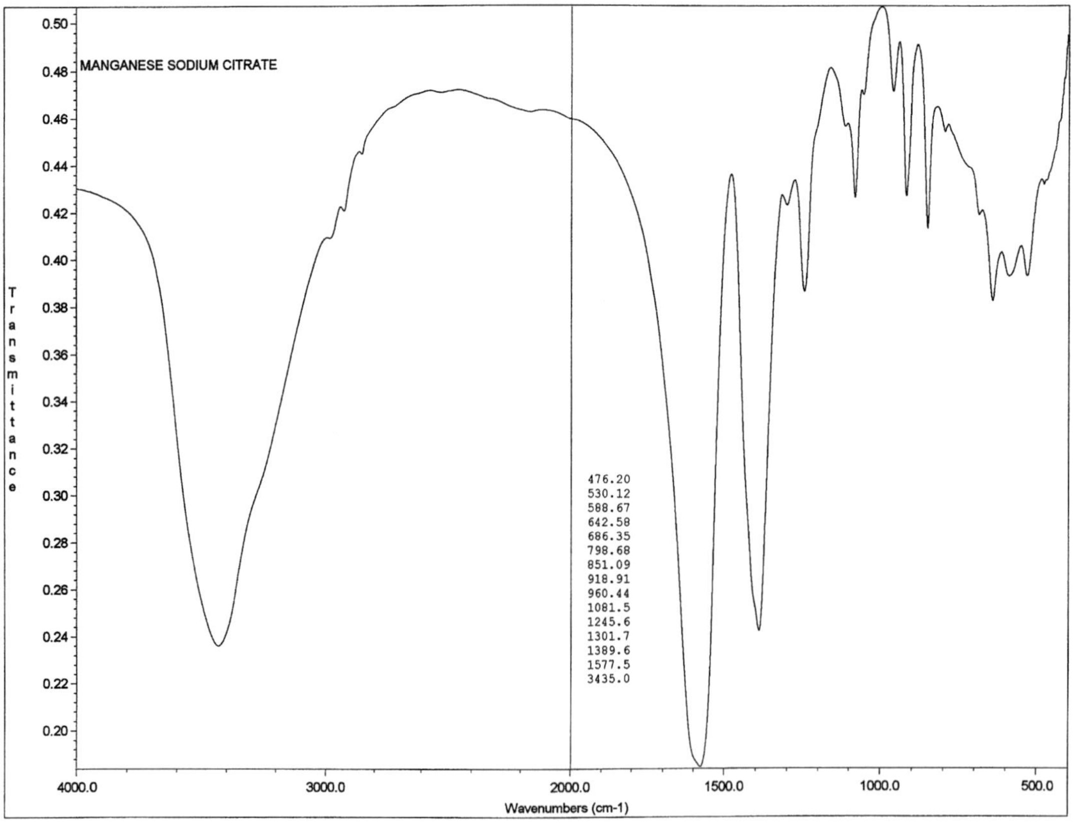

44 Manganese sodium citrate $((O_2CCH_2)C(OH)(CO_2))MnNa$

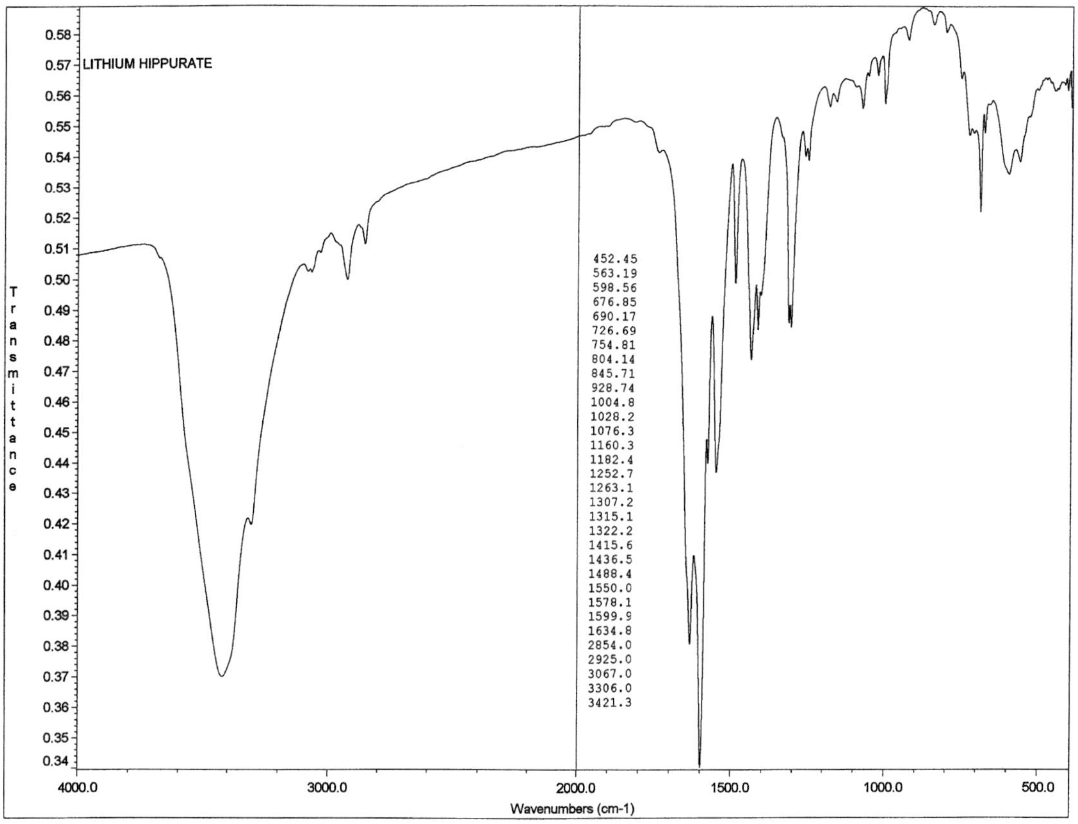

46 Lithium hippurate $(C_6H_5C(=O)NHCH_2CO_2)Li$

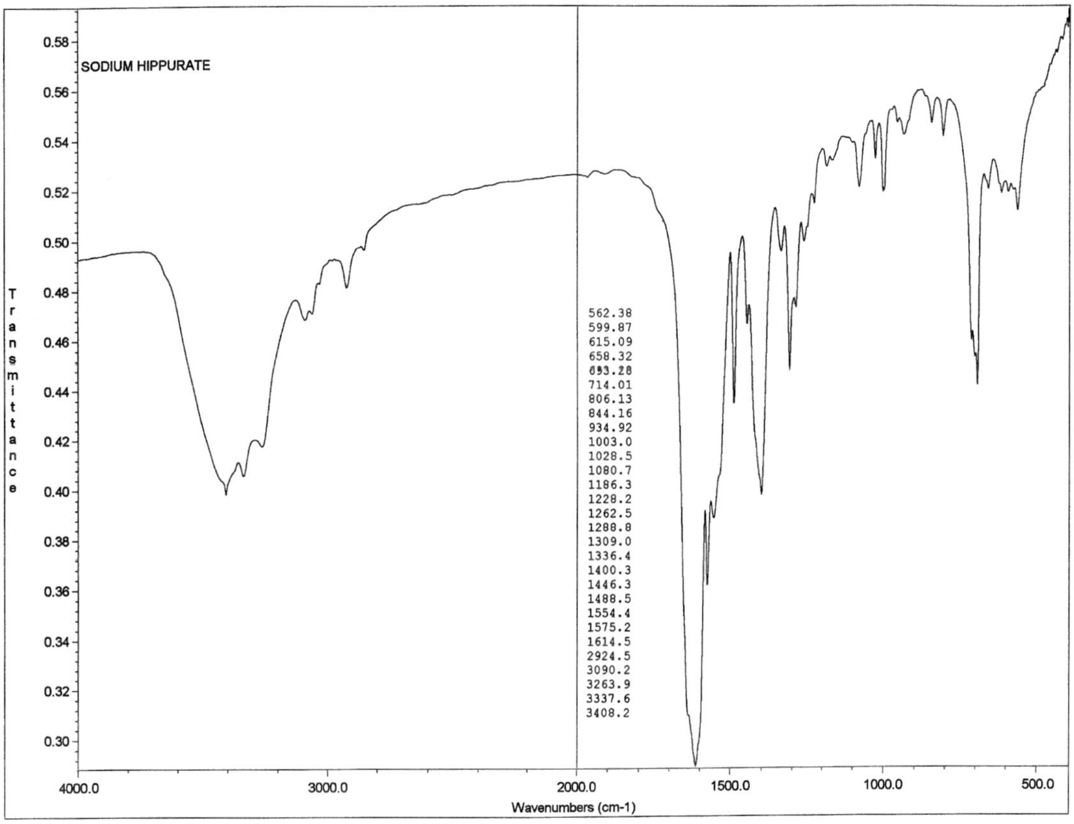

47 Sodium hippurate $(C_6H_5C(=O)NHCH_2CO_2)Na$

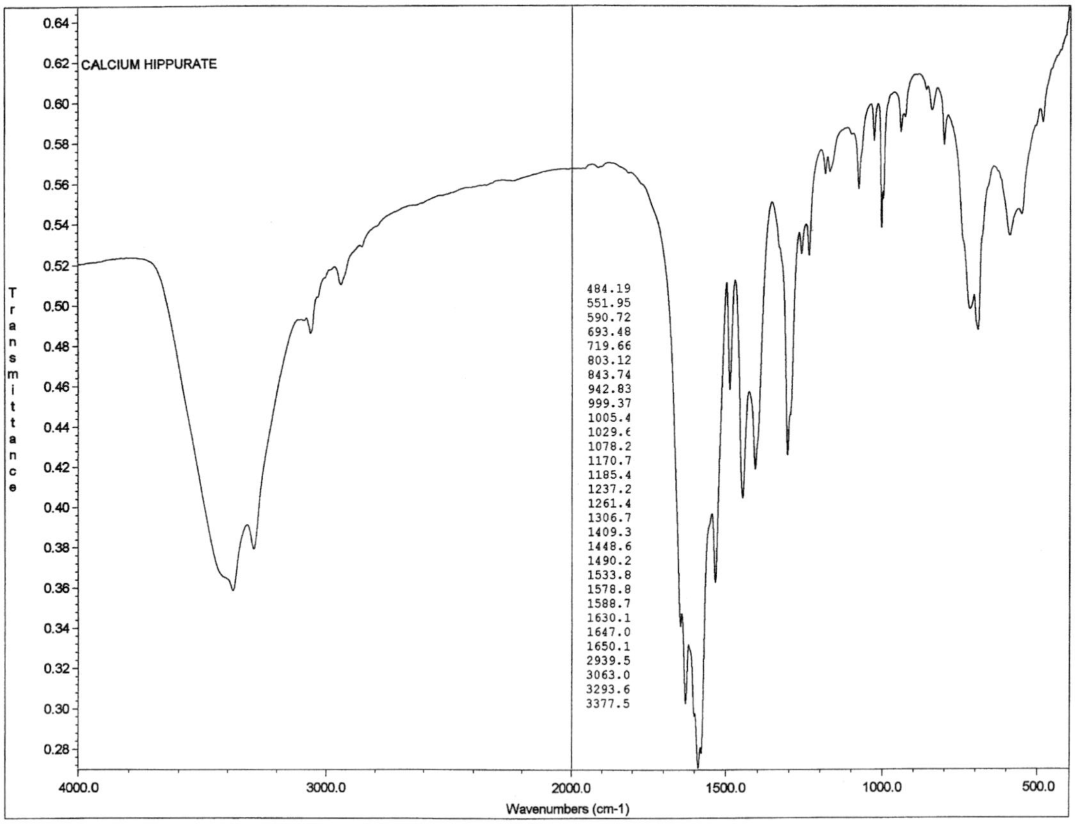
CALCIUM HIPPURATE
Transmittance
0.64
0.62
0.60
0.58
0.56
0.54
0.52
0.50
0.48
0.46
0.44
0.42
0.40
0.38
0.36
0.34
0.32
0.30
0.28
484.19
551.95
590.72
693.48
719.66
803.12
843.74
942.83
999.37
1005.4
1029.6
1078.2
1170.7
1185.4
1237.2
1261.4
1306.7
1409.3
1448.6
1490.2
1533.8
1578.8
1588.7
1630.1
1647.0
1650.1
2939.5
3063.0
3293.6
3377.5
4000.0
3000.0
2000.0
1500.0
1000.0
500.0
Wavenumbers (cm-1)

48 Calcium hippurate $[((C_6H_5C(=O)NHCH_2CO_2)]Ca$

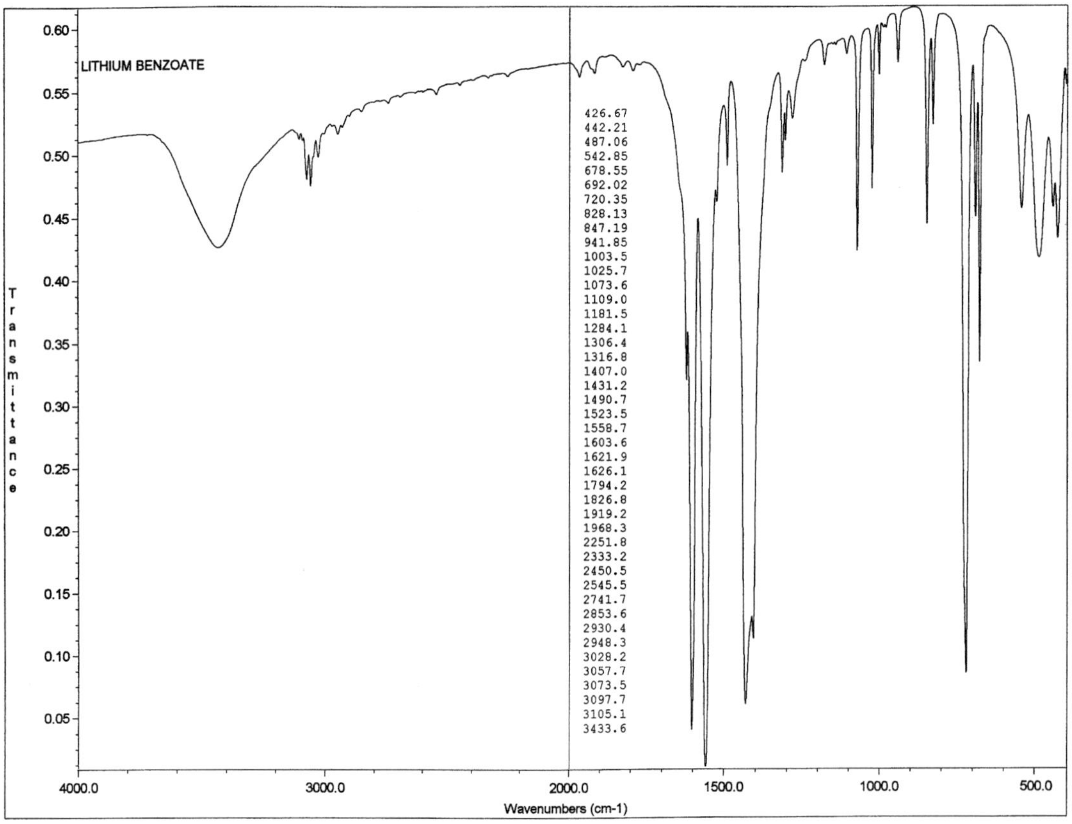
LITHIUM BENZOATE
Transmittance
0.60
0.55
0.50
0.45
0.40
0.35
0.30
0.25
0.20
0.15
0.10
0.05
426.67
442.21
487.06
542.85
678.55
692.02
720.35
828.13
847.19
941.85
1003.5
1025.7
1073.6
1109.0
1181.5
1284.1
1306.4
1316.8
1407.0
1431.2
1490.7
1523.5
1558.7
1603.6
1621.9
1626.1
1794.2
1826.8
1919.2
1968.3
2251.8
2333.2
2450.5
2545.5
2741.7
2853.6
2930.4
2948.3
3028.2
3057.7
3073.5
3097.7
3105.1
3433.6
4000.0
3000.0
2000.0
1500.0
1000.0
500.0
Wavenumbers (cm-1)

49 Lithium benzoate $(C_6H_5CO_2)Li$

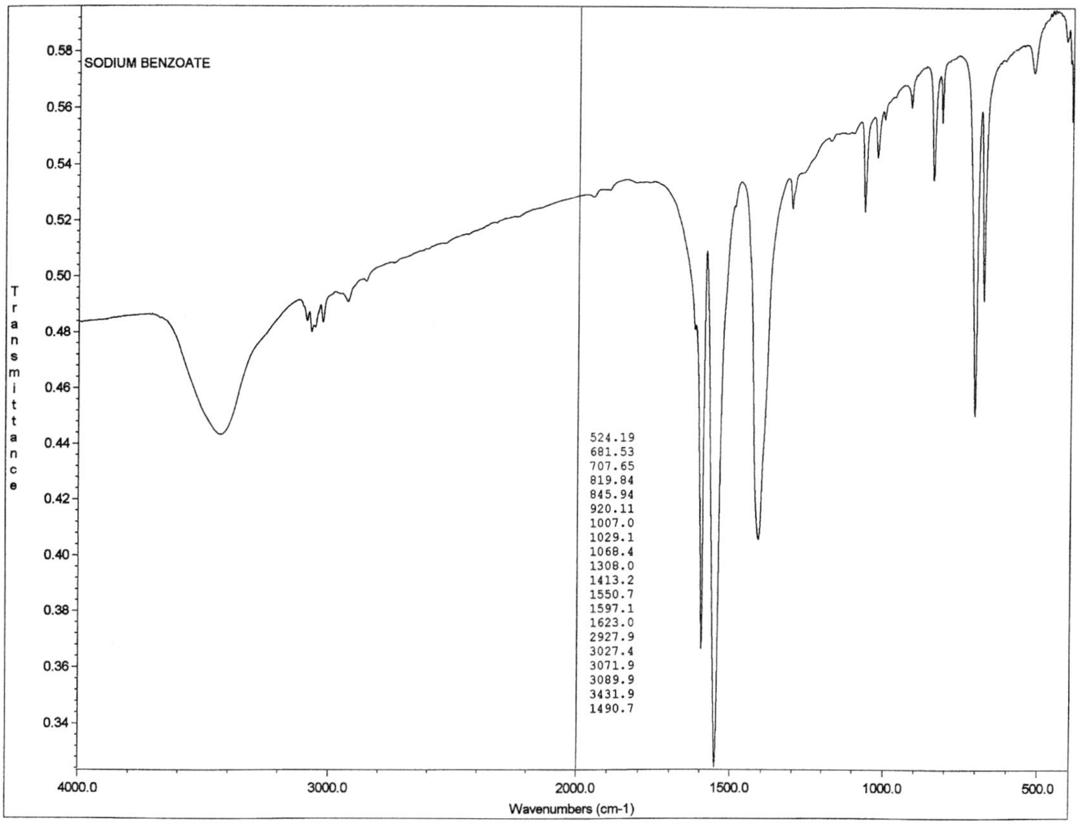

50 Sodium benzoate $(C_6H_5CO_2)Na$

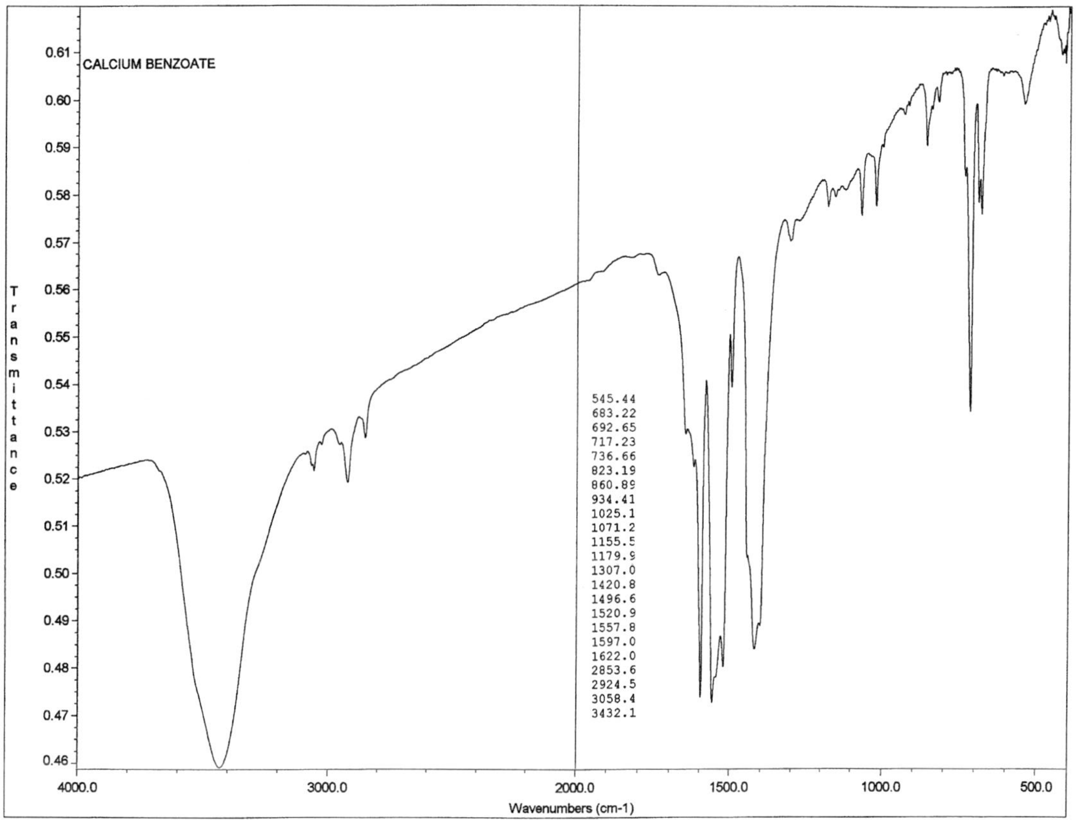

51 Calcium benzoate $(C_6H_5CO_2)_2Ca$

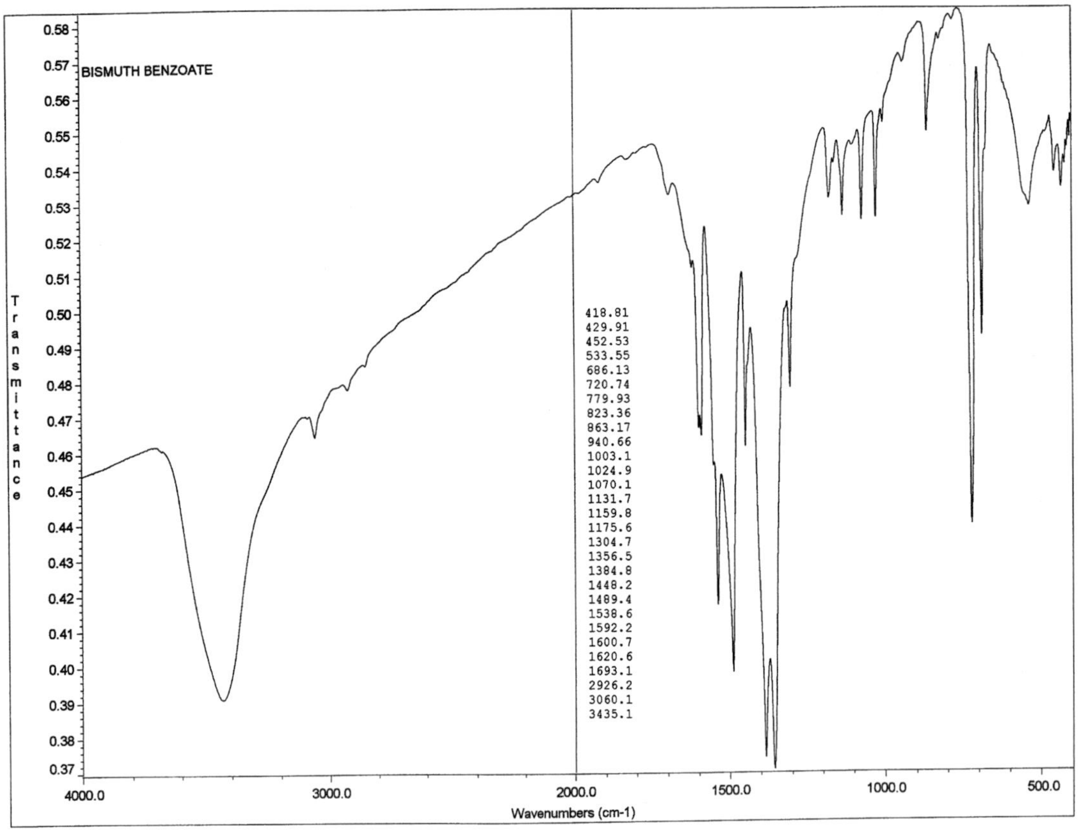
BISMUTH BENZOATE
Transmittance
0.58
0.57
0.56
0.55
0.54
0.53
0.52
0.51
0.50
0.49
0.48
0.47
0.46
0.45
0.44
0.43
0.42
0.41
0.40
0.39
0.38
0.37
418.81
429.91
452.53
533.55
686.13
720.74
779.93
823.36
863.17
940.66
1003.1
1024.9
1070.1
1131.7
1159.8
1175.6
1304.7
1356.5
1384.8
1448.2
1489.4
1538.6
1592.2
1600.7
1620.6
1693.1
2926.2
3060.1
3435.1
4000.0
3000.0
2000.0
1500.0
1000.0
500.0
Wavenumbers (cm-1)

52 Bismuth benzoate $(C_6H_5CO_2)_2Bi$

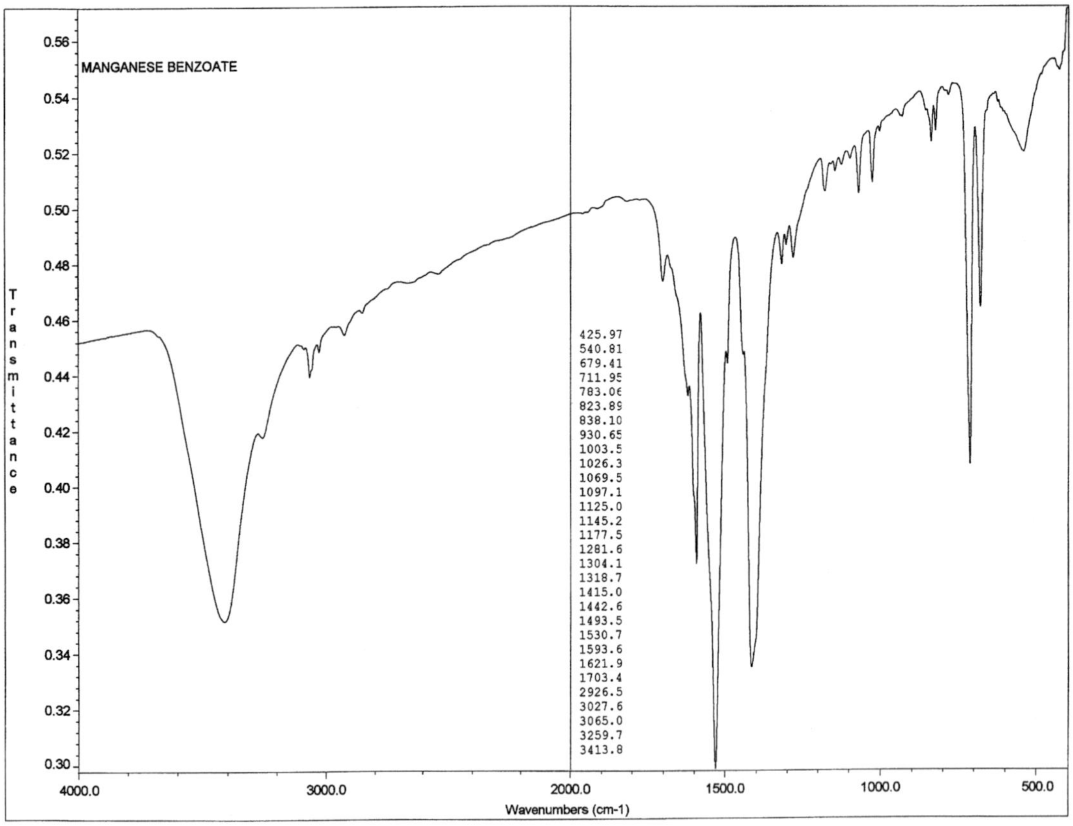
MANGANESE BENZOATE
Transmittance
0.56
0.54
0.52
0.50
0.48
0.46
0.44
0.42
0.40
0.38
0.36
0.34
0.32
0.30
425.97
540.81
679.41
711.95
783.06
823.89
838.10
930.65
1003.5
1026.3
1069.5
1097.1
1125.0
1145.2
1177.5
1281.6
1304.1
1318.7
1415.0
1442.6
1493.5
1530.7
1593.6
1621.9
1703.4
2926.5
3027.6
3065.0
3259.7
3413.8
4000.0
3000.0
2000.0
1500.0
1000.0
500.0
Wavenumbers (cm-1)

53 Manganese benzoate $(C_6H_5CO_2)_2Mn$

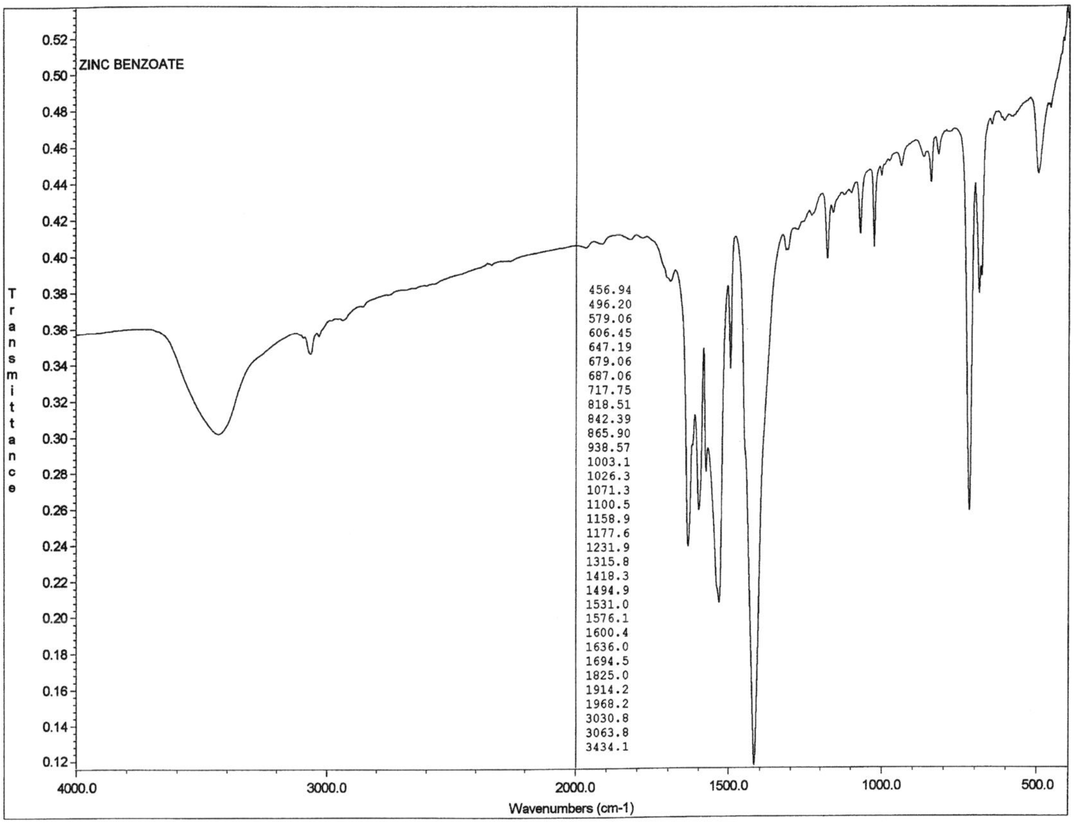

54 Zinc benzoate $(C_6H_5CO_2)_2Zn$

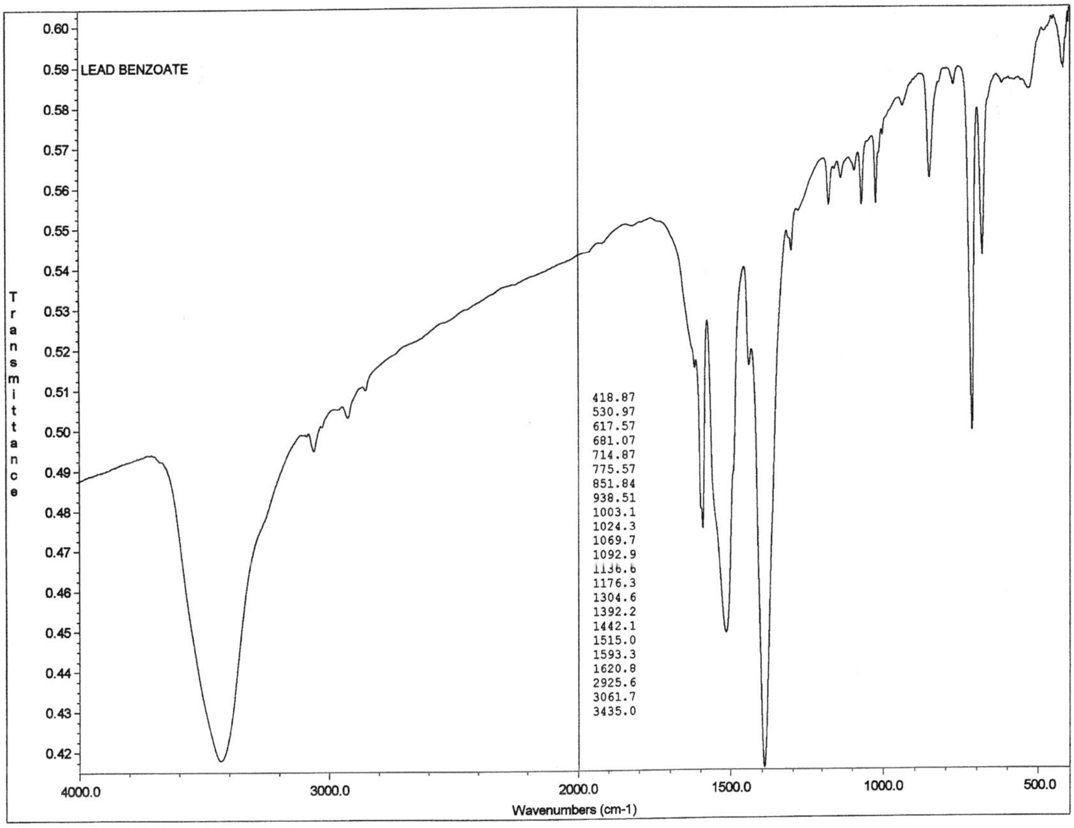

55 Lead benzoate $(C_6H_5CO_2)_2Pb$

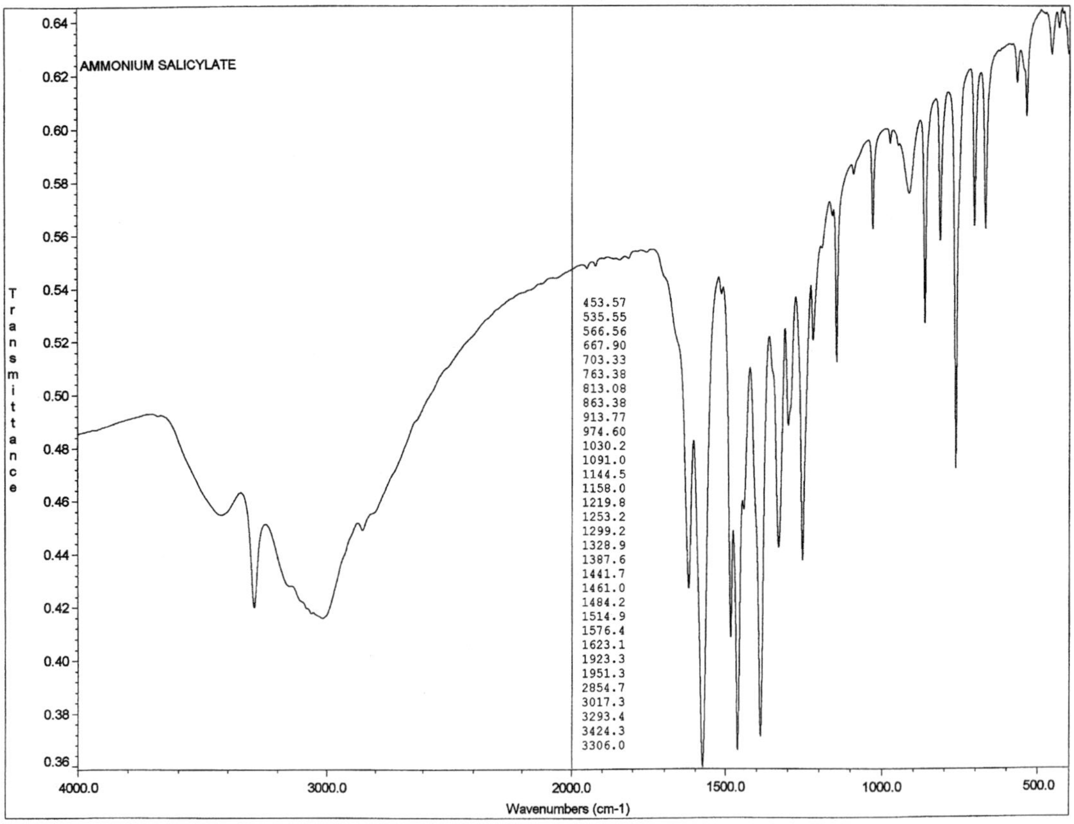

56 Ammonium salicylate (o-(OH)$C_6H_4CO_2$)NH_4

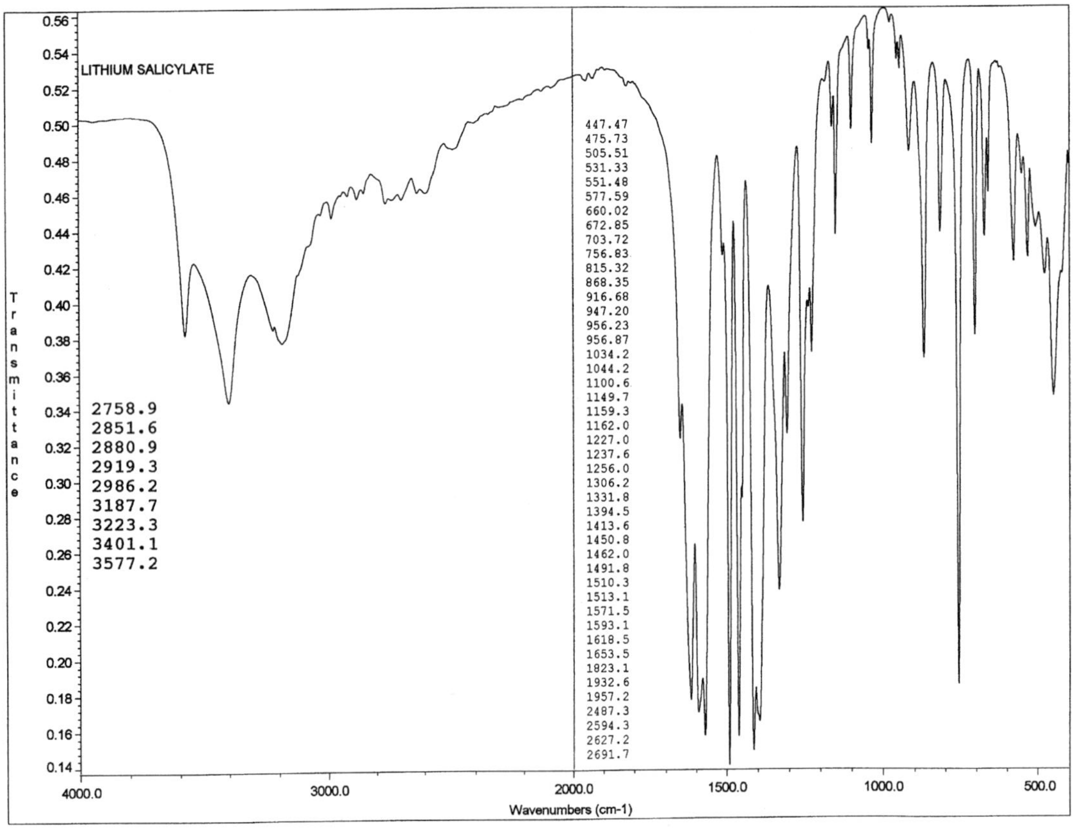

57 Lithium salicylate (o-(OH)$C_6H_4CO_2$)Li

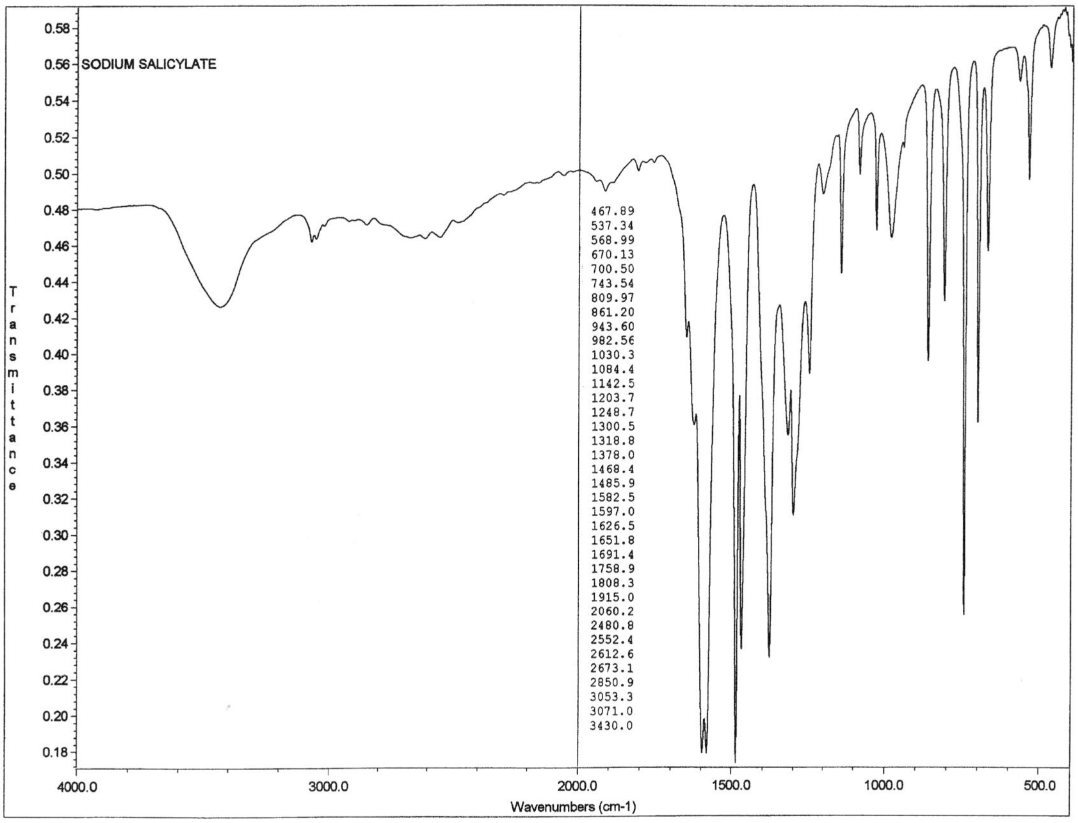

58 Sodium salicylate (o-(OH)$C_6H_4CO_2$)Na

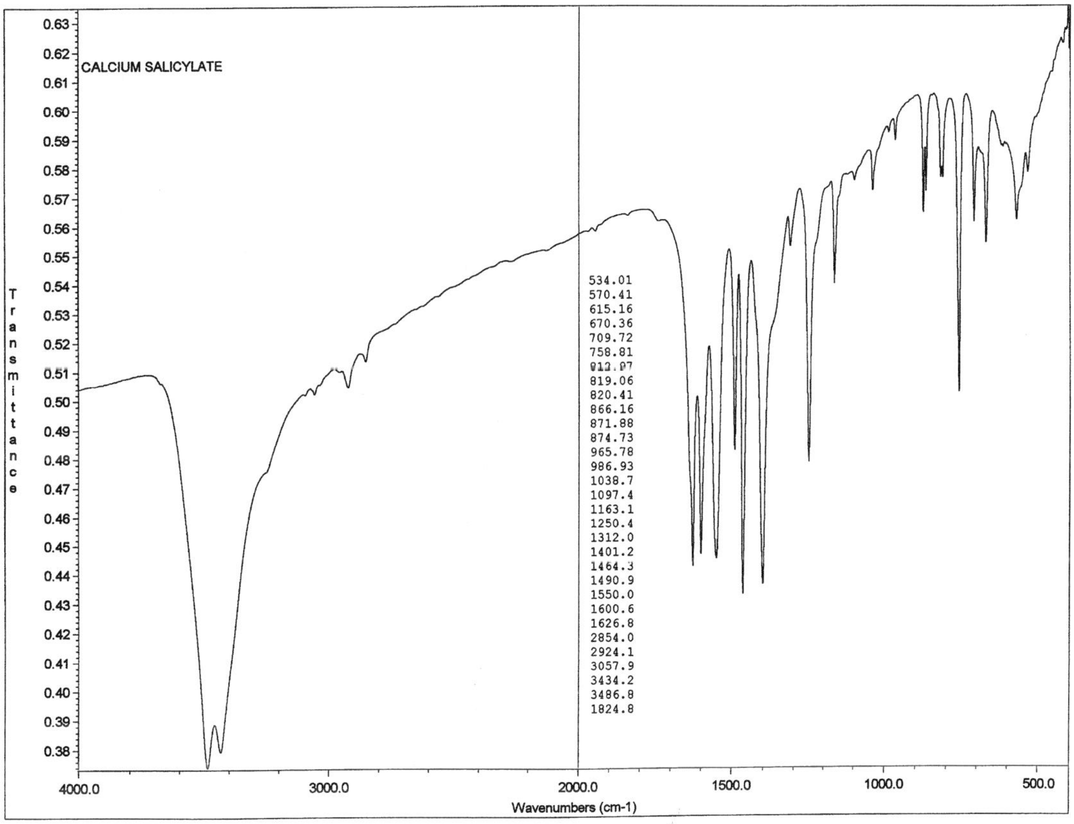

59 Calcium salicylate $(o\text{-}(OH)C_6H_4CO_2)_2Ca$

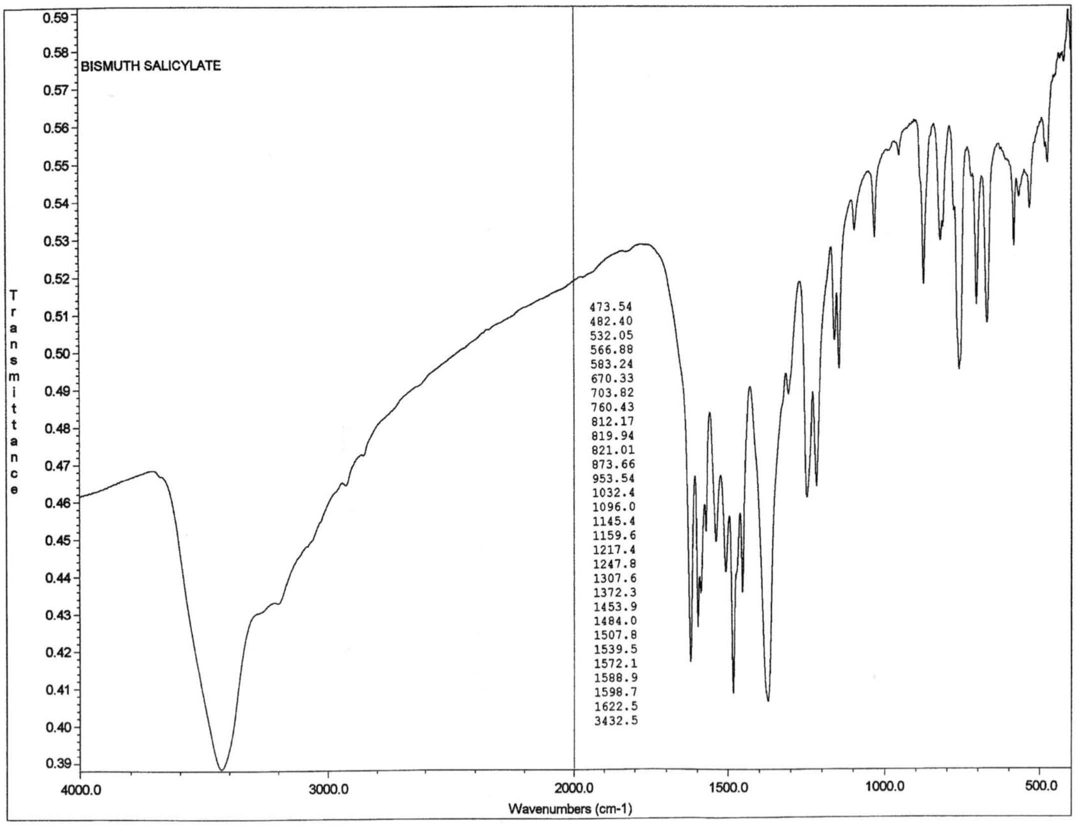

60 Bismuth salicylate (o-(OH)$C_6H_4CO_2)_2Bi$

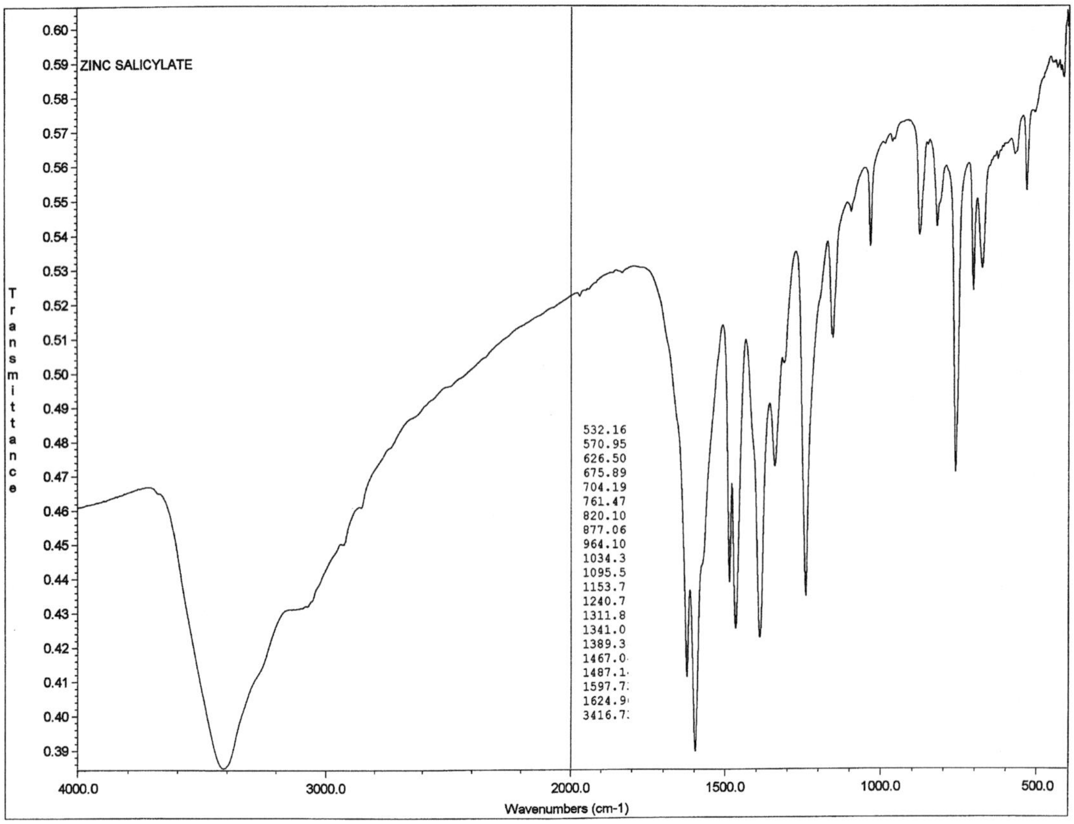

62 Zinc salicylate (o-(OH)$C_6H_4CO_2)_2Zn$

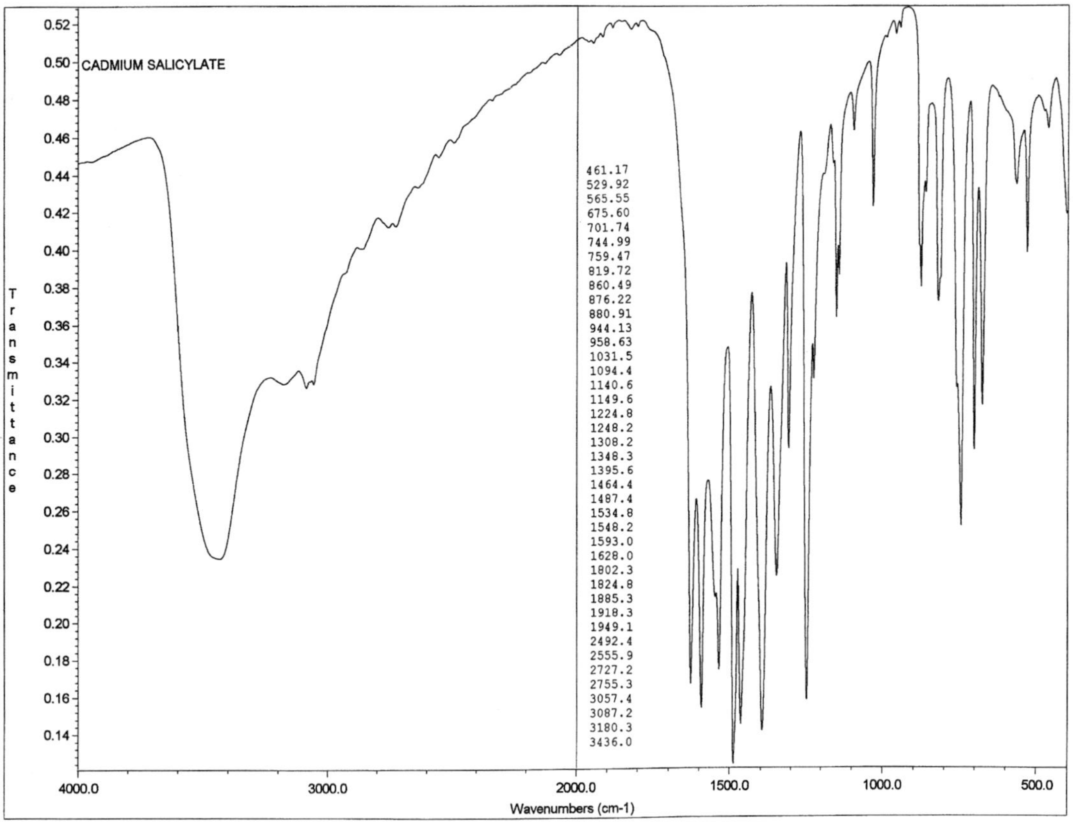
CADMIUM SALICYLATE
Transmittance
Wavenumbers (cm-1)
0.52
0.50
0.48
0.46
0.44
0.42
0.40
0.38
0.36
0.34
0.32
0.30
0.28
0.26
0.24
0.22
0.20
0.18
0.16
0.14
4000.0
3000.0
2000.0
1500.0
1000.0
500.0
461.17
529.92
565.55
675.60
701.74
744.99
759.47
819.72
860.49
876.22
880.91
944.13
958.63
1031.5
1094.4
1140.6
1149.6
1224.8
1248.2
1308.2
1348.3
1395.6
1464.4
1487.4
1534.8
1548.2
1593.0
1628.0
1802.3
1824.8
1885.3
1918.3
1949.1
2492.4
2555.9
2727.2
2755.3
3057.4
3087.2
3180.3
3436.0

63 Cadmium salicylate (o-(OH)$C_6H_4CO_2)_2Cd$

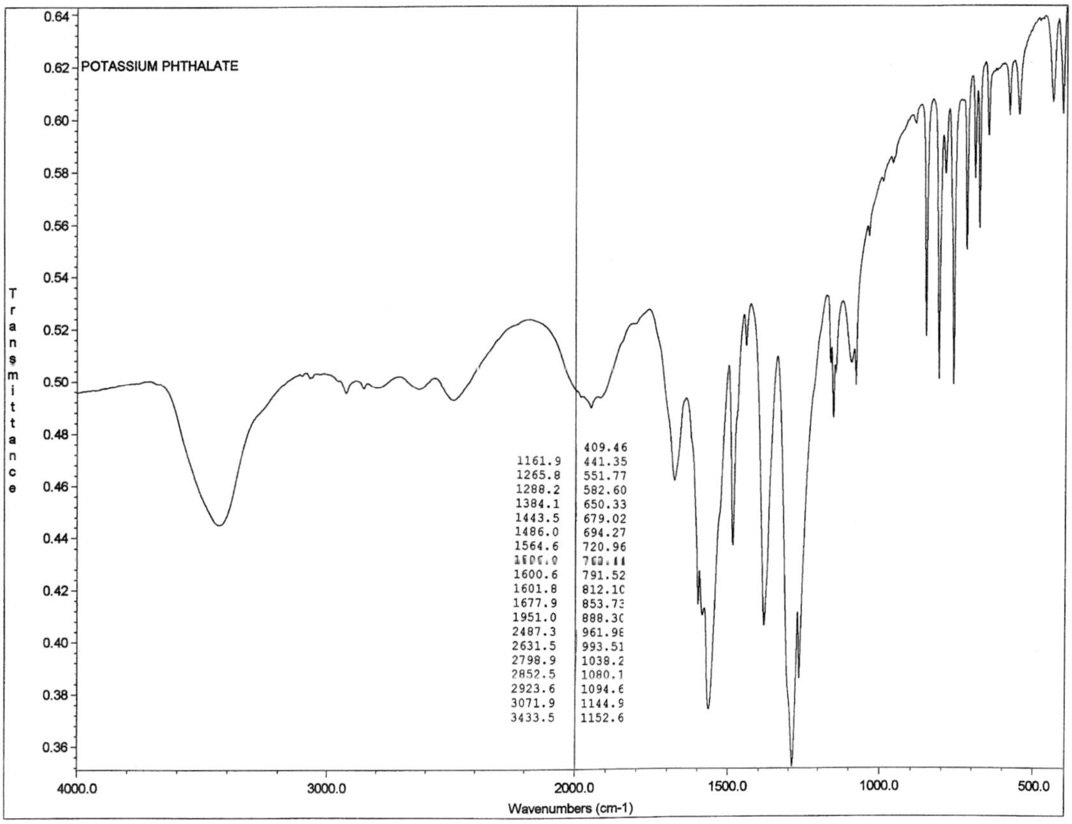
POTASSIUM PHTHALATE
Transmittance
Wavenumbers (cm-1)
0.64
0.62
0.60
0.58
0.56
0.54
0.52
0.50
0.48
0.46
0.44
0.42
0.40
0.38
0.36
4000.0
3000.0
2000.0
1500.0
1000.0
500.0
1161.9
1265.8
1288.2
1384.1
1443.5
1486.0
1564.6
1600.6
1601.8
1677.9
1951.0
2487.3
2631.5
2798.9
2852.5
2923.6
3071.9
3433.5
409.46
441.35
551.77
582.60
650.33
679.02
694.27
720.96
791.52
812.10
961.9
993.51
1038.2
1080.1
1094.6
1144.9
1152.6

64 Potassium phthalate $[o\text{-}C_6H_4(CO_2)_2]K_2$

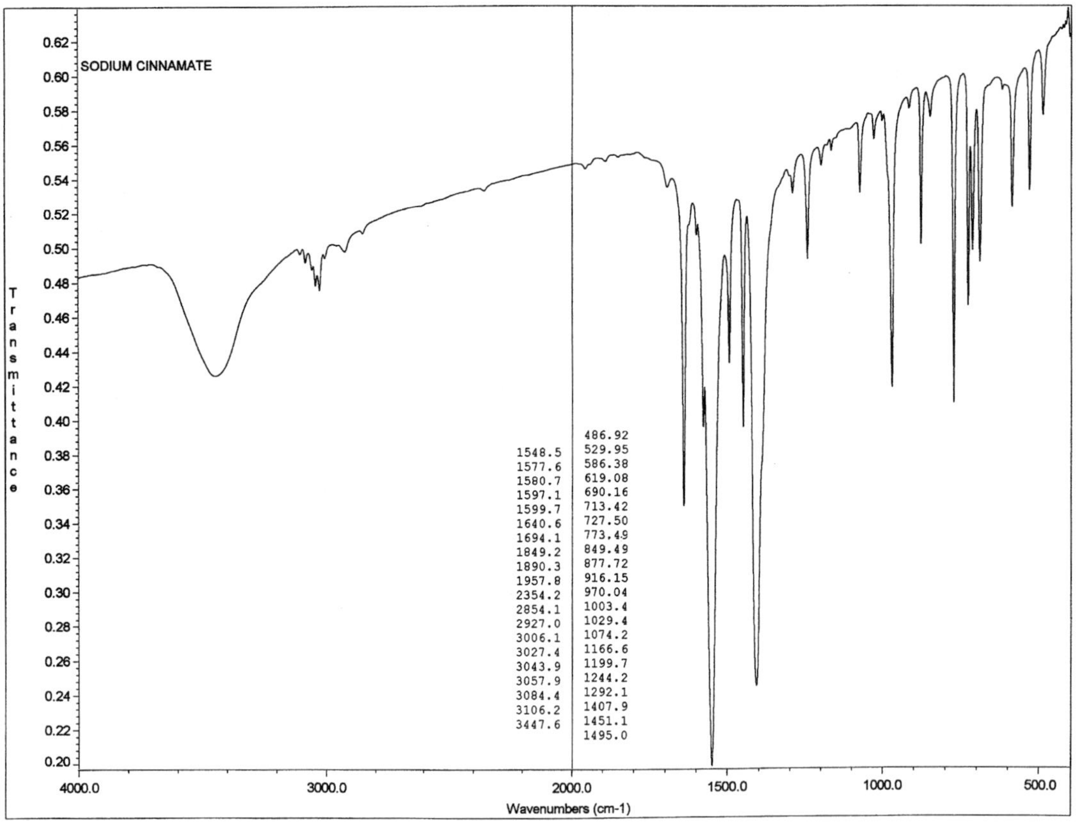

65 Sodium cinnamate ($C_6H_5CH{=}CHCO_2$)Na

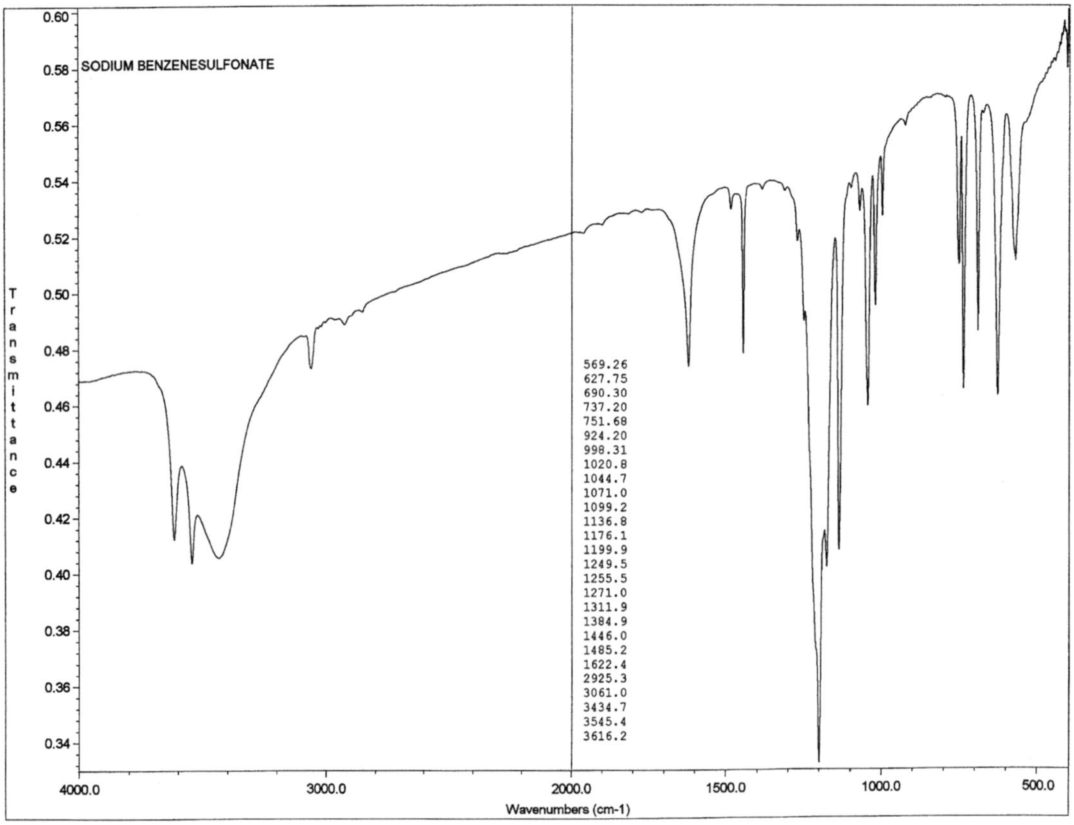

68 Sodium benzenesulfonate ($C_6H_5SO_3$)Na

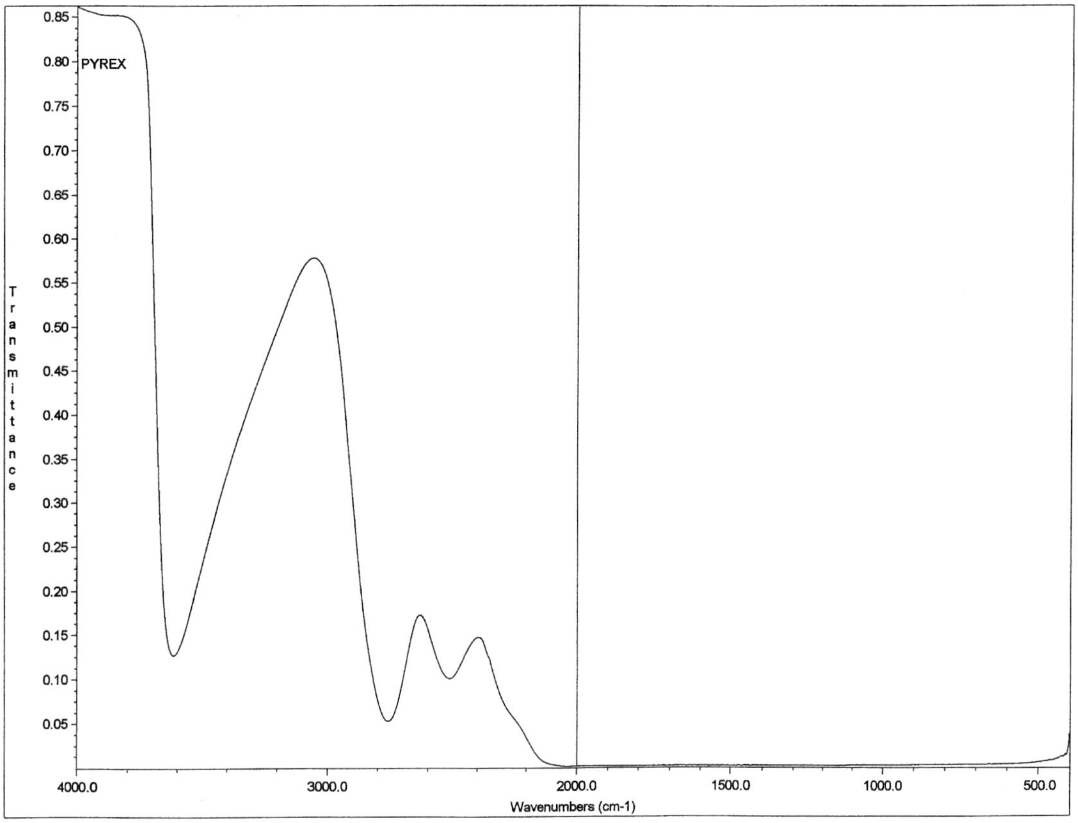

W1 Pyrex

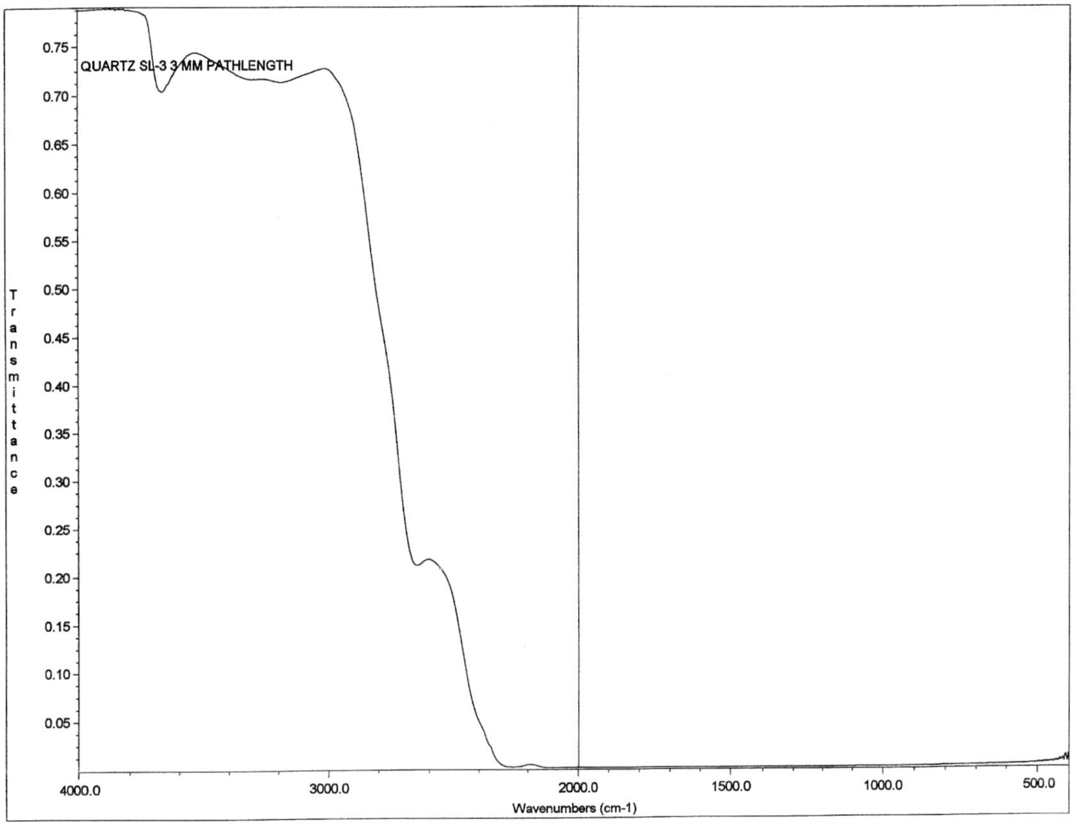

W2 Quartz

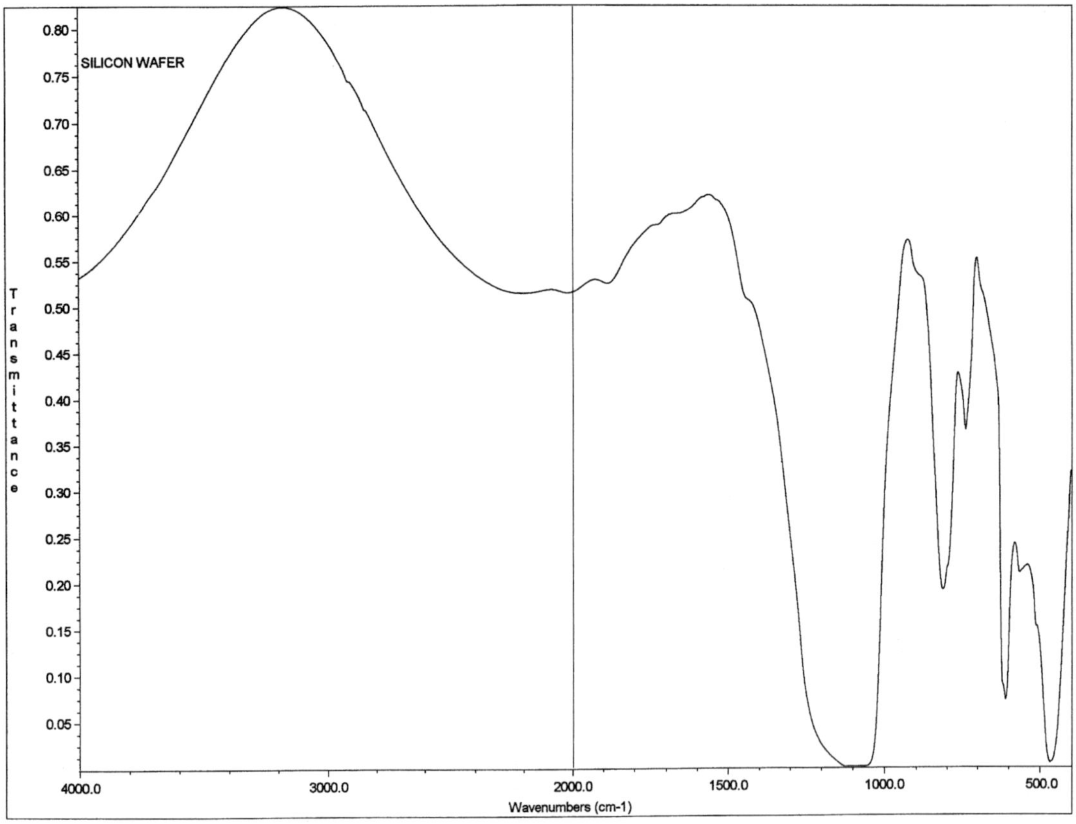

W3 Silicon wafer

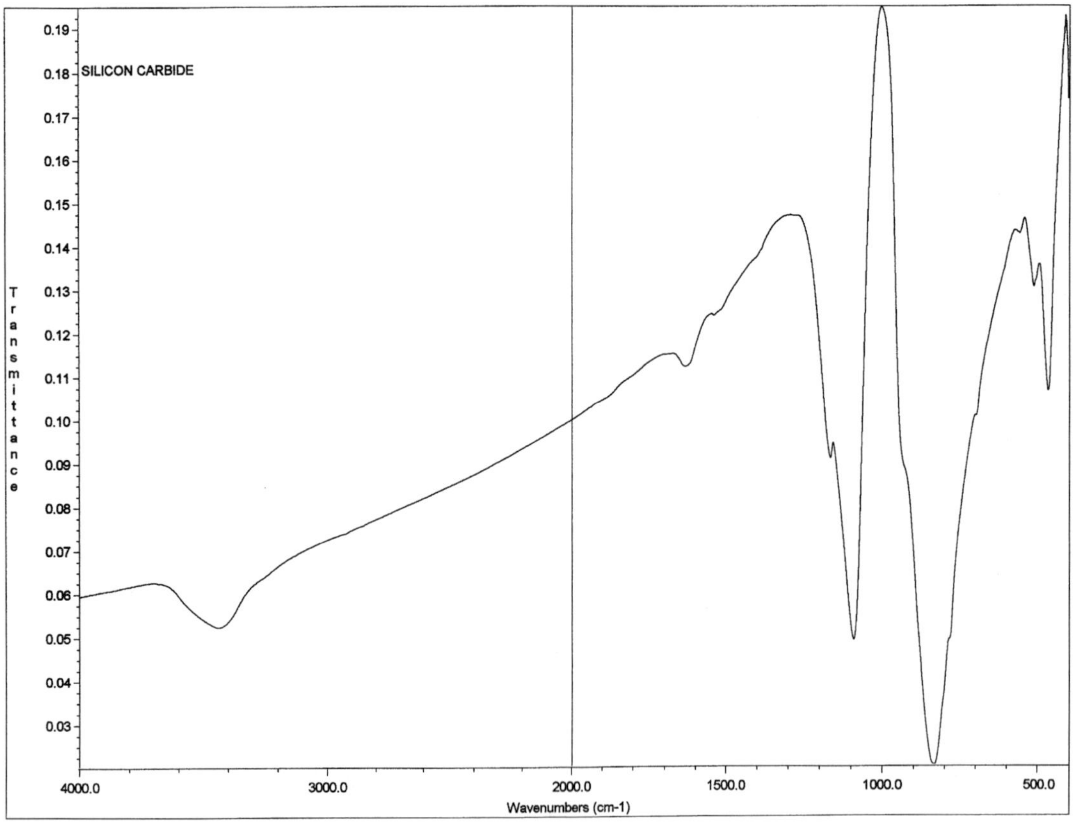

W4 Silicon carbide

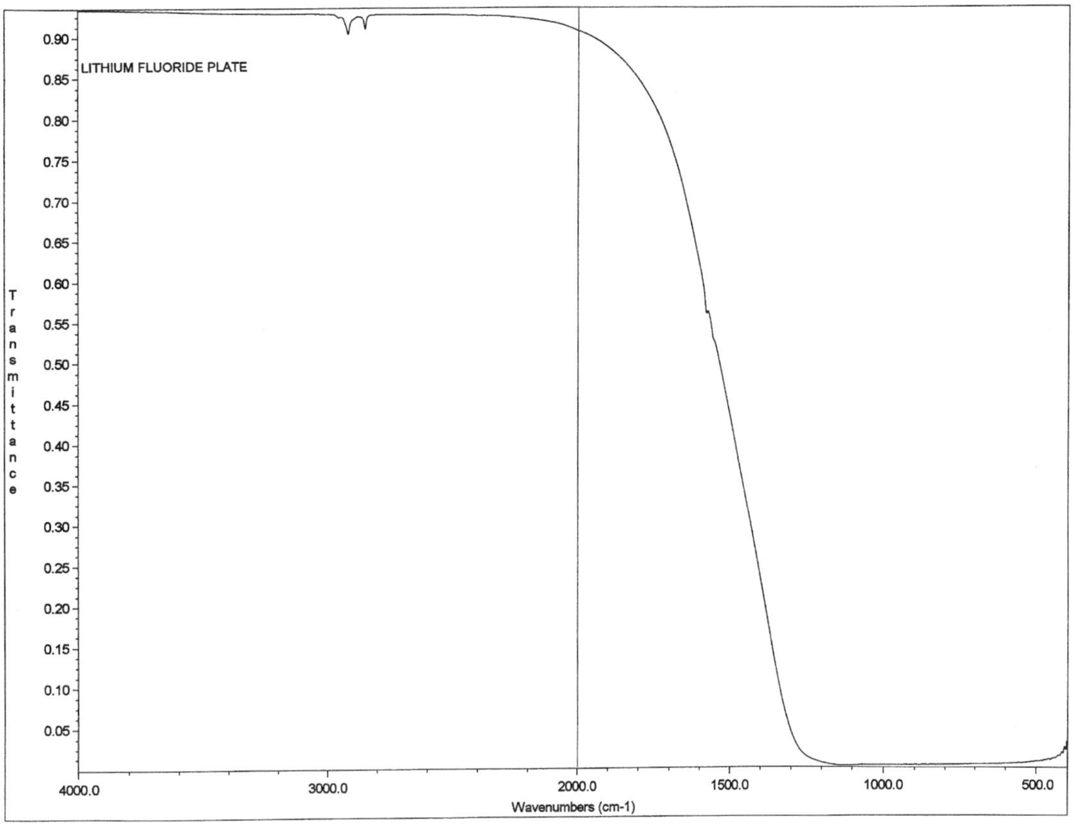

W5 Lithium fluoride

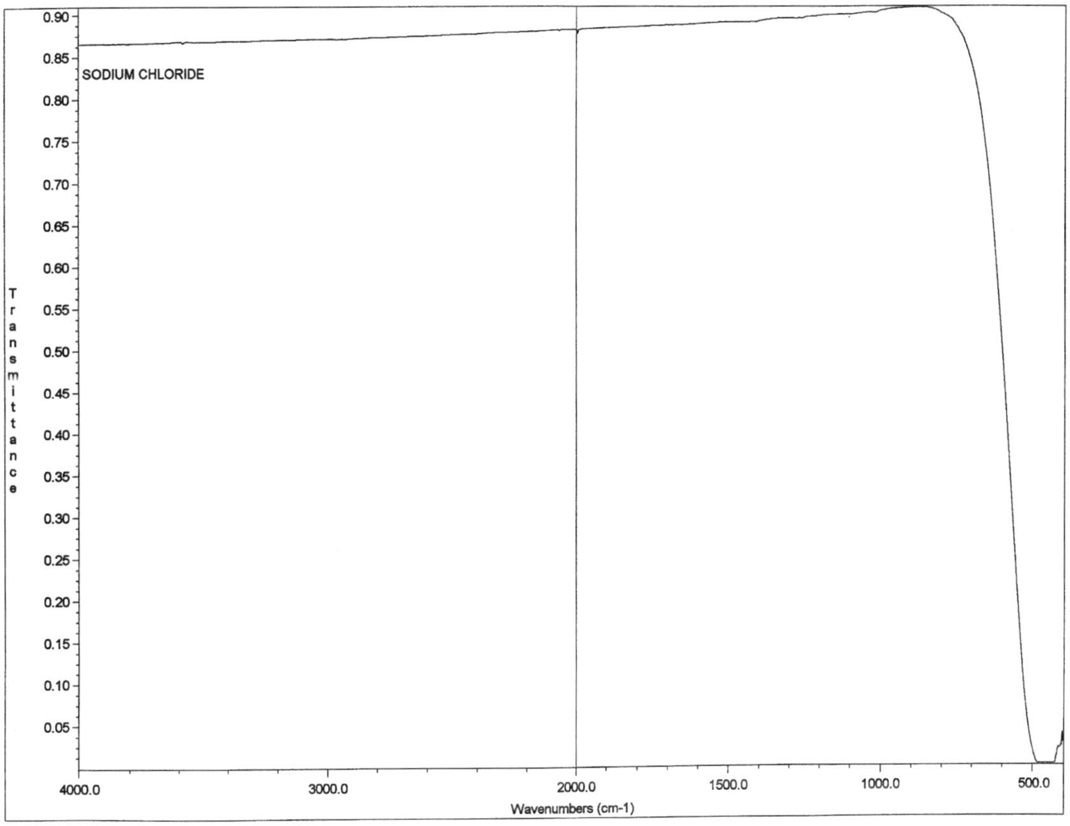

W6 Sodium chloride

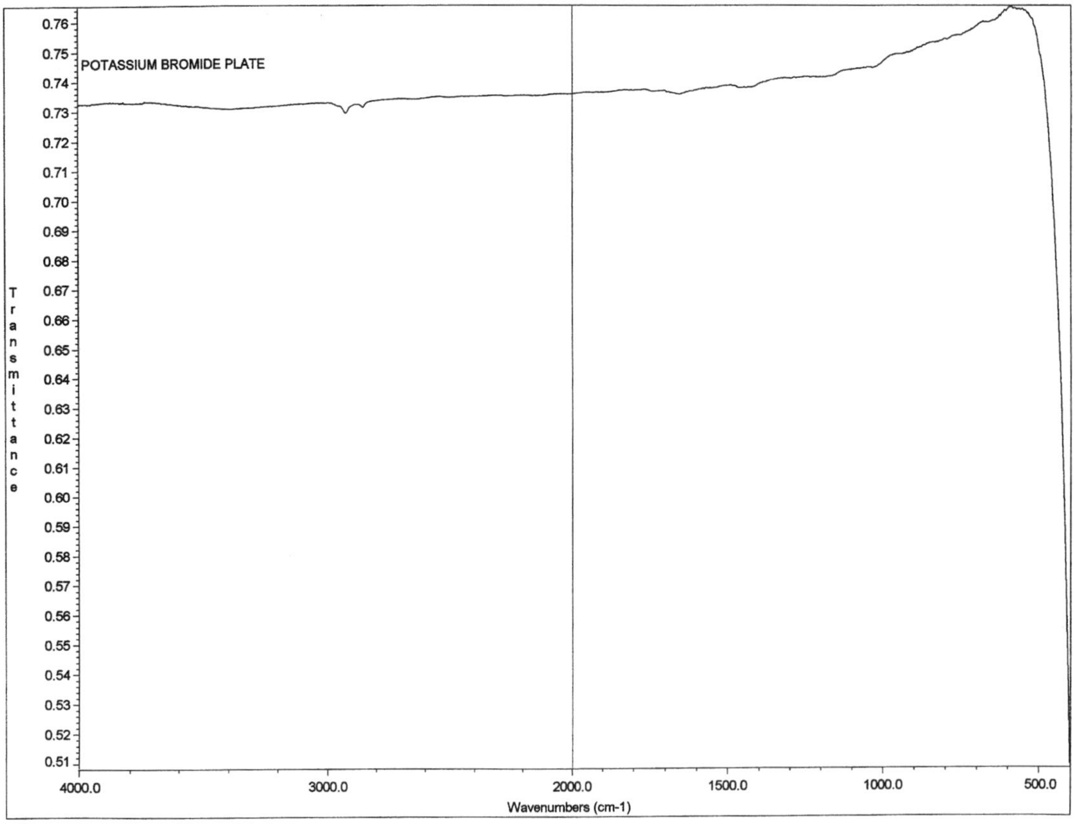

W7 Potassium bromide

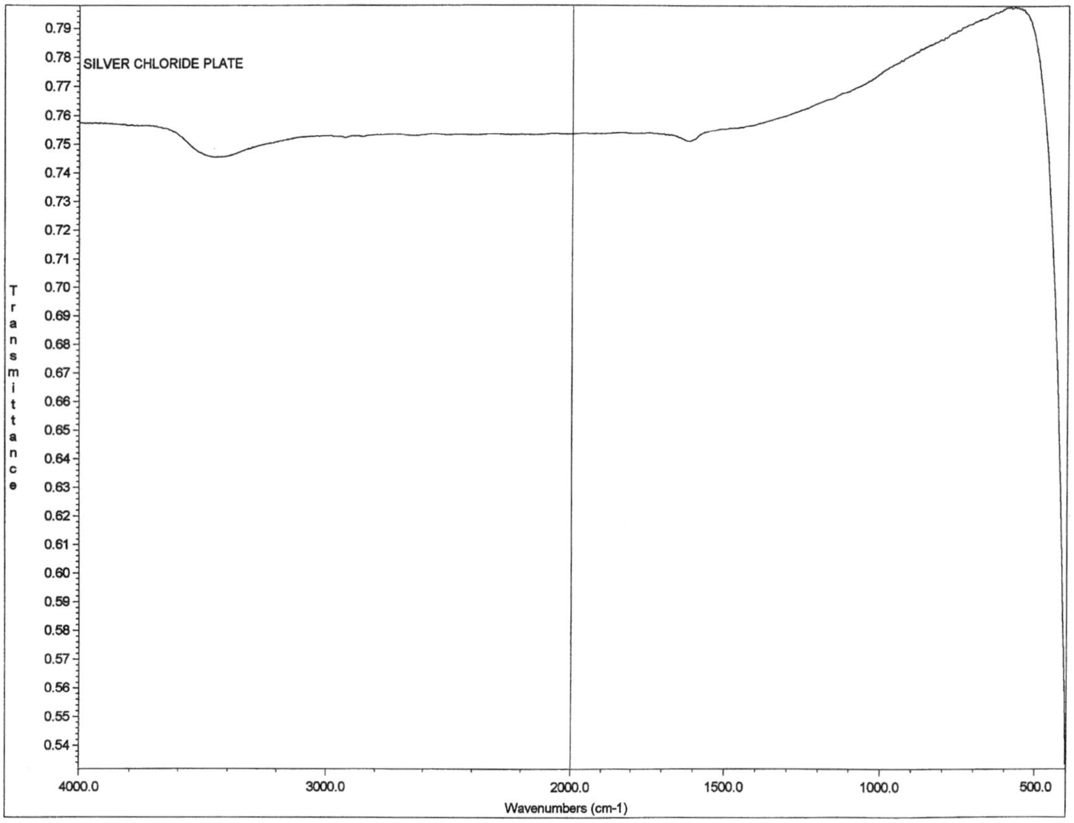

W8 Silver chloride

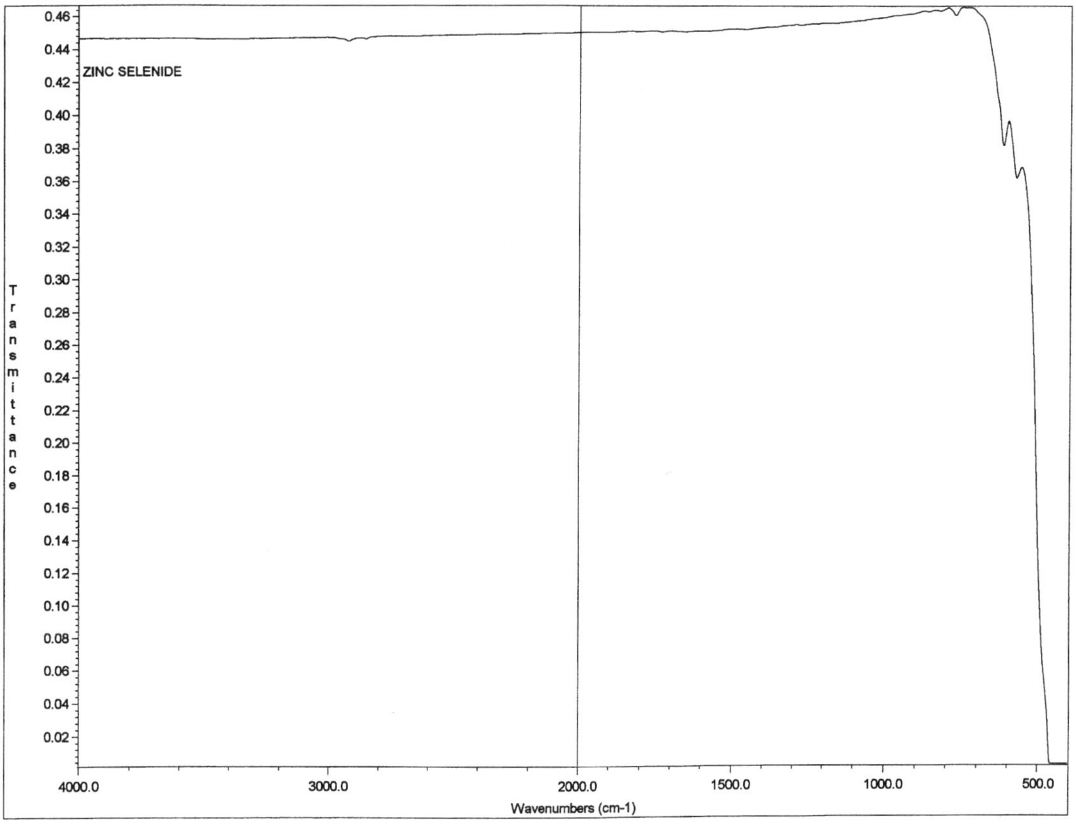

W9 Zinc selinide

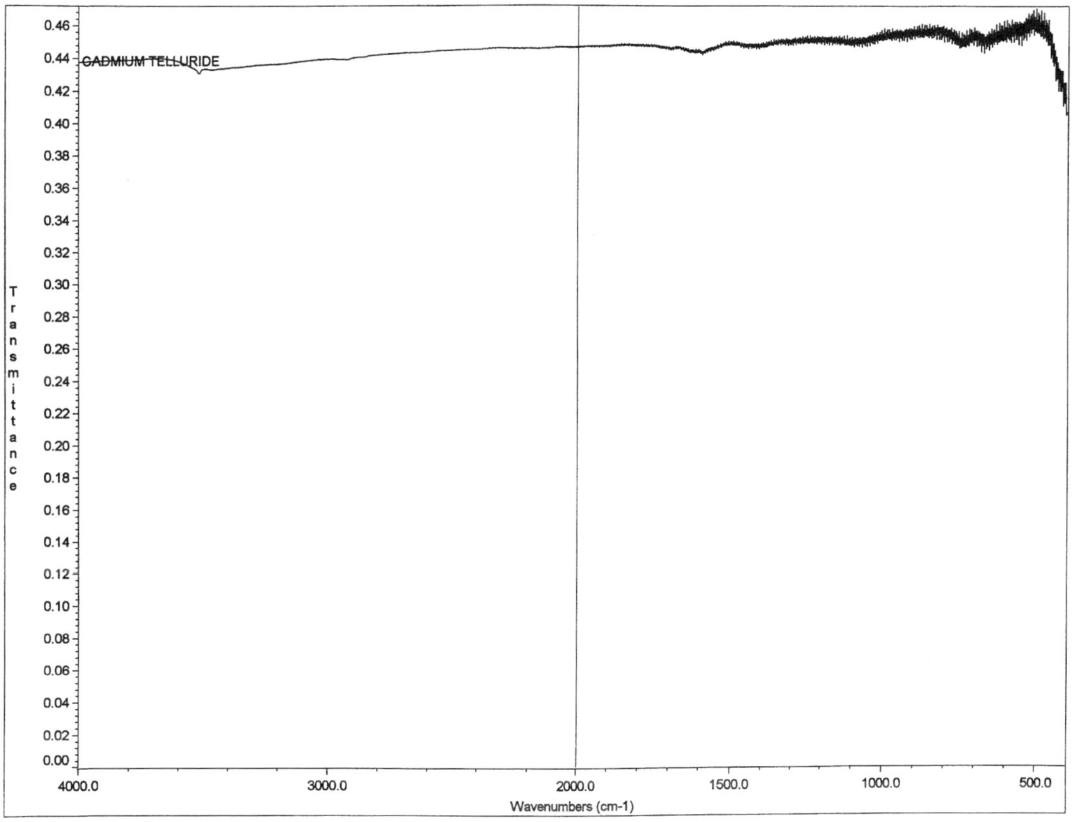

W10 Cadmium telluride

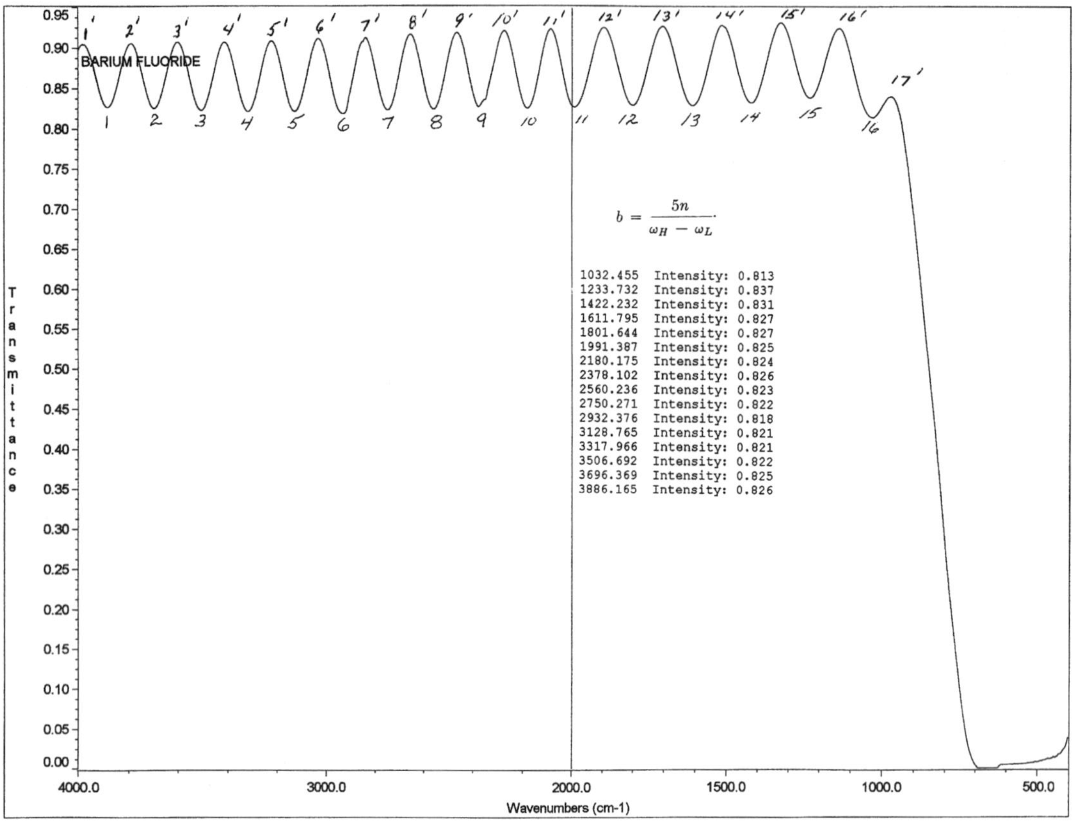
BARIUM FLUORIDE
$b = \frac{5n}{\omega_H - \omega_L}$
1032.455 Intensity: 0.813
1233.732 Intensity: 0.837
1422.232 Intensity: 0.831
1611.795 Intensity: 0.827
1801.644 Intensity: 0.827
1991.387 Intensity: 0.825
2180.175 Intensity: 0.824
2378.102 Intensity: 0.826
2560.236 Intensity: 0.823
2750.271 Intensity: 0.822
2932.376 Intensity: 0.818
3128.765 Intensity: 0.821
3317.966 Intensity: 0.821
3506.692 Intensity: 0.822
3696.369 Intensity: 0.825
3886.165 Intensity: 0.826
Transmittance
Wavenumbers (cm-1)

W11 Barium fluoride sealed cell (0.026 mm pathlength)

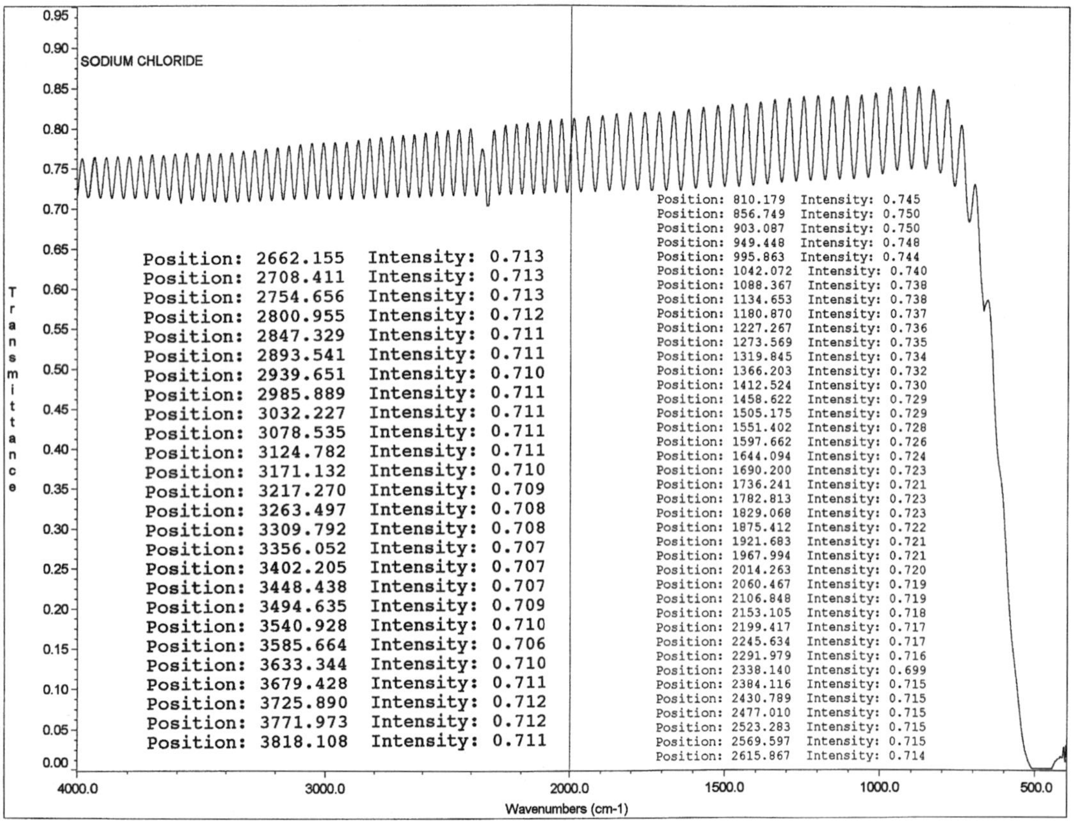
SODIUM CHLORIDE
Position: 2662.155 Intensity: 0.713
Position: 2708.411 Intensity: 0.713
Position: 2754.656 Intensity: 0.713
Position: 2800.955 Intensity: 0.712
Position: 2847.329 Intensity: 0.711
Position: 2893.541 Intensity: 0.711
Position: 2939.651 Intensity: 0.710
Position: 2985.889 Intensity: 0.711
Position: 3032.227 Intensity: 0.711
Position: 3078.535 Intensity: 0.711
Position: 3124.782 Intensity: 0.711
Position: 3171.132 Intensity: 0.710
Position: 3217.270 Intensity: 0.709
Position: 3263.497 Intensity: 0.708
Position: 3309.792 Intensity: 0.708
Position: 3356.052 Intensity: 0.707
Position: 3402.205 Intensity: 0.707
Position: 3448.438 Intensity: 0.707
Position: 3494.635 Intensity: 0.709
Position: 3540.928 Intensity: 0.710
Position: 3585.664 Intensity: 0.706
Position: 3633.344 Intensity: 0.710
Position: 3679.428 Intensity: 0.711
Position: 3725.890 Intensity: 0.712
Position: 3771.973 Intensity: 0.712
Position: 3818.108 Intensity: 0.711
Position: 810.179 Intensity: 0.745
Position: 856.749 Intensity: 0.750
Position: 903.087 Intensity: 0.750
Position: 949.448 Intensity: 0.748
Position: 995.863 Intensity: 0.744
Position: 1042.072 Intensity: 0.740
Position: 1088.367 Intensity: 0.738
Position: 1134.653 Intensity: 0.738
Position: 1180.870 Intensity: 0.737
Position: 1227.267 Intensity: 0.736
Position: 1273.569 Intensity: 0.735
Position: 1319.845 Intensity: 0.734
Position: 1366.203 Intensity: 0.732
Position: 1412.524 Intensity: 0.730
Position: 1458.622 Intensity: 0.729
Position: 1505.175 Intensity: 0.729
Position: 1551.402 Intensity: 0.728
Position: 1597.662 Intensity: 0.726
Position: 1644.094 Intensity: 0.724
Position: 1690.200 Intensity: 0.723
Position: 1736.241 Intensity: 0.721
Position: 1782.813 Intensity: 0.723
Position: 1829.068 Intensity: 0.723
Position: 1875.412 Intensity: 0.722
Position: 1921.683 Intensity: 0.721
Position: 1967.994 Intensity: 0.721
Position: 2014.263 Intensity: 0.720
Position: 2060.467 Intensity: 0.719
Position: 2106.848 Intensity: 0.719
Position: 2153.105 Intensity: 0.718
Position: 2199.417 Intensity: 0.717
Position: 2245.634 Intensity: 0.717
Position: 2291.979 Intensity: 0.716
Position: 2338.140 Intensity: 0.699
Position: 2384.116 Intensity: 0.715
Position: 2430.789 Intensity: 0.715
Position: 2477.010 Intensity: 0.715
Position: 2523.283 Intensity: 0.715
Position: 2569.597 Intensity: 0.715
Position: 2615.867 Intensity: 0.714
Transmittance
Wavenumbers (cm-1)

W12 Sodium chloride sealed cell (0.108 mm pathlength)

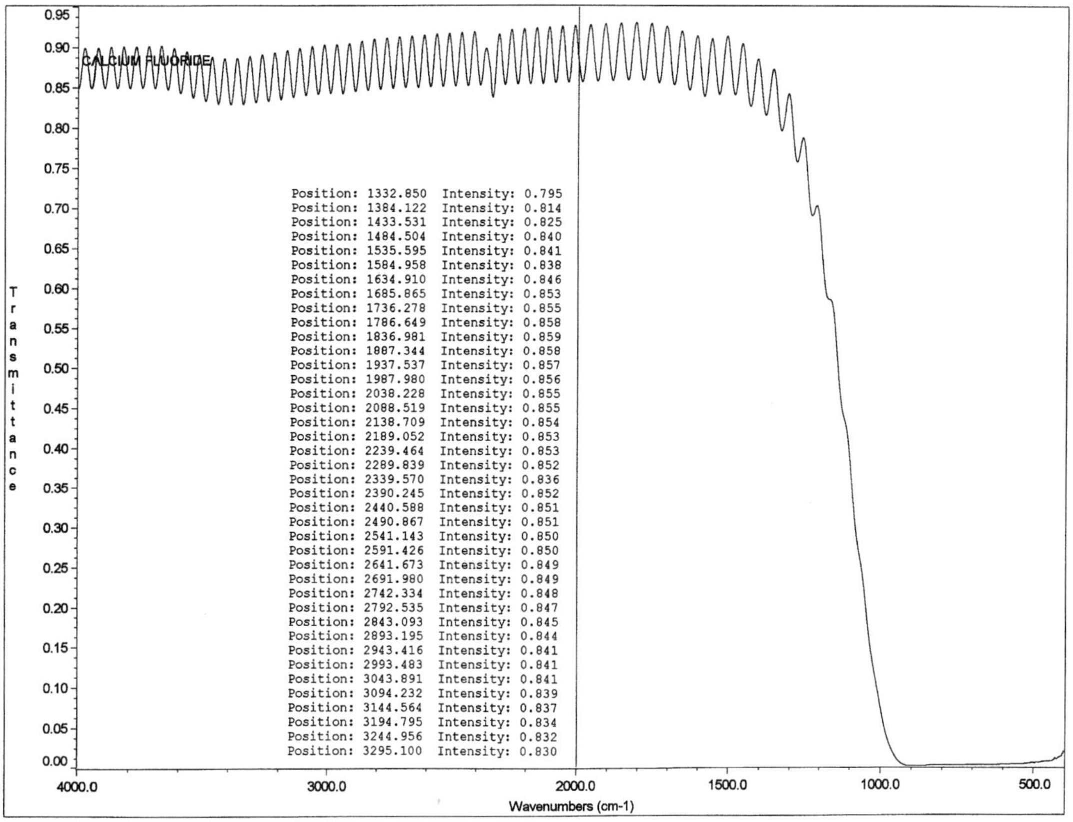

W13 Calcium fluoride sealed cell (0.099 mm pathlength)

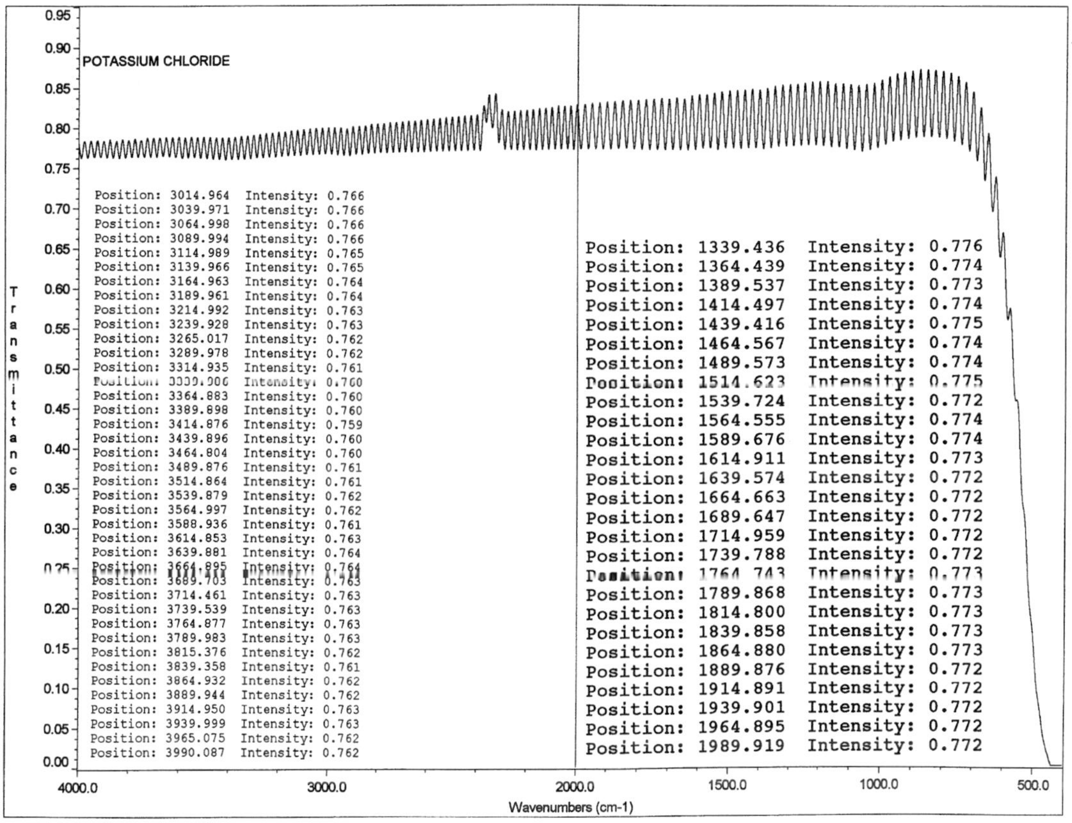

W14 Potassium chloride sealed cell (0.200 mm pathlength)

ISBN 0-12-523447-3